TALK TO ME IN KOREAN

LEVEL 2

Conjunctions, Tenses, Telling Time,
and More

This book is based on a series of published lessons, divided into ten levels, which are currently available at TalkToMeInKorean.com.

Talk To Me In Korean - Level 2

1판 1쇄	1st edition published	2015. 11. 16
1판 12쇄	12th edition published	2020. 5. 12

지은이	Written by	TalkToMeInKorean
책임편집	Edited by	선경화 Kyung-hwa Sun, 스테파니 베이츠 Stephanie Bates
디자인	Designed by	선윤아 Yoona Sun
삽화	Illustrations by	김경해 Kyounghae Kim
녹음	Voice Recordings by	선현우 Hyunwoo Sun, 최경은 Kyeong-eun Choi
펴낸곳	Published by	롱테일북스 Longtail Books
펴낸이	Publisher	이수영 Su Young Lee
편집	Copy-edited by	김보경 Florence Kim
주소	Address	04043 서울 마포구 양화로 12길 16-9(서교동) 북앤빌딩 3층
		3rd Floor Book-And Bldg. 16-9 Yanghwa-ro 12-gil, Mapo-gu, Seoul, KOREA
이메일	E-mail	TTMIK@longtailbooks.co.kr
ISBN		979-11-86701-08-9 14710

*이 교재의 내용을 사전 허가 없이 전재하거나 복제할 경우 법적인 제재를 받게 됨을 알려 드립니다.

*잘못된 책은 구입하신 서점이나 본사에서 교환해 드립니다.

*정가는 표지에 표시되어 있습니다.

TTMIK - TALK TO ME IN KOREAN

MESSAGE
FROM
THE AUTHOR

Welcome to Level 2 of the Talk To Me In Korean book series! Whether you have already studied with the Level 1 book, or you have chosen this book because it is the right level for you, we hope that you enjoy learning Korean with us.

When learning a new language, especially if embarking on a self-study journey, it is very important to find a variety of ways to help improve your listening, speaking, reading, and writing skills. We strongly recommend seeking out other resources to help with your language study. There is a workbook available to accompany this book in addition to free MP3 audio files to download and take with you wherever you go. We, and a community of Korean learners just like you, are always available on your favorite social media network to help you practice.

After studying with this book, you will be able to hold simple conversations in Korean and have an expanded vocabulary. Level 1 and Level 2 introduce the most essential sentence structures, grammar points, tenses, and vocabulary which give you the strong foundation you need to take your Korean language skills even further through subsequent lessons and practice.

Thank you for giving us your support and for studying with Talk To Me In Korean. Good luck with your studies, and enjoy Level 2!

TABLE OF
CONTENTS

LESSON 1

Future Tense

-(으)ㄹ 거예요

Track 01

Welcome to Level 2 and congratulations on making it through Level 1!

In Level 2, you will build upon what was learned in Level 1 with new grammar points and expressions.

Let's get started with the first lesson where you will learn how to use the sentence ending expressing the future in Korean.

Future Tense

The most common way of making future tense sentences in Korean is by adding

-(으)ㄹ 거예요.
[-(eu)l kkeo-ye-yo]

> *Conjugation:*
>
> Verb + -(으)ㄹ 거예요 = future tense

8

Determining whether to use -ㄹ 거예요 or -을 거예요:

1. Verb stems ending with a vowel (보다, 가다, 자다) are followed by -ㄹ 거예요.

보다 + -ㄹ/을 거예요 = 볼 거예요.
[bo-da]   [bol kkeo-ye-yo.]
가다 + -ㄹ/을 거예요 = 갈 거예요.
[ga-da]   [gal kkeo-ye-yo.]
자다 + -ㄹ/을 거예요 = 잘 거예요.
[ja-da]   [jal kkeo-ye-yo.]

2. Verb stems ending with a consonant (먹다, 찾다, 붙다) are followed by -을 거예요.

먹다 + -ㄹ/을 거예요 = 먹을 거예요.
[meok-tta]   [meo-geul geo-yeo-yo.]
찾다 + -ㄹ/을 거예요 = 찾을 거예요.
[chat-tta]   [cha-jeul geo-yeo-yo.]
붙다 + -ㄹ/을 거예요 = 붙을 거예요.
[but-tta]   [bu-teul geo-yeo-yo.]

(* There is no complex reason for this. It is simply for the ease of pronunciation.)

Track 01

3. Exception: Verb stems already ending with ㄹ (놀다, 멀다, 살다) are followed only by 거예요.

놀다 + -ㄹ/을 거예요 = 놀 거예요.
[nol-da]   [nol kkeo-ye-yo.]
멀다 + -ㄹ/을 거예요 = 멀 거예요.
[meol-da]   [meol kkeo-ye-yo.]
살다 + -ㄹ/을 거예요 = 살 거예요.
[sal-da]   [sal kkeo-ye-yo.]

When a verb is changed into this form, it takes on the meaning of "to be going to" do something or "will" do something, but as you will find out when you hear more conversations between native speakers, the present tense can also serve to express the future when the context is very clear.

For example, "I'm going to go tomorrow" is "내일 갈 거예요" in the future tense, but "내일
[nae-il]
가요" (which is in the present tense) may still make perfect sense depending on the situation.

9

1. 가다 = to go   가 + ㄹ 거예요.

  → 갈 거예요. = I'm going to go. / I will go.

  Ex)

  지금 갈 거예요. = I am going to go (there) now.
  [ji-geum]
  혼자 갈 거예요. = I am going to go alone.
  [hon-ja]
  내일 갈 거예요. = I am going to go tomorrow.

2. 하다 = to do   하 + ㄹ 거예요.
  [ha-da]
    → 할 거예요. = I am going to do (it). / I will do (it).
    [hal kkeo-ye-yo.]

  Ex)

  뭐 할 거예요? = What are you going to do?
  [mwo]
  언제 할 거예요? = When are you going to do (it)?
  [eon-je]
  이거 언제 할 거예요? = When are you going to do this?
  [i-geo eon-je]
  이거 정말 할 거예요? = Are you really going to do it?
  [i-geo jeong-mal]

Track 01

3. 입다 = to wear   입 + 을 거예요.
  [ip-tta]
    → 입을 거예요. = I am going to wear (it). / I will wear (it).
    [i-beul kkeo-ye-yo.]

  Ex)

  청바지 입을 거예요. = I am going to wear blue jeans.
  [cheong-ba-ji]
  뭐 입을 거예요? = What are you going to wear?
  [mwo]
  티셔츠 입을 거예요. = I am going to wear a t-shirt.
  [ti-syeo-cheu]
  치마 입을 거예요. = I am going to wear a skirt.
  [chi-ma]

4. 만나다 = to meet   만나 + ㄹ 거예요.
[man-na-da]
→ 만날 거예요. = I am going to meet (him/her/that person/them). / I will meet (him/
[man-nal kkeo-ye-yo.]
her/that person/them).

Ex)

누구 만날 거예요? = Who are you going to meet?
[nu-gu]
어디에서 만날 거예요? = Where are you going to meet?
[eo-di-e-seo]
언제 만날 거예요? = When are you going to meet?

5. 팔다 = to sell   팔 + 거예요.
[pal-da]
→ 팔 거예요. = I am going to sell (it). / I will sell (it).
[pal kkeo-ye-yo.]

Ex)

Track
01

뭐 팔 거예요? = What are you going to sell?

어디에서 팔 거예요? = Where are you going to sell it?

얼마에 팔 거예요? = At what price are you going to sell it?
[eol-ma-e]

Sample Dialogue

A: 밥 언제 먹을 거예요?
[bap eon-je meo-geul kkeo-ye-yo?]

B: 지금 먹을 거예요.
[ji-geum meo-geul kkeo-ye-yo.]

A: 어디에서 먹을 거예요?
[eo-di-e-seo meo-geul kkeo-ye-yo?]

B: 밖에 나가서 먹을 거예요.
[ba-kke na-ga-seo meo-geul kkeo-ye-yo.]

A: When are you going to eat?

B: I am going to eat now.

A: Where are you going to eat?

B: I am going to go out to eat.

✎ Exercises for Lesson 1

Translate the following sentences to Korean:

Check the answers on **p.196**

1. "I'm going to wear blue jeans."
   * 입다 = to wear, 청바지 = blue jeans
     [ip-tta]   [cheong-ba-ji]

   (   )

2. "What are you going to sell?"
   * 팔다 = to sell
     [pal-da]

   (   )

3. "Who are you going to meet?"
   * 만나다 = to meet
     [man-na-da]

   (   )

4. "When are you going to eat lunch?"
   * 점심 = lunch, 먹다 = to eat
     [jeom-sim]   [meok-tta]

   (   )

5. "What are you going to do tomorrow?"

   (   )

LESSON 2

Object Marking Particles

-을, -를

Track 03

In Level 1 Lesson 9, topic marking particles (-은, -는) and subject marking particles (-이, -가)
[-eun] [-neun]　　　　　　　　　　　　　　　　　　　　　　[-i]　[-ga]
were introduced. Particles may still be new and different to many people, and it may seem
like an impossible task to truly grasp the function of these particles, but with this lesson,
learning how and when to use object marking particles is broken down to make it easier to
understand.

Object marking particles create a relation to the verb in the sentence. Although quite a
few specific verbs have been introduced previously, in general, verbs can be divided into
transitive (verbs which need a direct object) and intransitive verbs (verbs which do not
require a direct object). This is clearer in English than it is in Korean. Take a look at the
following exchange in English:

Speaker A: "Did you find your wallet?"
Speaker B: "Yes, I found it."

14

"Find"/"found" is a transitive verb and needs a DIRECT OBJECT. "Wallet" is the direct object in the first sentence, and "it" (object pronoun) in the second sentence.

In Korean, however, the sentences are as follows:

Speaker A: "지갑 찾았어요?" (Literal translation: "Wallet found?")
[ji-gap cha-ja-sseo-yo?]
Speaker B: "네. 찾았어요." (Literal translation: "Yes. Found.")
[ne. cha-ja-sseo-yo.]

There is no direct object in the second sentence, but Speaker A knows what Speaker B is referring to without it. The distinction between transitive and intransitive is not as strong in Korean as in English or other languages.

How is that possible?!

Track 03

That is where object marking particles come into play.

Object marking particles:

> ### *Conjugation:*
> -을 - used after a noun ending in a consonant
> -를 - used after a noun ending in a vowel

우유(milk) + -를 = 우유를
[u-yu-reul]
책(book) + -을 = 책을
[chae-geul]
모자(hat) + -를 = 모자를
[mo-ja-reul]
카메라(camera) + -를 = 카메라를
[ka-me-ra-reul]
방(room) + -을 = 방을
[bang-eul]

So what exactly do particles in Korean do anyway?

To explain it simply, they help listeners/readers predict the verb (to an extent).

In English, if you say or write "an apple", it is simply a noun; a round, shiny, sweet fruit. If you write or say a sentence and do not use a verb to go with it, the reader/listener has no idea what ACTION is directly happening to the apple in the sentence.

Ex)

"Did you _____ an apple?" ⟶ The verb can be any action verb: buy, sell, trade, eat, throw, etc. (transitive verb)

Track 03

Likewise, if you say or write just "the apple", the reader/listener has no clue ABOUT the apple. Did the apple DO an action? Is there something about the apple that he/she needs to know?

Ex)

"The apple." ⟶ The apple "what"? In this case, either an intransitive verb (rolled, disappeared, fell, emerged, vanished, etc.) or adjective (is good, bad, ugly, pretty, shiny, etc.) can be used to complete the sentence.

In Korean, 사과 is "apple". By adding only -를 (object marking particle), to 사과, making 사과
[sa-gwa]   [-reul]
를, one can predict that 사과 is the direct OBJECT of the verb in the sentence, meaning that the verb's ACTION (transitive verb) will be directly transferred to the 사과.

Ex)

사과를 먹었어요? (Did you eat an apple?)
[sa-gwa-reul meo-geo-sseo-yo?]

16

사과를 사요? (Are you buying an apple?)
[sa-gwa-reul sa-yo?]

By adding -가 (subject marking particle) to 사과, it becomes the SUBJECT of the sentence, meaning that the verb will be ABOUT the 사과 (absolutely NO action is being directly transferred to the 사과). It is easy to predict the verb or adjective (known as a "descriptive verb" in Korean) here as well.

Ex)

이 사과가 맛있어요. (This apple is delicious.)
[i sa-gwa-ga ma-si-sseo-yo.]
사과가 떨어졌어요. (The apple fell.)
[sa-gwa-ga tteo-reo-jyeo-sseo-yo.]

When adding -는 (topic marking particle) to create 사과는, the reader/listener knows that 사과 will be compared to something else, or that 사과 is being brought up in the conversation for the first time. All this without any other words!

Track 03

How particles are dropped

In Korean, particles are sometimes necessary in order to clarify the meaning of a sentence, especially when changing the word order or forming long sentences. Sometimes, however, there are certain situations where particles can be dropped if the meaning of the sentence is clearly understood or for ease of pronunciation and for the sake of shortening the phrase.

Ex)

사과를 사요? → 사과 사요? (Are you buying an apple?)
[sa-gwa-reul sa-yo?]
이 사과가 맛있어요. → 이 사과 맛있어요. (This apple is delicious.)
[i sa-gwa-ga ma-si-sseo-yo.]

The meaning of these sentences stays the same with or without a particle.

"When do I need to use object or subject marking particles?"

You need to use them when you want to clarify the relationship between the object or subject and the verb. When the object or subject is close to the verb, such as in the sentences before, using a particle or omitting it does not make much of a difference since the meaning is still the same. However, when sentences become longer, there are more elements, the word order can change, and the object or subject gets further away from the verb. Using a particle is absolutely necessary in this situation to clarify the meaning.

Sample Sentences

Track 03

만났어요.
[man-na-sseo-yo.]
= I met.

→ 만났어요?

= Did you meet?

→ 누구 만났어요?
[nu-gu]
= Who did you meet?

→ 어제 여기에서 누구(를) 만났어요?
[eo-je yeo-gi-e-seo nu-gu-(reul) man-na-sseo-yo?]
= Who did you meet here yesterday?

→ 어제 누구를 여기에서 만났어요?

= WHO did you meet here yesterday?

텔레비전 봐요.
[tel-le-bi-jeon bwa-yo.]
= I watch TV.

→ 텔레비전 봐요?

= Do you watch TV?

Conjunctions, Tenses,

→ 텔레비전 자주 봐요?
　　　[ja-ju]
= Do you watch TV often?

→ 일주일에 몇 번 텔레비전 봐요?
　[il-jju-i-re myeot beon]
= How many times per week do you watch TV?

→ 텔레비전(을) 일주일에 몇 번 봐요?

= How many times a week do you watch TV?

Don't worry too much about the other elements of the sentences above for now. Just focus on remembering that the longer the sentence is, the more necessary it is to use particles!

**Track
03**

19

Sample Dialogue

A: 핸드폰을 잃어버렸어요.
[haen-deu-po-neul i-reo-beo-ryeo-sseo-yo.]

B: 어디에서 잃어버렸어요?
[eo-di-e-seo i-reo-beo-ryeo-sseo-yo?]

A: 잘 모르겠어요.
[jal mo-reu-ge-sseo-yo.]

A: I have lost my cell phone.

B: Where did you lose it?

A: I am not sure.

Conjunctions, Tenses,

✎ Exercises for Lesson **2**

-을 and -를 *are object marking particles in Korean. Do you remember how to decide which one is used? Please fill in the blanks with either* "-을" *or* "-를".

1. 사과 (   )

2. 핸드폰 (   )
[hean-deu-pon]

3. 공부 (   )
[gong-bu]

4. 시계 (   )
[si-gye]

5. 여행 (   )
[yeo-haeng]

Check the answers on **p.196**

21

LESSON **3**

And, And then, Therefore, So

그리고, 그래서

Track 05

The last two lessons contained fairly heavy topics (future tense and object marking particles), but in this lesson, your brain gets a bit of a break!

Korean has conjunctions (part of speech which connects words, sentences, phrases, or clauses) just like many other languages around the world. There are many of them in Korean, but you will learn two of the most common in this lesson.

그리고

그리고 has the meaning of "and" or "and then" depending on the context. 그리고 can
[geu-ri-go]
be used for both linking nouns and phrases, but in colloquial situations, 그리고 is more commonly used for linking phrases.

Ex) (linking nouns)

커피, 빵, 그리고 물 = coffee, bread, and water
[keo-pi, ppang, geu-ri-go mul]

22

서울 그리고 부산 = Seoul and Busan
[seo-ul geu-ri-go bu-san]

런던 그리고 파리 = London and Paris
[leon-deon geu-ri-go pa-ri]

미국 그리고 호주 = United States and Australia
[mi-guk geu-ri-go ho-ju]

독일 그리고 필리핀 = Germany and the Philippines
[do-gil geu-ri-go pil-li-pin]

Ex) (linking phrases)

(1) 친구를 만났어요.
[chin-gu-reul man-na-sseo-yo.]

친구 = friend

를 = object marking particle

만나다 = to meet
[man-na-da]

만났어요 = past tense of 만나다

(2) 밥을 먹었어요.
[ba-beul meo-geo-sseo-yo.]

밥 = rice, meal
[bap]

을 = object marking particle
[eul]

먹다 = to eat
[meok-tta]

먹었어요 = past tense of 먹다

Track 05

(1) and (2) = 친구를 만났어요 and 밥을 먹었어요.

= 친구를 만났어요. 그리고 밥을 먹었어요.

그래서

그래서 has the meaning of "therefore" and "so", and just as in English, using this word
[geu-rae-seo]
between two sentences shows a logical relation between sentences.

23

Ex)

(1) 오늘은 비가 왔어요.
[o-neu-reun bi-ga wa-sseo-yo.]

비가 오다 = to rain
[o-da]

비가 왔어요 = past tense of 비가 오다

(2) 집에 있었어요.
[ji-be i-sseo-sseo-yo.]

집 = house, home
[jip]

있다 = to be
[it-tta]

있었어요 = past tense of 있다

(1) + (2) = 오늘은 비가 왔어요. Therefore, 집에 있었어요.

= 오늘은 비가 왔어요. 그래서 집에 있었어요.

Track 05

Sample Sentences

김치는 맛있어요. 그리고 한국 음식이에요.
[gim-chi-neun ma-si-sseo-yo. geu-ri-go han-guk eum-si-gi-e-yo.]
= Kimchi is delicious. And it is Korean food.

김치 = kimchi

맛있다 = to be delicious
[ma-sit-tta]

한국 음식 = Korean food
[han-guk eum-sik]

저는 학생이에요. 그리고 프랑스어를 공부해요.
[jeo-neun hak-ssaeng-i-e-yo. geu-ri-go peu-rang-sseu-eo-reul gong-bu-hae-yo.]
= I am a student. And I am studying French.

저 = I (humble)

학생 = student

프랑스어 = French (language)

공부하다 = to study
[gong-bu-ha-da]

24

저는 학생이에요. 그래서 돈이 없어요.
[jeo-neun hak-ssaeng-i-e-yo. geu-rae-seo do-ni eop-sseo-yo.]
= I am a student. So, I do not have money.

　　돈 = money

　　없다 = to not be, to not exist
　　[eop-tta]

김치는 맛있어요. 그래서 김치를 많이 먹어요.
[gim-chi-neun ma-si-sseo-yo. geu-rae-seo gim-chi-reul ma-ni meo-geo-yo.]
= Kimchi is delicious. So, I eat a lot of kimchi.

　　많이 = a lot, many (in quantity or frequency)

　　먹다 = to eat

저는 한국인이에요. 그래서 김치를 많이 먹어요.
[jeo-neun han-gu-gi-ni-e-yo. geu-rae-seo gim-chi-reul ma-ni meo-geo-yo.]
= I am Korean. So, I eat a lot of kimchi.

　　한국인 = Korean (person)
　　[han-gu-gin]

Track 05

저는 김치를 많이 먹어요. 그래서 튼튼해요.
[jeo-neun gim-chi-reul ma-ni meo-geo-yo. geu-rae-seo teun-teun-hae-yo.]
= I eat a lot of kimchi. Therefore, I am strong.

　　튼튼하다 = to be strong
　　[teun-teun-ha-da]

Sample Dialogue

A: 오늘 많이 아팠어요. 그래서 회사를
못 갔어요.
[o-neul ma-ni a-pa-sseo-yo. geu-rae-seo hoe-sa-reul
mot ga-sseo-yo.]

B: 진짜요? 병원 갔다 왔어요?
[jin-jja-yo? byeong-won gat-tta wa-sseo-yo?]

A: 아니요. 지금 갈 거예요.
[a-ni-yo. ji-geum gal kkeo-ye-yo.]

A: I was very sick today.
Therefore, I could not go to work.

B: Really? Have you been to the
hospital?

A: No. I am going to go now.

✏ Exercises for Lesson *3*

Please fill in the blanks with **"그리고"** *or* **"그래서"**.

I. 책, 연필 (   ) 공책
[chaek, yeon-pil]   [gong-chaek]
= A book, a pencil, and a notebook.

2. 저는 학생이에요. (   ) 돈이 없어요.
[jeo-neun hak-ssaeng-i-e-yo.]   [do-ni eop-sseo-yo.]
= I am a student. Therefore, I don't have money.

3. 김밥은 맛있어요. (   ) 김밥을 자주 먹어요.
[gim-ppa-beun ma-si-sseo-yo.]   [gim-ppa-beul ja-ju meo-geo-yo.]
= Kimbap is delicious. So, I eat kimbap often.

4. 서울 (   ) 부산
[seo-ul]   [bu-san]
= Seoul and Busan

5. 예지 씨는 예뻐요. (   ) 노래도 잘해요.
[ye-ji ssi-neun ye-ppeo-yo.]   [no-rae-do ja-rae-yo.]
= Yeji is pretty. And she also sings well.

Check the answers on **p.196**

27

LESSON 4

And, With

-하고, -(이)랑

Track 07

As mentioned in the previous lesson, there are many conjunctions in Korean, especially when it comes to the word "and". Continue the quest of learning conjunctions in Korean with this lesson on -하고 and -(이)랑.
[-ha-go]   [-(i)-rang]

-하고 = and

> **Conjugation:**
>
> -하고 is used like a particle and attached to a noun without space.
> [-ha-go]

Ex)

이거
[i-geo]
= this, this thing

이거하고 이거
[i-geo-ha-go i-geo]
= this and this

28

이거하고 이거 주세요.
[i-geo-ha-go i-geo ju-se-yo.]
= Give me this and this.

-(이)랑 = and

> **Conjugation:**
>
> If a noun ends in a vowel, attach **-랑** at the end, and if it ends with a consonant,
> [-rang]
> use **-이랑**. This makes it easier to pronounce.
> [-i-rang]

* *-(이)랑 and -하고 are almost always interchangeable, but -(이)랑 is more colloquial and casual,*
and not often used in formal settings.

Track 07

Ex)

우유 = milk
[u-yu]

빵 = bread
[ppang]

우유랑 빵 = milk and bread

빵이랑 우유 = bread and milk

우유하고 빵 = milk and bread

우유랑 빵 샀어요. = I bought milk and bread.
[sa-sseo-yo.]

우유하고 빵 샀어요. = I bought milk and bread.

빵이랑 우유 샀어요. = I bought bread and milk.

Another meaning of -하고 and -(이)랑

Depending on the context of the sentence, both -하고 and -(이)랑 can also mean "with", and it is usually very easy to tell whether it is used as "and" or "with".

친구하고 영화 봤어요.
[chin-gu-ha-go yeong-hwa bwa-sseo-yo.]
= I saw a movie with a friend.*

* *It is very unlikely that this sentence means "I watched a friend and a movie".*

누구랑 갔어요?
[nu-gu-rang ga-sseo-yo?]
= Who did you go with?

Track 07

To make the meaning of a sentence clearer, add the word 같이 after -하고 or -(이)랑. 같이 [ga-chi] means "together", so -하고 같이 or -(이)랑 같이 means "together with". While saying "친구하고 영화 봤어요" makes perfect sense, if you say "친구하고 같이 영화 봤어요", it is even better. The same can be said for "누구랑 갔어요?" and "누구랑 같이 갔어요?"

Sample Sentences

동생하고 공부할 거예요.
[dong-saeng-ha-go gong-bu-hal kkeo-ye-yo.]
= I'm going to study with my younger brother/sister.

선생님하고 밥을 먹을 거예요.
[seon-saeng-ni-ma-go ba-beul meo-geul kkeo-ye-yo.]
= I'm going to eat with my teacher.

내일 선생님하고 경복궁에 갈 거예요.
[nae-il seon-saeng-ni-ma-go gyeong-bok-kkung-e gal kkeo-ye-yo.]
= I am going to go to Gyeongbok Palace with my teacher tomorrow.

어제 홍대하고 신촌에 갔어요.
[eo-je hong-dae-ha-go sin-cho-ne ga-sseo-yo.]
= I went to Hongdae and Sinchon yesterday.

* 홍대 *and* 신촌 *are both popular hang out spots in Seoul for younger people.*

Track 07

Sample Dialogue

A: 여행 누구랑 갔다 왔어요?
[yeo-haeng nu-gu-rang gat-tta wa-sseo-yo?]

B: 가족들이랑 갔다 왔어요.
[ga-jok-tteu-ri-rang gat-tta wa-sseo-yo.]

A: 어디로 갔다 왔어요?
[eo-di-ro gat-tta wa-sseo-yo?]

B: 보라카이로 갔다 왔어요.
[bo-ra-ka-i-ro gat-tta wa-sseo-yo.]

A: Who did you travel with?

B: I traveled with my family.

A: Where did you go?

B: We went to Boracay.

Conjunctions, Tenses,

✏️ Exercises for Lesson **4**

Fill in the blanks to complete the Korean sentences.

1. 친구(   ) 영화 봤어요.
= I saw a movie with a friend.

2. 누구(   ) 같이 갔어요?
= Who did you go with?

3. 김밥(   ) 라면 좋아해요.
[gim-ppap]   [ra-myeon jo-a-hae-yo.]
= I like kimbap and ramen noodles.

4. 동생(   ) 스케이트장 갈 거예요.
[dong-saeng]   [seu-ke-i-teu-jang gal kkeo-ye-yo.]
= I'm going to go ice skating with my younger brother/sister.

5. 노트(   ) 펜 가지고 오세요.
[no-teu]   [pen ga-ji-go o-se-yo.]
= Please bring your notebook and pen.

Check the answers on **p.196**

LESSON 5

Days of the Week

After completing this lesson, you will be able to recognize and use the Korean words for each day of the week.

Sunday	Monday	Tuesday	Wednesday	Thursday	Friday	Saturday
일요일	월요일	화요일	수요일	목요일	금요일	토요일
[i-ryo-il]	[wo-ryo-il]	[hwa-yo-il]	[su-yo-il]	[mo-gyo-il]	[geu-myo-il]	[to-yo-il]

The syllables 요 and 일 together mean "day of the week" in Korean. Each day has its own unique first syllable.

Let's glance at the 한자 characters (한자 is the Korean word for Chinese characters) that are used in the names of the days of the week.

月 = 월 = moon
[wol]
火 = 화 = fire
[hwa]
水 = 수 = water
[su]
木 = 목 = tree
[mok]
金 = 금 = gold, metal, iron
[geum]
土 = 토 = earth, soil, ground
[to]
日 = 일 = sun
[il]

The names for the days of the week can also be related to some of the planets in our solar system.

Track 09

화요일 = Tuesday / 화성 = Mars
[hwa-seong]
수요일 = Wednesday / 수성 = Mercury
[su-seong]
목요일 = Thursday / 목성 = Jupiter
[mok-sseong]
금요일 = Friday / 금성 = Venus
[geum-seong]
토요일 = Saturday / 토성 = Saturn
[to-seong]

Sample Sentences

토요일에는 소풍을 갈 거예요.
[to-yo-i-re-neun so-pung-eul gal kkeo-ye-yo.]
= I'm going to go on a picnic on Saturday.

어제는 신나는 금요일이었어요.
[eo-je-neun sin-na-neun geu-myo-i-ri-eo-sseo-yo.]
= Yesterday was an exciting Friday.

저는 월요일에 영화를 봤어요.
[jeo-neun wo-ryo-i-re yeong-hwa-reul bwa-sseo-yo.]
= I watched a movie on Monday.

35

Sample Dialogue

A: 오늘 무슨 요일이에요?
[o-neul mu-seun yo-i-ri-e-yo?]

B: 화요일이요.
[hwa-yo-i-n-yo.]

A: 아, 오늘 수요일 아니었어요?
[a, o-neul su-yo-il a-ni-eo-sseo-yo?]

B: 네. 오늘 화요일이에요.
[ne. o-neul hwa-yo-i-ri-e-yo.]

A: *What day is it today?*

B: *It is Tuesday.*

A: *Oh, wasn't today Wednesday?*

B: *No, today is Tuesday.*

Conjunctions, Tenses,

✏ Exercises for Lesson **5**

Match the Korean words to the English equivalent.

1. 일요일   a. Saturday

2. 화요일   b. Sunday

3. 토요일   c. Thursday

4. 목요일   d. Monday

5. 수요일   e. Friday

6. 월요일   f. Wednesday

7. 금요일   g. Tuesday

Check the answers on **p.196**

LESSON 6

But, However

그렇지만, 그런데

Track 11

Jump right back into Korean conjunctions with this lesson, since now we will introduce two more words that can be used at the beginning of sentences!

그렇지만 = but, however
그런데 = but, however

(1) 피곤해요. 그렇지만 영화 보고 싶어요.
[pi-gon-hae-yo. geu-reo-chi-man yeong-hwa bo-go si-peo-yo.]
= I am tired, but I want to see a movie.

(2) 피곤해요. 그런데 영화 보고 싶어요.
[pi-gon-hae-yo. geu-reon-de yeong-hwa bo-go si-peo-yo.]
= I am tired. However, I want to see a movie.

그렇지만 and 그런데 both mean "but" or "however", but there is some difference in the usage of these two words.

(1) 어제 이거 샀어요. 그렇지만 정말 커요.
[eo-je i-geo sa-sseo-yo. geu-reo-chi-man jeong-mal keo-yo.]
= I bought this yesterday. "그렇지만" it is really big.

(2) 어제 이거 샀어요. 그런데 정말 커요.
[eo-je i-geo sa-sseo-yo. geu-reon-de jeong-mal keo-yo.]
= I bought this yesterday. "그런데" it is really big.

In sentence (1), 그렇지만 means "but" or "however". The speaker is contrasting two facts: having purchased "this" yesterday and "it" being too big. It sounds as if the speaker is disappointed that it is very big.

In sentence (2), the intended meaning is "but", however at the same time it can also mean "and". If the speaker is implying the meaning of "and", the entire sentence can mean "I bought this yesterday, and as I have come to find out, it is really big".

Track 11

In summary,
그렇지만 = "but"
그런데 = "but" or "and" (depending on the context)

To contrast two sentences, "A + however/but + B", you can choose to use either 그렇지만 or 그런데.

To introduce two actions or states which occurred one after another, and if the first sentence is background information for the second, only use 그런데.

어제 학교에 갔어요. 그렇지만 일요일이었어요.
[eo-je hak-kkyo-e ga-sseo-yo. geu-reo-chi-man i-ryo-i-ri-eo-sseo-yo.]
= I went to school yesterday, but it was Sunday.

어제 학교에 갔어요. 그런데 일요일이었어요.
[eo-je hak-kkyo-e ga-sseo-yo. geu-reon-de i-ryo-i-ri-eo-sseo-yo.]
= I went to school yesterday, but it was Sunday.

= I went to school yesterday, and by the way, it was Sunday.

= I went to school yesterday, and as I found out after I went, it was Sunday.

그런데 can be used for a wider variety of meanings than 그렇지만, which has a very formal nuance to it and is used more in writing. In actual everyday conversations, 그런데 is used more often than 그렇지만.

Sample Sentences

어젯밤 늦게 잤어요. 그런데 피곤하지 않아요.
[eo-jet-ppam neut-kke ja-sseo-yo. geu-reon-de pi-gon-ha-ji a-na-yo.]
= I went to bed late last night, but I am not tired.

  늦게 = late, at a late hour

  피곤하다 = to be tired

저는 매일 운동을 해요. 그런데 살이 빠지지 않아요.
[jeo-neun mae-il un-dong-eul hae-yo. geu-reon-de sa-ri ppa-ji-ji a-na-yo.]
= I work out every day, but I do not lose any weight.

  매일 = every day

  살이 빠지다 = to lose weight

저는 친구가 없어요. 그런데 왕따는 아니에요.
[jeo-neun chin-gu-ga eop-sseo-yo. geu-reon-de wang-tta-neun a-ni-e-yo.]
= I do not have friends, but I am not a loner.

  왕따 = outcast, loner, someone who is bullied by others

Sample Dialogue

Track 12

A: 저 어젯밤에 일찍 잤어요.
[jeo eo-jet-ppa-me il-jjik ja-sseo-yo.]

B: 윤아 씨가요?
[yu-na ssi-ga-yo?]

A: 네. 그런데 오늘 아침에 늦게 일어났어요.
[ne. geu-reon-de o-neul a-chi-me neut-kke i-reo-na-sseo-yo.]

A: I went to bed early last night.

B: Who? You?

A: Yes, but I got up late this morning.

41

Telling Time, and More

✏️ Exercises for Lesson 6

Translate the following words or phrases to Korean:

1. "But" or "however"

( )

2. "I'm tired, but I want to see a movie."

( )

Check the answers on **p.196**

3. "It's good, but it's expensive."

( )

4. "Yesterday, it rained, but now, it doesn't rain."

( )

5. "I went to school yesterday, but it was Sunday."

( )

LESSON 7

"To" someone, "From" someone

-한테, -한테서

Track 13

When it comes to particles in Korean, there are not always direct (or correct) translations from Korean to English. It is important to understand the roles the particles play within the sentence rather than just trying to memorize a similar English counterpart.

Keep that in mind as you learn about the particles -한테 and -한테서!
[-han-te] [-han-te-seo]

In order to express "to" or "from" someone in Korean, the particles -한테 and -한테서 are used most commonly. There are two other particles which have similar characteristics (-에게 [-e-ge] and -에게서) but are used mainly in written language and will not be covered in this lesson.
[-e-ge-seo]

-한테 = "to" someone, "from" someone

-한테서 = "from" someone

43

-한테 can mean both "to" and "from" someone, whereas -한테서 can only mean "from" someone. The meaning of -한테 can only be completely understood by examining the context of a sentence.

-한테 and -한테서 can ONLY be used about people or animals, NOT objects or places.

- "to a friend" = friend + -한테 (○)
- "to Seoul" = Seoul + -한테 (✕)

Ex)

저한테 = to me, from me
[jeo-han-te]
친구한테 = to a friend, from a friend
[chin-gu-han-te]
누구한테 = to whom, from whom
[nu-gu-han-te]

Track 13

저한테서 = from me
[jeo-han-te-seo]
친구한테서 = from a friend
[chin-gu-han-te-seo]
누구한테서 = from whom
[nu-gu-han-te-seo]

* When used with a verb that already expresses passive voice, -한테 can also mean "by".
For example, 맞다 generally means "to be correct", but in another sentence, it can mean "to be beaten" or "to be hit". Therefore, A한테 맞다 can be translated to English as "to be beaten by A".
[mat-tta]

Sample Dialogue

Track 14

A: 저한테 이메일 보냈어요?
[jeo-han-te i-me-il bo-nae-sseo-yo?]

B: 네.
[ne.]

A: 언제 보냈어요?
[eon-je bo-nae-sseo-yo?]

B: 왜요? 안 왔어요?
[wae-yo? an wa-sseo-yo?]

A: Did you email me?

B: Yes.

A: When did you send it?

B: Why? It hasn't arrived?

✏️ *Exercises for Lesson* **7**

1. 받다 means "to receive" in English. How do you say "I received it from a friend" in Korean?
[bat-tta]

(   )

2. If 물어보다 is "to ask", how would you write "(to) Whom did you ask?"
[mu-reo-bo-da]

(   )

3. 질문 is "question". How do you say "Do you have a question for me?"
[jil-mun]

(   )

4. Since 동생 is "younger brother/sister" and 주다 is "to give", how do you say "I will give this to my younger brother/sister"?
[dong-saeng]   [ju-da]

(   )

5. 얻다 is "to obtain; to acquire; to get". How do you write "I got this from my friend"?
[eot-tta]

(   )

LESSON **8**

Telling Time

한 시, 두 시, 세 시, 네 시 …

Now it's TIME to talk about **TIME**!

Track 15

As you may have already studied (if you studied with the Level 1 book in this series, you have definitely already studied this!), there are two number systems in Korean. Most of the time, the two number systems are used for different things or they are interchangeable. When it comes to telling time, however, both systems are used at the same time.

Quickly review some **native Korean numbers**:

1 하나
[ha-na]
2 둘
[dul]
3 셋
[set]
4 넷
[net]

5 다섯
[da-seot]
6 여섯
[yeo-seot]
7 일곱
[il-gop]
8 여덟
[yeo-deol]

9 아홉
[a-hop]
10 열
[yeol]
11 열하나
[yeo-ra-na]
12 열둘
[yeol-ttul]

Telling Time, and More

When saying the hour, use these native Korean numbers (1, 2, 3 and 4 are irregular and change form a little).

> ### Conjugation:
>
> Number + 시 = hour

하나 + 시 = 한 시 = 1 o'clock (not 하나 시)
[han si]

둘 + 시 = 두 시 = 2 o'clock (not 둘 시)
[du si]

셋 + 시 = 세 시 = 3 o'clock (not 셋 시)
[se si]

넷 + 시 = 네 시 = 4 o'clock (not 넷 시)
[ne si]

다섯 시 = 5 o'clock
[da-seot si]

여섯 시 = 6 o'clock
[yeo-seot si]

일곱 시 = 7 o'clock
[il-gop si]

여덟 시 = 8 o'clock
[yeo-deol si]

아홉 시 = 9 o'clock
[a-hop si]

열 시 = 10 o'clock
[yeol si]

열한 시 = 11 o'clock
[yeo-ran si]

열두 시 = 12 o'clock
[yeol-ttu si]

🎙 **Track 15**

Now, take a minute to review some **sino-Korean numbers**:

1 일	2 이	3 삼	4 사	5 오
[il]	[i]	[sam]	[sa]	[o]
6 육	7 칠	8 팔	9 구	10 십
[yuk]	[chil]	[pal]	[gu]	[sip]

* Numbers 11 and onward are combinations of these 10 numbers.

When saying minutes in Korean, use sino-Korean numbers.

Conjugation:

Number + **분** = minute
[bun]

일 분 = 1 minute

이 분 = 2 minutes

오 분 = 5 minutes

십 분 = 10 minutes

십오 분 = 15 minutes
[si-bo bun]

삼십 분 = 30 minutes
[sam-sip bun]

오십오 분 = 55 minutes
[o-si-bo bun]

Track 15

1:05 = 1 + 시 + 5 + 분 = 한 시 오 분

1:15 = 1 + 시 + 15 + 분 = 한 시 십오 분

3:20 = 3 + 시 + 20 + 분 = 세 시 이십 분
[i-sip bun]

10:00 = 10 + 시 = 열 시

10:30 = 10 + 시 + 30 + 분 = 열 시 삼십 분

* *"# o'clock sharp" is expressed with the word* **정각**.
[jeong-gak]

** *Rather than saying* **삼십 분**, *the word* **반**, *meaning "half", can also be used.*
[ban]

How to ask the time

지금 몇 시예요?
[ji-geum myeot si-ye-yo?]
= What time is it now?

지금 몇 시 몇 분이에요?
[ji-geum myeot si myeot bu-ni-e-yo?]
= What is the hour, and what is the minute?

Sample Sentences

저는 매일 아침 9시까지 출근해요.
[jeo-neun mae-il a-chim a-hop-si-kka-ji chul-geu-nae-yo.]
= I get to work by 9 o'clock every morning.

매일 = every day

출근하다 = to go to work
[chul-geu-na-da]

Track 15

내일 수업이 4시 반에 끝나요.
[nae-il su-eo-bi ne-si ba-ne kkeun-na-yo.]
= My classes finish at 4:30 tomorrow.

내일 = tomorrow

수업 = class
[su-eop]
끝나다 = to finish
[kkeun-na-da]

오늘 몇 시에 친구를 만나요?
[o-neul myeot si-e chin-gu-reul man-na-yo?]
= What time do you meet your friend today?

만나다 = to meet
[man-na-da]

Sample Dialogue

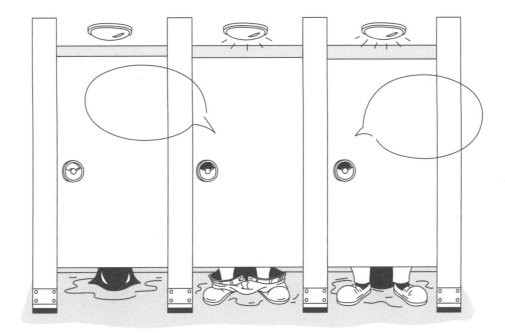

🎙️
Track 16

A: 오늘 몇 시에 출근했어요?
[o-neul myeot si-e chul-geu-nae-sseo-yo?]

B: 아홉 시 반에 출근했어요. 유정 씨는요?
[a-hop si ba-ne chul-geu-nae-sseo-yo. yu-jeong ssi-neun-nyo?]

A: 여덟 시 십 분에 출근했어요.
[yeo-deol si sip bu-ne chul-geu-nae-sseo-yo.]

A: *What time did you come to work today?*

B: *I came to work at 9:30. How about you, Yujeong?*

A: *I came to work at 8:10.*

✏ Exercises for Lesson **8**

1. How do you say "What time is it?" in Korean?

( )

2. Please write out "**3** o'clock" using only 한글.

( )

3. In Korean, how do you say "**1:15**" (time)?

( )

4. Please write out "**5:47**" using only 한글.

( )

5. How is "**10:30**" (time) read in Korean?

( )

Check the answers on **p.197**

Conjunctions, Tenses,

LESSON 9

Counters

개, 명

Track 17

When counting in English, the number is followed by the word for what is being counted (i.e. a person, two cats, three houses). In Korean, there are many words used as counting units for different subjects which are similar to words in English such as "loaf" of bread, "glass" of water, "sticks" of butter, and "cubes" of ice.

There are SO many counters in Korean that it is impossible to memorize them all at once. Learning the counters one by one as you practice or as you need them is a little less overwhelming and may help you learn them more efficiently.

Ex)

English: number + noun	Korean: noun + number + counter
1. a car	1. "car" + one + "counter for cars"
2. two pencils	2. "pencil" + two + "counter for pencils"
3. three books	3. "book" + three + "counter for books"

53

There are literally hundreds of counters in the Korean language, but not all of them are always used. As long as the speakers understand each other, some people just use the simplest and easiest counter to count certain words and it does not confuse anyone. For example, in Korean, a pencil is 연필 and the counter for pencils is 자루. The word 자루 is also
[yeon-pil]   [ja-ru]
used for counting pens, bags containing grain, and knives. Instead of using the word 자루 all the time for 연필, many people just use the general counter for things, which is 개.
[gae]

연필 한 자루 = one pencil
[yeon-pil han ja-ru]
연필 한 개 = one pencil
[yeon-pil han gae]

This does NOT work for all counters. Some common counters are almost never replaced with 개. For example, the counter for cars is 대, and it is never replaced with 개. In other
[dae]
words, changing 연필 한 자루 to 연필 한 개 is okay, but changing 차 한 대 to 차 한 개 is not okay and considered incorrect.

🎙️
Track 17

The counter 대 is used more frequently than the counter 자루. However, as a learner of the Korean language, if you find yourself using the wrong counter, you will be given feedback so you will remember better next time. It is better to say something in Korean than choosing not to say anything at all! Making mistakes is part of the learning process, so do not be too hard on yourself when you mess up. The person listening to you will, more than likely, be impressed with your skills anyway and just offer the correction without judgment.

In this lesson, remember these two most frequently used counters, 개 and 명.
[myeong]

개 as a noun in Korean means "dog", but when used as a counter, it is used for counting things and objects. 명 is used for counting people.

54

The majority of the time, counters are used with native Korean numbers.

Conjugation:

Numbers + 개 (counter for things)

1 = 하나 → 한 개
    [ha-na]   [han]

2 = 둘 → 두 개
    [dul]   [du]

3 = 셋 → 세 개
    [set]   [se]

4 = 넷 → 네 개
    [net]   [ne]

5 = 다섯 → 다섯 개
    [da-seot]

6 = 여섯 → 여섯 개
    [yeo-seot]

7 = 일곱 → 일곱 개
    [il-gop]

8 = 여덟 → 여덟 개
    [yeo-deol]

9 = 아홉 → 아홉 개
    [a-hop]

10 = 열 → 열 개
    [yeol]

Do you remember the irregularity rule for these numbers (plus 20)?

Track 17

From 11 to 20

열한 개, 열두 개, 열세 개, 열네 개, 열다섯 개, 열여섯 개, 열일곱 개, 열여덟 개,
[yeol-han] [yeol-ttu] [yeol-sse] [yeol-le] [yeol-tta-seot] [yeol-lyeo-seot] [yeol-lil-gop] [yeol-lyeo-deol]

열아홉 개, 스무 개
[yeo-ra-hop] [seu-mu]

From 21 to 30

스물한 개, 스물두 개, 스물세 개, 스물네 개, 스물다섯 개, 스물여섯 개, 스물일곱 개,
[seu-mul-han] [seu-mul-ttu] [seu-mul-sse] [seu-mul-le] [seu-mul-da-seot] [seu-mul-lyeo-seot] [seu-mu-ril-gop]

스물여덟 개, 스물아홉 개, 서른 개
[seu-mul-lyeo-deol] [seu-mu-ra-hop] [seo-reun]

Ex)

one apple = 사과 + 1 + 개 = 사과 한 개
[sa-gwa]

two stones = 돌 + 2 + 개 = 돌 두 개
[dol]

five balls = 공 + 5 + 개 = 공 다섯 개
[gong]

how many (things) = 몇 + 개 = 몇 개
[myeot]

Use the counter 명 for "people".

one person = 한 명

two students = 학생 + 2 + 명 = 학생 두 명
[hak-ssaeng]

three friends = 친구 + 3 + 명 = 친구 세 명
[chin-gu]

how many (people) = 몇 + 명 = 몇 명

Track 17

The word for "people" or "person", 사람, is also used when generally referring to a small
[sa-ram]
number of people without specifying who they are.

Ex)

Q: How many people are there?

A: There are 10 people.

= Q: 몇 명 있어요?
[myeot myeong i-sseo-yo?]
A: 10명 있어요.
[yeol myeong i-sseo-yo.]

= Q: 몇 사람 있어요?

A: 열 사람 있어요. (This is unnatural).

→ A: 두 사람 있어요. (two people - this is okay).

Check out a few more commonly used counters:

병 = bottles
[byeong]

    몇 병 = how many bottles
    [myeot byeong]

마리 = animals
[ma-ri]

    개 한 마리 = one dog
    [gae han ma-ri]

    새 한 마리 = one bird
    [sae han ma-ri]

    오리 세 마리 = three ducks
    [o-ri se ma-ri]

대 = vehicles, machinery
[dae]

    차 한 대 = one car
    [cha han dae]

    비행기 세 대 = three airplanes
    [bi-haeng-gi se dae]

권 = books
[gwon]

    책 한 권 = one book
    [chaek han gwon]

    책 두 권 = two books
    [chaek du gwon]

장 = paper, pages, tickets
[jang]

    종이 한 장 = a sheet of paper
    [jong-i han jang]

Track 17

Sample Sentences

아줌마 김치찌개 한 개 주세요.
[a-jum-ma gim-chi-jji-gae han gae ju-se-yo.]
= Ma'am, please give me one kimchi stew.

    찌개 = stew

콜라 한 병 주세요.
[kol-la han byeong ju-se-yo.]
= Please give me a bottle of cola.

Sample Dialogue

A: 의자 몇 개 필요해요?
[ui-ja myeot gae pi-ryo-hae-yo?]

B: 스무 개요.
[seu-mu gae-yo.]

A: 지금 스무 명 있어요?
[ji-geum seu-mu myeong i-sseo-yo?]

B: 아니요. 그런데 곧 올 거예요.
[a-ni-yo. geu-reon-de got ol kkeo-ye-yo.]

A: How many chairs do you need?

B: 20 chairs.

A: Are there 20 people now?

B: No, but people will come soon.

✏️ Exercises for Lesson 9

Translate the following to Korean.

1. When counting objects: "three things".

( )

2. When counting people: "five people".

( )

3. How do you write "three chairs" in Korean? The word for "chair" is 의자.
[ui-ja]

( )

4. "How many people are there?"

( )

5. "There are two people."

( )

Check the answers on **p.197**

59

LESSON **10**

Present Progressive

-고 있어요

Track 19

Don't be "tense" about another lesson on tenses! You will be able to form sentences in the present progressive tense (현재 진행형) in Korean.
[hyeon-jae ji-naeng-hyeong]

Examples of present progressive sentences in English:

1. I'm reading a book.

2. What are you watching?

3. He's helping me a lot.

> ### *Conjugation:*
>
> - to be -ing = Verb stem + **-고 있다**
> [-go it-tta]
> **보다** = to see
> [bo-da]
> **보고 있다** = to be seeing
> [bo-go it-tta]

Conjunctions, Tenses,

Present progressive:

- am/are/is -ing = Verb stem + -고 있어요
[-go i-sseo-yo]

밖에 비가 오고 있어요. = It is raining outside.
[ba-kke bi-ga o-go i-sseo-yo.]
밖에 눈이 오고 있어요. = It is snowing outside.
[ba-kke nu-ni o-go i-sseo-yo.]
밖에 바람이 불고 있어요. = The wind is blowing outside.
[ba-kke ba-ra-mi bul-go i-sseo-yo.]

Past progressive:

- was/were -ing = Verb stem + -고 있었어요
[-go i-sseo-sseo-yo]

눈이 오고 있었어요. = It was snowing.
[nu-ni o-go i-sseo-sseo-yo.]
비가 오고 있었어요. = It was raining.
[bi-ga o-go i-sseo-sseo-yo.]
바람이 불고 있었어요. = The wind was blowing.
[ba-ra-mi bul-go i-sseo-sseo-yo.]
경은 씨가 자고 있었어요. = Kyeong-eun was sleeping.
[gyeong-eun ssi-ga ja-go i-sseo-sseo-yo.]

Track 19

Future progressive:

- will be -ing = Verb stem + -고 있을 거예요
[-go i-sseul kkeo-ye-yo]

Past and future progressive sentences are quite common in Korean and are used almost every day. Having a thorough understanding of how to use the present progressive form will make learning past and future progressive quite easy.

61

When using the present progressive tense, there are two important points to remember:

1

Literal translation between Korean present progressive sentences and English present progressive sentences does not always work, especially when using the present progressive form in English to indicate the future.

For example, "I'm not going to work tomorrow" in English is talking about the future; therefore in Korean, -고 있어요 cannot be used.

2

In everyday conversations, sentences which need to be in the present progressive form do not always take the -고 있어요 form. Koreans often just use the plain present tense form even for sentences that would normally be present progressive tense in English.

Track 19

Ex)

Instead of saying:

A: 지금 뭐 하고 있어요? = What are you doing now?
[ji-geum mwo ha-go i-sseo-yo?]
B: 공부하고 있어요. = I am studying.
[gong-bu-ha-go i-sseo-yo.]

many people say:

A: 지금 뭐 해요? = What are you doing now?
[ji-geum mwo hae-yo?]
B: 공부해요. = I am studying.
[gong-bu-hae-yo.]

Sample Sentences

일하다 = to work
[i-ra-da]
일하고 있어요. = I am working.
[i-ra-go i-sseo-yo.]
일하고 있었어요. = I was working.

일하고 있을 거예요. = I will be working.

듣다 = to listen
[deut-tta]
듣고 있어요. = I am listening.
[deut-kko i-sseo-yo.]
듣고 있었어요. = I was listening.

듣고 있을 거예요. = I will be listening.

생각하다 = to think
[saeng-ga-ka-da]
생각하고 있어요. = I am thinking.
[saeng-ga-ka-go i-sseo-yo.]
생각하고 있었어요. = I was thinking.

생각하고 있을 거예요. = I will be thinking.

Track 19

졸다 = to doze off
[jol-da]
졸고 있어요. = I am dozing off.
[jol-go i-sseo-yo.]
졸고 있었어요. = I was dozing off.

졸고 있을 거예요. = I will be dozing off.

Sample Dialogue

Track
20

A: 그 영상 봤어요?
[geu yeong-sang bwa-sseo-yo?]

B: 지금 보고 있어요.
[ji-geum bo-go i-sseo-yo.]

A: 재미있어요?
[jae-mi-i-sseo-yo?]

B: 네, 재미있어요.
[ne, jae-mi-i-sseo-yo.]

A: Have you watched the video?

B: I am watching it now.

A: Is it interesting?

B: Yes, it is interesting.

✎ Exercises for Lesson 10

Translate the following sentences to Korean:

1. "I am reading a book."
(읽다 = to read)
[ik-tta]
(   )

2. "What are you doing?"
(   )

3. "What were you doing?"
(   )

4. "I was sleeping."
(   )

5. "I will be studying."
(   )

Check the answers on **p.197**

BLOG

NAMSAN
(남산)

남산 (Namsan, literally "South Mountain") stands in the middle of Seoul, surrounded by major shopping districts and an ever-growing and modernizing city. However, many generations ago, 남산 marked the southern border of Seoul.

This mountain is easily accessible from many different points in Seoul because of its central location. For example, it is a 20-30 minute walk from Subway lines 1 or 2, 시청역 (City Hall Station) in Jung-gu. It is also right outside of Subway line 6, 한강진역 (Hangangjin Station) and very close to Subway line 3, 동대입구역 (Dongguk University Station).

There is more to 남산 than N. Seoul Tower, a.k.a. Namsan Tower or 남산타워. One of the most popular destinations aside from the tower for tourists and Seoulites alike during the springtime is the Namsan Circular Road that connects the Namsan Library to the Palgakjeong. The cherry blossom trees that line this road are absolutely beautiful and well worth the hike to get there.

Almost every part of 남산 is full of lush, natural green landscape that offers a great contrast to the tall buildings and paved streets of the surrounding metropolis. The entire mountain and surrounding area is known as 남산 공원 (Namsan Park). 남산 공원 contains many places of interest, including the National Theater, Namsan Public Library, and several statues in memorial of Korean patriots. The park also contains Palgakjeong (an octagonal pavilion), an aquarium, a fountain, and a cable car leading to Seoul Tower.

Since 남산 is, well, a 산, an added benefit of the placement of this mountain is that you can enjoy hiking without having to travel very far away. While hiking one of the many trails on 남산, you can enjoy the multitude of trees, plants, and animals as well as take advantage of the exercise equipment. You might have to fight off some 아줌마 or 아저씨 to use it, but it'll be a good way to practice your Korean!

남산 is also one of the best places in Seoul to get a panoramic view of the city. Whether you go during the day or at night, you won't be disappointed. There are various photo spots and viewing platforms along the walking trails that give you the best view possible and help you catch spectacular photos of your memories that will last a lifetime.

Congratulations!
You've made it past lesson 10!
You're nearly half way finished with Level 2!
화이팅!

LESSON **11**

Self Introduction

Track 21

| 자기소개 |

By using what you have learned so far, you can already express many things about yourself. In this lesson, you will add to that knowledge and learn vocabulary, phrases, and sentence patterns which are specific and absolutely necessary for introducing yourself in Korean.

자기소개 self-introduction
[ja-gi-so-gae]

There are thousands of different things you could reveal when introducing yourself, but to generalize, some of the most common information is:

- name
- age
- place of living
- work

- school

- family members

- hobby

- greetings

Self-introductions are personal, and each situation is different. You may feel like revealing a lot of information about yourself, or just a little, so there is no need to try to memorize every sentence related to introductions. No single detailed chapter on self-introductions can cover everything you need to know every time you introduce yourself.

There are a few frequently used sentence patterns to use whenever you introduce yourself.

I. ABC은/는 XYZ이에요. = ABC is XYZ.
[ABC-eun/neun XYZ-i-e-yo.]

Track 21

Ex)

I'm a student. = 저는 학생이에요.
[jeo-neun hak-ssaeng-i-e-yo.]

I'm a teacher. = 저는 선생님이에요.
[jeo-neun seon-saeng-ni-mi-e-yo.]

I'm James. = 저는 제임스예요.
[jeo-neun je-im-sseu-ye-yo.]

My name is Stephen. = 제 이름은 스티븐이에요.
[je i-reu-meun seu-ti-beu-ni-e-yo.]

My sister's name is Taliana. = 제 여동생 이름은 탈리아나예요.
[je yeo-dong-saeng i-reu-meun tal-li-a-na-ye-yo.]

I am 30 years old. = 저는 30살이에요.
[jeo-neun seo-reun-sa-ri-e-yo.]

My name is Choi Kyeungeun. = 제 이름은 최경은이에요.
[je i-reu-meun choe-gyeong-eu-ni-e-yo.]

My age is a secret. = 제 나이는 비밀이에요.
[je na-i-neun bi-mi-ri-e-yo.]

And I am a Korean teacher. = 그리고 저는 한국어 선생님이에요.
[geu-ri-go jeo-neun han-gu-geo seon-saeng-ni-mi-e-yo.]

2. ABC은/는 XYZ이/가 + VERB = As for ABC, XYZ + VERB.
[ABC-eun/neun XYZ-i/ga]

Ex)

저는 여동생이 있어요. = I have a younger sister. (lit. "As for me, a younger sister exists".)
[jeo-neun yeo-dong-saeng-i i-sseo-yo.]
저는 남동생이 있어요. = I have a younger brother.
[jeo-neun nam-dong-saeng-i i-sseo-yo.]
저는 언니가 있어요. = I have an older sister.
[jeo-neun eon-ni-ga i-sseo-yo.]
저는 취미가 없어요. = I don't have any hobbies. (lit. "As for me, the hobby doesn't exist".)
[jeo-neun chwi-mi-ga eop-sseo-yo.]
저는 취미가 수영이에요. = My hobby is swimming. (lit. "As for me, the hobby, swimming is".)
[jeo-neun chwi-mi-ga su-yeong-i-e-yo.]

3. ABC은/는 XYZ에/에서 + VERB = ABC + VERB + in XYZ.
[ABC-eun/neun XYZ-e/e-seo]

Track 21

Ex)

저는 서울에 살아요. = I live in Seoul.
[jeo-neun seo-u-re sa-ra-yo.]
저는 은행에서 일해요. = I work in a bank.
[jeo-neun eu-naeng-e-seo i-rae-yo.]
저는 대학교에서 중국어를 가르쳐요. = I teach Chinese in college.
[jeo-neun dae-hak-kkyo-e-seo jung-gu-geo-reul ga-reu-chyeo-yo.]
저는 미국에서 태어났어요. = I was born in the USA.
[jeo-neun mi-gu-ge-seo tae-eo-na-sseo-yo.]

Important and useful vocabulary words:

나이 = age
[na-i]
취미 = hobby
[chwi-mi]
직장 = workplace
[jik-jjang]
직업 = job = 하는 일
[ji-geop]
사는 곳 = place of living
[sa-neun got]
가족 = family
[ga-jok]

72

친척 = relatives, extended family
[chin-cheok]

대학생 = university student
[dae-hak-ssaeng]

고등학생 = high school student
[go-deung-hak-ssaeng]

중학생 = middle school student
[jung-hak-ssaeng]

초등학생 = elementary school student
[cho-deung-hak-ssaeng]

Useful greetings:

처음 뵙겠습니다. = How do you do?
[cheo-eum boep-kke-sseum-ni-da.]

반갑습니다. = It's nice to meet you.
[ban-gap-sseum-ni-da.]

제 명함이에요. = It's my business card.
[je myeong-ha-mi-e-yo.]

다음에 또 봬요. = See you again next time.
[da-eu-me tto bwae-yo.]

이야기 많이 들었어요. = I've heard a lot about you.
[i-ya-gi ma-ni deu-reo-sseo-yo.]

Track 21

Sample Dialogue

A: 안녕하세요. 처음 뵙겠습니다.
[an-nyeong-ha-se-yo. cheo-eum boep-kke-sseum-ni-da.]

B: 안녕하세요.
[an-nyeong-ha-se-yo.]

A: 저는 지금 대학교에서 한국어를
공부하고 있어요.
[jeo-neun ji-geum dae-hak-kkyo-e-seo han-gu-geo-reul
gong-bu-ga-go i-sseo-yo.]

B: 아! 반갑습니다. 저는 온라인에서
한국어를 가르치고 있어요.
[a! ban-gap-sseum-ni-da. jeo-neun ol-la-i-ne-seo
han-gu-geo-reul ga-reu-chi-go i-sseo-yo.]

A: Hello. How do you do?

B: Hello.

A: I am currently studying the Korean
language at university.

B: Oh! Nice to meet you. I am teaching
the Korean language online.

Conjunctions, Tenses,

✐ Exercises for Lesson 11

Translate the following phrases to Korean:

1. "I am a student."

(   )

2. "My name is Minsu."
(이름 = name, 제 이름 = "My name")

(   )

3. "I am *20* years old."

(   )

4. "I live in Seoul."

(   )

5. "It's nice to meet you."

(   )

Check the answers on **p.197**

75

LESSON 12

What is the Date?

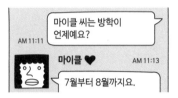

마이클 씨는 방학이
언제예요?
AM 11:11

마이클 ♥   AM 11:13

7월부터 8월까지요.

날짜

Track 23

After studying with this lesson, you will be able to say and identify the months of the year and the days in a month in Korean. You will also be able to answer questions regarding the date as well as ask questions related to dates.

Names of the months

In Korean, the names for the 12 months in a year are very simple. Just add the word 월,
[wol]
which means "month", after every corresponding sino-Korean number.

January = 1월
[i-rwol]

February = 2월
[i-wol]

March = 3월
[sa-mwol]

April = 4월
[sa-wol]

May = 5월
[o-wol]

June = 6월
[yu-wol]

July = 7월
[chi-rwol]

August = 8월
[pa-rwol]

September = 9월
[gu-wol]

October = 10월
[si-wol]

November = 11월
[si-bi-rwol]

December = 12월
[si-bi-wol]

Which month: 몇 월
[myeot wol = myeo-dwol]

76

Days in a month

Simply add the sino-Korean number to the Korean word 일, which means "day".
                                                                    [il]

Ex)

1 + 일 = 1일
            [i-ril]
2 + 일 = 2일
            [i-il]
⋮

29 + 일 = 29일
             [i-sip-kku-il]
30 + 일 = 30일
             [sam-si-bil]

What date: 며칠
            [myeo-chil]

Track 23

* 몇 월 *has* 몇 *as a standalone word whereas* 며칠 *is a combination of* 몇 *and* 일. *For the sake of smoother and easier pronunciation, the* ㅊ *from* 몇 *is carried over to take the place of the* ㅇ *in* 일.

What month and what date: 몇 월 며칠
                          [myeo-dwol myeo-chil]

Sample Sentences

몇 월 며칠이에요? = What is the date?
[myeo-dwol myeo-chi-ri-e-yo?]
오늘 몇 월 며칠이에요? = What is today's date?
[o-neul]
생일이 몇 월 며칠이에요? = What date is your birthday?
[saeng-i-ri]

When mentioning a specific day, 언제, which means "when", can also be used.
                                 [eon-je]
생일이 언제예요? = When is your birthday?
[eon-je-ye-yo?]

77

Sample Dialogue

Track
24

A: 마이클 씨는 방학이 언제예요?
[ma-i-keul ssi-neun bang-ha-gi eon-je-ye-yo?]

B: 7월부터 8월까지요.
[chi-rwol-bu-teo pa-rwol-kka-ji-yo.]

A: 7월 1일부터요?
[chi-rwol i-ril-bu-teo-yo?]

B: 아니요. 7월 5일부터요.
[a-ni-yo. chi-rwol o-il-bu-teo-yo.]

A: When is your school vacation, Michael?

B: It is from July to August.

A: Starting July 1st?

B: No. It starts July 5th.

✎ Exercises for Lesson 12

1. In Korean, the word for month is 월. How do you say September?

( )

2. What is the word for "day" or "days" in Korean?

( )

3. How do you say "September 25th"?

( )

4. How do you ask "What month?"

( )

5. How do you ask "What date?"

( )

6. How do you ask "What date is your birthday?"

( )

Check the answers on **p.197**

Telling Time, and More

LESSON 13

Too, Also

-도 (Part 1)

If you have been studying with this book series starting with Level 1, you have learned a handful of different particles up to this point: -이/가 (subject marking particles), -은/는(topic
[-i/ga]   [-eun/neun]
marking particles), and -을/를 (object marking particles). Are you ready to add one more
              [-eul/reul]
particle to the bunch? :D

-도 is used to represent the meaning of **"also"** and **"too"**.
[-do]

In English, the placement of the words "too", "also", or "as well" varies depending on the speaker. Most of the time they are added to the end of a sentence, but sometimes they can be placed in the middle or near the beginning next to the subject. In Korean, however, -도 is treated as a particle and ALWAYS follows the noun or pronoun.

Ex)

1. I like it, too.

   저도 좋아요.
   [jeo-do jo-a-yo.]

2. I think so as well.

저도 그런 것 같아요.
[jeo-do geu-reon geot ga-ta-yo.]

3. I, too, saw it.

저도 봤어요.
[jeo-do bwa-sseo-yo.]

In these sentences "too" and "as well" were used to modify different things. In the last sentence, "I, too, saw it", the word "too" is modifying "I". If you literally translate this to Korean, it becomes "저도 봤어요". Adding -도 right after 저, which means "I", in this case
[jeo-do bwa-sseo-yo.]
modifies "I" just as in the English sentence.

When the particle -도 needs to be attached to a noun or a pronoun which already has a particle behind it, -도 can replace the particle.

Track
25

Sample Sentences

I am a student.

= 저는 학생이에요.
[jeo-neun hak-ssaeng-i-e-yo.]

I am a student, too.

= 저도 학생이에요.
[jeo-do hak-ssaeng-i-e-yo.]

 * Note that it is NOT "저는도 학생이에요".

I brought this.

= 이것 가져왔어요.
[i-geot ga-jeo-wa-sseo-yo.]

I brought this, too.

= 이것도 가져왔어요.
[i-geot-tto ga-jeo-wa-sseo-yo.]

Do you work today?

= 오늘 일해요?
[o-neul il-hae-yo?]

Do you work today as well?

= 오늘도 일해요?
[o-neul-do il-hae-yo?]

Depending on the location of the particle -도, the meaning of the entire sentence can change.

In Korean, "please give me water" is said as "물 주세요".
[mul ju-se-yo]

To say "give water to me, too, not just other people", say: 저도 물 주세요.
[jeo-do]

Track 25

"Please give some water to me, too". = 저도 물 주세요.

To say "give me, not only other things, but water as well", say: 저 물도 주세요.
[jeo mul-do ju-se-yo.]

"Please also give some water to me". = 저 물도 주세요.

Sample Dialogue

Track 26

A: 오늘도 야근해요?
[o-neul-do ya-geun-hae-yo?]

B: 네. 알렉스 씨도 야근하고 있어요?
[ne. al-lek-sseu ssi-do ya-geun-ha-go i-sseo-yo?]

A: 네.
[ne.]

B: 힘내세요. 파이팅!
[him-nae-se-yo. pa-i-ting!]

A: Do you work overtime today as well?

B: Yes. Are you also working overtime, Alex?

A: Yes.

B: Cheer up. Let's do this!

🖋 Exercises for Lesson 13

1. "I am a teacher" is "저는 선생님이에요."
   [jeo-neun seon-saeng-ni-mi-e-yo.]
   Please write "I am a teacher, too" in Korean.

   (   )

2. "Do you study Korean?" is "한국어 공부해요?"
   [han-gu-geo gong-bu-hae-yo?]
   How do you ask "Do you study Korean, too (in addition to other languages)?"

   (   )

3. "Do you work today?" is "오늘 일해요?"
   [o-neul il-hae-yo?]
   How do you ask "Do you work today as well?"

   (   )

Check the answers on **p.197**

4. "There is water" is "물이 있어요"
   [mu-ri i-sseo-yo.]
   Please write "There is water, too" in Korean.

   (   )

5. Write "Give me this, too" in Korean. There can be two ways.

   (   )

Conjunctions, Tenses,

LESSON **14**

Too, Also

-도 (Part 2)

In the previous lesson, you learned how to use -도 with pronouns and nouns to mean
[-do]
"[noun], too" or "[pronoun] also." Do you remember the formula?

Track 27

Take a moment to review:

내일 = Tomorrow
[nae-il]
내일도 = Tomorrow, too.
[nae-il-do]

우유 = Milk
[u-yu]
우유도 = Milk, also.
[u-yu-do]

나 = Me
[na]
나도 = Me, too.
[na-do]

85

물 주세요. = Give me water, please.
[mul ju-se-yo.]
물도 주세요. = Give me water, too, please.
[mul-do ju-se-yo.]

내일 갈 거예요. = I will go tomorrow.
[nae-il gal kkeo-ye-yo.]
내일도 갈 거예요. = I will go (again) tomorrow, too.
[nae-il-do gal kkeo-ye-yo.]

Now that using -도 with nouns and pronouns is fresh in your memory, you can learn how to use -도 with verbs! However, using -도 with verbs as they are is not possible!

Wait. What?!

"How will I learn to use -도 with verbs if it's not possible?"

Well, if you change the verb into its noun form, it is absolutely possible to use -도 with verbs.

By changing a verb into its noun form and adding the verb 하다, it literally translates to "to
[ha-da]
do + verb in noun form + also". It may seem complicated at first, but try to think of -도 하다 as a set when it comes to using -도 with verbs.

How to change a verb to its noun form

There are a few different ways to change a verb into its noun form, but the simplest and most common way is by adding -기 to the verb stem. This is similar to using verbs in the "to
[-gi]
do [verb]" and "[verb]ing" format.

Ex)

보다 = to see
[bo-da]

Noun form: 보 + -기 = 보기 (= to do the act of seeing; seeing)
[bo-gi]

보다 → 보기도 하다 = to also see, to even see
[bo-gi-do ha-da]

먹다 = to eat
[meok-tta]

Noun form: 먹 + -기 = 먹기 (= to do the act of eating; eating)
[meok-kki]

먹기 → 먹기도 하다 = to also eat, to even eat
[meok-kki-do ha-da]

잡다 = to catch
[jap-tta]

→ 잡기도 하다 = to also catch; to even catch
[jap-kki-do ha-da]

팔다 = to sell
[pal-da]

→ 팔기도 하다 = to also sell; to even sell
[pal-gi-do ha-da]

사다 = to buy
[sa-da]

→ 사기도 하다 = to also buy; to even buy
[sa-gi-do ha-da]

Track 27

* *Verbs in "noun + 하다" form already (i.e. 공부하다, 청소하다, 노래하다, 준비하다, 요리하다,*
[gong-bu-ha-da], [cheong-so-ha-da], [no-rae-ha-da], [jun-bi-ha-da], [yo-ri-ha-da]

etc.) don't have to be changed in this manner. Just separate the noun from 하다 and add -도 after

the noun (i.e. 공부도 하다, 청소도 하다, 노래도 하다, 준비도 하다, 요리도 하다, etc.)

Sample Sentences

저는 영어를 가르쳐요.
[jeo-neun yeong-eo-reul ga-reu-chyeo-yo.]
= I teach English.

저는 영어도 가르쳐요.
[jeo-neun yeong-eo-do ga-reu-chyeo-yo.]
= I teach English as well.

저는 영어를 가르치기도 해요.
[jeo-neun yeong-eo-reul ga-reu-chi-gi-do hae-yo.]

= I also teach English.

= I even teach English.

= I also work as an English teacher.

컴퓨터를 고쳐요.
[keom-pyu-teo-reul go-chyeo-yo.]
= I fix computers.

컴퓨터도 고쳐요.
[keom-pyu-teo-do go-chyeo-yo.]
= I fix computers as well.

컴퓨터를 고치기도 해요.
[keom-pyu-teo-reul go-chi-gi-do hae-yo.]
= I also fix computers.

= I even fix computers.

Track 27

Sample Dialogue

Track 28

A: 여기는 서점이에요, 도서관이에요?
[yeo-gi-neun seo-jeo-mi-e-yo, do-seo-gwa-ni-e-yo?]

B: 서점이에요. 그런데 책을 빌려주기도 해요.
[seo-jeo-mi-e-yo. geu-reon-de chae-geul bil-lyeo-ju-gi-do hae-yo.]

A: 우와!
[u-wa!]

A: Is this place a bookstore or a library?

B: It is a bookstore. However, we also lend out some books.

A: Wow!

✏ Exercises for Lesson 14

1. "To see" is "보다". How do you say "to also see" or "to even see"?

(   )

2. "To sell" is "팔다". How do you write "to also sell" or "to even sell"?

(   )

3. How do you say "I teach English"?

(   )

4. How do you write "I also teach English" or "I even teach English" with focus being on the act of teaching?

(   )

5. "수학" is "mathematics". How do you say "I also teach math" with focus being on the act of
[su-hak]
teaching?

(   )

LESSON 15

Only

-만

There are a few different ways to say "only" in Korean, but to prevent your brain from being overloaded, only one of those ways will be covered in this lesson.

**Track
29**

Using -만 is one of the most widely used and basic ways of saying "only". Simply add -만 after
[-man]
a noun, pronoun, or noun form (-기) of a verb.
                              [-gi]

I. Adding -만 after nouns and pronouns

이것 + 만 = 이것만 = only this
              [i-geon-man]

    Ex) 이것만 살 거예요. = I will only buy this.
    [i-geon-man sal kkeo-ye-yo.]

저 + 만 = 저만 = me only, I only
         [jeo-man]
    Ex) 저만 들었어요. = Only I heard.
[jeo-man deu-reo-sseo-yo.]

커피 + 만 = 커피만 = only coffee
[keo-pi-man]

Ex) 아침에는 커피만 마셔요. = I only drink coffee in the morning.
[a-chi-me-neun keo-pi-man ma-syeo-yo.]

아침에만 커피(를) 마셔요. = I drink coffee only in the morning.
[a-chi-me-man keo-pi-(reul) ma-syeo-yo.]

2. Adding -만 after noun forms of verbs

* *To add* -**만** *after a verb, change the verb into its noun form using* -**기**, *then add* -**만 하다** *which*
[-man ha-da]
literally translates to "*only do [noun]*".

듣다 = to hear; to listen
[deut-tta]

듣 + 기 = 듣기 = listening (noun form)
[deut-kki]

듣 + -기 + -만 하다 = 듣기만 하다 = to only listen
[deut-kki-man ha-da]

Ex) 듣기만 했어요. = I only listened (and didn't talk).
[deut-kki-man hae-sseo-yo.]

보다 = to see, to look
[bo-da]

보 + 기 = 보기 = seeing, looking
[bo-gi]

보 + -기 + -만 하다 = 보기만 하다 = to only see, to just look
[bo-gi-man ha-da]

Ex) 보기만 할 거예요. = I will only look (and not touch it).
[bo-gi-man hal kkeo-ye-yo.]

Sample Sentences

오늘만 일찍 왔어요.
[o-neul-man il-jjik wa-sseo-yo.]
= I got here early only today.

오늘 = today

일찍 = early

왔어요. = I came, I got here.

책 한 권만 주문했어요.
[chaek han gwon-man ju-mun-hae-sseo-yo.]
= I only ordered one book.

책 한 권 = one book

주문했어요. = I ordered.

왜 이것만 샀어요?
[wae i-geon-man sa-sseo-yo?]
= Why did you only buy this?

사다 = to buy
[sa-da]
샀어요. = I bought it.

이것 = this, this stuff
[i-geot]
왜 = why

**Track
29**

어제 놀기만 했어요.
[eo-je nol-gi-man hae-sseo-yo.]
= I did nothing but play yesterday.

놀다 = to play
[nol-da]
어제 = yesterday

영화는 집에서만 봐요.
[yeong-hwa-neun ji-be-seo-man bwa-yo.]
= I watch movies only at home.

영화 = a movie

집에서 = at home

Sample Dialogue

A: 왜 책상만 있어요? 의자는 없어요?
[wae chaek-sang-man i-sseo-yo? ui-ja-neun eop-sseo-yo?]

B: 의자도 올 거예요.
[ui-ja-do ol kkeo-ye-yo.]

A: 언제요?
[eon-je-yo?]

B: 내일 올 거예요.
[nae-il ol kkeo-ye-yo.]

A: Why is there only a desk? There's no chair?

B: A chair will come, too.

A: When?

B: It will come tomorrow.

94

✏ Exercises for Lesson 15

1. What is the word for "only" which is attached after nouns and pronouns?

(   )

2. How do you say "this only"?

(   )

3. "To see" is "보다". How do you say "to only see"?

(   )

4. How do you write "I only drink coffee"?

(   )

5. "To order" is "주문하다". How do you say "I only ordered one book"?
[ju-mu-na-da]

(   )

Check the answers on **p.197**

LESSON 16

A bit, Really, Very, Not really, Not at all

조금, 정말, 진짜, 아주, 별로, 전혀

Track 31

By the end of this lesson, you will be able to create sentences with stronger emphasis and richer context. You CAN keep your sentences very simple, but being able to add "really", "truly", "a little", "very", or "not really" to emphasize a point can really kick your Korean fluency up a notch!

Please take a look at the following five words and how they are used in Korean sentences:

조금 = a little, a bit, a little bit
[jo-geum]

정말 = really, truly
[jeong-mal]

아주 = very, quite
[a-ju]

별로 = not really, not particularly
[byeol-lo]

전혀 = not at all
[jeo-nyeo]

* 조금, 아주, *and* 정말 *can be used with any sentence, but* 별로 *and* 전혀 *can only be used with negative sentences.*

조금 = a little, a bit, a little bit

Sample Sentences

조금 비싸요.
[jo-geum bi-ssa-yo.]
= It's a little expensive.

조금만 주세요.
[jo-geum-man ju-se-yo.]
= Give me only a little bit.

물 조금만 주세요.
[mul jo-geum-man ju-se-yo.]
= Give me only a little bit of water.

Track 31

소금 조금만 주세요.
[so-geum jo-geum-man ju-se-yo.]
= Give me only a little bit of salt.

* When pronounced quickly, **조금** often becomes **좀** (often pronounced like **쫌**) and is frequently
[jom]   [jjom]
written this way as well.

** The use of **조금** to mean "quite" or "very" is possible based on the assumption that the other person in the conversation understands what you mean. For example, in the first sample sentence, **조금 비싸요**, can mean both "it is a little expensive" or "it is quite expensive" depending on tone and context.

<h1 style="text-align:center">정말 = really, truly</h1>

Sample Sentences

정말 빨라요.
[ppal-la-yo.]
= It's really fast.

정말 이상해요.
[i-sang-hae-yo.]
= It's really strange.

* A word which has almost the same meaning as 정말 is 진짜. It is considered a little less formal
[jin-jja]
than 정말.

** Whereas other words introduced here are used to describe the extent to which something is
done or to describe the intensity of a certain state (i.e. "very" good, "a little" expensive or "quite"
fast), 정말 and 진짜 can also be used to just express whether or not what is being said is true. (i.e.
I "really" did it).

Sample Conversation

A: 제가 방 청소했어요!
[je-ga bang cheong-so-hae-sseo-yo!]
= I cleaned up my room!

B. 아... 진짜?
[ah...jin-jja?]
= Oh, really?

A: 예, 진짜! 보고 싶어요?
[ye, jin-jja! bo-go si-peo-yo?]
= Yeah, really! Do you want to see it?

아주 = very, quite

Sample Sentences

아주 맛있어요.
[ma-si-sseo-yo.]
= It's very delicious.

아주 멀어요.
[meo-reo-yo.]
= It's very far away.

* 아주 *is the most standard way of saying* "very" *in the written form, but more often than not, in spoken Korean,* 아주 *is replaced with* 정말 *or* 진짜.

Track 31

별로 = not really; not particularly

* 별로 *is always used in negative sentences, regardless of whether the verb that follows has a negative or a positive meaning.*

** *Rather than just using* 별로, *sometimes, in Korean,* 안 *must be added to the sentence to*
[an]
actually make the sentence a negative. Using 별로 *when speaking will allow the listener to guess that the end of the sentence will be something in negative form.*

Sample Sentences

별로 안 비싸요.
[an bi-ssa-yo.]
= It's not so expensive.

별로 재미없어요.
[jae-mi-eop-sseo-yo.]
= It's not that interesting.

* 재미없어요 *is one word, but because* 없어요 *is already within the word itself, it is possible to say* "별로 재미없어요".

별로 안 나빠요.
[an na-ppa-yo.]
= It's not too bad. (It's not the worst, but it's still bad. Note: this does not mean the same thing as the English phrase "it's not bad").

* *Even if the word* 나쁘다 *has a negative meaning, saying only* "별로 나쁘다" *does not work.*
[na-ppeu-da]   [byeol-lo na-ppeu-da]

전혀 = not at all

Track 31

Sample Sentences

전혀 안 바빠요.
[an ba-ppa-yo.]
= I'm not busy at all.

전혀 안 더워요.
[an deo-wo-yo.]
= It's not hot at all.

* *In spoken Korean, the expression* 하나도 *is used more commonly than* 전혀.
[ha-na-do]

Sample Dialogue

Track
32

A: 저랑 제 동생이랑 닮았어요?
[jeo-rang je dong-saeng-i-rang dal-ma-sseo-yo?]

B: 아니요, 전혀 안 닮았어요.
[a-ni-yo, jeon-hyeo an dal-ma-sseo-yo.]

A: 저하고 저희 엄마랑은요?
[jeo-ha-go jeo-hui eom-ma-rang-eun-nyo?]

B: 조금 닮았어요.
[jo-geum dal-ma-sseo-yo.]

A: *Do my younger sister/brother and I look alike?*

B: *No. You guys don't look like each other at all.*

A: *What about my mother and I?*

B: *You two look a little bit alike.*

101

Check the answers on **p.198**

✏ Exercises for Lesson 16

Translate the following sentences to Korean.

1. "It's a bit expensive."

( )

2. "It's very interesting."

( )

3. "It's really strange."

( )

4. "It's not that expensive."

( )

5. "It's not interesting at all."

( )

Conjunctions, Tenses,

LESSON **17**

Can, Cannot

-(으)ㄹ 수 있다/없다

When speaking Korean, whether just practicing or speaking out of necessity, there will come a point when knowing how to say "can (do something)" or "cannot (do something)" will come in handy.

Track 33

To say "can (do something)", use **-(으)ㄹ 수 있다**
[-(eu)l ssu it-tta]

> ### Conjugation
>
> **보다** = to see
> [bo-da]
> → 보 + -ㄹ 수 있다 = **볼 수 있다** = can see
> [bol ssu it-tta]
>
> **먹다** = to eat
> [meok-tta]
> → 먹 + -을 수 있다 = **먹을 수 있다** = can eat
> [meo-geul ssu it-tta]

* *Verb stems ending in a vowel are followed by* -ㄹ 수 있다, *and verb stems ending with a consonant are followed by* -을 수 있다. *The difference is whether there is an extra* 으 *or not in*

103

front of -ㄹ 수 있다 for the ease of pronunciation.

Regarding -(으)ㄹ 수 있다, the word 수 means an "idea" or "way" for solving a problem or for getting something finished. 수 has the same meaning as 방법 (a method); therefore,
[bang-beop]
-(으)ㄹ 수 있다 literally means "to have a way/idea (for doing something)".

When there is no "way" or "idea" to do something, it means that it cannot be done, and in Korean, this becomes **-(으)ㄹ 수 없다**. 없다 has the opposite meaning of 있다.
[-(eu)l ssu eop-tta]

Conjugation

자다 = to sleep
[ja-da]
→ 자 + -ㄹ 수 없다 = 잘 수 없다 = cannot sleep
[jal ssu eop-tta]
⟶ 잘 수 있다 = can sleep

잡다 = to catch
[jap-tta]
→ 잡 + -을 수 없다 = 잡을 수 없다 = cannot catch
[ja-beul ssu eop-tta]
⟶ 잡을 수 있다 = can catch

Another way to say -(으)ㄹ 수 없다 is by using the word 못 before a verb.
[mot]

-(으)ㄹ 수 없다 is the most basic way to express "cannot", but it is not always used in spoken Korean. A more common way to say "cannot" or "to be unable to" in spoken Korean is by adding 못 before a verb.

Conjunctions, Tenses,

갈 수 없다 = 못 가다 [verb: 가다] = cannot go
[gal ssu eop-tta]   [mot ga-da]

볼 수 없다 = 못 보다 [verb: 보다] = cannot see

먹을 수 없다 = 못 먹다 [verb: 먹다] = cannot eat

할 수 없다 = 못 하다 [verb: 하다] = cannot do
[hal ssu eop-tta]   [mot ha-da]

Sample Sentences

운전 할 수 있어요?
[un-jeon hal ssu i-sseo-yo?]
= Can you drive? (lit. "Can you do driving?")

일본어 할 수 있어요?
[il-bo-neo hal ssu i-sseo-yo?]
= Can you speak Japanese? (lit. "Can you do Japanese?")

Track 33

이거 읽을 수 있어요?
[i-geo il-geul ssu i-sseo-yo?]
= Can you read this?

못 읽어요.
[mot il-geo-yo.]
= I cannot read it.

지금 못 만나요.
[ji-geum mot man-na-yo.]
= I cannot meet you now.

Sample Dialogue

Track 34

A: 미경 씨, 기타 칠 수 있어요?
[mi-gyeong ssi, gi-ta chil ssu i-sseo-yo?]

B: 아니요. 그런데 곧 배울 거예요.
경화 씨는요?
[a-ni-yo. geu-reon-de got bae-ul kkeo-ye-yo.
gyeong-hwa ssi-neun-nyo?]

A: 저도 배울 거예요.
[jeo-do bae-ul kkeo-ye-yo.]

A: Mikyung, can you play the guitar?

B: No, but I am going to learn soon.
How about you, Kyung-hwa?

A: I am going to learn, too.

✎ Exercises for Lesson 17

1. "To go" is "가다". How do you say "I can go"?
[ga-da]

(   )

2. How do you say "I can't do it"?

(   )

3. Please write "Can you do this?"

(   )

4. Please write "Can we meet now?"

(   )

5. "To swim" is "수영하다". Please write "Can you swim?"
[su-yeong-ha-da]

(   )

Check the answers on **p.198**

LESSON 18

To be good/poor at ⋯

잘하다, 못하다

Track 35

In Lesson 17, you learned how to say "can" or "cannot" in Korean. Take that knowledge one step further by learning how to construct sentences to express that you are "good" or "bad" at doing something.

> ### Conjugation
>
> [object] + -을/를 (object marking particle) + 잘하다
> [-eul/reul]   [jal-ha-da]
> = to do [object] well; to be good at [object]
>
>
> [object] + -을/를 + 못하다
>   [mo-ta-da]
> = to do [object] poorly; to be bad at [object]

Ex)

노래 = singing; song
[no-rae]
노래를 잘하다 = to be good at singing; to sing well

Conjunctions, Tenses,

요리 = cooking, dish
[yo-ri]
요리를 못하다 = to be poor at cooking; to cook poorly

* Saying 못 하다 with a pause or space between 못 and 하다 gives the phrase the meaning of
[mot ha-da]
"to be unable to do (something)" or "cannot do (something)".

** 잘 is often added in front of 못하다 to make the meaning softer. By saying 잘 못하다, the
[jal]
meaning is literally "cannot do (something) well" or "unable to do (something) well".

요리를 못하다 = to be poor at cooking

요리를 잘 못하다 = to be poor at cooking

Ex)

**Track
35**

수영 = swimming
[su-yeong]
수영을 잘하다 = to be good at swimming
[su-yeong-eul jal-ha-da]
수영을 못하다 = to be bad at swimming
[su-yeong-eul mo-ta-da]
수영을 잘 못하다 = to be bad at swimming
[su-yeong-eul jal mo-ta-da]

* *IMPORTANT: Be very careful when saying* 잘 못하다. *Saying this phrase with a pause between*
잘 *and* 못, 잘 못하다, *gives the meaning "to be poor at (something)". Not placing a pause*
between 잘 *and* 못, *as in* 잘못 하다 *gives the impression of "to do (something) in the wrong*
[jal-mot ha-da]
way". Additionally, saying 잘못하다 *with no pause between any of the words means "to make a*
[jal-mo-ta-da]
mistake".

Are 잘 and 못 (or 잘 못) only used with -하다 verbs?

No. Other types of verbs can be used with 잘 and 못 as well. Since the first part of most
-하다 verbs are nouns, it is easy to detach the noun from -하다 and add 잘, 못, or 잘 못 in

109

front of -하다. For other types of verbs which are not in the "noun + -하다" form, just add 잘, 못, or 잘 못 in front of the verb with a space in between.

잘 달리다 = to run well, to be good at running
[dal-li-da]
잘 쓰다 = to write well, to be good at writing
[sseu-da]

When a verb is used on its own, however, often times the meaning is not very clear. For example, 쓰다 can mean both "to write" and "to use". The phrase sounds incomplete with only using a verb; therefore, a noun is added to the phrase to give the verb a more specific meaning.

Track 35

잘 쓰다 → 글을 잘 쓰다 (= to be good at writing; to be a good writer)
[geu-reul]
[lit. "to write well"]

글 is a noun meaning "written text", "a piece of writing", or "a composition".
[geul]

잘 쓰다 → 글씨를 잘 쓰다 (= to be good at handwriting; to have good penmanship)
[geul-ssi-reul]
[lit. "to write writing/letters well"]

Here, the word 글씨, meaning "writing" or "letters", is used to make the meaning of "writing" clearer and prevent people from thinking that it might mean "to use".

잘 달리다 → 달리기를 잘하다 (= to be good at running)
[dal-li-gi-reul]
[lit. "to do running well"]

달리다 was changed to its noun form here and followed by 잘하다.

110

Sample Sentences

저는 노래를 잘 못해요.
[jeo-neun no-rae-reul jal mo-tae-yo.]
= I can't sing well. / I'm not good at singing.

제 친구는 수영을 잘해요.
[je chin-gu-neun su-yeong-eul jal-hae-yo.]
= My friend is good at swimming.

저는 퍼즐을 잘 풀어요.
[jeo-neun peo-jeu-reul jal pu-reo-yo.]
= I am good at solving puzzles.

저는 글씨를 잘 못 써요.
[jeo-neun geul-ssi-reul jal mot sseo-yo.]
= My handwriting is not good.

저는 글을 잘 못 써요.
[jeo-neun geu-reul jal mot sseo-yo.]
= I'm not good at writing.

Track 35

매운 거 잘 먹어요?
[mae-un geo jal meo-geo-yo?]
= Are you good at eating spicy food?

111

Sample Dialogue

A: 경은 씨는 요리 잘해요?
[gyeong-eun ssi-neun yo-ri jal-hae-yo?]

B: 아니요, 잘 못해요. 석진 씨는요?
[a-ni-yo, jal mo-tae-yo. seok-jjin ssi-neun-nyo?]

A: 저도 잘 못해요.
[jeo-do jal mo-tae-yo.]

A: Are you a good cook, Kyeong-eun?

B: No, not really. How about you, Seokjin?

A: I am not good at it either.

✎ Exercises for Lesson 18

1. "To do" is "하다". How do you say "to do something well" or "to be good at doing something"?

(　　　　　　　　　　　　　　　　　　　　　　　　　　　)

2. How do you write "to be bad at doing something"?

(　　　　　　　　　　　　　　　　　　　　　　　　　　　)

3. What can you say to imply that you cannot do something or are unable to do something?

(　　　　　　　　　　　　　　　　　　　　　　　　　　　)

4. Write "I am good at swimming" in Korean.

(　　　　　　　　　　　　　　　　　　　　　　　　　　　)

5. How do you say "I'm not good at singing"?

(　　　　　　　　　　　　　　　　　　　　　　　　　　　)

Check the answers on **p.198**

113

LESSON 19

Making Verbs Into Nouns

-는 것

Track 37

In Level 2, Lesson 14, you learned how to add the meaning of "also" in Korean by adding -도 to a verb. In order to do this, however, the verb needs to be changed into its noun form [-do]

by adding -기 to the verb stem, then add -도, and end with 하다. (Is it all coming back to you [-gi] [ha-da]

now?)

In this lesson, you will expand that knowledge by looking at a more general way of making action verbs into nouns. Understanding this will help your understanding of how to form a number of expressions in Korean.

-는 것

This is the most general way of changing an action verb into a noun. 것 originally means "a thing", "an object", or "stuff", but when it is used in this way, it can also mean "a fact" or "an act".

114

Conjugation:

- Verb stem + -는 것
[-neun geot]

By changing verbs into nouns, the form [verb stem + -는 것] can take many different meanings:

1. "doing" something

2. the act of "doing" something

3. the thing which one "does"

4. what one "does"

5. the fact that one is "doing" or "does" something

Ex)

Track 37

보다 = to see
[bo-da]
보는 것 = seeing; the act of seeing; the thing which one sees; what one watches
[bo-neun geot]
가다 = to go
[ga-da]
가는 것 = going; the act of going
[ga-neun geot]
먹다 = to eat
[meok-tta]
먹는 것 = eating; the act of eating; the thing which one eats; what one eats
[meog-neun geot]
사다 = to buy
[sa-da]
사는 것 = buying; the act of buying; the thing which one buys; what one buys
[sa-neun geot]

산 것 = what one bought
[san-geot]
사는 것 = what one buys

살 것 = what one will buy
[sal geot]
먹은 것 = what one ate
[meo-geun geot]
먹는 것 = what one eats

먹을 것 = what one will eat
[meo-geul geot]

-는 것 vs -는 거

-는 것 is the standard form, but often at times the form -는 거 is used because it is easier to
pronounce. It is not, however, ever used in very formal situations.

[-neun geo]

지금 듣는 것은 노래예요.
[ji-geum deun-neun geo-seun no-rae-ye-yo.]
= What I am listening to now is a song.

→ 지금 듣는 거는 노래예요.

오늘 만나는 것 알아요?
[o-neul man-na-neun geot a-ra-yo?]
= Do you know that we are meeting today?

→ 오늘 만나는 거 알아요?

**Track
37**

매운 것 잘 먹어요?
[mae-un geot jal meo-geo-yo?]
= Are you good at eating spicy food?

→ 매운 거 잘 먹어요?

Sample Sentences

제 취미는 영화 보는 거예요.
[je chwi-mi-neun yeong-hwa bo-neun geo-ye-yo.]
= My hobby is watching movies.

요즘 공부하는 거는 뭐예요?
[yo-jeum gong-bu-ha-neun geo-neun mwo-ye-yo?]
= Recently, what is it that you are studying?

= 요즘 뭐 공부해요?

116

저는 친구랑 수다 떠는 거를 좋아해요.
[jeo-neun chin-gu-rang su-da tteo-neun geo-reul jo-a-hae-yo.]
= I like chitchatting with my friends.

Sample Dialogue

Track
38

A: 남편한테 말했어요?
[nam-pyeo-nan-te ma-rae-sseo-yo?]

B: 뭐를요?
[mwo-reul-lyo?]

A: 밖에서 저녁 먹는 거요.
[ba-kke-seo jeo-nyeok meong-neun geo-yo.]

B: 네, 말했어요.
[ne, ma-rae-sseo-yo.]

A: Have you told your husband?

B: What do you mean?

A: That you were going out to have dinner.

B: Yes, I told him.

Conjunctions, Tenses,

✎ Exercises for Lesson 19

1. "To eat" is "먹다". How do you write "eating", "the act of eating", or "what one eats" in Korean?

( )

2. "To go" is "가다". How do you say "going" or "the act of going" in Korean?

( )

3. Please write "I like reading books".

( )

4. How do you say "I don't like spicy things"?

( )

5. How do you write "My hobby is watching movies"?

( )

Check the answers on **p.198**

LESSON **20**

Have to, Should, Must

-아/어/여야 되다/하다

Track 39

By the end of this lesson, you will be constructing sentences using -아/어/여 + -야 되다/하다
[-a/eo/yeo]   [-ya doe-da/ha-da]
to say things such as "I have to go to work" or "You should buy it".

To use this ending, take the verb stem and add -아/어/여 PLUS -야 되다 or -야 하다.

> **Conjugation:**
>
> verb stem + -아/어/여 + -야 되다/하다

Ex)

자다 = to sleep
[ja-da]
자 + -아/어/여 + -야 되다/하다

➞ 자 + -아 + -야 되다/하다

　　(-아 is chosen because 자 ends with a vowel.)

➞ 자야 되다/하다 (Drop the -아 because it is the same as ㅏ.)
[ja-ya doe-da/ha-da]

➞ 자야 되다 and 자야 하다 are the same thing.

쓰다 = to use; to write
[sseu-da]

쓰 + -아/어/여 + -야 되다/하다

→ 쓰 + -어 + -야 되다/하다

    (-어 is chosen because 쓰 does not end in ㅏ or ㅗ.)

→ 써야 되다/하다 (쓰 + 어 together change to '써')
[sseo-ya doe-da/ha-da]

→ 써야 되다 and 써야 하다 mean the same thing.

> **Conjugation:**
>
> 1. verb stems ending in vowels ㅏ or ㅗ + -아야 되다/하다
>
> 2. verb stems ending in other vowels + -어야 되다/하다
>
> **3. 하 + -여야 되다/하다**

Track 39

However, it is more important to understand WHY -아/어/여야 되다/하다 means "to have to" or "should".

To understand this better, look at the two parts separately:

1. -아/어/여 + -야

This means "only when _____ is done" or "only when you do _____".

2. 되다 or 하다

되다 means "to be done" or "to be possible", and 하다 means "to do" something.

Therefore, when putting 1 and 2 together, it takes the meaning of "only when you do _____, it works", "only when you do this, everything is alright", or "only if _____ is done, it's okay". Thus, -아/어/여야 되다/하다 takes the meaning of "to have to" or "should".

121

Q : *What is the difference between* 하다 *and* 되다 *here?*

A : *The only difference is that using* 되다 *is more common in colloquial situations.*

Sample Sentences

집에 가야 돼요.
[ji-be ga-ya dwae-yo.]
= I have to go home.

저는 뭐 해야 돼요?
[jeo-neun mwo hae-ya dwae-yo?]
= What should I do?

Track 39

언제까지 여기에 있어야 돼요?
[eon-je-kka-ji yeo-gi-e i-sseo-ya dwae-yo?]
= Until when should I be here?

누구한테 줘야 돼요?
[nu-gu-han-te jwo-ya dwae-yo?]
= Who should I give this to?

어디에서 사야 돼요?
[eo-di-e-seo sa-ya dwae-yo?]
= Where should I buy it?

Sample Dialogue

Track 40

A: 지금 뭐 하고 있어요?
[ji-geum mwo ha-go i-sseo-yo?]

B: 숙제하고 있어요. 내일까지 해야 돼요.
[suk-jje-ha-go i-sseo-yo. nae-il-kka-ji hae-ya dwae-yo.]

A: 내일 몇 시까지 해야 돼요?
[nae-il myeot si-kka-ji hae-ya dwae-yo?]

B: 내일 10시까지 해야 돼요.
[nae-il yeol-si-kka-ji hae-ya dwae-yo.]

A: *What are you doing now?*

B: *I am doing my homework. I have to finish it by tomorrow.*

A: *By what time tomorrow do you have to finish it?*

B: *I have to finish it by 10 o'clock tomorrow.*

123

✏️ Exercises for Lesson 20

Check the answers on **p.198**

I. What is the difference between 하다 and 되다?

(   )

Translate the following to Korean:

2. "I have to go."

(   )

3. "I have to write" or "I have to use".

(   )

4. "I have to do it now."

(   )

5. "Where do you have to go tomorrow?"

(   )

BLOG

KIMCHI
FRIED RICE

김치 볶음밥 is super delicious, super easy to make, and it fries up so quickly that you'll barely have time to say "한국 음식 진짜 좋아해요!" (I really like Korean food!) before it's cooked!

One of the best things about Korean cooking is that you can add your own flair to it. If you want to add corn, do it! Want to add SPAM or 두부 (tofu)? Go ahead!

This is a pretty basic recipe for 김치 볶음밥, and it makes 2 very generous servings.

Let's get cooking!

You will need:

- 후라이팬 (fry pan)
- 2 cups (or 2 rice bowls) of cooked 밥 (rice)
- 1 cup of 김치 (kimchi) - do not drain or squeeze the liquid!
- ½ of a 양파 (onion)
- 1 clove of 마늘 (garlic)
- 1-2 teaspoons of 고추장 (gochujang – a.k.a. hot pepper paste: 1 tablespoon if you like it medium-hot, and 2 tablespoons if you'd like a death sentence).
- 1 tablespoon of 간장 (soy sauce)
- 2 teaspoons of 설탕 (sugar)
- 2 tablespoons of 김치 juice from the jar
- 2 달걀 (egg)
- 1 teaspoon of 참기름 (sesame oil)
- 2 tablespoons of oil for frying (vegetable, canola, olive etc).
- 깨소금 (sesame seeds) for garnish
- 1 파 (green onion) for garnish

Directions

1. Chop 파, mince 1 clove of 마늘, roughly chop 1 cup of 김치, and cut 양파. Set aside.

2. Heat 1 tablespoon of oil in the 후라이팬 over medium heat.

3. Once the oil is heated, fry the 2 달걀. Traditionally, the 달걀 is served sunny-side up.

(* Note: You can cook the 달걀 before you start to cook the rice, or you can cook it after you've plated the rice and wiped the 후라이팬 clean, or you can cook the 달걀 in a separate 후라이팬. Basically, you can cook the 달걀 whenever you want and however you want!)

4. Heat the remaining 1 tablespoon of oil in the 후라이팬.

5. When the oil is heated, add 마늘 and 양파. Sauté until you can smell them (about 1 minute).

6. Add chopped 김치. Fry for 2-3 minutes.

7. Add 밥 and stir well to combine.

8. Turn down the heat (medium-low) and add 김치 juice, 간장, 설탕, and 고추장.

9. Stir/fold to make sure it mixes well with the rice.

10. Turn off the heat and add 1 teaspoon of 참기름. Mix well.

11. Put the 김치 볶음밥 on a plate or in a bowl and put a fried egg on top. Garnish with 깨소금 and chopped 파!

Voilà! Delicious **김치 볶음밥***!*

You are half way finished with Level 2!
Cook up some **김치 볶음밥** *to replenish*
your strength and power through the rest of this book!

LESSON **21**

more ⋯ than ⋯

-보다 더

Track 41

After studying with this lesson, you will be able to compare two things or people in Korean by saying that something is better/taller/faster/prettier/nicer/etc. than something else.

How to say "more" in Korean

In Korean, the word for "more" is 더. In English, relatively short words change forms instead of having the word "more" in front, such as "shorter", "hotter", and "faster". In Korean, however, all words just have 더 in front of them.

[deo]

Ex)

빠르다 = to be fast
[ppa-reu-da]
더 빠르다 = to be faster
[deo ppa-reu-da]

비싸다 = to be expensive
[bi-ssa-da]
더 비싸다 = to be more expensive
[deo bi-ssa-da]

130

예뻐요. = It's pretty. / You're pretty. / She's pretty.
[ye-ppeo-yo.]

더 예뻐요. = It's prettier. / You're prettier. / She's prettier.
[deo ye-ppeo-yo.]

How to say "than" in Korean

The word for "than" or "compared to" is -보다. The basic construction for this is not very
[-bo-da]
complicated, but the word order in Korean is completely different from English. Take a look
at the following example:

English: A watermelon is bigger than an apple.

Korean: 수박은 사과보다 더 커요.
[su-ba-geun sa-gwa-bo-da deo keo-yo.]

* In the English sentence above, the word "than" comes BEFORE "apple", but in Korean, the word
-보다 (which means "than") comes AFTER 사과, which means "apple".

Track
41

> *Conjugation:*
>
> than A = A보다
>
> more (verb/adjective/adverb) than A = A보다 더 (verb/adjective/adverb)

Ex)

(1) to be big = 크다
[keu-da]

to be bigger = 더 크다
[deo keu-da]

It's bigger. = 더 커요.
[deo keo-yo.]

It's bigger than this one. = 이거보다 더 커요.
[i-geo-bo-da deo keo-yo.]

(2) to be nice = 좋다
[jo-ta]

to be nicer = 더 좋다
[deo jo-ta]

131

It's nicer. = 더 좋아요.
[deo jo-a-yo.]

It's nicer than this one. = 이거보다 더 좋아요.
[i-geo-bo-da deo jo-a-yo.]

(3) to be nice (to people) = 착하다
[cha-ka-da]

to be nicer = 더 착하다
[deo cha-ka-da]

Hyunwoo is nicer. = 현우 씨는 더 착해요.
[hyeo-nu ssi-neun deo cha-kae-yo.]

Hyunwoo is nicer than Kyeong-eun. = 현우 씨는 경은 씨보다 더 착해요.
[hyeo-nu ssi-neun gyeong-eun ssi-bo-da deo cha-kae-yo.]

* 더 *is not always necessary in Korean. Saying "she's busy than me" instead of "she's busier than me" in English is a bit weird, but in Korean, the meaning is perfectly clear even without the word* 더.

Track 41

Sample Sentences

오늘은 어제보다 더워요.
[o-neu-reun eo-je-bo-da deo-wo-yo.]
= Today is hotter than yesterday.

영어는 한국어보다 어려워요.
[yeong-eo-neun han-gu-geo-bo-da eo-ryeo-wo-yo.]
= English is more difficult than Korean.

어제보다 일찍 갈 거예요.
[eo-je-bo-da il-jjik gal kkeo-ye-yo.]
= I'm going to go earlier than yesterday.

현정 씨가 저보다 더 잘해요.
[hyeon-jeong ssi-ga jeo-bo-da deo ja-rae-yo.]
= Hyeonjeong is better than me (at doing that).

저는 책을 읽는 것보다 사는 것을 더 좋아해요.
[jeo-neun chae-geul ing-neun geot-bo-da saneun geo-seul deo jo-a-hae-yo.]
= I like buying books more than reading books.

Sample Dialogue

Track 42

A: 어제보다 오늘 손님이 더 많았어요?
[eo-je-bo-da o-neul son-ni-mi deo ma-na-sseo-yo?]

B: 아니요. 오늘보다 어제가 더 많았어요.
[a-ni-yo. o-neul-bo-da eo-je-ga deo ma-na-sseo-yo.]

A: 아, 그래요?
[a. geu-rae-yo?]

A: Were there more customers today than there were yesterday?

B: No. There were more customers yesterday than there were today.

A: Oh, there were?

✏️ Exercises for Lesson 21

1. "To be fast" is "빠르다". How do you write "to be faster"?

(   )

2. "To be good" is "좋다". How do you say "to be better"?

(   )

3. Please write "Coffee is more expensive than water".

(   )

4. How do you say "This book is more interesting than that book over there"?

(   )

5. How do you write "I came here earlier than yesterday"?

(   )

Check the answers on **p.198**

Conjunctions, Tenses,

LESSON 22

To like

좋다 vs 좋아하다

A verb which is often encountered in Korean is 좋다, which generally means "to be good".

However, there are a few instances where 좋다 takes on the meaning of "to like".
[jo-ta]

Track 43

Ex)

한국어 좋아요.
[han-gu-geo jo-a-yo.]
= I like the Korean language.

이거 좋아요.
[i-geo jo-a-yo.]
= I like this.

이 가수 좋아요.
[i ga-su]
= I like this singer.

Even though the verb 좋다 in these examples is used to mean "to like", the dictionary definition of the verb is "to be good". In principle, the nouns (한국어, 이거, 이 가수) are subjects of the sentences.

Therefore, the particles which are hidden after the nouns are NOT object marking particles, but in fact, are subject marking particles.

한국어 좋아요.

→ 한국어를 좋아요. (x)
[han-gu-geo-reul jo-a-yo.]
→ 한국어가 좋아요. (o)
[han-gu-geo-ga jo-a-yo.]

In this sentence, you are literally saying that "Korean is good, likable, enjoyable, and preferable" FOR YOU.

Track 43

The difference between 좋다 and 좋아하다

한국어 좋아해요.
[jo-a-hae-yo.]
→ 한국어를 좋아해요. (o)
→ 한국어가 좋아해요. (x)

By dropping the particles, there is no difference between 좋다 and 좋아하다.
[jo-a-ha-da]

(1) 이 가수 좋아요.
(2) 이 가수 좋아해요.

Sentences (1) and (2) have the same meaning - "This singer is good" or "I like this singer". To specify what is good and who likes whom, adding particles is recommended.

(3) 이 가수가 좋아요.
[i ga-su-ga]
(4) 이 가수를 좋아요.
[i ga-su-reul]

Sentence number (3) means that you like this singer, however sentence number (4) is not correct because 좋다 is a descriptive verb and cannot have an object.

(5) 이 가수를 좋아해요.
(6) 이 가수가 좋아해요.

Sentence number (5) means that you like (or someone else likes) this singer; this singer is the OBJECT of your affection. The SUBJECT of sentence (6) is this singer, and the sentence is translated as "This singer likes". Left as it is, the sentence is incomplete, and what/who this singer likes (OBJECT) needs to be added.

Track 43

Descriptive verbs + 하다 combination

> *Conjugation:*
> Verb stem + -아/어/여 + -하다

As in the case of 좋다 and 좋아하다, there can be many pairs of words which seem similar at first but are actually different in usage.

Ex)

(1) 싫다 / 싫어요.
[sil-ta]　[si-reo-yo.]
= to be unlikable; to be undesirable

싫어하다 / 싫어해요.
[si-reo-ha-da]　[si-reo-hae-yo.]
= to hate; to not like

(2) 예쁘다 / 예뻐요.
[ye-ppeu-da]　[ye-ppeo-yo.]
= to be pretty; to be cute

예뻐하다 / 예뻐해요.
[ye-ppeo-ha-da]　[ye-ppeo-hae-yo.]
= to consider someone pretty and treat them in such a manner

(3) 슬프다 / 슬퍼요.
[seul-peu-da]　[seul-peo-yo.]
= to be sad

슬퍼하다 / 슬퍼해요.
[seul-peo-ha-da]　[seul-peo-hae-yo.]
= to feel sad, and therefore, express such emotions

Track 43

In order to say "don't be sad" or "do not hate me", use -지 마세요 after the verb stem.
[-ji ma-se-yo]
However, "sad" (슬프다) and "hate" (싫다) in Korean are actually descriptive verbs, not
action verbs. To use -지 마세요, descriptive verbs must be made into action verbs by adding
-하다.

Ex)

Don't be sad. = 슬퍼하지 마세요. (o) 슬프지 마세요. (x)
[seul-peo-ha-ji ma-se-yo.]　　　[seul-peu-ji ma-se-yo.]
Don't hate me. = 싫어하지 마세요. (o) 싫지 마세요. (x)
[si-reo-ha-ji ma-se-yo.]　　　[sil-chi ma-se-yo.]

Sample Sentences

저는 우유를 좋아해요.
[jeo-neun u-yu-reul jo-a-hae-yo.]
= I like milk.

저는 우유를 안 좋아해요.
[jeo-neun u-yu-reul an jo-a-hae-yo.]
= I don't like milk.

우유가 좋아요? 주스가 좋아요?
[u-yu-ga jo-a-yo? ju-seu-ga jo-a-yo?]
= Do you like milk? Or do you like juice?

뭐가 제일 좋아요?
[mwo-ga je-il jo-a-yo?]
= What is your favorite?

Track 43

뭐를 제일 좋아해요?
[mwo-reul je-il jo-a-hae-yo?]
= What do you like best?

** Here, another difference between 좋다 and 좋아하다 is that 좋다 is used to mean "to like"
only about yourself, not about other people. If you want to say "Kyeong-eun likes coffee", use
the verb 좋아하다.*

> **Ex)** 경은 씨는 커피를 좋아해요.
> [gyeong-eun ssi-neun keo-pi-reul jo-a-hae-yo.]

한국 영화 좋아하세요?
[han-guk yeong-hwa jo-a-ha-se-yo?]
= Do you like Korean movies?

Sample Dialogue

A: 한국 드라마 좋아해요?
[han-guk deu-ra-ma jo-a-hae-yo?]

B: 아니요. 저는 드라마 잘 안 봐요.
[a-ni-yo. jeo-neun deu-ra-ma jal an bwa-yo.]

A: 한국 영화는요?
[han-guk yeong-hwa-neun-nyo?]

B: 영화는 좋아해요.
[yeong-hwa-neun jo-a-hae-yo.]

A: Do you like Korean dramas?

B: No. I don't really watch dramas.

A: What about Korean movies?

B: I do like movies.

✏ Exercises for Lesson **22**

I. "좋다" and "좋아하다" are similar in meaning but quite different in usage. Which one is closer to "actively" liking something?

(   )

2. Use the verb "좋다" to write "I like the Korean language."

(   )

3. Use the verb "좋아하다" to say "I like the Korean language."

(   )

4. Using the verb "좋아하다", how do you say "민수 likes milk"?

(   )

5. Using the verb "좋다", how do you say "What is your favorite?"

(   )

Check the answers on **p.198**

Telling Time, and More

LESSON **23**

If, In case

만약, -(으)면

Track 45

After studying with this lesson, you will know how to say "if" in Korean. You will also be able to use it in context in your Korean sentences.

In order to express the meaning "if", you need to know two expressions: one is a noun, and one is a verb ending.

만약 = in case, if

-(으)면 = verb ending for "if"

In English, the word "if" is used at the beginning of a sentence to make the sentence conditional, but in Korean, you can add the word 만약, but you also need to conjugate
[ma-nyak]
the verb as well to match. Do not worry, though! Conjugating verbs in this manner is very straightforward.

How to conjugate verbs

In order to add the meaning "if" to a verb, add -(으)면 to the verb stem.
[-(eu)-myeon]

> *Conjugation:*
>
> **1. Verb stems ending with a vowel + -면**
>
>   **Ex)** 자다 → 자면 (if you sleep)
>   [ja-da]   [ja-myeon]
> **2. Verb stems ending with ㄹ + -면**
>
>   **Ex)** 길다 → 길면 (if it's long)
>   [gil-da]   [gil-myeon]
> **3. Verb stems ending with consonants other than ㄹ + -으면**
>
>   **Ex)** 작다 → 작으면 (if it's small)
>   [jak-tta]   [ja-geu-myeon]

Track 45

To make the sentence clearer, add the word 만약 in front of the verb or at the beginning of the phrase. Since most Korean sentences are heavily affected by verb endings toward the end of sentences, adding 만약 at the beginning makes it easier to understand that the sentence will be conditional.

Ex)

(1) Verb: 자다 = to sleep

지금 자면 = if I sleep now
[ji-geum]
만약 지금 자면 = if I sleep now

(2) Verb: 비가 오다 = to rain
[bi-ga- o-da]
내일 밤에 비가 오면 = if it rains tomorrow night
[nae-il ba-me]
만약 내일 밤에 비가 오면 = if it rains tomorrow night

* In the second sentences for both examples on the previous page, the listener can figure out that the sentence is going to be an "if" sentence just by hearing "만약".

If what you are saying is simple and the sentence is not very long, you do not always have to use the word 만약 in each sentence.

More Examples

Track 45

먹다 = to eat
[meok-tta]
먹으면 = if you eat it; if I eat it
[meo-geu-myeon]

* Add the -았/었/였 suffix before -으면 to make a past tense clause.
[-at/eot/yeot]

먹었어요 = I ate
[meo-geo-sseo-yo]
먹 + 었 + 으면 = if you ate it; if I ate it
[meo-geo-sseu-myeon]

사다 = to buy
[sa-da]
사면 = if you buy it; if I buy it; if they buy it
[sa-myeon]
샀다 = I bought
[sat-tta]
샀으면 = if you bought it; if we bought it
[sa-sseu-myeon]

* Create future tense sentences by using -(으)ㄹ 거면.
[-(eu)l geo-myeon]

보다 = to watch
[bo-da]
보면 = if you watch it; if I watch it
[bo-myeon]
봤다 = I watched
[bwat-tta]

144

봤으면 = if I watched it; if they watched it
[bwa-sseu-myeon]

볼 거예요 = I am going to watch
[bol kkeo-ye-yo]

볼 거면 = if you are going to watch it
[bol geo-myeon]

Sample Sentences

내일 비가 오면, 집에 있을 거예요.
[nae-il bi-ga o-myeon, ji-be i-sseul kkeo-ye-yo.]
= If it rains tomorrow, I'm going to be at home.

이거 다 먹으면, 배가 아플 거예요.
[i-geo da meo-geu-myeon, bae-ga a-peul kkeo-ye-yo.]
= If you eat all of it, your stomach will hurt.

리모콘을 찾으면, TV를 볼 수 있어요.
[ri-mo-ko-neul cha-jeu-myeon, ti-bi-reul bol su i-sseo-yo.]
= If you find the remote control, you can watch TV.

Track 45

TTMIK으로* 공부하면, 재미있어요.
[TTMIK-eu-ro gong-bu-ha-myeon, jae-mi-i-sseo-yo.]
= If you study with TTMIK, it's fun.   *p. 173

지금 안 오면, 후회할 거예요.
[ji-geum an o-myeon hu-hoe-hal kkeo-ye-yo.]
= If you don't come now, you will regret it.

This is not everything.

This is, however, one of the most basic and frequently used ways to make "if" sentences in Korean. There are other expressions which can be used, but those will have to wait until future lessons to be introduced. In the meantime, enjoy practicing what you learned with us in this lesson!

Sample Dialogue

Track 46

A: 그거 사지 마세요.
[geu-geo sa-ji ma-se-yo.]

B: 왜요?
[wae-yo?]

A: 다른 곳에서 사면 더 싸요.
[da-reun go-se-seo sa-myeon deo ssa-yo.]

A: Don't buy that.

B: Why not?

A: It is cheaper if you buy it at another place.

Conjunctions, Tenses,

✏ Exercises for Lesson 23

1. If "to sleep" is "자다" in Korean, how do you say "If I sleep now"?

( )

Match the Korean word to its English equivalent.

2. 보다

a. if you are going to watch it

3. 보면

b. if you watch it, if I watch it

4. 봤으면

c. to watch

5. 볼 거면

d. if I watched it, if they watched it

6. Write the following sentence in Korean: "If it rains tomorrow, I'm going to be at home."

( )

Check the answers on **p.198**

LESSON **24**

Still, Already

아직, 벌써

The focus of this lesson is on two new expressions with opposite meanings, which can help you express "still" or "not yet" and "already".

아직 means "still" and "not yet".

In English, generally, the word "still" is used with positive sentences, and the word "yet" is more commonly used with negative sentences. However, in Korean, the word 아직 is used
[a-jik]
for both positive and negative sentences.

아직 10시예요.
[yeol-ssi-ye-yo.]
= It's still 10 o'clock.

아직 안 했어요.
[an hae-sseo-yo.]
= I haven't done it yet.

148

아직 아침이에요.
[a-chi-mi-e-yo.]
= It's still morning.

아직 몰라요.
[mol-la-yo.]
= I don't know yet.

To emphasize the meaning of "still happening" or "still not happening", add the particle -도
[-do]
after 아직 to form 아직도. 아직도 has a meaning of criticizing the other person or being a
[a-jik-tto]
little bit mad or angry.

아직 몰라요?
= You don't know yet?

Track
47

아직도 몰라요?
[a-jik-tto]
= You still don't know? / How could you still not know?

아직 안 왔어요?
[an wa-sseo-yo?]
= He's not here yet?

아직도 안 왔어요?
= He's still not here yet?

네, 아직도 안 왔어요.
[ne]
= No, he's still not here.

벌써 means "already".

The usage of the word 벌써 is very similar to the English word "already". It is generally placed
[beol-sseo]
at the beginning of sentences, but it does not always have to be at the beginning.

It's already three o'clock.

= 벌써 세 시예요.
[se si-ye-yo.]

It's three o'clock already!

= 세 시예요, 벌써!

Track 47

Both of the sentences above are correct.

Sample Sentences

벌써 왔어요?
[beol-sseo wa-sseo-yo?]
= Oh, you are already here!

벌써 끝났어요.
[beol-sseo kkeun-na-sseo-yo.]
= It's already over.

벌써 끝났어요?
[beol-sseo kkeun-na-sseo-yo?]
= Is it already over? Did it already finish?

이미 vs 벌써

Another word which also has the meaning of "already" is 이미. You will probably come
[i-mi]
across this word frequently when reading or listening to Korean.

Although 벌써 and 이미 appear to have the same meaning, native speakers often distinguish
the two by using them in different contexts.

The difference between 이미 and 벌써 lies in whether you are already aware of a fact or
not. When you and/or the speaker know about something already and talk about it, use 이
미. When you are just finding out about something as you speak, use 벌써. People do not
always stick to this rule, but this is the basic idea.

**Track
47**

Ex)
그 사람은 이미 학교를 졸업했어요.
[geu sa-ra-meun i-mi hak-kkyo-reul jo-reo-pae-sseo-yo.]
= He already graduated from school.

- You (and probably the other person) have known about this long before you said this
sentence.

그 사람은 벌써 학교를 졸업했어요!
= He already graduated from school.

- You may have found out about this fact recently, or you already knew about this, but the
other person may have not known about it before you said it.

Because of this difference, in normal everyday situations where new information is discovered, 벌써 is used.

벌써 비가 오고 있어요.
[bi-ga o-go i-sseo-yo.]
= It's already raining.

벌써 추워요.
[chu-wo-yo.]
= It's already cold.

벌써 끝났어요.

= It's already over.

Track 47

Sample Dialogue

Track 48

A: 경화 씨, 집이에요?
[gyeong-hwa ssi, ji-bi-e-yo?]

B: 아니요. 아직 사무실이에요.
[a-ni-yo. a-jik sa-mu-si-ri-e-yo.]

A: 아직도요? 지금 밤 10시예요!
[a-jik-tto-yo? ji-geum bam yeol-ssi-ye-yo!]

B: 벌써요?
[beol-sseo-yo?]

A: Kyung-hwa, are you home?

B: No. I am still at my office.

A: Still? It is 10PM!

B: Already?

✎ *Exercises for Lesson* **24**

1. How do you say "still" or "not yet" in Korean?

$$()$$

2. Please write "I don't know yet" in Korean.

$$()$$

3. "Already" is "벌써". How do you say "Is it already over?/Did it already finish?"

$$()$$

Check the answers on **p.199**

Remember, although 벌써 *and* 이미 *appear to have the same meaning, native speakers often distinguish the two by using them in different contexts.*

4. How do you say "He already graduated from school"?
 - You, and probably the other person, have known this information for a long time.

그 사람은 (   ) 학교를 졸업했어요.

5. How do you say "He already graduated from school"?
 - You may have found out this information just recently, or you already knew about this, but the other person may have not known about it prior to you telling him/her.

그 사람은 (   ) 학교를 졸업했어요!

LESSON 25

Someone, Something, Somewhere, Someday

누군가, 무언가, 어딘가, 언젠가

Track
49

In English, when changing the adverbs "when", "what", "who", or "where" to indefinite words (words with no definite meaning), the words change form and become compound words.

When = Someday

What = Something

Who = Someone

Where = Somewhere

In Korean, it is much easier to create these indefinite words. Just simply add -ㄴ가 to the end
[-(n)-ga]
of the word.

For example :

155

누구 (who) - **누군가** (someone)
[nu-gu]   [nu-gun-ga]
뭐 (what) - **뭔가 (= 무언가)** (something)
[mwo]   [mwon-ga]   [mu-eon-ga]
어디 (where) - **어딘가** (somewhere)
[eo-di]   [eo-din-ga]
언제 (when) - **언젠가** (someday)
[eon-je]   [eon-jen-ga]

Sample Sentences

언젠가 미국에 가고 싶어요.
[eon-jen-ga mi-gu-ge ga-go si-peo-yo.]
= I want to go to the United States someday.

언제 미국에 가고 싶어요?
[eon-je mi-gu-ge ga-go si-peo-yo?]
= When do you want to go to the United States?

Track 49

언젠가 일본에 갈 거예요.
[eon-jen-ga il-bo-ne gal kkeo-ye-yo.]
= I'm going to go to Japan one day.

언제 일본에 갈 거예요?
[eon-je il-bo-ne gal kkeo-ye-yo?]
= When are you going to go to Japan?

뭐 찾았어요?
[mwo cha-ja-sseo-yo?]
= What did you find?

뭔가 찾았어요?
[mwon-ga cha-ja-sseo-yo?]
= Did you find something?

뭔가 이상해요.
[mwon-ga i-sang-hae-yo.]
= Something is strange.

156

뭐가 이상해요?
[mwo-ga i-sang-hae-yo?]
= What is strange?

누구 만날 거예요?
[nu-gu man-nal kkeo-ye-yo?]
= Whom will you meet?

누군가 만날 거예요?
[nu-gun-ga man-nal kkeo-ye-yo?]
= Will you meet someone?

누군가 왔어요.
[nu-gun-ga wa-sseo-yo.]
= Someone came.

어디에 있어요?
[eo-di-e i-sseo-yo?]
= Where is it?

여기 어딘가에 있어요.
[yeo-gi eo-din-ga-e i-sseo-yo.]
= It is here somewhere.

*However in Korean, just as in other languages, this usage rule is not always kept by everyone. What does this mean? It means that EVEN when the intended meaning is "someday", 언제 can be used instead of 언젠가. Likewise, 뭐 can be used for "something", 어디 for "somewhere", and 누구 for "someone".

The distinction between 언제 and 언젠가 is stronger than the distinction between other words, but there are many situations in which 언젠가 can be replaced with 언제. When using the original interrogative word rather than -ㄴ가, pay attention to your intonation. The emphasis should be on the verbs, not the actual interrogative word.

157

Sample Sentences

뭐 샀어요? (stress is on 뭐)
[mwo sa-sseo-yo?]
= What did you buy?

뭐 샀어요? (stress is on 샀어요)

= Did you buy something?

언제 중국에 갈 거예요? (stress is on 언제)
[eon-je jung-gu-ge gal kkeo-ye-yo?]
= When are you going to go to China?

언제 중국에 갈 거예요? (stress is on 갈 거예요?)

= Are you going to go to China someday/one of these days?

Track 49

어디 가요? (stress is on 어디)
[eo-di ga-yo?]
= Where are you going?

어디 가요? (stress is on 가요?)

= Are you going somewhere?

오늘 뭐 배웠어요? (stress is on 배웠어요?)
[o-neul mwo bae-wo-sseo-yo?]
= Did you learn something today?

오늘 뭐 배웠어요? (stress is on 뭐)

= What did you learn today?

158

Sample Dialogue

Track 50

A: 여행 좋아해요?
[yeo-haeng jo-a-hae-yo?]

B: 네, 좋아해요. 어딘가로 떠나는 거
좋아해요.
[ne, jo-a-hae-yo. eo-din-ga-ro tteo-na-neun geo
jo-a-hae-yo.]

A: 저도 여행 정말 좋아해요. 항상
어딘가로 떠나고 싶어요.
[jeo-do yeo-haeng jeong-mal jo-a-hae-yo. hang-sang
eo-din-ga-ro tteo-na-go si-peo-yo.]

A: *Do you like traveling?*

B: *Yes, I do. I like leaving to go
somewhere.*

A: *I also really like traveling. I
always want to leave to go
somewhere.*

✏️ Exercises for Lesson 25

1. If "when" is "언제", how do you say "someday" in Korean?

   (   )

2. Since "what" is "뭐", how do you write "something" in Korean?

   (   )

3. How do you say "When are you going to go to Japan?"

   (   )

4. Please write "I'm going to go to Japan one day."

   (   )

5. How do you say "Something is strange"?

   (   )

LESSON **26**

Imperative

-(으)세요

Track 51

Learning to ask or tell someone to do something for you is one of the most essential things to learn in any language. Whether the intention is to be polite or not so polite, learning how to construct imperative sentences in Korean will come handy every single day.

To tell someone to do something, add **-(으)세요** to the verb stem.
[-(eu)-se-yo]

> *Conjugation*
>
> Verb stem ending in a consonant + -으세요
>
> Verb stem ending in a vowel or the consonant ㄹ + -세요

Ex)

시작하다 = to begin, to start
[si-ja-ka-da]

시작하 + -세요 = 시작하세요 = Please begin.
[si-ja-ka-se-yo]

161

오다 = to come
[o-da]
오 + -세요 = 오세요 = Please come.
[o-se-yo]

쉬다 = to rest
[swi-da]
쉬 + -세요 = 쉬세요 = Please get some rest.
[swi-se-yo]

고르다 = to choose, to pick
[go-reu-da]
고르 + -세요 = 고르세요 = Please choose.
[go-reu-se-yo]

접다 = to fold
[jeop-tta]
접 + -으세요 = 접으세요 = Please fold it.
[jeo-beu-se-yo]

Track 51

Exception:

When a verb stem ends with the consonant ㄹ, drop the ㄹ and add -세요.

팔다 = to sell
[pal-da]
팔 → 파 + 세요 = 파세요 = Please sell it.
[pa-se-yo]

The focus of this lesson is presenting -(으)세요 as a way to tell someone to do something. The honorific suffix -시 is included in this ending, and there are a couple variations of this depending on the type of language (honorific, informal), but please remember that this ending is considered "formal" or "polite".

Sample Sentences

내일 세 시에 오세요.
[nae-il se si-e o-se-yo.]
= Please come here at three o'clock tomorrow.

162

공부하세요!
[gong-bu-ha-se-yo!]
= Study! Do your studies!

경은 씨, 빨리 일하세요.
[gyeong-eun ssi, ppal-li i-ra-se-yo.]
= Kyeong-eun, hurry up and get some work done!

경은 씨, 쉬세요.
[gyeong-eun ssi, swi-se-yo.]
= Kyeong-eun, please get some rest.

이거 저한테 파세요.
[i-geo jeo-han-te pa-se-yo.]
= Please sell this to me.

조심하세요.
[jo-si-ma-se-yo.]
= Be careful!

Track 51

Some fixed expressions using -세요:

When going into a store or restaurant, an employee will most often say:

1. 어서 오세요.
[eo-seo o-se-yo.]
= (lit. Come quickly) Welcome.

When a person is leaving and you are staying:

2. 안녕히 가세요.
[an-nyeong-hi ga-se-yo.]
= (lit. Go peacefully) Goodbye.

If you are leaving, and the other person is staying:

3. 안녕히 계세요.
[an-nyeong-hi gye-se-yo.]
= (lit. Stay peacefully) Goodbye.

How to say "Goodnight" in Korean:

4. 안녕히 주무세요.
[an-nyeong-hi ju-mu-se-yo.]
= (lit. Sleep peacefully) Goodnight.

Some words change their forms specifically for polite/formal language, but those will be

covered in a future lesson.

Track 51

Conjunctions, Tenses,

Sample Dialogue

Track 52

A: 서점에서 TTMIK 책 사 오세요.
[seo-jeo-me-seo TTMIK chaek sa o-se-yo.]

B: 만약에 없으면요?
[ma-nya-ge eop-sseu-myeon-nyo?]

A: 없으면 그냥 오세요.
[eop-sseu-myeon geu-nyang o-se-yo.]

A: Please buy me a TTMIK book from the bookstore.

B: What if they don't have one?

A: If so, just come back (here).

✏ Exercises for Lesson **26**

Check the answers on **p.199**

1. When you want to tell or ask someone to do something, you add the ending -(으)세요 to
   the verb stem. How would you say "Do it"?

   ( )

2. "To rest" is "쉬다". How do you say "Get some rest"?

   ( )

3. "To be careful" is "조심하다". How do you write "Be careful!"?
   [jo-si-ma-da]

   ( )

4. "To study" is "공부하다" and "doing something difficult" is described in Korean as doing it
   [gong-bu-ha-da]
   "열심히". How do you say "Study hard!"?
   [yeol-ssi-mi]

   ( )

5. When you go into a shop or a restaurant, what will the people who are working there say
   to you to mean "Welcome"?

   ( )

Conjunctions, Tenses,

LESSON 27

Please do it for me

-아/어/여 주세요

In the previous lesson, you learned how to tell someone to do something using -(으)세요.
[-(eu)-se-yo]
Although this is perfectly acceptable, there is an even more polite way to ask the same

question.

Track 53

Rather than adding -(으)세요 after a verb stem, add **-아/어/여 + 주세요**. By adding this
[-a/eo/yeo]   [ju-se-yo]
verb ending, the sentence has a much nicer tone and has a nuance of asking someone for a

favor or asking the other person to do something "for you".

Ex)

오다 = to come
[o-da]
오세요. = Please come.
[o-se-yo.]
와 주세요. = Please do me a favor and come.
[wa ju-se-yo.]

하다 = to do
[ha-da]
하세요. = Do it.
[ha-se-yo.]

167

해 주세요. = Please do me a favor and do it for me.
[hae ju-se-yo.]

Using -아/어/여 주세요 rather than just -(으)세요 not only makes the sentence more polite, but it also adds the meaning of "please do it for me". There is no need to say the phrase "저를 위해서", which literally means "for me" if -아/어/여 주세요 is used.
[jeo-reul wi-hae-seo]

For example, "아이스크림 사세요" can mean "buy yourself some ice cream", "buy ice cream
[a-i-seu-keu-rim sa-se-yo]
for your friends", or simply just "buy some ice cream". On the other hand, using -아/어/여 주세요 to say "아이스크림 사 주세요" means "please buy ME some ice cream". If someone
[a-i-seu-keu-rim sa ju-se-yo]
selling ice cream says this, the meaning is "please buy ice cream from me if you want to help me".

Track 53

When asking for help, often at times, it is more natural to add -아/어/여 주세요. For example, it is not very natural to say "저를 도우세요!" (돕다 = to help) when the intended
[jeo-reul do-u-se-yo!]   [dop-tta]
meaning is "help me!" To sound more natural and a bit more polite, say "저를 도와 주세요"
[jeo-reul do-wa ju-se-yo]
or just "도와 주세요".

Take a look at the difference of meaning between -(으)세요 and -아/어/여 주세요.

가르치다 = to teach
[ga-reu-chi-da]
가르치세요. = Teach. / Please teach. (to whom is unknown)
[ga-reu-chi-se-yo.]
가르쳐 주세요. = Please teach me.
[ga-reu-cheo ju-se-yo.]
경은 씨한테 가르쳐 주세요. = Please teach Kyeong-eun (how to do that).
[gyeong-eun ssi-han-te ga-reu-cheo ju-se-yo.]
경은 씨한테 스페인어 가르쳐 주세요. = Please teach Kyeong-eun Spanish.
[gyeong-eun ssi-han-te seu-pe-i-neo ga-reu-cheo ju-se-yo.]
스페인어 가르쳐 주세요. = Please teach me Spanish.
[seu-pe-i-neo ga-reu-cheo ju-se-yo.]

보다 = to see
[bo-da]

보세요. = See it. / Please see it.
[bo-se-yo.]

봐 주세요. = Please see it, and I would appreciate it. / Please be kind and see it.
[bwa ju-se-yo.]

이거 봐 주세요. = Please look at this.
[i-geo bwa ju-se-yo.]

숙제 봐 주세요. = Please look at my homework.
[suk-jje bwa ju-se-yo.]

주세요 is derived from 주다, which means "to give". By adding 주세요 after a verb, the meaning of "do it for me, please" is also added. As for -아/어/여, think of it as a "helper" to make the pronunciation a bit easier.

To speak a little less formally, say 줘요 rather than 주세요. It is more casual than 주세요 but more polite than just -세요.

Track 53

Sample Sentences

영어를 배우고 있어요. 도와주세요.
[yeong-eo-reul bae-u-go i-sseo-yo. do-wa-ju-se-yo.]
= I am learning English. Please help me.

도와줄 수 있어요?
[do-wa-jul su i-sseo-yo?]
= Can you help me?

배고파요. 김밥 사 주세요.
[bae-go-pa-yo. gim-ppap sa ju-se-yo.]
= I am hungry. Buy me some kimbap.

무서워요. 같이 가 주세요.
[mu-seo-wo-yo. ga-chi ga ju-se-yo.]
= I am scared. Please go with me.

Sample Dialogue

Track 54

A: 석진 씨, 잠깐 이야기할 수 있어요?
[seok-jjin ssi, jam-kkan i-ya-gi-hal ssu i-sseo-yo?]

B: 아... 지금이요?
[a... ji-geu-mi-yo?]

A: 지금 바쁘면 3시까지 1층으로
와 주세요.
[ji-geum ba-ppeu-myeon se-si-kka-ji il-cheung-eu-ro
wa ju-se-yo.]

B: 네, 알겠습니다.
[ne, al-get-sseum-ni-da.]

A: Seokjin, can we talk for a moment?

B: Ah... now?

A: If you are busy now, please come
down to the first floor by 3 o'clock.

B: Okay, I will.

✏ Exercises for Lesson *27*

1. The expression that makes a sentence translate to "for me" or "do it for me" is -아/어/여 주세요. How do you say "Do this for me, please"?

( )

2. The verb "to teach" is "가르치다". How do you say "Please teach me English"?

( )

3. The verb "to buy" is "사다". How do you say "Please buy me that over there"?
[sa-da]

( )

4. How do you say "Please have a look at this"?

( )

5. "Can you come with me?" is "같이 갈 수 있어요?". How do you add the nuance of "Can you do
[ga-chi gal su i-sseo-yo?]
me a favor and come with me?" to the sentence?

( )

Check the answers on **p.199**

171

LESSON 28

Method, Way

-(으)로

Track 55

You have already learned a handful of Korean particles and how to use them through the previous lessons in this book. Get ready to add a new one to the bunch! Learn the meaning and usage of -(으)로 with this lesson.

[-(eu)-ro]

> *Conjugation:*
>
> **Nouns ending with a consonant + -으로**
>
> **Nouns ending in a vowel or the consonant "ㄹ" + -로**

-(으)로 connects a noun and a verb very closely and can have various functions. -(으)로 can mark the ingredients an object is made of, the cause of a disease or something that happened, the direction in which someone is going, or the status or identity of a person doing something. Take a look at some examples:

Ex)

(1) 나무로 만들다
[na-mu-ro man-deul-da]

= 나무 (wood) + -로 + 만들다 (to make)

= to make (something) with wood

Someone made this table with wood. = 누가 이 테이블을 나무로 만들었어요.
[nu-ga i te-i-beu-reul na-mu-ro man-deu-reo-sseo-yo.]

(2) 왼쪽으로 가다
[oen-jjo-geu-ro ga-da]

= 왼쪽 (left side) + -으로 + 가다 (to go)

= to go to the left

= to go through the left side

(3) 이 길로 가다
[i gil-lo ga-da]

= 이 (this) 길 (street / road) + -로 + 가다 (to go)

= to go down this path

= to go down this road

Track 55

(4) 펜으로 쓰다
[pe-neu-ro sseu-da]

= 펜 (pen) + -으로 + 쓰다 (to write)

= to write with a pen

(5) 한국어로 말하다
[han-gu-geo-ro ma-ra-da]

= 한국어 (Korean) + 로 + 말하다 (to speak / to talk)

= to speak in Korean

(6) 치즈로 유명하다
[chi-jeu-ro yu-myeong-ha-da]

= 치즈 (cheese) + 로 + 유명하다 (to be famous)

= to be famous for cheese

(7) 사고로 다치다
[sa-go-ro da-chi-da]

= 사고 (accident) + 로 + 다치다 (to get hurt)

= to get hurt in (from) an accident

There is a common factor in the way -(으)로 was used in the previous sentences. Can you identify it?

By using -(으)로, something is used as a channel, tool, device, or a method.

Sample Sentences

이거 뭐로 만들었어요?
[i-geo mwo-ro man-deu-reo-sseo-yo?]
= What did you make this with?

= What is this made of?

오늘 택시로 왔어요?
[o-neul taek-ssi-ro wa-sseo-yo?]
= Did you come by taxi today?

버스로 갈 거예요.
[beo-sseu-ro gal kkeo-ye-yo.]
= I'm going to go by bus.

저를 친구로 생각해요?
[jeo-reul chin-gu-ro saeng-ga-kae-yo?]
= Do you think of me as a friend?

2번 출구로 나오세요.
[i-beon chul-gu-ro na-o-se-yo.]
= Come out through exit number 2.

저는 Talk To Me In Korean으로 한국어 공부해요.
[jeo-neun Talk To Me In Korean-eu-ro han-gu-geo gong-bu-hae-yo.]
= I study Korean through Talk To Me In Korean.

Track 55

175

Sample Dialogue

A: 2월에 캐나다로 돌아가요?
[i-wo-re kae-na-da-ro do-ra-ga-yo?]

B: 네. 그런데 다시 올 거예요.
[ne. geu-reon-de da-si ol kkeo-ye-yo.]

A: 언제요?
[eon-je-yo?]

B: 여름에요.
[yeo-reu-me-yo.]

A: Are you going back to Canada in February?

B: Yes, but I will come here again.

A: When?

B: In the summer.

176

✏ Exercises for Lesson **28**

1. The word that indicates a method in which, or an ingredient with which, an object is made is "-으로" or "-로". When do you use "-으로" instead of "-로"?

( )

2. How do you say "with a pen"?

( )

3. The word for "a chair" is "의자", and the word for "wood" is "나무". Please write "They made this chair out of wood."
[ui-ja]   [na-mu]

( )

4. How do you say "Please speak in Korean for me"?

( )

5. Please write "What did you make this with?"

( )

Check the answers on **p.199**

177

LESSON **29**

All, More

다, 더

Track
57

With this lesson, you will learn the Korean words for "all" and "more" as well as how to apply these words to Korean sentences to sound more natural.

다 = all, entirely, whole

더 = more

For many sentences in English where a speaker would use adjectives and nouns, Korean speakers use adverbs and verbs. This often becomes a challenge when translating, as things do not quite translate directly, but having this knowledge as a learner of Korean will ultimately lead to more natural-sounding Korean.

Take a look at how 다 is used:
[da]

Ex)

(1) 다 주세요.
[da ju-se-yo.]
= Give me all of it.

(2) 우유 다 주세요.
[u-yu da ju-se-yo.]
= Give me all the milk.

(3) 다 했어요.
[da hae-sseo-yo.]
= I've done all of it.

Track 57

(4) 다 왔어요?
[da wa-sseo-yo?]
= Are we there yet? (lit. Did we all come? / Did we come to all of it?)

= Did everyone come?

(5) 다 살 거예요?
[da sal kkeo-ye-yo?]
= Are you going to buy all of it?

In some of the examples above, it looks as if the word 다 is working as a noun, and it is, but it has a stronger influence on the verbs and acts as more of an adverb.

커피를 마시다
[keo-pi-reul ma-si-da]
= to drink coffee

커피를 다 마시다

= to drink all the coffee

179

In the second sentence previously, the English word "all" was used to describe "the coffee", but in Korean, the word 다 was used to describe the action of drinking (마시다).

책을 읽다
[chae-geul ik-tta]
= to read a book

책을 다 읽다
[chae-geul da ik-tta]
= to read all of the book

= to finish reading the book

> Q : Then how do you say "all of the book" or "the entire book", if the word 다 only modifies verbs?
>
> A : You can use other words like 전체 or 전부. "The entire book" is 책 전체 or 책 전부, but
> [jeon-che] [jeon-bu]
> this might not sound very natural when used out of proper context. In most cases, it is better to use 다.

Let's look at how 더 is used.
[deo]

Ex)

(1) 더 주세요.
[deo ju-se-yo.]
= Please give me more.

(2) 더 있어요.
[deo i-sseo-yo.]
= There is more.

(3) 더 사고 싶어요.
[deo sa-go si-peo-yo.]
= I want to buy more.

(4) 옷 더 사고 싶어요.
[ot deo sa-go si-peo-yo.]
= I want to buy more clothes.

(5) 뭐가 더 좋아요?
[mwo-ga deo jo-a-yo?]
= Which is better?

The explanation for 다 also applies to the word 더, especially when modifying verbs. It may look as if 더 is used as a noun in sentences (3) and (4), but, it is not! When saying "더 사고 싶어요" or "옷 더 사고 싶어요", the meaning is closer to "I want to do the 'action of buying' more" rather than "I want to buy more" or "I want to buy more clothes".

Track 57

10분 기다려 주세요.

= Please wait for 10 minutes.

10분 더 기다려 주세요.
[sip-ppun deo gi-da-ryeo ju-se-yo.]
= Please wait for 10 more minutes.

In English, the phrase is said as "10 more minutes", but in Korean, it literally translates to "do the action of waiting for 10 minutes + more".

Sample Sentences

전화 다 했어요?
[jeo-nwa da hae-sseo-yo?]
= Did you finish talking on the phone?

= Did you make all the phone calls?

= Did everyone make a phone call?

준비 다 했어요.
[jun-bi da hae-sseo-yo.]
= I did all the preparation.

= I prepared everything.

= I finished the preparation.

= All of us are prepared.

Track
57

더 보여 주세요.
[deo bo-yeo ju-se-yo.]
= Show me more.

= Show me more of it.

더 공부하고 싶으면, TTMIK에 오세요.
[deo gong-bu-ha-go si-peu-myeon TTMIK-e o-se-yo.]
= If you want to study more, come to TTMIK.

= If you want to do more studying, come to TTMIK.

Conjunctions, Tenses,

Sample Dialogue

A: 한국어를 더 잘하고 싶어요.
[han-gu-geo-reul deo ja-ra-go si-peo-yo.]

B: 지금도 잘해요.
[ji-geum-do ja-rae-yo.]

A: 아니에요.
[a-ni-e-yo.]

B: 그럼 더 열심히 하세요.
[geu-reom deo yeol-ssi-mi ha-se-yo.]

A: I want to be better at Korean.

B: You are already good at it.

A: No, I am not.

B: Then study harder.

✏ Exercises for Lesson **29**

1. What is the word for "more" in Korean?

(　　　　　　　　　　　　　　　　　　　　　　　　　)

2. What is the word for "all" in Korean?

(　　　　　　　　　　　　　　　　　　　　　　　　　)

3. How do you say "Did you do all of it?" or "Did you finish doing it?"

(　　　　　　　　　　　　　　　　　　　　　　　　　)

4. How do you say "I did all my homework"?

(　　　　　　　　　　　　　　　　　　　　　　　　　)

5. Please write "I want to buy more" in Korean.

(　　　　　　　　　　　　　　　　　　　　　　　　　)

6. How do you say "I want to buy all"?

(　　　　　　　　　　　　　　　　　　　　　　　　　)

Check the answers on **p.199**

Conjunctions, Tenses,

LESSON 30

Don't do it

-지 마세요

You have already learned how to tell or ask someone to do something for you, but how do you tell someone to "stop doing" something or "do not do" something?

Track 59

Use the following verb + -(으)세요:
[-(eu)-se-yo]

말다 = to quit doing; to not do; to stop doing
[mal-da]

When using -(으)세요 with this word, it becomes 마세요. When combining 마세요 with
[ma-se-yo]
other verbs to say "do not do" or "stop doing" something, the suffix -지 is needed after the
[-ji]
verb stem.

> ### Conjugation:
> Verb stem + -지 마세요

185

Telling Time, and More

Ex)

가지 마세요. = Don't go.
[ga-ji ma-se-yo.]

아직 가지 마세요. = Don't go yet.
[a-jik ga-ji ma-se-yo.]

하지 마세요. = Don't do it. / Drop it. / Stop it. / Forget about it.
[ha-ji ma-se-yo.]

사지 마세요. = Don't buy it.
[sa-ji ma-se-yo.]

Sample Sentences.

만지지 마세요.
[man-ji-ji ma-se-yo.]
= Don't touch it.

**Track
59**

웃지 마세요.
[ut-jji ma-se-yo.]
= Don't laugh.

걱정하지 마세요.
[geok-jjeong-ha-ji ma-se-yo.]
= Don't worry.

경은 씨한테 말하지 마세요.
[gyeong-eun ssi-han-te ma-ra-ji ma-se-yo.]
= Please don't tell Kyeong-eun (about it).

아직 보내지 마세요. 아직 다 안 썼어요.
[a-jik bo-nae-ji ma-se-yo. a-jik da an sseo-sseo-yo.]
= Don't send it yet. I haven't finished writing it.

Sample Dialogue

Track 60

A: 내일 아침에 강남역으로 오는 거 잊지 마세요.
   [nae-il a-chi-me gang-nam-nyeo-geu-ro o-neun geo it-jji ma-se-yo.]

B: 네. 몇 시까지 가요?
   [ne. myeot si-kka-ji ga-yo?]

A: 9시까지 오세요.
   [a-hop-ssi-kka-ji o-se-yo.]

A: Don't forget to come to Gangnam Station tomorrow morning.

B: Okay. What time should I be there?

A: Please come by 9 o'clock.

Telling Time, and More

✏ Exercises for Lesson *30*

Check the answers on **p.199**

1. The Korean word for "to quit doing/to not do/ to stop doing" is "말다". How do you say "Don't do it"?

(   )

2. "To buy" is "사다". Please write "Don't buy it."
[sa-da]

(   )

3. The word for "not yet" or "yet" is "아직". How do you say "Don't do it yet"?

(   )

4. The word for "to give up" is "포기하다". Please write "Don't give up."
[po-gi-ha-da]

(   )

5. "A lot" is "많이" and "too much" is "너무 많이". How do you say "Don't buy too much of it"?
[ma-ni]   [neo-mu ma-ni]

(   )

BLOG

T-MONEY
(티머니 카드)

T-money is quite possibly the greatest invention to ever grace the streets of Seoul and surrounding Gyeonggi-do, and it'll be the best investment of your life to get one of these to carry around with you when you come here. T-money comes in all shapes and sizes, is rechargeable, and is useful in every means of public transportation that Seoul and Gyeonggi-do has to offer (hence the name "T-money").

So let's say that you've arrived in Korea and don't have T-money yet. How do you get it?

Luckily, you can purchase and re-fill T-money at all subway ticket booths. These automated machines are pretty nifty. You can also purchase and recharge T-money at almost every convenience store in Seoul. Most stores have a T-money logo in the window so you know for sure that you can purchase and re-charge there. There are even a few convenience stores at Incheon Airport on the arrival floor where you can do this, so when you get to

Seoul or Gyeonggi-do, you'll already have it. This saves you from being super awkward and basically wearing a sign on your forehead that says "I'm a tourist!" when you try to take a bus ride by paying with cash. Actually, it's not THAT awkward to pay with cash, but why pay with cash when you can get a discount by paying with T-money?!

Discount? Yeah, that's right! Everyone loves discounts, and T-money gives you 100W off the basic cash fare, which is essentially 1,150W for every 10km traveled. Since transportation cost in Seoul is figured by distance, having a T-money card will provide you with a discount on up to 4 transfers on the subways and buses when you need to.

You can get a regular T-money card for 3,000W, and other speciality cards, key chains, phone charms, etc. range from 6,000W to 15,000W. Different cards are sold at different locations, so check out this link to see all the different kinds of T-money cards and where they're sold: http://t-zone.co.kr/

T-money is also refundable, but you have to pay a 500W fee. If your balance is under 20,000W, just take your T-money to a GS25, 7-11, Buy the Way, MiniStop, HomePlus 365, or GS Watsons store to receive the refund on the balance only. If your balance is up to or less than 30,000W, you may only receive a refund at CU convenience stores. If your balance is up to or less than 50,000W, take your card to the T-money Service Desk on any Seoul subway

line at a number of stations in Seoul to get your money back (it may be difficult to find a T-money Service Desk outside the Seoul Metropolitan Area). Or, you can just keep the

T-money card and the money on it for the next time you come to Korea because it NEVER expires!!

If you won't be in Seoul for an extended amount of time and don't want to purchase a T-money card, another option is the M-Pass card or the Seoul City Pass Plus. With the M-Pass card, also known as Metropolitan Pass, you can ride the Seoul Subway Lines 1-9, the standard AREX (Incheon Airport Rail Express), standard trains (not express), metro trains (except the Shinbundang Line) and Seoul buses (except red buses). You can take advantage of these great modes of transportation up to 20 times per day without a limit on distance. The M-pass has a T-money function and can be used in taxis and when making convenience store purchases even if you have used it 20 times on the aforementioned public transportation methods. Passes are valid for the designated time period and expire at midnight on the last day.

There are five different types of M-passes: 1-day, 2-day, 3-day, 5-day, and 7-day which are available for purchase at Seoul Travel Information Centers (I-Tour Centers) in the Passenger Terminal at Incheon Airport. When purchasing an M-pass, you must pay a completely refundable deposit of 4,500 won in addition to a non-refundable service charge of 500 won. The refundable deposit will be returned to you in addition to any remaining T-money balance when you return the pass at any of the Seoul Travel Information Centers.

M-Pass Prices

1-day = 10,000W
2-days= 18,000W
3-days= 25,500W
5-day = 42,500W

7-day = 59,500W

The Seoul City Pass Plus Card is a pretty flippin' sweet deal if you're a tourist and plan to be in Seoul for a while. It's essentially a T-money card with added benefits designed for tourists. You can ride any bus or subway in Seoul until you run out of money and have to re-fill just like a regular T-money card, but you also have the ability to use the card at any of the four royal palaces in Seoul as well as for

most convenience store purchases. The benefits don't stop there! You can take any of the Seoul City Tour Bus routes at a 5% discount, too! With your Seoul City Pass Plus card, you also receive a booklet and discount coupons to use everywhere in Seoul. This pass also gets you discounts at 60+ participating stores that include restaurants, attractions, beauty stores, and many more! You get all of this great stuff for only 500W more than a regular T-money card. Um, yeah...totally awesome!

You can purchase and recharge the Seoul City Pass Plus Card at any GS25, CU, Mini Stop, Buy The Way, or 7-11 convenience stores in Korea. You can also recharge at any automatic subway ticket booth. This card is also refundable, but there is a 500W convenience fee to get your money back.

Now that you know how to get around Seoul with a few different payment options, we hope to see you here soon!

Before you close this book,
we want to say "congratulations" for finishing
TTMIK Level 2!
Way to go, and we'll see you in Level 3!

ANSWERS
for Level 2, Lessons 1 ~ 30

Answers for Level 2, Lesson 1

1. 청바지 입을 거예요.
[cheong-ba-ji i-beul kkeo-ye-yo.]
2. 뭐 팔 거예요?
[mwo pal kkeo-ye-yo?]
3. 누구 만날 거예요?
[nu-gu man-nal kkeo-ye-yo?]
4. 언제 점심 먹을 거예요? or
[eon-je jeom-sim meo-geul kkeo-ye-yo?]
점심 언제 먹을 거예요?
[jeom-sim eon-je meo-geul kkeo-ye-yo?]
5. 내일 뭐 할 거예요?
[nae-il mwo hal kkeo-ye-yo?]

Answers for Level 2, Lesson 2

1. 를
2. 을
3. 를
4. 를
5. 을

Answers for Level 2, Lesson 3

1. 그리고
2. 그래서
3. 그래서
4. 그리고
5. 그리고

Answers for Level 2, Lesson 4

1. 랑 / 하고
2. 랑 / 하고
3. 이랑 / 하고
4. 이랑 / 하고
5. 랑 / 하고

Answers for Level 2, Lesson 5

1. 일요일 = b. Sunday
2. 화요일 = g. Tuesday
3. 토요일 = a. Saturday
4. 목요일 = c. Thursday
5. 수요일 = f. Wednesday
6. 월요일 = d. Monday
7. 금요일 = e. Friday

Answers for Level 2, Lesson 6

1. 그렇지만 / 그런데
2. 피곤해요. 그렇지만 / 그런데 영화 보고 싶어요.
3. 좋아요. 그렇지만 / 그런데 비싸요.
[jo-a-yo] [bi-ssa-yo.]
4. 어제는 비 왔어요. 그렇지만 /
[eo-je-neun bi wa-sseo-yo.]
그런데 지금은 비 안 와요.
[ji-geu-meun bi an wa-yo.]
5. 어제 학교에 갔어요. 그렇지만 /
그런데 일요일이었어요.

Answers for Level 2, Lesson 7

1. 친구한테 / 친구한테서 받았어요.
[chin-gu-han-te / chin-gu-han-te-seo ba-da-sseo-yo.]
2. 누구한테 물어봤어요?
[nu-gu-han-te mu-reo-bwa-sseo-yo?]
3. 저한테 질문 있어요?
[jeo-han-te jil-mun i-sseo-yo?]
4. 동생한테 이거 줄 거예요. or
[dong-saeng-han-te i-geo jul kkeo-ye-yo.]
이거 동생한테 줄 거예요.
[i-geo dong-saeng-han-te jul kkeo-ye-yo.]
5. 친구한테 / 친구한테서 이거 얻었어요. or
[chin-gu-han-te/chin-gu-han-te-seo i-geo eo-deo-sseo-yo.]
이거 친구한테 / 친구한테서 얻었어요.
[i-geo chin-gu-han-te/chin-gu-han-te-seo eo-deo-sseo-yo.]

Answers for Level 2, Lesson 8

1. 몇 시예요?

2. 세 시

3. 한 시 십오 분

4. 다섯 시 사십칠 분
   [sa-sip-chil bun]

5. 열 시 삼십 분 or 열 시 반

Answers for Level 2, Lesson 9

1. 세 개

2. 다섯 명

3. 의자 세 개

4. 몇 명 있어요? or 몇 사람 있어요?

5. 두 명 있어요. or 두 사람 있어요.

Answers for Level 2, Lesson 10

1. 책 읽고 있어요.
   [chaek il-kko i-sseo-yo.]

2. 뭐 하고 있어요?

3. 뭐 하고 있었어요?

4. 자고 있었어요.
   [ja-go i-sseo-sseo-yo.]

5. 공부하고 있을 거예요.

Answers for Level 2, Lesson 11

1. 저는 학생이에요.

2. 제 이름은 민수예요.
   [min-su-ye-yo.]

3. 저는 20살이에요.
   [seu-mu-sa-ri-e-yo.]

4. 저는 서울에 살아요.

5. 반갑습니다.

Answers for Level 2, Lesson 12

1. 9월

2. 일

3. 9월 25일
   [gu-wol i-si-bo-il]

4. 몇 월

5. 며칠

6. 생일이 몇 월 며칠이에요?

Answers for Level 2, Lesson 13

1. 저도 선생님이에요.
   [jeo-do]

2. 한국어도 공부해요?
   [han-gu-geo-do]

3. 오늘도 일해요?
   [o-neul-do]

4. 물도 있어요.
   [mul-do]

5. 저도 이것 주세요. / 저 이것도 주세요.
   [jeo-do i-geot ju-se-yo.] [jeo i-geot-tto ju-se-yo.]

Answers for Level 2, Lesson 14

1. 보기도 하다

2. 팔기도 하다

3. 저는 영어를 가르쳐요.

4. 저는 영어를 가르치기도 해요.

5. 저는 수학을 가르치기도 해요.
   [jeo-neun su-ha-geul ga-reu-chi-gi-do hae-yo.]

Answers for Level 2, Lesson 15

1. 만

2. 이것만

3. 보기만 하다

4. 커피만 마셔요.
   [keo-pi-man ma-syeo-yo.]

5. 책 한 권만 주문했어요.

Answers for Level 2, Lesson 16

1. 조금 비싸요.

2. 아주 재미있어요.
[a-ju jae-mi-i-sseo-yo.]

3. 정말 이상해요.

4. 별로 안 비싸요.

5. 전혀 재미없어요.

Answers for Level 2, Lesson 17

1. 갈 수 있어요.
[gal su i-sseo-yo.]

2. 할 수 없어요. / 못 해요.
[hal su eop-sseo-yo.] [mot hae-yo.]

3. 이거 할 수 있어요?
[i-geo hal su i-sseo-yo?]

4. 지금 만날 수 있어요?
[ji-geum man-nal su i-sseo-yo?]

5. 수영할 수 있어요?
[su-yeong-hal su i-sseo-yo?]

Answers for Level 2, Lesson 18

1. -을/를 잘하다

2. -을/를 못하다

3. 못 하다

4. 저는 수영을 잘해요.

5. 저는 노래를 잘 못 해요.

Answers for Level 2, Lesson 19

1. 먹는 것

2. 가는 것

3. 책 읽는 것 좋아해요.
[chaek ing-neun geot jo-a-hae-yo.]

4. 매운 것 안 좋아해요.
[mae-un geot an jo-a-hae-yo.]

5. 제 취미는 영화 보는 거예요.

Answers for Level 2, Lesson 20

1. Using 되다 is more common in colloquial situations.

2. 가야 돼요. / 가야 해요.
[ga-ya dwae-yo.] [ga-ya hae-yo.]

3. 써야 돼요. / 써야 해요.
[sseo-ya dwae-yo.] [sseo-ya hae-yo.]

4. 지금 해야 돼요. / 지금 해야 해요.
[ji-geum hae-ya dwae-yo.]

5. 내일 어디 가야 돼요? / 내일 어디 가야 해요?
[nae-il eo-di ga-ya dwae-yo?]

Answers for Level 2, Lesson 21

1. 더 빠르다

2. 더 좋다

3. 커피는 물보다 더 비싸요.
[keo-pi-neun mul-bo-da deo bi-ssa-yo.]

4. 이 책은 저 책보다 더 재미있어요.
[i chae-geun jeo chaek-ppo-da deo jae-mi-i-sseo-yo.]

5. (저는) 어제보다 더 일찍 왔어요.
[(jeo-neun) eo-je-bo-da deo il-jjik wa-sseo-yo.]

Answers for Level 2, Lesson 22

1. 좋아하다

2. 한국어 좋아요.

3. 한국어를 좋아해요. or 한국어 좋아요.

4. 민수 씨는 우유를 좋아해요.
[min-su ssi-neun u-yu-reul jo-a-hae-yo.]

5. 뭐가 제일 좋아요?

Answers for Level 2, Lesson 23

1. 만약 지금 자면

2. 보다 = c. to watch

3. 보면 = b. if you watch it, if I watch it

4. 봤으면 = d. if I watched it, if they watched it

5. 볼 거면 = a.if you are going to watch it

6. 내일 비가 오면, 집에 있을 거예요.

Answers for Level 2, Lesson 24

I. 아직

2. 아직 몰라요.

3. 벌써 끝났어요?

4. 이미

그 사람은 이미 학교를 졸업했어요.

5. 벌써

그 사람은 벌써 학교를 졸업했어요!

Answers for Level 2, Lesson 25

I. 언젠가

2. 뭔가

3. 언제 일본에 갈 거예요?

4. 언젠가 일본에 갈 거예요.

5. 뭔가 이상해요.

Level 2 Lesson 26

I. 하세요
[ha-se-yo]

2. 쉬세요

3. 조심하세요!

4. 열심히 공부하세요!

5. 어서오세요. (lit. Come quickly)

Level 2 Lesson 27

I. 이거 해 주세요.

2. 영어 가르쳐 주세요.

3. 저거 사 주세요.
[jeo-geo sa ju-se-yo.]

4. 이거 봐 주세요.
[i-geo bwa ju-se-yo.]

5. 같이 가 줄 수 있어요?
[ga-chi ga jul su i-sseo-yo?]

Level 2 Lesson 28

I. after the nouns ending with a consonant

2. 펜으로

3. 이 의자는 나무로 만들었어요.
[i ui-ja-neun na-mu-ro man-deu-reo-sseo-yo.]

4. 한국어로 말해 주세요.
[han-gu-geo-ro ma-rae ju-se-yo.]

5. 이거 뭐로 만들었어요?

Level 2 Lesson 29

I. 더

2. 다

3. 다 했어요?

4. 숙제를 다 했어요.
[suk-jje-reul da hae-sseo-yo.]

5. 더 사고 싶어요.

6. 다 사고 싶어요.

Level 2 Lesson 30

I. 하지 마세요.

2. 사지 마세요.

3. 아직 하지 마세요.

4. 포기하지 마세요.
[po-gi-ha-ji ma-se-yo.]

5. 너무 많이 사지 마세요.

199

MP3 audio files can be downloaded at https://talktomeinkorean.com/audio.

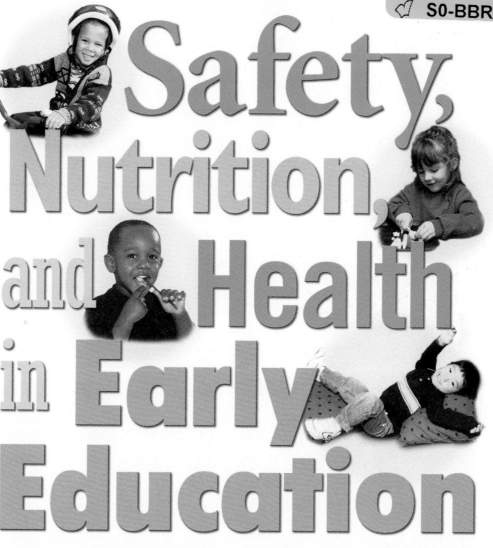

Safety, Nutrition, and Health in Early Education

SECOND EDITION

Join us on the web at

EarlyChildEd.delmar.com

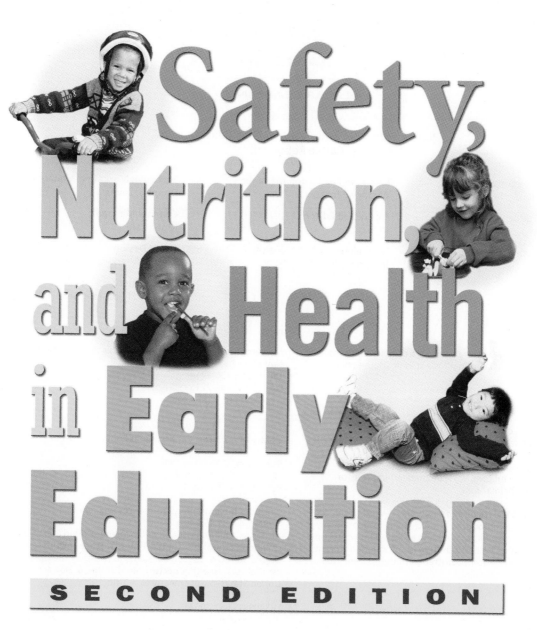

Safety, Nutrition, and Health in Early Education

SECOND EDITION

Cathie Robertson

DELMAR

THOMSON LEARNING

Australia Canada Mexico Singapore Spain United Kingdom United States

Safety, Nutrition, and Health in Early Education, 2e
Cathie Robertson

Business Unit Executive Director:
Susan L. Simpfenderfer

Acquisitions Editor:
Erin O'Connor

Editorial Assistant:
Ivy Ip

Executive Production Manager:
Wendy A. Troeger

Production Editor:
Joy Kocsis

Technology Project Manager:
Joseph Saba

Executive Marketing Manager:
Donna J. Lewis

Channel Manager:
Nigar Hale

Cover Design:
Joseph Villanova

Composition:
Stratford Publishing Services

Library of Congress Cataloging-in-Publication Data

Robertson, Catherine, 1946-
  Safety, nutrition, and health in early education / Cathie Robertson.-- 2nd ed.
    p. cm.
  Includes bibliographical references and index.
  ISBN 1-40181-255-4
  1. School children--Health and hygiene--United States. 2. Early childhood education--United States. 3. School health services--United States. 4. Schools--United States--Safety measures. 5. Day care centers--Health aspects--United States. 6. Day care centers--United States--Safety measures. I. Title.

LB3409.U5 R63 2002
372.17'1--dc21   2002025712

NOTICE TO THE READER

Contents

Preface

Cathie Robertson

Working with children today is different than it was ten years ago. There has been a societal shift and the daily lives of children are not the cultural images of childhood popularized in the media and on children's Web sites. *Safety, Nutrition, and Health in Early Education* includes vital information for those who work with children and addresses the challenges they will encounter in today's diverse world. Although adequate preparation in the areas of safety, nutrition, and health is imperative, even the best child development knowledge for learning and teaching will not be useful if the children are unhealthy, in unsafe environments, or malnourished.

This text focuses on the safety, nutrition, and health of children in child care. The audience for this text are child development students who are or are preparing to be teachers, paraprofessionals, caregivers, family home child care owners, or who will be working in other jobs that directly relate to young children. My experience teaching a variety of students who became nannies, preschool teachers, and family home care providers has helped me understand that although each type of caregiver will have many similar experiences, there will also be differences. This text is organized so that both the similarities and differences are recognized and discussed.

Organization

The whole child is addressed with respect to safety, nutrition, health, and special topics. All areas of the environment are examined to create policies that emphasize children's status and minimize any risk to children's well-being. *Safety, Nutrition, and Health in Early Education* combines basic information and theory, as well as practical applications, resources, and caregiving skills needed today for working with children, families, and staff.

This book is divided into four sections: safety, nutrition, health, and current issues in child care. This text serves for courses that may include all of those subjects, but was meant to stand alone for each of the subjects as needed. Every college and every instructor has a unique way of organizing the course that corresponds with this text. If one thinks of the sections in terms of modules, it may help both the student and the instructor find the information they need. The Reality Checks serve to enhance the information found in the chapters.

Safety

Creating safe child care environments is the major goal of this section of the text. The type of care and the developmental ages of the children in care are carefully examined in order to produce an appropriate safety plan. Accessories, behaviors, and conditions for safety risk are carefully explained in order for the caregiver to anticipate, monitor, and modify any risks to safety in the child care environment. Both indoor and outdoor environments are examined for common risks such as toys, equipment, traffic, fires, and burns. In addition, interpersonal safety and environmental factors are considered in relation to child care.

Nutrition

Providing nutritional balance in child care is covered in this section of the text. Using the Food Guide Pyramid, child caregivers can create nutritionally balanced menus. Infants, toddlers, preschoolers, school-age children, and special needs children are examined to help the caregiver meet the needs of children in each group. Exercise is addressed as a vital part of providing proper nutrition. Food safety and supplemental food programs are covered so that the caregiver can minimize health risks in the child care environment. Reinforcement of the information is provided through strategies and methods.

Health

Strategies for maintaining a healthy child care environment are covered in this section of the text. Tools are provided for observation, assessment, and screening of physical and mental health. Information on staff health, infection control, and health care in child care will help caregivers manage good child care with minimum health risks. Methods and strategies for using education, cultural competence, role modeling, and supervision are highlighted for the student to reinforce understanding of the health needs of children in care.

Current Issues in Child Care

This section covers topics of special interest to caregivers, such as child abuse, inclusion of children with special needs, care of children with chronic illnesses, the impact of stress on children, and how to meet the needs of children from families where drugs are abused. Communication skills, managing diversity, accessing resources, using advocacy for improved child care, and creating teams for child care are discussed. Curriculum for children, including a large reference section, is also offered in this section. As in previous sections, reinforcement is provided through discussion of methods and strategies in education, cultural competence, and supervision.

Special Features

Reality Checks address current issues that have an impact on the well-being of children. They bring an in-depth approach to some of the more critical areas that are affecting child care and children today. Reality Checks include information that is often absent in the popular cultural images of children found in many textbooks and the media regarding children's development. The following issues are discussed in Reality Checks:

- quality child care
- a safety checklist for parents
- kids and guns
- neighborhood violence
- dealing with natural disasters in child care
- sudden infant death syndrome
- secondhand smoke
- the effects of lead poisoning
- the effects of poverty on children
- child custody and its impact on child care
- peanut allergies
- effects of advertising on children's food choices
- children of the fast food generation
- the resilient child
- lice in child care
- otitis media in child care
- special care in mildly ill children
- shaken baby syndrome
- domestic violence and its effects on children's lives
- children and AD/HD
- children with HIV/AIDS in child care

Pedagogy

The chapters are organized for ease of use beginning with an outline that includes expected outcomes. The outline format is used so the student can easily assimilate the information. Each chapter section ends with Key Concepts that summarize the important points of that portion of the chapter. Vignettes, or stories based on real-life observations or events, are placed throughout each chapter. Vignettes reflect practical application and can help the child caregiver improve the health, safety, and well-being of children. For example:

Tamara, an autistic child, was acquiring some sign language capabilities. She spent part of her morning in a special school and then went to Kate's family day care before lunch. Her favorite food was watermelon, and whenever Kate served Tamara watermelon she could sign the word *more*.

Kate felt that there was an opportunity for learning here, so she went to the special education teacher at Tamara's school and learned how to sign the word *watermelon*. She used it every opportunity she could when she gave Tamara watermelon for lunch or snack. Eventually, Tamara learned how to sign the word. Her mother was so excited when she informed Kate several days later that Tamara had asked through signing for watermelon for dinner. It was a real milestone in Tamara's limited language.

Generalizable skills

common skills that can be practiced and used in different settings

Important terms are highlighted in color in the text and defined on the page where they first appear. This allows students to understand the term when they come to it and be familiar with it before they continue. There is also a complete glossary at the end of the text for reference.

Chapters 1–13 include **Implications for Caregivers**. This section of these chapters helps to reinforce the information given and reflects the responsibilities of the caregiver to perform the practices, strategies, and methods discussed in that chapter.

Chapter 14 is devoted to issues that directly relate to the caregiver's ability to provide the best environment possible for all children in care. Entitled "Creating Linkages," this chapter deals with communication, managing diversity, accessing resources, acting as an advocate, and creating teams.

The final chapter, Chapter 15, addresses curriculum for caregivers to use with children. Some of my reviewers felt that these should be sprinkled throughout within the individual chapters. Feel free to use them in that way. I concentrated them in one chapter because I felt that a whole week in class devoted to the creation of curriculum was important. This chapter includes the basics of curriculum planning and provides 14 lesson plans that represent the different chapters for caregivers to use with children. This should give students a head start, but it is important for instructors and students to understand the importance of creating a curriculum for safety, nutrition, and health. This chapter also includes an extensive and up-to-date list of children's books, both classic and new, to use as resources for working with children.

The end of every chapter is entitled **To Go Beyond**. This section gives the instructor ideas for classroom discussion, individual and group projects, and assignments. It also includes extensive references and suggestions for further reading.

Tables, graphs, checklists, figures, and photos are placed throughout each chapter to help present information in an organized manner. These features reinforce important concepts. For example:

TABLE 13–2 Stressors in a Child's Life

- Divorce/single parent family/stepfamily adjustments
- Birth of a sibling
- Separation anxiety
- Loss (death) of a loved one or pet
- Too many scheduled activities
- A new care situation or being placed in care for the first time
- A friend leaves child care
- Lack of bonding or attachment
- Financial problems at home
- Fears, real or imagined
- Special needs or chronic illness
- Victim of child abuse
- Drug abuse in the home
- Frequent relocation
- Cultural considerations, including language and immigration
- Observing violence in the home, neighborhood, or other real situation
- Poverty
- Homelessness

Supplemental Materials

An extensive Instructor's Manual is available for this text. This manual includes an outline guide, a test bank, enhancement activities, case studies, a video and film list, and other resources for each chapter. The enhancement activities offer ideas for meaningful projects that include many community links. The case studies will provide opportunities for critical thinking and practical application of the information provided in the text.

There are also Online Resources™ for this text to be found at http://www.delmarlearning.com/companions. Included on this site are extensive chapter quizzes, PowerPoint outlines, Web links, a discussion forum, and various other activities to help the instructor better use the material in each chapter. For the student there are chapter practice quizzes, a view of the PowerPoints, a discussion board, and Web links that will help them understand each chapter better. This site will be updated regularly so you may check back often to receive the latest information about the subjects in this chapter.

The author and Delmar Learning affirm that the Web site URLs referenced herein were accurate at the time of printing. However, due to the fluid nature of the Internet, we cannot guarantee their accuracy for the life of the edition.

Acknowledgments

The author wishes to extend her gratitude to a number of people who continue to make this text a valuable tool for child development professionals. Erin O'Connor, my editor, has been very supportive throughout this edition and I appreciate her help. Melissa Riveglia also contributed to the process of gathering and organizing the material and sending it out to reviewers, and then back to me. I would also like to thank Ivy Ip, who worked hard to put everything together at the end of the process. In addition I appreciate the work of Joy Kocsis in the production department and Linda DeMasi at Publisher's Studio.

I want to extend my heartfelt thanks to the following reviewers for sharing their expertise with me. Their constructive suggestions and recommendations were helpful in shaping the final product.

Billie Armstrong
Beaufort County Community College
Columbia, NC

Nancy Carlson
Orange County Community College
Middletown, NY

Linda Claussen
New River Community College
Dublin, VA

Jeannie Edwards
St. Louis Community College
St. Louis, MO

Linda S. Estes, Ed. D
St. Charles County Community
   College
St. Peters, MO

Leanna Manna
Villa Maria College
Buffalo, NY

Dedication

I would like to dedicate this book to my husband, Dan, for his loving support that has allowed me the time, energy, and effort to complete this ongoing project. I would like to thank my family, including my children Tara, Matt, and Anne and their spouses Frank, Angie, and Erin. A special tribute to my late brother Paul, who always encouraged me to be the best that I could be, and to the memory of my parents, Helen and Glen, who raised my consciousness level of what was happening in this world. All of my grandchildren—Zarli, Tatiana, Jake, Madilyn, and Jessica, are works in progress who have helped me rediscover the joys of childhood. This was the factor that made me decide to write this book, because it has reinforced for me the importance of good child care and inspired me to renew my efforts to make sure all children have what I expect for the children in my life.

The Author

Cathie Robertson received her BS and MS degrees from San Diego State University. She teaches courses in Family and Consumer Studies and Child Development at Grossmont College. She has taught food and nutrition courses, specializing in childhood nutrition, for a number of years. She is the former president of the International Nanny Association and presently serves on several local and state committees for issues that involve child care. She has made numerous state, local, and national professional presentations. Ms. Robertson has been the recipient of a number of grants, including one that funded the writing of a curriculum and resource guide for working with prenatally substance exposed children and their families. Ms. Robertson is married, the mother of three adult children, and a grandmother.

Safety, Nutrition, and Health in Child Care: A Holistic Environmental Approach

After reading this chapter, you should be able to:

1.1 Holistic Approach

Define a holistic approach to the safety, nutrition, and health of children.

1.2 The Environment

Describe an ecological perspective and explain how the environment may affect the safety, nutrition, and health of a young child.

1.3 Health Promotion, Protection, and Disease Prevention

Describe and discuss the differences between health promotion, protection, and disease prevention as they apply to child care.

1.4 Risk and Risk Management of Children's Well-Being

Define risk and discuss how risk management is crucial to the safety, nutrition, and health of children in child care.

1.5 Providing High-Quality Child Care in Safety, Nutrition, and Health

Discuss how a child caregiver would provide high-quality child care for safety, nutrition, and health.

1.1 Holistic Approach

It can no longer be assumed that all of the safety, nutritional, and health needs of children are met at home by parents. The U.S. Department of Labor estimates that more than 13 million children under the age of six have mothers in the workforce and it is expected that these numbers will continue to increase. It is estimated that more than 53 percent of mothers return to work within a year of a child's birth (Young, 1994). By the age of six, 84 percent of children in the United States have received supplemental child care and education (CCAC, 2001). Public and private center-based child care programs, family child care, and nanny in-home care are providing nonparental care for the majority of children while their mothers are working. These nonparental **caregivers** need to help the parents meet the health, safety, and nutritional needs of the children in their care.

Teachers, family child caregivers, nannies, and other nonparental caregivers spend their days working with children to provide intellectual stimulation, social and emotional support, and physical care. Good physical care is of primary importance to support the health, safety, and nutritional well-being of children. Children who are unhealthy or whose physical well-being is **at risk** may have difficulty performing cognitive tasks and relating to others in terms of social and emotional development. Cognitive, social, and emotional deficits as well as physical difficulties may result in poor health. Health should be defined in terms of a person's physical, mental, social, and emotional well-being. These areas are interrelated and a **holistic** approach will allow the effects of all areas of development to be observed for health and well-being.

Good health is the result of reducing unnecessary risk, preventing illness, and promoting the well-being of an individual. Child caregivers need to create an atmosphere for children that provides this protective type of environment. In order to accomplish this task, the child caregiver needs to focus on three basic areas: safety, nutrition, and health. Lack of good health practices, an unsafe environment, or providing poor nutrition may all contribute to failure in protecting children. The interrelationship of the areas of health, safety, and nutrition will be easier to understand if a holistic approach is used.

The **environment** of children's safety, nutrition, and health is the focus of this text. Each chapter begins with a lead-in paragraph and then points out current research findings that reinforce the need for concern for that issue. The issues presented indicate how children may be put at risk in center-based child care as well as family child care and nonparental care given to a child in the home. The body of each chapter provides the child caregiver with the information and strategies to deal with these issues.

As an example, the following research findings indicate and support the need for dealing with safety, nutrition, and health in a holistic manner:

■ "The whole child has been fragmented"; early childhood educators must have the knowledge, training, and skills to support the development of the whole child (Hyson, 2001).

■ Good quality child care can help reduce the magnitude of the effects of problems children may encounter such as poverty, violence, and the ability to achieve their whole potential (Schweinhart, 1994).

Caregivers
persons who provide care for children: teachers, family child care providers, nannies

At risk
exposure to chance of injury, damage, or hazard

Holistic
consideration of the whole being

Environment
all the conditions, circumstances, and influences surrounding and affecting the development of an individual

Research findings support the
need for dealing with safety,
nutrition, and health in a
holistic manner.

■ Good quality child care should meet standards that protect the basic health and safety of children and should also consider developmental needs. Most child care centers in the United States do not meet the children's needs for safety, health, or caring relationships (University of Colorado at Denver et al., 1995).

■ Children in this country are experiencing a greater number of at-risk difficulties than previously reported. These include psychological problems, emotional disorders, and chronic physical conditions (U.S. Department of Health and Human Services, 2000).

■ A holistic approach is needed to address the needs of children at risk for severe health problems and school failure (Newman et al., 2000).

■ Feeding practices related to growth can help predict the outcome of children's health, cognitive development, and social adjustment (Briley & Roberts-Gray, 1999).

■ Excellence of child care is directly related to compliance with a high standard of care (Grubb, 1993).

■ The first and second generation immigrant children are the fastest growing segment of U.S. population under the age of 15 (Board of Children and Families, 1995).

KEY CONCEPT 1.1

Holistic Approach

A holistic approach is the sensible way to deal with the interrelationship of safety, nutrition, and health on the well-being of young children (National Health Education Consortium, 1992). Those who provide nonparental child care should consider the environment of every child in care. Growth, health, development, and safety are a result of each child's environment.

Ecological

pertaining to the relationship of the individual to the environment

1.2 The Environment

Environment includes all the conditions, circumstances, and influences that surround a person. All of the complex factors in the environment can be simplified by using an ecological point of view (see Figure I–1). The ecological perspective examines the physical, social and emotional, economic, and cultural environments that affect a child. It relates all of the factors that might influence children's lives in terms of growth, health, safety, development, and well-being. Child care is an essential part of environment for those children who receive nonparental care. Those who are caregivers need to be aware of all the environmental factors.

The Physical Environment

The physical environment of a child begins in the mother's womb. A child born to a mother who had regular prenatal checkups and proper nutrition during pregnancy is less likely to have physical complications at birth and more likely to experience good health later in life than a child born to a mother who had

Figure I–I

Holistic View Ecological Approach

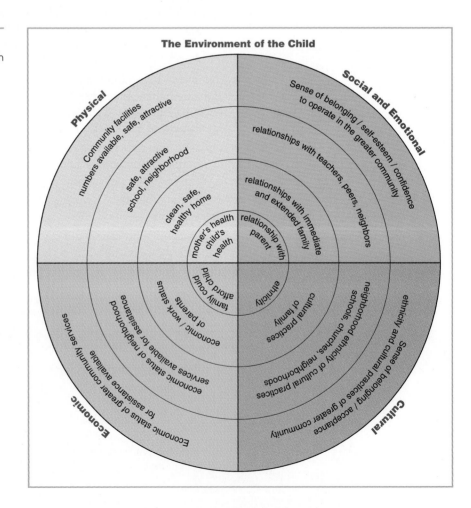

no prenatal care (U.S. Department of Health and Human Services, 2000). A child whose mother had no prenatal care is more likely to be born at a low birth weight and is far more likely to have physical problems at birth and health difficulties later in life.

After birth, the physical environment includes the family, home, school, neighborhood, and greater community. Children who are raised in poor circumstances are more vulnerable to inadequate nutrition, family violence, and exposure to environmental toxins *and are likely to have diminished physical health* (Brooks-Gunn & Duncan, 1997). Children who live in neighborhoods where they are protected from harm and are carefully watched are less likely to become injured or victims of violence than children who live in unsafe neighborhoods (Lynch & Cicchetti, 1998). This is significant because in the past 15 years, violence, poverty, physical illness, and family stress have increased in the United States (Bowman, 1995).

Another factor in the physical environment is **heredity**. Heredity plays a key role in the health and nutrition of children. A child's **genetic** background can influence a number of environmental risk factors (Plomin, Reiss, Hetherington, & Howe, 1994). Body type, temperament, and inherited diseases are just some of the characteristics that are expressed through genetic contributions from both parents in the reproduction process. There can also be inherited traits that may not be present at birth but may show up later.

An example of a disease that shows up at birth is phenylketonuria (PKU). It causes an inability in the child to **metabolize** one type of protein in the normal manner. Left untreated, this condition can cause brain damage and mental retardation. These harmful effects can be prevented if PKU is diagnosed in early infancy and if the proper diet is followed. Hospitals in many states routinely test for PKU at birth. The proper environment through correct diet measures can eliminate the risk factor.

Diabetes, cancer, obesity, and heart disease are inherited family factors that may appear later in life. These conditions may be prevented or their effects may be reduced through proper diet and exercise throughout life. By managing the environmental factors, those risks can be diminished and possibly eliminated.

Heredity

the transmission from parent to child of certain characteristics

---

Genetic

the origin of features of an individual

Metabolize

change occuring by chemical and physical processes in living cells

---

Andrea was ten months old when she was diagnosed with diabetes. Her family struggled to control the disease through diet and insulin. Even though several members of the extended family had the disease, none had been as young as Andrea at its onset. At age two and a half, her disease was finally managed with insulin in the morning and through careful diet control. When Andrea was three, her mother went back to work part-time, and she put Andrea in a family child care home. Andrea's child caregiver worked closely with her mother to make sure Andrea's diet was closely monitored. Today, Andrea is a healthy seventeen-year-old high school senior. The cooperation of her family child caregiver contributed to maintaining a positive environment for Andrea so she could be healthy and grow.

Children enter child care from many different physical home environments. Some children have had good physical environments and are healthy and protected from harm. Other children may come from at-risk physical environments. Families may not provide good health practices, or children may have an inherited condition or disease. Some children may be at risk for safety due to abuse or neighborhood violence. Children from at-risk home environments who have access to quality child care greatly increase the likelihood that they will grow up without problem behaviors and will contribute to society rather than becoming violent teens or adults (Newman et al., 2000). Children who attend a good child care environment are more likely to develop properly even if they are considered at risk in their own home environments (Cesarone, 1993).

A good child care environment using the holistic approach screens for health difficulties, provides good health and safety practices, and promotes proper nutrition. Caregivers integrate health, safety, and nutrition into the curriculum and value them as highly as social skills, language, or any other aspects of curriculum. This means that caregivers include all of these areas in the program every day. By providing this instruction to children in care, a good quality child care environment can provide the foundation for good health and well-being in adulthood. Child care may offer many children a better chance for an improved physical environment for at least part of the day.

The Social and Emotional Environment

The social and emotional environment of a child begins with the parent–child relationship. As the child grows, this environment expands to include the family, neighbors, teachers, peers, and other members of the community. Children's mental health and sense of well-being are very important factors in overall health. A family that provides a stable environment and creates the opportunity for a secure **attachment** for a child is more likely to raise a happy, cheerful child. A family that exposes a child to a high-risk situation and fails to form a secure attachment is more likely to produce a child who is at risk for many social and emotional problems (Shonkoff & Meisels, 2000; Sullivan, 2001). Children raised in healthy, functional families are more likely to retain good mental health and be well adjusted than those raised in dysfunctional, violent households (Bowlby, 1988; Osofsky, 1999; Spaccarelli, Sandler, & Rooss, 1994).

The consistency of caregiving and emotional investment on the part of a child caregiver has a direct relationship to the healthy development of children (Raikes, 1996; Young Children, 2001). Quality care contributes to children's sense of well-being. A good child care environment is one in which there are good one-on-one relationships between caregivers and children in care. Larger child care situations may have to provide a **primary caregiver** for each child to accomplish this optimal type of relationship. The caregiver who relates to the children in care is more likely to be alert and observant. A caregiver who has noticed any social or emotional effects of nonparental care can help the child adjust (Honig, 1993; Shonkoff & Meisels, 2000; Currie, 2000). The caregiver can also work with families to offer them strategies for providing a home environment that makes a child feel more secure and mentally healthy.

The quality of peer relationships may be a good indicator of a child's mental and emotional health status. A child's ability to cope with new situations, her sense of self-esteem, and her level of confidence affects how the

Attachment
the bond that develops between a child and another person as a result of a long-term relationship

Primary caregiver
the person assigned to be a child's main caregiver throughout the day in order to form a positive attachment bond

child deals with her peers. The observant caregiver will notice these things. A child's sense of self will affect how he grows and develops into a member of the greater community as an adult. It is widely recognized that early intervention by a caregiver provides a more secure environment for children who are at risk for adjustment difficulties (Zero to Three, 2002; American Public Health Association & American Academy of Pediatrics, 2002).

Mary Elizabeth is a four-year-old with a healthy appetite, a hearty laugh, and the ability to move from activity to activity with little need for transition. When she was born to a cocaine-addicted mother, the doctors were not sure of her prognosis for growth or behavior. She was briefly removed from her mother's custody and returned when her mother went into a parent supportive recovery program. Her mother, Ellen, received help for her addiction as well as help in learning how to parent, including the importance of early bonding in the mother–child relationship. Ellen studied to be a computer operator at a local community college and has been working for the past two years. Mary Elizabeth has been in the same child care center since she was 11 months old.

The staff at the child care center have been supportive of Ellen and understood that Mary Elizabeth might need some special help as a result of prenatal substance exposure. When Mary Elizabeth exhibited a high degree of frustration in certain types of play, the staff were able to provide emotional assurance and reduce the stimulation around her while redirecting her behavior. Mary Elizabeth is a good example of what early intervention and a good environment can do for the healthy development of a child at risk. Studies that have followed substance-exposed children from birth have concluded that, in many cases, a secure and supportive environment may overcome most of any possible side effects of prenatal exposure to drugs (Robertson, 1993).

The Economic Environment

Economic
the satisfaction of the material needs of people

The **economic** environment of the child is established in the home and is influenced by the parents' work history, the economic health of the neighborhood, the community, and the nation. Low income is the primary factor for the majority of childhood health and nutritional risks in this country (Children's Defense Fund, 2001b). Many children who are economically at risk are in child care situations.

One in every five young children in the United States lives below the poverty level. More than three out of four poor children live in a home where one family member was employed at least part of the time. One in three poor children lives in a family where at least one parent is employed full-time, year round (CDF, 2001b). The impact of financial stress on the home environment can affect children's emotions and behavior (Brooks-Gunn & Duncan, 1997). Financial limitations can also affect children's health. Lack of good medical care, poor nutrition, and an environment where parental attention is limited can affect children's well-being. Another effect of low income may be the inability to afford quality child care. Poor children are more at risk for serious illness and death. Some childhood health problems related to poverty are:

- low birthweight
- accidental deaths
- lead poisoning
- asthma
- lack of immunizations; deaths due to childhood diseases
- iron deficiency anemia

Economic factors that include the lack of preventive care and access to care can seriously impair the potential of many children in this country for maximum growth, healthy development, and protection from harm.

The person who provides child care will need to be aware of the impact that the economic environment of families has on the health, safety, and well-being of children. Child caregivers may be able to improve the impact of the economic environment on children by providing good nutrition and preventive health and safety measures. Caregivers can also help families to access resources, create community linkages, and advocate for children. These efforts and collaborations may provide families with critical information on health, safety, and nutritional issues. Child caregivers who collaborate with the greater community on these issues can improve their community environments.

The Cultural Environment

Cultural
relationship to traits and ascribed membership of a given group

The **cultural** environment includes the beliefs and practices of the family, the neighborhood, and the greater community. It has been estimated that by the year 2030, less than one-half of the U.S. population of children will be of

How can an at-risk environment where parental attention is limited negatively affect a child's well-being?

European ancestry (Shonkoff & Meisels, 2000). The United States has become a multiethnic society. With so many cultural traditions, practices, and values present, there may be value conflicts among different cultures. There may be bicultural conflict within families that represent several generations of values. One outcome of these conflicts may be the reinforcement of cultural values within families.

Practices for maintaining traditional cultural values in daily life, such as food choices and child care, are seen as meaningful declarations of family heritage. For example, whether or not the mother accesses prenatal care may depend upon the social practices of her cultural background (Kahler, O'Shea, Duffy, & Buck, 1993). It is important that the professional child caregiver support the family cultural values of the children in care (Shonkoff & Phillips, 2000). In instances where these cultural values put children at risk, cultural differences and legal practices will need to be addressed.

Characteristics of family health attitudes may relate directly to culture. For example, Latin American families appear to have lower expectations for children's health and therefore may be less likely to use preventive services (Vilchez & Tinsley, 1993; Carballo & Nerukar, 2001). The combined impact of social problems due to culture and economic hardship may cause harm to children. Children from these environments are more likely to experience social, emotional, and behavioral problems and suffer from poor mental health (Duarte & Rafanello, 2001).

It is important for the child caregiver to be aware of the diversity of the children and families in care (Derman-Sparks, 1999). In 2000, this diversity of children was apparent. Sixteen percent of the population of children were Hispanic, 15 percent were African American, four percent were Asian/Pacific Islander and one percent was Native American (America's Children, 2001). These numbers are expected to increase in the next three decades, especially in the Hispanic and Asian/Pacific Islander categories. As caregivers we need to go beyond cultural sensitivity or awareness which call for responsiveness, but go no further. We need to be culturally competent in our interactions with the children in care and their parents so that our relationships are mutually beneficial, even though we may have diverse cultural heritages and practices. This competence will allow us to better understand ways to communicate information on issues concerning safety, nutrition, and health.

KEY CONCEPT 1.2

Environment

An ecological perspective allows one to view the environment of a child. A risk factor in the health and well-being of children can come from any area of the environment. The physical, social and emotional, economic, and cultural environments all influence children's growth and development. Negative conditions from any part of a child's environment may place that child at risk. Poor physical and mental health, injury, or an impaired sense of well-being and self-esteem may prevent the maximum growth potential and development of a child. Using an ecological perspective, the child caregiver can approach the safety, nutrition, and health of children considering their total environment.

1.3 Health Promotion, Protection, and Disease Prevention

This text deals with the developmental aspects and issues that can help promote and protect children's well-being. The text also illustrates ways to prevent childhood illness, disease, or accidents. Caregivers should establish and maintain a healthy environment using health promotion. Caregivers promote health by checking for immunization and encouraging the use of proper hand washing and diapering techniques. They provide adequate nutrition and arrange for hearing, vision, and dental screening tests. Caregivers protect children in care by promoting safety practices such as using childhood safety seats in travel, checking toys and other equipment for hazards, and providing a low-risk environment.

The holistic approach to child care includes other measures to promote and protect children. Many organizations and efforts concerned with the health, safety, and nutrition of children contribute to a holistic approach. Some contributions will be examined in order to understand how issues concerning children's health, safety, nutrition, and well-being impact child care. Awareness of these outside efforts may help clarify the role of a caregiver in terms of the importance of providing good health, safety, and nutrition practices in child care. This knowledge may also help the caregiver understand the necessity of community linkages and of advocacy for children.

Healthy People 2010

Healthy People 2010: National Health Promotion and Disease Prevention Objectives is a report that is a product of a national process that has set health objectives for the year 2010. The major purpose of the program is to improve the health and well-being of Americans (Tate & Patrick, 2000). Many of the major targets for improvement are issues involving children. Some of the objectives that affect children are:

- Consider the environmental risks that cause emotional, physical, psychological, and learning problems.
- Provide culturally appropriate educational and support programs for parents in high-risk environments to help reduce child abuse and other health problems.
- Increase the proportion of children whose intakes from snacks at school (or day care) contribute proportionally to overall diet quality.

A caregiver can help improve the health and well-being of children in care by addressing these issues. Topics in this text provide the caregiver with a base of knowledge to effectively consider the issues.

National Health and Safety Performance Standards for Child Care

The American Public Health Association (APHA) and the American Academy of Pediatrics (AAP) collaborated and produced *National Health and Safety Performance Standards: Guidelines for Out-of-Home Child Care Programs.* Funding for this project and its in-process update has been provided by the Maternal

Health promotion
the improvement of health conditions by encouraging healthful characteristics and customs

KEY CONCEPT 1.3

Health Promotion, Protection, and Disease Prevention

Health promotion, protection, and disease prevention are ineffective if caregivers fail to understand the effects of the environment. Clearly, some programs and initiatives are trying to help parents and caregivers promote and protect the health and well-being of children. Caregivers play an essential role in the holistic approach to child care. They should be able to provide good nutrition and healthy environments that are safe from harm for the children in care. By modeling this environment, the caregivers can help children feel secure and help parents recognize the value of quality care.

and Child Health Bureau of the Department of Health and Human Services. These guidelines recognize the need for some consistency and guidance to help child caregivers provide the optimal environment for health, safety, and nutrition. The Pennsylvania Chapter of the American Academy of Pediatrics (ECELS, 1997) published *Model Child Care Health Policies,* and this document was adopted by the American Academy of Pediatrics. It may help to provide caregivers with some specific tools to create optimal child care.

The National Association for the Education of Young Children (NAEYC) is another organization concerned with the well-being of children. Although in agreement with many of the standards set by the APHA and AAP, they encourage caregivers to make decisions based on information from several points of view. Caregivers must first have the information and an understanding of specific procedures before making any decision regarding the health, safety, and nutritional needs of children in care. Caregivers need training to do this. This text was written to help caregivers acquire training in the areas of health, safety, and nutrition.

Other Efforts

Many federal and state programs such as Project Head Start, WIC (USDA's Supplemental Food Program for Women, Infants, and Children) and Project Healthy Start in Hawaii (Stein, 1995) are promoting good health and nutrition habits. Groups such as the Consumer Product Safety Commission promote safety measures that will improve the well-being of children.

Many of the initiatives that fund health promotion, protection, and prevention operate at all levels of government. There is a clear indication of the need for all entities involved with caring for young children to work together. Some collaborative efforts to promote safety, nutrition, and health for young children include:

- improving the health and nutrition of the developing child
- providing health and nutrition instruction for preschoolers
- providing parent education in health and nutrition

■ preparing preschool teachers to educate children and parents to use the skills themselves for health, safety, and nutrition issues

There are implications for caregivers from these governmental efforts. Child caregivers need to be prepared to perform the preceding tasks. They also need to understand how to communicate with families and collaborate with others in the community.

1.4 Risk and Risk Management of Children's Well-Being

Risk is defined as a chance or gamble that is often accompanied by danger. Risk management is a way to minimize the chance that danger may occur. Risk management takes on specific meaning when it is applied to taking care of children. Results of health risks include illness, infection, disease, mental illness, developmental difficulty, disability, and death. Results of safety risks include accidents, disability, and death. Nutritional risk results include developmental delay, growth retardation, poor health, and lack of resistance to infection or disease.

The opposite of risk in relation to health is well-being. Well-being is measured by wellness, degree of activity, resiliency, proper growth, at-level development, and general vitality. Children who are healthy, safe, and well nourished will exhibit those characteristics. Children who are at risk for problems will display one or more of the risk factors previously discussed.

Joey, a bright, happy two-year-old boy, was small for his age and seemed not to have grown in the six months that he had been at the child care center. Occasionally, he was listless. His teacher was concerned and spoke to Joey's mother, who had noticed the same thing. Joey's mother took him to the doctor for a checkup. The doctor inquired about Joey's diet and discovered that the mother was giving Joey large amounts of fruit juice and not enough milk and other foods. The doctor put Joey on a balanced diet. The mother explained that she had had a problem of being overweight when she was a child and did not want to feed him foods that had too much fat in them. The doctor explained that too much fruit juice may hinder growth and that Joey needed some fat and more milk in his diet. To stay healthy and grow properly, children need a variety of food sources (Bittman, 1994; Briley & Roberts-Gray, 1999).

Proper risk management strategies remove risk factors from children's health, safety, and nutrition. For the child caregiver, the strategies of health promotion, safety protection, and nutritional education are necessary risk management tools. Modeling good health, safety, and nutrition practices is a positive risk management strategy. The guidelines to managing risk in relation to the well-being of children are to set thorough standards and guidelines for child care facilities, training, and staffing.

KEY CONCEPT 1.4

Risk and Risk Management

Risk management is an effective way to protect, promote, and prevent difficulties regarding children's health, safety, and nutrition. A number of strategies such as modeling good practices and complying with standards and guidelines are good risk management tools for child caregivers.

1.5 Providing High-Quality Child Care in Safety, Nutrition, and Health

According to Bredekamp and Copple (1997), high-quality child care programs should provide "a safe and nurturing environment that promotes the physical, social, emotional, and cognitive development of young children while responding to the needs of families" (p.1). In terms of the health, safety, and well-being of children, the child caregiver needs to have four basic goals in mind to ensure a high-quality child care program:

1. Maximize the health status of the children.
2. Minimize risks to the health, safety, and well-being of the children.
3. Utilize education as a tool for health promotion and risk reduction for both children and adults.
4. Recognize the importance of guidelines, standards, and laws as they apply to the health, safety, and well-being of children.

Goal One: Maximizing Children's Health Status

Health status
the condition of health of an individual

A person's **health status** reflects the condition of health of that person. Child caregivers have the opportunity to provide optimal conditions to maximize the health and sense of well-being of the children in their care. In order to accomplish this goal, a set of objectives for health promotion and the prevention of illness and disease should be planned, carried out, and monitored through the creation of health policies. Regardless of whether care is in a child care center, a family child care home, or in the child's own home, many of the objectives will be the same. In some instances, the objectives may apply more specifically to the type of setting in which the care is performed (see Table I–1).

TABLE I–I   Objectives for the Optimal Health and Well-Being of Children

For care of children, all caregivers should:

- Respect the developmental needs, characteristics, and diversity of each child.
- Support a child's development based on knowledge of the general health and unique characteristics of the individual child. This includes emotional support as well as attention to physical needs.
- Reduce and prevent the transmission of infectious and communicable diseases.
- Understand the management of ill children, including exclusion policies.
- Use universal health procedures for toileting, diapering, maintaining toys, and handling and storing food.
- Utilize the health status of the staff as an important component of job performance.
- Ensure good nutrition and food safety by following the requirements of the USDA child care component, the Child Care Food Program, and the Code of Federal Regulations.

For parent education, all caregivers should:

- Help parents understand the importance of developing child care routines that contribute to children's sense of well-being.
- Utilize community health and nutrition professionals to create helpful linkages for children, families, and staff.
- Promote good health and nutrition through education for children, parents, and staff.
- Provide education and support to parents for the management of infectious illness and disease.

A child care center staff should:

- Provide a primary caregiver for each child.
- Provide someone to communicate in the children's and parents' first language.

Family and in-home child caregivers should:

- Work closely with the parents to provide nutritional information, healthy food choices, and good food for children.
- Act as a resource and role model for the parents by providing a healthy home environment for children in care.

Goal Two: Minimizing Risks for Childhood Safety, Nutrition, and Health

Proactive planning to reduce risk for children is an essential element in providing quality child care. The vulnerability of children places them at risk for many problems that can be prevented. Historically, infectious diseases have been perceived as the major risk associated with childhood. The threat of many childhood diseases has been lessened or eliminated with the availability of widespread immunizations to eliminate those diseases. However, these immunizations are only effective if they are administered to children. Other risks for spread of disease could decrease through proper sanitation practices.

Today, in reality, the major risks to children are unintentional injury, child abuse and neglect, homicide, lead poisoning, and developmental difficulties. The vulnerability of children at risk for unintentional injuries is influenced by age, cognitive development, motor skills, and the home environment (CDC, 1999). The danger of child abuse and neglect and homicide have become major issues in the health and well-being of children in America. Children are more at risk for violence when drug and alcohol abuse, poverty, and family violence are present in the environment.

Lead poisoning is another problem that poses risk to many children through environmental exposure. Developmental difficulties can cause permanent harm if they are not detected early. Intervention can reduce many problems associated with the difficulties.

This text includes a number of Reality Checks to help the reader understand the significance of current issues that affect the health, safety, or nutrition of children. The first Reality Check indicates an overview of issues that often go unnoticed due to lack of awareness.

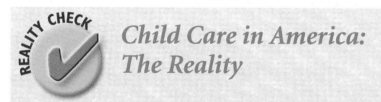

Child Care in America: The Reality

Historically, the care, protection, and supervision of children has been performed within families. The shift from family care to nonparental care has taken place mostly in the last half of the last century. Today, 84 percent of children who reach kindergarten age have been in some form of nonparental child care (CCAC, 2001). Seventy-three percent of infants and toddlers are in nonparental care at least part of the time (Ehrle, Tout, & Adams, 2000). Child care enrollments will continue to rise as more mothers enter the workplace for economic reasons (NIHCD, 1997). One reason for increased workplace entry is the change in the welfare system referred to as the Personal Responsibility and Work Opportunity Reconciliation Act of 1996 (PRWORA), which compels people formerly on welfare to enter the workforce. Considering the number of children in care, child care is no longer an option, but a necessity for most families. The majority of families must rely on others to provide for the care, protection, and supervision of their children at least part of the time.

Since child care is such an important part of most young children's lives, one would assume that quality child care would be the norm. Of children in nonparental care, approximately 30 percent are in center-based care, 23 percent are in family child care, and 5 percent are at home with a nanny or baby-sitter. Ninety percent of parents rate the child care center programs that their children are in as very good. However, trained observers rating the same programs noted that the great majority of care was poor to mediocre (Cost, Quality and Outcomes Study Team, 1995). In fact, many studies on the same subject lead us to believe that quality center-based care is not the norm, but is available in only a small percentage (14 percent) of cases. The Cost, Quality and Outcomes study also found that the quality at most child care centers does not meet children's needs for health, safety, and secure attachments. Galinsky et al. (1994) did a similar study on family child care and found that only 9 percent of the homes were

(continued)

rated as good quality. This study also found that 13 percent of the regulated and 50 percent of the nonregulated family child care homes were inadequate in their ability to provide good care to children. In these same homes only half the caregivers provided secure attachment to the children in their care.

There are approximately 3 million child caregivers in this country who work in 102,458 licensed child care centers and 290,000 regulated family child care homes (CCAC, 2001). The remainder work in nonregulated family child care homes and as nannies in families where there is no supervision provided for them. In this country there is no formal system in place to oversee family child care homes (Shallcross, 1999) or nanny care, and no consistent federal regulations for center-based care. Many states have marginal licensing laws for child care (Gordon, 2000). Regardless of state, age of children, or family income of the children in care, consistent state and federal policies for child care would help children receive the quality care they deserve. (Capizzano, Adams, & Sonenstein, 2000).

If we were to have the quality of child care that children deserve, what would it look like? Many people in the fields of child development, health education, and safety education, and others that support children have their opinions. A combination of the best of these would be:

■ Caregivers who have adequate training in the areas of child development, health, and safety, and what provides for the well-being of children (Gordon, 2000; Hyson, 2001; Shallcross, 1999; CCA, 2001; Los Angeles County Child Care Directory, 2001)

■ Caregivers who provide sensitive, responsive care that allows for secure attachment. (Shonkoff & Phillips, 2001; CCB, 2000b; Patten & Ricks, 2000; Raikes, 1996)

■ Caregivers who have skills to engage parents in communication and who promote parental nurturing for the well-being of the children (Lally, Lerner, & Lurie-Hurvitz, 2001; Gordon, 2000; Koshanksy, 1997; Winik, 1999)

■ Caregivers who are competent with diverse cultural and language backgrounds of children (Derman-Sparks, 1999; Shonkoff & Phillips, 2000; Burnette, 1999)

■ An environment that allows for good health and safety in child care and provides good working conditions for caregivers (Gordon, 2000; Los Angeles County Child Care Directory, 2001; Shonkoff & Phillips, 2000; Koshansky, 1997)

■ Adequate compensation for caregivers (Shonkoff & Phillips, 2000; Gordon, 2000; Winik, 1999; Cost, Quality and Outcomes Study Team, 1995) so that they will remain on the job and be a stable part of the children's lives

■ Adequate caregiver to child ratio (Gordon, 2000; CCA, 2001; CCB, 2000b; Shonkoff & Phillips, 2000)

■ For care that includes meals and snacks caution should be taken to provide adequate nutrition and food safety (Briley & Roberts-Gray, 1999; Koshanksy, 1997; Johnson & Kennedy, 2000).

■ An environment in which toys and equipment are age appropriate and developmentally appropriate practice is an integral part of the program. (Bredekamp & Copple, 1997; Koshanksy, 1997; Cost, Quality and Outcomes Study Team, 1995; Shonkoff & Phillips, 2000)

The importance of the need for quality child care in the United States is overlooked by many people, including legislators and some families who utilize this care, and by some of the people who are performing this care. *It is critical to the development of young children who are in care to be in high quality care. This type of care best can provide a stable, safe, and consistent environment.* This would allow children of all incomes, ethnic and cultural backgrounds, and family circumstances to have equal opportunities for good child development. This has been proven by several recent studies (Peisner-Feinberg et al., 2000; Newman et al., 2000; Shonkoff & Phillips, 2000).

There are many ways that high-quality child care can be accomplished (Gordon, 2000; Kinch & Schweinhart, 1999; Hyson, 2001). It can best be summed up by a caregiver, Peggy Haack of Madison, Wisconsin, who said, "The key to quality is the person providing it" (Winik, 1999). It is the responsibility of caregivers to be caring, consis-

(continued)

tent, well-educated, and well-trained so that they can support the children in their care with the best of quality available. But, beyond that, we need to educate parents as to what quality care looks like.

The public should be made aware that these changes will need legislative guidelines, standards, and regulations, as well as funding to ensure that quality child care is a reality for all children in care.

Prevention, recognition, protection, and early intervention are the major tools child caregivers can use to reduce risks to children in their care. Table I–2 lists some risk management objectives for child care safety, nutrition, and health.

TABLE I–2 Risk Management for Child Care

All child caregivers should:

- Require proof of immunizations before admitting children to care.
- Meet immunization requirements personally.
- Follow health and safety licensing guidelines.
- Provide a safe staff-to-child ratio.
- Develop good observational skills.
- Use health appraisals and assessment as risk management tools.
- Follow sanitary guidelines for hygiene and food handling.
- Protect the facility from neighborhood violence.
- Recognize and manage mild childhood illnesses.
- Provide backup or substitute caregivers to replace ill caregivers.
- Develop an inclusion/exclusion policy for ill children.
- Communicate by written notice about exposure to communicable disease.
- Provide a hazard-free environment.
- Prevent accidents in the indoor environment by following safety guidelines and practices.
- Prevent accidents in the outdoor environment by selection and placement of equipment and by following safety guidelines and practices.
- Create a safety plan for the facility.
- Create a disaster preparedness plan for fire and other dangers.
- Prevent fire by following local fire code standards and practices.
- Post and be ready to follow emergency procedures.
- Have knowledge of pediatric first aid and be able to practice it in case of an emergency.
- Be able to perform cardiopulmonary resuscitation (CPR).
- Detect, prevent, and report child abuse.
- Understand and utilize acceptable methods of discipline.
- Arrange the facility so there is no opportunity for isolation or privacy of individual caregivers with children.
- Develop a written plan for nutritious meals and snacks.
- Provide nutritious foods.
- Provide relief time for all staff.

Family child and in-home caregivers should:

- Organize the home for child care.
- Organize for mixed age child care.

Goal Three: Education as a Tool for Children's Health Promotion and Risk Reduction

A holistic approach to health promotion and illness and disease prevention is needed because health and well-being cannot be achieved without awareness. An educational component must be present in order to create a safe and nurturing environment for children. The educational component must impact the staff, the children, and the parents involved in the child care program or relationship.

Education and training for quality child care are essential (American Public Health Association & American Academy of Pediatrics, 1992; Gordon, 2000). The caregiver should be educated in promotional, preventive, and protective practices in order to provide the maximum environment and minimum risk for the child (Table I–3). A fundamental role of the child caregiver is to pass along knowledge. Modeling good health and safety measures and good food choices teaches children by example. Role modeling also allows children and their parents to see the caregiver put this knowledge to practice.

Teaching children about good health and proper nutrition helps them contribute to their own health. Instructing children in preventive and protective measures permits them to participate in their own well-being. The children can pass that information on to others by modeling and through discussion. This may motivate parents to be more receptive to the caregiver's modeling and information.

Caregivers educate parents by sending handouts, holding miniworkshops, and discussing health, safety, and nutrition directly with them. If necessary, the caregiver can access community groups' help to aid with this task. Parents who are supported through continual contacts with caregivers and educational assistance are better at providing holistic health for their children (Johnson, 1993).

Knowledgeable child caregivers who work with children, parents, and the community contribute to a team effort to promote good health, safety, prevention, and nutrition. Creating these linkages allows the child caregiver to effect a holistic approach to ensure a quality environment for the children.

Goal Four: Recognizing the Importance of Guidelines, Standards, and Laws for the Health, Safety, and Well-Being of Children

Guidelines
statements of advice or instruction pertaining to practice

Standards
statements that define a goal of practice

Laws
rules of conduct established and enforced by authority

Guidelines, standards, and laws affecting child care have been created for the purpose of protecting children and promoting quality environments for them. Child care centers in states where there are stringent regulations tend to provide higher quality care than those in states that have less stringent regulations (Child Care Bureau, 2000b). When nonparental child caregivers in all settings comply with standards, there is a lower turnover rate, more sensitive care, and staff with better training, resulting in better quality child care. NAEYC's position on licensing and regulation states "The fundamental purpose of public regulation is to protect children from harm, not only threats to their immediate physical health and safety, but also threats of long-term development impairment" (1997). Compliance with minimum standards can affect environmental practices, relationships with parents, and the general attitude of caregivers (Grubb, 1993).

TABLE I–3   Educational Tools for Caregivers

A caregiver should have knowledge of:

- Health promotion and the importance of modeling health promotion behavior
- Observational skills
- Immunizations and when they are to be given
- Health appraisals and use of assessment tools
- Mechanisms of communicable diseases and how they are spread
- Universal sanitary practices
- Common childhood illnesses, including management and exclusion policies
- Environmental health and safety hazards
- Safety standards and practices for both indoor and outdoor equipment
- Disaster preparedness
- Emergency response procedures
- Cardiopulmonary resuscitation (CPR) and first aid
- Child abuse detection and reporting
- Child abuse prevention
- Nutritional needs of children
- Good feeding practices for children
- Any special health or nutritional needs of children in care
- Communication skills
- Diversity and how it can affect health, safety, and nutrition
- Advocacy for children
- Access to community resources
- Development of family and community coalitions for improved safety, nutrition, and health

Regulations
recommendations that are made a requirement by law

Staff-to-child ratio
the number of staff required to provide proper care for the number of children of a certain age group

Whenever a child is injured or dies in the care of a professional caregiver, the media is quick to report it. Although the sensationalism may hurt the profession at the time, good may come from these unfortunate accidents or poor care. Parents have been calling for tougher regulations for safe child care (Chisolm, 1992). Some legislators in this country are more receptive to recommendations from organizations such as the National Association for the Education of Young Children, Children's Defense Fund, The American Academy of Pediatrics, The National Center for Clinical Infant Programs, The American Dietetic Association, and The American Public Health Association. Those organizations have developed standards and recommended guidelines for child caregivers to follow concerning the safety, nutrition, and health of young children. These and other groups are helping to effect legislation that originates regulations or enacts laws that protect children's well-being. For example, the staff-to-child ratio is an issue covered by regulations.

The American Academy of Pediatrics and the American Public Health Association believe that standards and guidelines should be established for all nonparental child care. The United States Department of Health and Human Services oversees federal regulations that have been enacted to help children. Individual states can enact legislation that creates regulations for child care. Many states have strict licensing regulations for child care settings, although some states have few, if any, licensing requirements. These licensing requirements basically relate to center-based care and family child care. There are virtually no regulations for in-home child caregivers.

Guidelines, standards, and regulations affect the child caregiver. They exist to support and promote the health and well-being of children. If guidelines, standards, and regulations exist, they should be followed. In a center-based facility, it is up to the director to ensure that the staff complies with and understands the guidelines, standards, and regulations. In a family child care home, it is the caregiver who monitors guidelines, standards, and regulations to ensure compliance. A caregiver who cares for a child in the child's own home must use common sense and form guidelines based on information from classes and available support such as this text or a network of community resources.

If the state in which the child care is performed has no regulations, it is imperative that the caregiver follow guidelines and standards suggested by the organizations previously discussed in this introduction. Many of the guidelines and standards are reflected in this text. It is basic good child care practice to follow them. The caregiver who uses them will be able to provide a healthy, protective environment for the children in care.

KEY CONCEPT 1.5

Providing High-Quality Child Care

High-quality care should be the objective of every child caregiver. For good safety, nutrition, and health in child care, the caregiver should have four basic goals: to maximize the health status of children; to minimize risks to children; to utilize education as a tool for health promotion and risk reduction; and to recognize the importance of guidelines, standards, and laws as they apply to child care.

CHAPTER SUMMARY

A holistic approach allows the caregiver to look at the interrelationships of safety, nutrition, and health for the care of young children. An ecological perspective views the total environment of the child. The physical, social and emotional, economic, and cultural environments all have an effect on the growth and development of children. Safety, nutritional, and health risk factors may come from any of these environments.

Awareness of efforts on national, state, and local levels may help clarify the role of the child caregiver concerning safety, nutrition, and health and nutritional practices, and recognizing signs and symptoms of health problems for early intervention.

Quality child care involves maximizing the health status of children and minimizing risk. Health promotion and risk management will enable the caregiver to ensure this. A caregiver who recognizes the importance of guidelines, standards, and laws has the tools for maximizing the child's environment. These tools help the caregiver set up healthy and safe practices, risk management strategies, and other tools needed to create a quality environment for the children in care.

TO GO BEYOND

In this section you will find a number of activities that you can use to apply and improve your knowledge of this chapter. There is also a thorough Online Resource that accompanies this text that can be found at: http://www.early childed.delmar.com/resources/robertson/index.html. Included on this site are chapter practice quizzes, PowerPoint outlines, Web links, a discussion forum, and various other activities to help you better understand the material in this chapter. This site is updated regularly so check back often to receive the latest information about the subjects in this chapter.

Chapter Review Critical Thinking Applications

1. Discuss the holistic approach to children's safety, nutrition, and health. Why do you suppose so many people who work with young children fragment or select one portion to look at and do not view the whole child? Does the interrelationship between safety, nutrition, and health affect issues regarding any one of them when applied to child care?

2. Describe the ecological perspective of the total environment. Consider a child whom you know. How does each of these areas affect a child's safety? Nutrition? Health?

3. Discuss the changes in diversity in this country. How might these changes impact child care? What could be done to minimize the impact?

As an Individual

1. Look at your own environment at home. What risks do you see in it? What could you do to minimize those risks? What can be done to maximize the health and safety of your environment? What if your environment were used for child care—would it be a safe and healthy place for children?

2. Write down everything you have eaten for one typical weekday and one typical weekend day. How could you improve your own nutritional status?

3. Observe a child care situation. Look at it with a holistic approach. What are the caregiver and the facility doing to contribute to the children's safety, nutrition, and health? How would you improve the child care by thinking of the whole child?

4. What are the health and safety standards or licensing regulations for child care in your community? Your state? If possible, obtain a copy.

As a Group

1. Examine the health promotion activities on your own campus. Are you aware of them? Are they adequate? What suggestions for improvement do you have? Remember to consider the whole person.

2. Obtain and analyze the local licensing requirements for health and safety measures in child care. Would you consider them adequate? How would you change these requirements to improve the health, safety, and well-being of children? Are those changes practical?

3. Assess your community's environment. Be sure to consider all the elements: physical, social, emotional, economic, and cultural. How would you rate your community in relation to safety, nutrition, health, or a place to raise children? What might be done to improve it? List 10 things that could be done to improve your community.

4. Analyze the quality of child care on your campus. If you do not have child care on-site, choose an off-campus site to evaluate. Compare the quality in relation to items reported in the Reality Check on Child Care in America (p. 15).

5. Design a quality child care environment considering both a holistic approach and the total environment.

CHAPTER REFERENCES

American Academy of Pediatrics. (2002, June/July). Warning to parents who smoke. *Healthy Kids,* 52.

American Public Health Association & American Academy of Pediatrics. (2002). *Caring for our children: National health and safety performance standards: Guidelines for out-of-home care.* Washington, DC: American Public Health Association.

America's children: Key national indicators of well-being, 2001. (2001) Vienna, VA: National Maternal and Child Health Clearinghouse.

Bittman, M. (1994, March 18). Eating well: Why would a child exasperate his parents by refusing to eat? Maybe he isn't hungry. *New York Times,* B7, C4.

Board of Children and Families, National Research Council (1995). Immigrant children and their families: Issues for research and policy. *The Future of Children, 5*(2), 72–89.

Bowlby, J. (1988). *A secure base.* New York: Basic Books.

Bowman, B. (1995). The professional development challenge: Supporting young children and families. *Young Children, 51*(1), 30–34.

Briley, M., & Roberts-Gray, C. (1999). Nutrition standards for child care programs—Position of ADA. *Journal of American Dietetic Association, 99*(6), 981–988.

Bredekamp, S., & Copple, C. (Eds.). (1997). *Developmentally appropriate practice.* Washington DC: National Association for the Education of Young Children.

Brooks-Gunn, J., & Duncan, G. (1997). The effects of poverty on children. *The Future of Children, 7*(2), 55–71.

Burnette, J. (1999). *Critical behaviors and strategies of teaching culturally diverse students.* (ERIC Digest) Champaign, IL: Eric Clearinghouse.

Capizzano, J., Adams, G., & Sonenstein, C. (2000). *Arrangements for children under five: Variation across states.* New Federation: National Survey of America's Families Series. Washington, DC: Urban Institute.

Carballo, M., & Nerukar, A. (2001). Migration, refugees and health risks. *Emerging Infectious Diseases, 7*(3), 556–560.

Centers for Disease Control (CDC). (1999). *Childhood injury fact sheet.* Atlanta, GA: Author. Retrieved May 15, 2002, from http://www.cdc.gov/ncipc/factsheets/childh/htm.

Cesarone, B. (1993). *Health care, nutrition and goal one.* ERIC Digest. Champaign, IL: Eric Clearinghouse on Elementary and Childhood Education.

Child Care Action Campaign (CCAC). (2001). *Key facts on child care and early education.* New York: Author. Retrieved May 15, 2002, from http://www.childcareaction.org/rfacts.html.

Child Care Aware (CCA). (2001). *Five steps to choosing quality child care.* New York, Author. Retrieved May 15, 2002, from http://www.childcareaware.org/en/5steps. html.

Child Care Bureau (CCB). (2000a). *Child care for young children demographics: Frequently asked questions.* Department of Health and Human Services, Washington, DC: Author. Retrieved May 15, 2002, from http://www.acf.dhhs.gov/programs/ccb/faq/demogra.htm.

Child Care Bureau (CCB). (2000b). *Child care for young children: Quality. Frequently asked questions.* Department of Health and Human Services, Washington, DC: Author. Retrieved May 15, 2002, from http://www.acf.dhhs.gov/programs/ccb/ faq/quality.htm.

Children's Defense Fund (CDF). (2000). *Child abuse and neglect: Fact sheet.* Washington, DC: Author.

Children's Defense Fund (CDF). (2001a). *Child care basics: Facts and figures.* Washington, DC: Author. Retrieved May 15, 2002, from http://www.childrensdefense.org/cc_facts.htm.

Children's Defense Fund (CDF). (2001b). *The state of America's children: Yearbook 2001.* Washington, DC: Author.

Chisholm, P. (1992). The search for safe day care. *Maclean's, 105*(25), 30.

Cost, Quality and Outcomes Study Team. (1995, January). *Cost, quality and child care outcomes in child care centers.* [Executive Summary] Denver, CO: Economics Department, University of Colorado at Denver.

Currie, J. (2000). *Early childhood intervention programs: What do we know?* Working paper from the Children's Roundtable. Washington, DC: The Brookings Institute.

Derman-Sparks, L. (1999). Markers of multicultural/antibias education. *Young Children, 54*(5), 43.

Duarte, G., & Rafanello, D. (2001). The migrant child: A special place in the field. *Young Children, 56*(2), 26–34.

Early Childhood Education Linkage Systems (ECELS). (1997). *Model child care health policies.* Elk Grove, IN: American Academy of Pediatrics.

Ehrle, J., Tout, K., & Adams, G. (2000). *Who's caring for our youngest children: Childcare patterns for infants and children.* New Federation: National Survey of America's Families Series. Washington, DC: Urban Institute.

Galinsky, E., Howes, C., Kontos, S., & Shinn, M. (1994). *The study of children in child care and relative care.* New York: Families and Work Institute.

Gordon, J. (2000). How our field participates in undermining quality child care. *Young Children, 55*(6), 31–34.

Grubb, P. (1993). The quality of regenerated family day care homes and compliance with minimum standards. *Child Welfare, 72*(5), 461–472.

Honig, A. (1993). Mental health for babies: What do theory and research tell us? *Young Children, 48*(3), 69–76.

Hyson, M. (2001). Better futures for young children, better preparation for their teachers: Challenges emerging from recent national reports. *Young Children, 56*(1), 60–62.

Johnson, D. (1993, March). Teaching low-income mothers to teach their children. Paper presented at the meeting for Society for Research in Child Development, New Orleans.

Johnson, R., & Kennedy, E. (2000). The 2000 dietary guidelines for Americans: What are the changes and why were they made? *Journal of the American Dietetic Association, 100*(7), 769–774.

Kahler, L., O'Shea, R., Duffy, L., & Buck, G. (1993). Factors associated with rates of participation in WIC by eligible women. *Public Health Reports, 107*(1), 60–65.

Kinch, A., & Schweinhart, L. (1999). Making childcare work for everyone: Lessons from the Program Recognition Project. *Young Children, 54*(1), 68–73.

Koshanksy, D. (1997). High-quality child care: Luxury options or standard equipment. *Young Children, 52*(2), 80–81.

Lally, J., Lerner, C., & Lurie-Hurvitz, E. (2001). National survey reveals gaps in the public's and parent's knowledge about every childhood development. *Young Children, 56*(2), 49–53.

Los Angeles County Child Care Directory. (2001). *What to look for in quality child care.* Los Angeles: Author. Retrieved May 15, 2002, from http://childca.co.la.us.quality cc1.htm.

Lynch, M., & Cicchetti, D. (1998). An edological-transactional analysis of children and context: The longitudinal interplay among child maltreatment, community violence and children's symptomatology. *Developmental Psychopathology, 98*(10), 235–258.

NAEYC. (1997). *Position statement on licensing and public regulation of early childhood programs.* Available at http://www.naeyc.org/resources/position_statements/pslicense.htm.

Newman, S., Brazelton, T., Zigler, E., Sherman, L., Bratton, W., Sanders, J., & Christeson, W. (2000). *America's child care crisis: A crime prevention tragedy.* Washington, DC: Fight Crime: Invest in Kids.

NICHD. (1997, April). Mother-child interaction and cognitive outcomes associated with child care: Results from the NICHD study. Paper presented at a meeting for the Society for Research in Child Development, Washington, DC.

Osofsky, J. (1999). The impact of violence on children. *The Future of Children, 9*(3), 33–49.

Pattern, P., & Ricks, O. (2000). *Child care quality: An overview for parents.* (ERIC Digest) Champaign, IL: Eric Clearinghouse on Elementary and Early Childhood Education.

Peisner-Feinberg, E., Bruchinal, M., Clifford, R., Culkin, M., Howes, C., Kagan, S., Yozcojian, N., Byler, P., Rustici, J., & Zelazo, J. (2000). *The children of the cost, quality and outcomes report go to school: Technical report.* Chapel Hill, NC: Frank Porter Graham Child Development Lab, University of North Carolina.

Plomin, R., Reiss, D., Hetherington, M., & Howe, G. (1994). Nature and nurture: Genetic contributions to measures of family environment. *Developmental Psychology, 30*(1), 32–33.

Raikes, H. (1996). A secure base for babies. *Young Children, 51*(4), 59–67.

Robertson, C. (1993). *California community college curriculum and resource guide for working with prenatally substance exposed children and their families.* Sacramento, CA: Chancellor's Office California Community Colleges.

Schweinhart, L. (1994). *Lasting benefits of preschool programs* (ERIC Digest). Champaign, IL: Eric Clearinghouse on Elementary and Early Childhood Education.

Shallcross, M. (1999). Family child care homes need health and safety training and an emergency rescue system. *Young Children, 54*(5), 70–73.

Shonkoff, J., & Meisels, M. (Eds.). (2000). *Handbook of early childhood intervention.* New York: Cambridge University Press.

Shonkoff, J., & Phillips, J. (Eds.). The Committee on Integrating the Science of Early Childhood Development. (2000). *Neurons to neighborhoods.*

Committee on Integrating the Science of Early Childhood Development, Board of Children, Youth and Families. Washington, DC: National Academy Press. Retrieved May 15, 2002, from www. nap.edu.

Spaccarelli, S., Sandler, I., & Rooss, M. (1994). History of spouse violence against mother: Correlated risks and unique effects on child mental health. *Journal of Family Violence, 8*(1), 79–98.

Stein, M. (2000, July 23). We're breaking the cycle of abuse. *Parade Magazine,* 8.

Sullivan, R. (2001, March 11). What makes a child resilient? *Time Magazine.* http://www.time.com/time/magazine/archive/.

Tate, M., & Patrick, S. (2000). Healthy People 2010 targets healthy diet and healthy weight as critical goals. *Journal of the American Dietetic Association, 100*(3), 300.

University of Colorado at Denver, University of California at Los Angeles, University of North Carolina, & Yale University. (1995, January). *Cost, quality and child outcomes in child care centers.* [Executive Summary].

U.S. Department of Health and Human Services. (2000). *Healthy people year 2010: National health promotion and disease prevention objectives.* Washington, DC: U.S. Government Printing Office.

Vilchez, K., & Tinsley, B. (1993, March). *Latino families' childhood health socialization: Theoretical and applied issues.* Paper presented at the meeting of the Society for Research in Child Development, New Orleans.

Winik, L. (1999, January 24). Every child deserves the best. *Parade Magazine,* 4–6.

Young Children. (2001). The irreducible needs of children: An interview with T. Barry Brazelton and Stanley Greenspan. *Young Children, 56*(2), 6–14.

Young, K. (1994, May 1). From zero to three. *San Diego Union-Tribune,* G-4.

Zero to Three/National Center for Clinical Infant Program. (1997). Caring for infants and toddlers in groups. Arlington, VA: Author.

SUGGESTIONS FOR READING

Aronson, S., Smith, H., & Martin, J. (1993). *Model health care policies.* Bryn Mawr, PA: Pennsylvania Chapter American Academy of Pediatrics.

Barbarin, O. (1993). Emotional and social development of African American children. *Journal of Black Pathology, 19*(4), 381–390.

Belsky, J. (1988). The effects of infant day care reconsidered. *Early Childhood Research Quarterly, 3*(3), 19–34.

Child care and early education program participation of infants, toddlers, and preschoolers. The National Data Resource Center. NCES 95–213. Retrieved May 15, 2002, from http://www.ed.gov:80/NCES/Sbriefs/sbielec2.html.

Children's Defense Fund. *Maybe America really is going to hell in a handbasket.* [Brochure]. Washington, DC: Author.

Frede, E. (1995). The role of program quality in producing early childhood program benefits. *The Future of Children, 5*(3), 115–132.

Griffin, A. (1993). *Preventing preventable harm to babies: Promoting health and safety in child care.* Arlington, VA: Zero to Three.

Herbst, A. (1999). What's wrong with our children? *Parents Magazine, 9,* 108–115.

Kelly, J., & Booth, C. (1999). Child care for infants with special needs: Issues and applications. *Infants and Young Children, 12*(1), 26–33.

LEAD! No. 1 environmental pediatric health problem. (1994). *Young Children, 49*(4), 9.

Loeb, P., Friedman, D., Lord, M., Guttman, M., & Kukula, G. (1993). To make a nation: How immigrants are changing America for better and worse. *U.S. News and World Report, 115*(13), 47–52.

National household education survey—Child care and early education program participation of infants, toddlers, and preschoolers. (1995). U.S. Department of Education National Center for Education Statistics [Internet].

Phillips, D., Howes, C., & Whitebook, M. (1992). The social policy context of child care: Effects on quality. *American Journal of Community Psychology, 20*(1), 25–51.

Recer, P. (1999, March 1). No lasting harm found in children of working moms. *San Diego Union Tribune,* A-5.

Schweinhart, L. (1993). Observing young children in action: The key to early childhood assessment. *Young Children, 48*(7), 29–33.

For additional information on safety, nutrition, and health in early education, visit our Web site at **http://www.earlychilded.delmar.com**

Safety in Child Care

In this section, we will discuss elements of safety in child care:

1. Setting Up and Managing a Safe Environment
2. Indoor Safety
3. Outdoor Safety
4. Emergency Response Procedures for Child Care

Setting Up and Managing a Safe Environment

After reading this chapter, you should be able to:

1.1 Safety Policies

Define and discuss safety policies and their use as tools for safety, risk prevention, protection, and promotion.

1.2 Creating Safe Environments

Discuss the importance of safe environments and describe a safe environment for all types of child care.

1.3 Injury Prevention Management

Discuss the factors involved in childhood injury and describe strategies for use in injury prevention.

1.4 Constructing a Safety Plan for Child Care

Explain the development of a safety plan for a child care setting.

1.5 Implications for Caregivers

Describe the importance of and strategies for education, supervision, and observation for maintaining a safe environment.

1.1 Safety Policies

Developing safety policies for the caregiver to manage risk, provide protection, and promote safety in child care is important. Some factors that indicate the need for these safety policies are:

- Unintentional injury is now the leading cause of death in childhood (Deal et al., 2000).

- In 1997, about 31,000 children under four were treated in U.S. hospital emergency rooms for injuries that occurred at child care/school settings. At least 56 children have died in child care settings since 1990 (CPSC, 1999).

- Forty percent of parents believe that children's serious injuries are "random acts of fate or accidents" and therefore they do not think in terms of prevention (NCHS, 1991).

- We can no longer assume that children are safe in their own environments of home and school (Hatted, 1994).

- Playground design, lack of attention, falls, and choking are common hazards in child care. SIDS deaths as a hazard in child care can be prevented if babies are put to sleep on their backs (Aronson, 2001).

- Children's sense of safety may be at risk as a result of what they observe in their world (Levin, 1994).

Caregivers should realize that most injuries to children are preventable. An accident infers a chance occurrence that is accompanied by no control or responsibility. Many injuries that children suffer can be prevented and do carry with them a degree of control for prevention and responsibility for protection. Because of developmental factors that limit children's physical, cognitive, and emotional abilities, they are more vulnerable to injury. Children are natural risk takers who attempt actions for which they may lack skills. Children want to test and master their environments. Children need a sense of trust and security

Because children may lack the capacity to judge whether or not an activity is safe, they must be provided with a secure, safe environment to ensure their well-being and protection.

that their environment is friendly and safe. Depending on their developmental level, children may lack the capacity to judge the safety of their environment.

Designing a Safety Policy

Safety policies should be developed and directed toward the children and staff. They should promote safe practices for the child, the caregiver, and the family. Basic safety policies lay the foundation for quality child care.

Policies establish a process, assign responsibility, and offer guidance for action. Safety policies may take the form of checklists, injury reports, guidelines, practices, and strategies to improve risk. When policies are being developed, the following questions should be asked (Kendrick, Kaufmann, & Messenger, 1995):

- What needs to be done?
- What process will be followed?
- Who is responsible for making sure the process is followed?
- Are there any time perimeters or limitations?

The question "What needs to be done?" provides the child caregiver with information needed to create a specific safety policy for each particular safety hazard that might be present in care. The caregiver needs to know what hazards are addressed by the local licensing regulations and fire board. An example of this is a state mandate that the child caregivers must report any suspected abuse. The caregiver then creates a policy for dealing with how, when, and where to make a report of suspected abuse. Some local areas have county or city fire regulation and zoning codes that may affect the design of safety policies.

Addressing the process involved in a safety policy will help the caregiver understand how the policy should be carried out. The process explains when, and perhaps where, an action should be performed. The caregiver should be aware of what safety hazards exist in both the indoor and outdoor environments. Viewing the environment through the eyes of a child will help the caregiver find safety hazards and create safety checklists and other policies that offer maximum protection. It is essential that the caregiver heave the knowledge of developmental abilities of the children in care. Developmental level safety checklists are important tools that may be used to manage the environment for risk.

Knowledge of environmental hazards will help the caregiver create specific policies for child care. Each type of safety hazard should have a process of actions to be followed to avoid risk. For example, if field trips are to be taken, there should be a definite policy for travel with children. This policy would include actions to be taken prior to the trip as well as actions needed during the trip.

Time limitations or parameters may be a critical factor in some areas of safety in child care. This is especially true for emergency situations. A child who has fallen and is unconscious for more than a few seconds should have immediate emergency medical care.

The child care setting will determine who is responsible for carrying out the policy. In a child care center, responsibility may fall to the director or primary caregiver (see Chapter Eight), or assigned safety advocate. In family child care, the responsibility will usually fall to the child caregiver. For in-home care, the nanny will probably share the responsibility with the parents. It is important to define the responsible party so that the policy does not go unenforced. A good health policy will have checks and balances for responsibility built into the policy. All staff should be encouraged to understand all safety precautions needed in the child care environment. Every child caregiver should be encouraged to carry out actions that provide for the greatest degree of safety.

Safety policies should be clearly written and include guidelines, limitations, and suggested methods of communication to be used. Safety policies help the caregiver develop proper practices based on the knowledge of safety, risk prevention, protection, and promotion. Basic policies should be created for safety, nutrition, health, and special topics and should incorporate the four major goals of high-quality child care:

- maximizing health status
- minimizing risk
- using education as a tool
- recognizing the importance of guidelines

A responsible caregiver would help to encourage safety and safe behaviors. Educating the children and their families so that they also know how to recognize dangers in any setting will ensure further protection. There should be several policies addressing the educational aspects for safety.

General child care safety policies should cover:

- *Creating Safe Environments:* practices for creating and managing safe facility specific environments
- *Injury Prevention Management:* understanding of injury and practices for preventing injury and protecting children
- *Developing a Safety Plan:* strategies for developing guidelines for prevention and protection in child care
- *Implications for Caregivers:* methods and practices for conducting education, observation, and supervision that provide maximum safety and minimum risk

KEY CONCEPT 1.1

Safety Policies

Safety policies should be planned and executed to prevent unintentional injury, protect the children from harm, and promote the use of safety practices for the caregiver, the child, the family, and the people in the environment of the greater community. These policies should be clearly written and should be based on standard safety practices and licensing regulations. The policies should consider developmental stages of the children and should be applicable to the specific child care environment. These safety policies would guide the caregiver in methods of practicing safety prevention, using protection and promotion to maximize the environment and minimize the risk to children.

Injury prevention
forestalling or anticipating
injury risk

1.2 Creating Safe Environments

The caregiver will need to use all the risk management and **injury prevention** tools available in order to create the safe environment children need to grow to their greatest potential. Knowledge of the ABCs of potential for injury will help the caregiver be aware of what is needed to create the protective and secure environment. Safety policies for modifying the environment, modifying behavior, monitoring children, and teaching injury preventive behaviors to children will help the caregiver to provide more safety, protection, and prevention in every child care situation. Most of the practices and behaviors that create a safe environment can be applied to all child care environments. See Table 1–1 for a guide to safe practices and injury prevention. Safety policies can be created from the list.

Something as simple as making sure all footwear is properly worn and tied may prevent an accident from occurring. What are other preventive measures to avoid accidents?

TABLE 1–1	A Caregiver's Guide to Safe Practices and Injury Prevention for a Safe Environment

- Know all applicable safety practices for the child care environment.
- Screen environment for hazards and remove, where possible.
- Use safety devices, where applicable.
- Monitor environment for hazards that are part of the environment.
- Know developmental levels of children including capabilities and limitations.
- Promote safety through action, word, and deed.
- Role model safety practices to children and parents.
- Be aware of conditions that contribute to injury.
- Closely observe children, giving special consideration during at-risk conditions.

There may be some differences in child care safety policies that are dependent upon several considerations. How these policies apply to specific safety protection, prevention, and promotion practices may relate to:

■ What type of environment are you applying these safety practices?
■ What is the age of children in care?
■ What is the greater community surrounding the environment like?
■ What is the child's family environment?

The Type of Environment

The type of child care environment has a definite impact on the degree of safety the caregiver is able to provide. Protective and preventive measures may differ depending upon the type of environment. Child care centers may be able to control for safety more than a family child care home. The level of safety in an in-home care situation may vary widely.

Child Care Centers.   Child care centers are different from homes. In most states, child care centers must follow certain licensing safety codes and practices (APHA and AAP, 2002). These basic codes and practices help the caregiver lay the foundation for normal safety practices for that environment. Child care centers generally are not multi-use facilities. The sole purpose of the child care center is to perform care and to provide a safe environment for the children in care.

Some child care centers are very different from single-purpose child care centers. A child care center in a church-related environment may not be subject to the same safety rules and regulations as those in the public sector. In addition, the church facility may be used by a number of different groups for a number of different activities, thus introducing a greater degree of safety risk factors.

Multi-use facilities

child care sites that are used for other functions

Depending on the environment, different degrees of protective and preventive measures must exist.

The same hazardous situation may be true for child care center environments that are located in some public facilities. Ski resorts, fitness centers, and elementary schools may have child care centers on site. These sites may not be subject to the same licensing safety codes or regulations and may be used for other purposes at other times. Modifying the environment in these unregulated, multi-use facilities may be a challenge to the caregiver. Modification would be a constant, ongoing process. These unregulated environments may make it more imperative that the caregiver know safety practices, be a role model, and promote safety through actions, words, and deeds. Teaching the children about these safety risk factors may help the caregiver have an added level of monitoring for these environments. The responsibility for maintaining a safe environment rests with the caregivers. Some examples of shared space are:

- a college or university preschool used in the evenings for classroom space
- a ski lodge that uses a corner of its lounge for child care while parents ski
- a church preschool room, used as a Sunday school and meeting room
- a corporate child care center that is used for meetings and training classes on weekends
- a community recreation center that has child care while parents attend classes

Family Child Care Homes.   Family child care homes are multi-purpose by definition. If the state or local area requires licensing, the home must pass certain safety requirements, such as a fire code. Some states or local jurisdictions do not require licensing for family child care homes. Other states may only license larger family child care homes with twelve or more children. This puts the responsibility of providing safety and protection directly on the caregiver in whose home the child care takes place. Self-regulation and monitoring the environment are vital for the prevention of injuries and protection of the children.

There may be local programs through the resource and referral services that help to support the family child caregiver. This support can help the family child caregiver create a safe environment using specific safety policies that are similar to licensing regulations in other areas. Another source of help for the caregiver is the National Family Child Care Association. This organization offers a program for accreditation that includes safety standards, policies, and practices.

In-Home Child Care.   An in-home situation where the caregiver comes to the child's home presents different challenges. Both the family child care home and child care center have the caregiver as the person responsible for creating and monitoring the environment for safety. An in-home child caregiver shares this responsibility with the parents. It would be easy to assume that this is a fairly straightforward task. Unfortunately, this is not always the case. Some parents do not understand the need for making the environment as safe as possible. The environment is the home they have carefully selected and decorated for comfort and style and it meets their needs.

When an infant arrives in the home, that child makes no demands on the home environment other than a place to sleep. As the child grows older and

The caregiver at a home care center with a pool should take all appropriate safety steps to avoid the possible "accident waiting to happen."

goes through the developmental stages, the need for modifying the home environment becomes important. Some parents are intent on making these modifications, while others do not see the need because "Joey is just going through a phase." It is on the shoulders of the nanny or in-home caregiver to make sure the parents participate in modifying and monitoring the home environment for safety. If the parents choose not to childproof the home environment, it is recommended that the caregiver not stay in this situation.

Not all situations like Damon's turn out so well. A home environment needs to be just as safe as any child care environment.

Damon was a quiet, curious toddler. Mary Ann, his nanny, was concerned that as he was becoming more mobile, Damon would get into unsafe situations. Mary Ann asked Damon's parents to remove the cleaning chemicals from under the sinks in the kitchen and bathroom. She asked that they remove small decorative objects from his reach. Some of these objects had sharp edges; while others were small enough for him to choke on if he put them in his mouth. The parents did not see the need. They felt that Mary Ann should rely solely on monitoring the child, and not worry about the environmental hazards.

Mary Ann served her two-week notice when they refused to cooperate. The following weekend, while in the care of his aunt, Damon got under the sink and drank some cleaning solution. He was rushed to the hospital and had his stomach pumped. He was very lucky that the cleaning product he swallowed did not do permanent damage. The aunt felt terrible, the parents realized their mistake, and Damon had to go through a very scary situation. The family begged Mary Ann to stay and offered their full cooperation for childproofing their home.

The Age of Children in Care

Because of the developmental stages children go through (see Table 1–2, page 37), the age of children in care will affect the type of safety policies that the caregiver will need (CDC, 1999). If the environment is for a particular age group where children are all at about the same developmental level, as is true in most large child care centers, the safety modifications that the caregiver makes to the child care environment will be standardized to fit that age range.

Infants.   Some child care may involve caring for infants. This may be a center where infant care is available, a family child care that specilizes in infants, or it may be a nanny caring for one or two infants. Infants are totally dependent and thus very vulnerable to injury if not carefully monitored. Infants develop their motor abilities in the **cephalocaudal** and **proximodistal** direction. Development in the cephalocaudal direction moves from the head to toe. As a child grows, development progresses down the body. For example, one of the first milestones for an infant is the ability to lift his head. One of the last infant milestones is the ability to walk. These **gross motor skills** develop earlier than **fine motor skills**. Proximodistal direction motor development works from the center of the body to the outside. An infant can roll over and use the arms long before he can reach and grasp (see Figure 1–1).

During the first few months of life infants are not mobile and do not encounter many risks. The major risk that infants of all ages encounter is Sudden Infant Death Syndrome (SIDS). The caregiver should use protective and preventive measures to reduce the possibility of a child being at risk for SIDS (see Reality Check, page 62).

Once an infant rolls over, mobility, thus risk, increases. A child could turn over and fall from a changing table or infant seat set on a counter. As the cephalocaudal motor direction develops, skills, thus mobility, increase. Children

Cephalocaudal
development from the top to the bottom of the body or from the head down toward the toes

Proximodistal
development of the body from the inside toward the outside or the torso through the arms and out to the fingers

Gross motor skills
physical skills using large body movements such as running, jumping, and climbing

Fine motor skills
physical skills related to small body movements, particularly of the hand and fingers. These skills include using scissors, holding a crayon, or working a puzzle.

Children who are at the same developmental level in a child care setting should be provided with a safe environment that accommodates their developmental stage.

Figure 1–1

An Infant Showing Proximodistal and Cephalocaudal Development

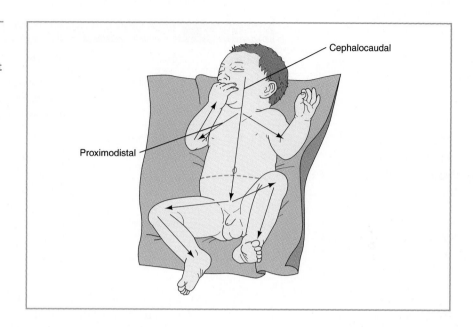

Sensorimotor cognitive development

first stage of cognitive development that utilizes motor abilities and senses

who creep, then crawl are apt to get into more and more territory that may pose risk to them. The need for safety devices increases at this stage. This is the time for safety gates on stairs, closed doors to bathrooms, and so forth.

Proximodistal motor development allows children to become more agile when using their hands and arms to reach for things and pick up things. Combined with sensorimotor cognitive development (see Table 1–2), this can lead to danger. Children who are able to pick up objects usually explore those objects by placing them in their mouths. The agile infant can get into practically any cabinet and may also be able to open containers in those cabinets. Safety latches should be used for cabinets, doors, and so forth. Any cleaning solutions or other chemical hazards should be removed to a high, locked cabinet. All electrical sockets should have safety plugs blocking inspection by curious infants.

Toddlers. Once a child has begun walking, his skills as well as his abilities to access dangerous situations increase. Cephalocaudal development will progress to abilities that include running and climbing. At the beginning of this stage the balance of the toddler is somewhat unsteady. Being mobile allows the toddler different ways to look at the environment. It can also give the toddler the ability to overcome obstacles that may have previously prevented action.

TABLE 1–2	**Piaget's Sensorimotor Developmental Stages**	
Stage	**Age**	**Actions**
1	0–1 month	Mostly sucking and looking.
2	1–4 months	Making interesting things happen repeatedly with the body, like kicking legs or sucking a finger. Pleasure from repetition.

(continued)

TABLE 1–2	Piaget's Sensorimotor Developmental Stages *(continued)*	
Stage	**Age**	**Actions**
3	4–8 months	Repeated actions focusing on objects and events. Picking up rattle and shaking over and over. Pleasure from repetition.
4	8–12 months	Combine actions to reach a goal.
5	12–18 months	Experiments to find new and different ways to solve problems or reach goal. This stage often referred to as "little scientist."
6	18–24 months	Beginning of thought using symbols or language to solve problems mentally.

Proximodistal development leads to greater manipulative abilities. Sensorimotor development presents cognitive abilities in children that will challenge any caregiver to keep one step ahead. Children at this stage are perhaps most at risk for dangerous situations. They are exploring and trying to master their environments, but they do not have the cognitive abilities to understand cause and effect. This can be a deadly combination.

Children in the toddler stage need to be supervised very closely. Their physical abilities and cognitive limitations will have them performing dangerous acts, so they must be carefully watched. All physical and environmental hazards need to be examined. Safety devices should be in place and all hazards that can be, should be removed.

Preschoolers. Preschool children have mastered most of their gross and fine motor skills. They are capable of most physical tasks. Cognitive abilities of children this age have also developed and they are in the **preoperational stage** (see Table 1–3) that offers some limitations in their thought processes. These limitations cause preschool children to see the world from their point of view. Children of this age may not perceive risk when it is present. For example, a four year old may be certain that she can climb to the top of playground equipment, jump off it, and land on the ground without getting hurt because she saw her favorite cartoon character do this very thing.

This age group responds well to role modeling and education. Preschool children are less likely to need safety devices such as stair gates and plastic plugs in electrical sockets, because they understand the perceived risk from these items. The preschool child can be trained to understand much risk from their environment. They will need monitoring, but not at the intense level of the older infant and toddler.

School Age. School-aged children are at far less risk for safety because they have cognitive abilities that can help keep them out of danger. Children of this age are at the **concrete operational stage** of cognitive development and have the ability to understand most situations that involve safety risk or hazards. Children of this age like to test their abilities to perform. Accidents and injuries

Preoperational stage
second stage of cognitive development in which logic is limited

Concrete operational stage
third stage of cognitive development in which logical ideas can be applied to concrete or specific situations

TABLE I–3	Limitations of the Preoperational Stage
Limitation	**Meaning**
Egocentrism	World is centered around "me." Nothing else exists. Sharing is hard. All toys seem to be "mine."
Centration	Child focuses only on one aspect of a situation or object. Child sees a toy, heads for it, regardless of what is in the way.
Fantasy	Children love to make believe and role play.
Irreversibility	Inability to reverse a situation or an action. Difficult for child to retrace steps of thoughts or action.
Animism	Everything is "alive" and all objects are capable of human feelings or actions.
Transductive Reasoning	Child cannot relate general to specific or a part to the whole. They only relate specific to specific. For example, if Sparky, the dog, is friendly, any dog that is encountered is friendly.

involving this age group are often from sports activities such as bicycling, skating, or organized sports such as soccer and baseball. Another area of concern for this age group is the curiosity about firearms. Guns are objects that provide great risk to children of any age, but this age group is more likely to be able to access them (Jackman et al., 2001).

School-aged children respond well to education and role modeling. The issue of firearms and the risk they pose should be discussed with these children (Eller, 1998). School-aged children can be excellent examples when they role model safety to other children. Although school-aged children need some monitoring, they can also be their own monitors for safety if they are armed with safety knowledge.

Multi-age Groups.   If the children in care are of varying ages and thus developmental levels, the caregiver will need to take a different look when planning for safety in the environment. If the environment needs to be designed for multi-age groups, then it should be modified as closely as possible to fit the youngest child's developmental abilities. This may cause some frustration for older children, but safety issues must come first. Role modeling and talking with the older children about the need for safety can help buffer their frustration and lead to greater understanding. Depending on their ages, older children may even help the caregiver monitor the potential risks in the child care environment and observe unsafe behaviors that younger children may exhibit.

The Community Surrounding Child Care

The safety of the children in care can no longer be taken for granted. It is impossible to consider the environment of child care as only the premises and

In addition to violence and traffic, discarded drug paraphernalia may be a potential hazard and liability for child caregivers using inner city public playgrounds with their children.

Liabilities

safety risks or hazards

the surrounding yard or outdoor play area. Child care takes place in the middle of cities, in suburbs, and in rural areas. The holistic approach for child care safety must consider the community area that surrounds the care site (Earls & Buka, 2000). No matter where the child care takes place, there are safety hazards, conditions, and behaviors that may affect the child care situation.

It is the caregiver's responsibility to be aware of the safety aspects or liabilities surrounding the child care premises. In some inner city areas violence may be a liability while in other areas, traffic may be the key liability. Rural and suburban areas may be isolated and distance may be a liability in case of an emergency. Rural areas may be more likely to have hazards such as animals in the environment.

It is the caregiver's responsibility to understand the risks and liabilities of the surrounding neighborhood community. The children should be taught safety and prevention strategies that apply to the community surrounding the child care. The promotion of safety should not end at the door of the child care situation.

The Child's Family Environment

A child's family environment may affect the child care environment. If the child's home environment is safe and secure, the child trusts that the caregiver's is also. A child who is free to explore and master a safe environment at home will also explore the child care environment. It is essential that the caregiver teach the child the rules and limitations for the care environment that will help to keep the child safe while in care.

A child who comes from an environment that is less safe and secure will also need consideration. Low income or poverty can affect the home environment. Maslow explained that the most important basic needs of humans are shelter, food, and clothing. Safety and security are second level needs (Maslow, 1968) (see Figure 1–2). If the family is poor, the parents may be trying to meet the basic needs and may not have the time or energy to think

Maslow's Hierarchy of Human Needs

Self-Actualization

Self-Esteem

Social

Love, Friendship

Safety and Security

Food, Shelter, Clothing

Figure I–2

According to Maslow's Hierarchy of Human Needs, a person's needs for such basics as food, shelter, and cothing must be met before higher level needs can be addressed.

about safety and security as being as important. Nine of ten Native American children, one in two African American children, one in three Hispanic children, and one in five white children live in poverty. One-fourth of the homeless today are children, and families are the fastest growing segment of the homeless population (Jones, 1998).

Note: Before the needs of a particular level can be addressed, the needs of the previous level must be met. For example, before the needs of safety and security can be met, one must already have food, shelter, and clothing.

The number of children living in poverty is significant considering the safety risks that may be present. Children from low-income families may need help understanding the need for safety and protective measures. In this case, role modeling and safety promotion will be important tools. Some of these children may also be unfamiliar with a secure environment that allows them to

Children living in poverty situations may be unaware of the potential safety and health risks their environment presents.

explore and develop a sense of independence. These children will need a predictable, supportive environment so they can develop a sense of trust.

Violence and child abuse are also safety risks that may come from the home environment of some children.

Child Custody and the Impact on a Child Care Center

With the high divorce and cohabitation rates, more children are coming to child care centers with unresolved custody issues. Included with this may be a risk for the child to be taken by a parent who does not have custody, or liability to the center for allowing a child to leave the premises with a parent who has no legal right to remove the child. It is extremely important for every center to have a policy on how to handle the risks involved.

It is helpful to understand exactly what the term "custody" means. There are some common terms in regard to this and they include:

▪ *Sole legal custody* gives one parent the right to make all decisions regarding the health, education, and welfare of the child. The other parent has no say in these matters (Nolo.com, 2001).

▪ *Joint legal custody* gives both parents the ability to participate in the decisions regarding the health, education, and welfare of the child. (NCCUSL, 1997).

▪ *Sole physical custody* gives one parent the sole physical custody of the child and prevents the other parent from having physical custody of the child. This often occurs if a parent has neglected or abused the child or has a drug addiction that prevents that parent from acting responsibly.

▪ *Joint physical custody* gives both parents the ability to be with the child. Custody as far as days and dates are included with this and a co-parenting plan may be inserted to this custody order.

▪ *Shared custody* gives an equal share to each parent in the legal and physical custody

issues concerning the child. This type of order is only issued if the parents are in full agreement and cooperation about the welfare of the child.

▪ *Bird's Nest custody* allows the child to remain in the family home while the parents take turns moving in and out (Nolo.com, 2001).

▪ *Noncustodial parent* refers to the parent who has the child the lesser amount of time, and *custodial parent* refers to the parent who spends more time with the child, and with whom the child lives.

▪ *Child visitation* encompasses the time that the noncustodial parent spends with the child.

Historically, custody rights were usually given to the mother due to the underlying prevalent theory that mothers were better suited to raise children. When divorce rates began their dramatic rise during the 1960s, the focus shifted to what was in the best interest of the child. Fathers were recognized for their contribution to children's lives. This led to more joint custody after divorce. By 1991, more than 40 states included joint custody as a common option (Kelly, 1997).

Divorce often creates anger and animosity between the parents that results in battles over the children in a number of ways. This can filter down to issues that may affect a child or children in your care. The major concern of the caregiver should be the protection of the child and keeping child care facility from any safety or liability issues that may be involved.

How does the center or caregiver deal with this? Where there is a joint custody order, and the parents have given the center or caregiver a copy of the order, there are clear guidelines for the pick-

(continued)

ing up of children. If there is a sole custody order, there should be clear guidelines as to who is allowed to pick up the child. Joint legal custody does not necessarily mean both parents have the rights to joint physical custody and the custody order would reflect this (Co-parenting.com, 2001).

The line may become blurred. When a custody order is on hand, and the custodial parent presents a document to the child care center authorizing the noncustodial parent to pick up the child, the center should be able to release the child without liability and without risk to the child. It may be wise to check state law (DivorceSource.com, 2001). If a noncustodial parent tries to pick up the child without authorization, there should be no question that you would not allow the child to go with this parent.

Particular cases should be very clearly defined for the child care and may not need a policy, other than to follow the court order, unless there is clear authorization from the custodial parent to allow the other parent pick-up rights. This should be more than a phone call. It should be a document that has been notarized, that acknowledges that the custodial parent has given this authorization.

In a case where the child is born to parents who are unmarried and there is no custody agreement order, it is more difficult to determine who has pick-up rights for the child. This situation may also apply to parents who are married, but are separated and have no legal document for custody or visitation. If there is no legal document available,

some type of policy must be created to deal with this issue.

The child care center should not act as a mediator or judge. In polling a number of centers about this issue, the majority had a policy based on common sense, but also considered liability. The consensus was that when a child is signed up for care, unless one parent indicated the other parent was not to pick up the child, both were allowed to pick up the child. In the case of one-parent pick-up only, the center would ask for a legal document stating that only that parent was authorized. If this was not forthcoming, the policy stated that if this "unauthorized" parent picked up the child, the child would no longer be enrolled in this program. Each parent would be advised of this. Legally, a child care center has no right to withhold a child from a parent unless there is a court document. Although dropping the child from the child care center rolls may appear to be a harsh response, the centers polled said that this worked well. Even though many parents are angry with each other, the child's welfare is still the main concern. These centers stated that when faced with the loss of child care for the child, the "unauthorized" parent did not attempt to take the child.

Whatever the situation, child care centers must be aware of this issue and their role in it. Court documents are the safest and best measure for a policy on child pick-up rights. When the rights for child pick-up are not clear, a policy should be carefully developed.

KEY CONCEPT 1.2

Creating a Safe Environment

Creating a safe environment by using safe practices allow the caregiver to provide the sense of security and protection from harm that children need to be free to develop, learn, and grow. Developing safety policies should directly relate to the type of child care that is being provided. Understanding the developmental needs, capabilities, and limitations due to the age of children in care helps the caregiver to lay a foundation of safety and protection. Knowing about the community and the family will enable the caregiver to more adequately prepare the safest environment possible for the children in care.

1.3 Injury Prevention Management

A safe environment for a child is one that provides freedom from harm and offers a sense of security in which to play, develop, and learn. The caregiver is responsible for providing this type of environment for the children in care. A major goal for a caregiver is to manage the child care environment for injury prevention. Injury prevention promotes safety, protects the child, and minimizes risk. Injury prevention also offers a plan to manage injuries as they occur with the least distress to everyone concerned. The child care environment should prepare for reducing risk, protecting children from harm, and planning for occurrence of injury. Injury prevention offers children the sense of safety and security needed to develop to the fullest potential.

ABCs of Childhood Injuries

Every accident has a cause and effect. Accidental injuries generally occur when a risk is taken or a hazard is present in the environment. To avoid unintentional injuries, causal factors must be understood and anticipated.

The injury triad is a valuable tool for injury prevention (see Figure 1–3). When an injury occurs, certain questions can be asked to understand the circumstances:

- What type of injury occurred?
- How did the injury happen?
- Why did the injury occur?
- Where did the injury occur?
- When did the injury happen?

As these questions are explored, a clearer picture may form as to what could have been done to prevent the injury to a child. Table 1–4 provides common factors for childhood injury.

Accessory. Accessories that are involved in injuries include physical and environmental hazards and lack of safety devices. Accessories help explain

Figure 1–3
The injury triad is used to understand the circumstances surrounding an injury to help prevent future injuries.

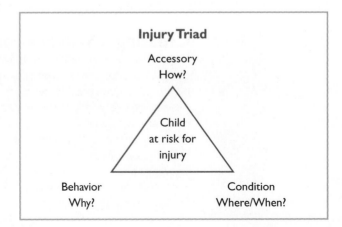

TABLE I–4	The ABCs of Injury Risk to Children			
A	**=**	**Accessory**	**=**	**How**
		Physical and environmental hazards		
		Lack of safety devices		
B	**=**	**Behavior**	**=**	**Why**
		By Child:		
		Developmental level		
		Mastery/Exploration		
		Don't know/understand		
		Lack of physical ability		
		Don't grasp cause and effect		
		Lack of fear		
		Inattention		
		Emotions		
		Stress		
		Imitation		
		By Adult:		
		Inattention, no supervision		
		Lack of knowledge/understanding		
		Lack of communication		
		Lack of safety precautions		
		Emotions		
		Stress		
C	**=**	**Conditions**	**=**	**Where or When**
		Where:		
		Place		
		Indoor/outdoors		
		When:		
		Time of day		
		Tired, hungry, in a hurry		

how the injury happened. An accessory is a known factor. A physical hazard could be an object, such as a penny on the floor, a cleaning solution stored under a sink, or a piece of equipment, such as a jungle gym. Environmental hazards might include a swimming pool or traffic around the child care center.

Lack of safety devices might include an open electrical outlet without a plug cap or a car without a proper safety seat.

The most effective risk management tool to remove accessories as a risk factor in the injury triad is to use preventive and protective strategies and practice. Since accessories are known factors, the caregiver can modify the environment to remove risk due to them. Modification might include moving cleaning solutions to a high, locked cabinet or installing electrical outlet plug covers.

Behavior. Behaviors contribute action or inaction that leads to an injury. This can help explain why an injury occurred. Behavior bears most of the responsibility for injury. Action of a child is the most common behavior to the injury triad. The majority of behaviors the child displays are related to the developmental level of the child (CDC, 1999). The common developmental tasks children perform as they go from stage to stage are the very behaviors that lead them to injury. A child explores his environment, masters his skills and abilities, and uses his cognitive processes to solve problems. These behavioral factors can lead a child into situations that can cause injury.

Knowledge of the developmental levels of children can help alleviate risky situations. Being aware of the developmental stages and situations a child is prone to encounter at a particular age can help the caregiver monitor the environment and be a keen observer of the child.

The adult behaviors that can contribute to a child's injury can be active or inactive. In the case of child abuse, violence, or running over a child with an automobile, the adult behavior is active. In the majority of cases, however, the adult contributes inactive behavior to an injury. Lack of supervision, knowledge, communication, and understanding of a situation are causes of inaction (Shallcross, 1999). Inattention to what is going on around oneself can also be

Regardless of the cause, when an injury occurs it must be taken care of properly by a child caregiver or nurse.

Rodney was a caregiver for two-year-olds at an inner city day care center. The two-year-olds and three-year-olds shared a large room and often played together during free time. Rodney was well aware of the differences of the younger twos in his group and the older three-year-olds in the other group. He carefully monitored the free play time. One morning he stopped Joshua from putting a small toy part in his mouth. Kelley, a three-year-old, had brought a small car from home. One of the wheels had fallen off and Joshua picked it up and attempted to put it in his mouth. Although Rodney had no choice about his group playing with the older children and their toys, he was very careful in what he watched for, because he knew the developmental level limitations of his two-year-olds.

inaction. A caregiver who is under stress or who is experiencing emotional difficulties may not be as attentive as normal. Inaction presents itself as the absence of preventive, protective, and promotional safety measures.

The same risk management tools for safety that are used for children apply to adult behaviors. A full knowledge of safety practices through education are critical to provide the necessary supervision for a safe and secure environment for children (Aronson, 2001). The caregiver also needs to be aware how his stress and emotions may affect the care given to the children. The use of education, promotion, and good role modeling by the caregiver can help children learn more safe practices. The caregiver should also be practical and use good judgment. These risk management tools may also lead children to an earlier understanding of cause and effect and provide them with preventive strategies that would protect them from harm in dangerous situations. Using education, role modeling, and communication, the caregiver can also help the parent lay the foundation for a safer, more secure environment in the home.

Condition

circumstance or situation under which safety is at risk

Condition.   The **condition** factor of the injury triad indicates the circumstances surrounding an injury. The questions as to when and where the injury took place are answered as conditions are explored (Smith, 2001). The place, the time, and the situation under which an injury takes place may have contributed to the injury. Injuries take place in child care centers, in homes, on playgrounds, and many other places.

Certain types of injuries are more likely to happen in certain places (Figure 1–4). For example, falls from equipment such as climbing structures are more likely to occur on playgrounds or in child care centers than in a home because this type of equipment is more likely to be found at child care centers than in a private home. A child is more likely to have a bicycle accident in the street than on a sidewalk because streets have traffic and pedestrians, while sidewalks contain pedestrians only. Certain types of injuries are more likely to happen indoors, while other injuries commonly occur outdoors.

Time may be a critical factor that contributes to injury. Children are more likely to get injured in late morning or late afternoon when they are tired. If a child or adult is in a hurry, an injury is more likely to occur. A shift in environment or routine at child care can present distractions or conflicts that are

Figure 1–4
Pie Chart with Common Conditions for Childhood Accidents

stressful and lead to accidents. Developing an awareness that certain conditions in child care contribute to injury can help the caregiver be more alert when those conditions are present in the child care situation.

Table 1–5 applies the causal factors from the injury triad to specific situations that may be found in injuries that might occur during child care.

When Injury Does Occur

Even in the safest environments, injuries do happen. How the caregiver handles the injury can contribute to keeping the child care environment as secure as possible. Careful planning for injury prepares the caregiver to handle accidents and injuries as they occur with as little stress as possible. This can help reinforce the trust of the children present in child care environment. Safety policies should include injury response methods and practices to help provide good injury management.

TABLE I–5   Causal Factors in Childhood Injuries

Who = Children of all devlopmental stages and ages

What	How	Why	Where	When
Motor vehicle accident	Lack of seat belt or safety seat Inattention of driver	Inattention to importance of using safety device	In automobile	Anytime
Riding bicycle near cars	Darting in front of car	Inattention Don't grasp cause/effect Lack of fear In a hurry	Near home, school neighborhood	Anytime Unsupervised
Fall	Unsafe equipment Mastery Exploration	Lack of safety knowledge Lack of ability Don't grasp cause/effect Imitation	Outdoor playgrounds Indoor climbing	Late morning Late afternoon Unsupervised Tired
Collision with objects	Mastery Exploration	Hazards in environment Lack of ability Don't grasp cause/effect In a hurry Imitation	Anywhere	Anytime Tired Unsupervised
Poisoning	Exploration Mastery	Hazards in environment Don't grasp cause/effect Imitation Inability to read	Kitchen, bathroom bedroom, garage living room, yard	Unsupervised Anytime
Choking	Exploration	Hazards in environment Don't grasp cause/effect	Anywhere	Unsupervised Anytime
Burns	Lack of safety devices Mastery Exploration	No smoke detector Water too hot Don't grasp cause/effect Imitation Access to fire device	Anywhere Bathroom Kitchen	Unsupervised Anytime
Drowning	Exploration Mastery	Lack of ability Imitation Lack of safety precautions Lack of understanding cause/effect Hazards in environment	Bathtub Pool Any body of water	Unsupervised Anytime
Child abuse	Parent Someone child knows Stranger	Repeat of cycle of abuse Poverty Dysfunction	Anywhere	Anytime Under stress
Violence	Lack of safety precautions Firearms available	Guns and other hazards Inattention to safety	Neighborhood/ Home School	Anytime Unsupervised

KEY CONCEPT 1.3

Injury Prevention Management

Injury prevention is a major responsibility of the child caregiver. To prevent injury and protect children, the caregiver must first understand how injuries occur. A caregiver who understands how accessories, behaviors, and conditions contribute to injury will have the ability to anticipate injury. Monitoring the children and modifying the environment will allow the caregiver to prevent injury and promote safety.

1.4 Constructing a Safety Plan for Child Care

The safety policy designed for each type of child care situation includes the construction of a safety plan. This plan prevents risk and promotes safety, and consists of the guidelines the caregiver develops to promote safety in the child care environment (Kendrick, Kaufman, & Messenger, 1995). The guidelines address the areas where risks are anticipated and the environment is modified and monitored for safety. These applications will lessen risk due to accessories, behaviors, and conditions.

Anticipation

The anticipation process begins with a room-by-room indoor inspection and overall outdoor inspection for safety with checklists that the caregiver creates for that particular child care environment. These checklists apply to the type of child care, the ages of the children in care, the surrounding community, and the family environments the children represent.

Caregivers should search for the accessories, behaviors, and conditions that affect injury prevention. The caregiver should anticipate from the developmental level of the children who are present in child care. Seeing the environment room by room from a child's eye view will help the caregiver to identify risks that an adult-only point of view may have missed.

The next step is to anticipate the behaviors that lead to injury that might occur in the caregiver's type of child care environment. In order to best meet the needs of the children in the child care environment the caregiver must consider the factors of age, community, and family. Knowledge of behaviors that contribute to injury helps the caregiver prepare to promote safety through education and good role modeling. Children who learn safe practices and preventive strategies are less at risk for behavior factors that contribute to injury.

Conditions that contribute to injury must be anticipated next. Creating a plan for safety and careful observation during times when children are more likely to be injured will help to reduce the possibility of injury. The caregiver who understands the conditions and common times that injuries occur will be especially alert when faced with those circumstances.

Children who come to child care from conditions that make them more at risk for injury can especially benefit from efforts to help them understand safety and prevention. Children need a supportive and caring environment to explore in and be protected from harm. Children from at-risk environments may not feel this protection at home. Children in violence prone neighborhoods may feel especially vulnerable. For these children, child care or school may serve as a safe haven. Giving these children tools of safe practices and the sense of security in the child care environment may help them to be more resilient in their home environment (Levin, 1994). It may also help them be more alert in their community environment (Levin, 1999).

Communicating with parents about conditions, such as stress, that contribute to injury may help them avoid situations that can lead to injury. Role modeling for safety under stressful conditions delivers the message to the parent that injury can be prevented and that a safer environment can be created for children.

Modifications

Careful screening of the environment for hazards, removing the hazards, and placing safety devices where needed are simple tasks that a caregiver can perform to ensure a safe and secure physical environment for children. The use of checklists can assist the caregiver in this process.

Behaviors can be modified through teaching and exhibiting safe, protective, and preventive practices. The caregiver's safety plan would use the most applicable and suitable mode of communication for child care situations. Injury prevention can be taught at all levels, to some extent. Preschool children are more receptive and have greater capabilities than toddlers or infants. School-aged children are very receptive to safety behaviors and practices. There are several steps that the caregiver can use to help children of all ages modify their behaviors to protect themselves and prevent injury. The three most important teaching tools for promoting behavior change are:

- ■ feedback
- ■ modeling
- ■ role playing through practice drills

Teachers or caregivers can role model safe behavior in a variety of ways.

Feedback
a technique for encouraging desired behaviors in children through communication

Positive reinforcement
reward given in response to a particular behavior that increases the chance of that behavior occurring again

Diversion
something that changes the focus of attention

Feedback about safety can include **positive reinforcement** for good safety behavior practices, **diversion** away from unsafe situations and practices, and a two-way communication channel about both safe and unsafe practices.

Modeling can include role modeling by the caregiver, the use of safety posters and signs, and the use of videos, stories, and other modes of communicating about safety and how it is achieved.

Role playing helps prepare children to act in unsafe or dangerous situations. It is a preventative tool that allows children to be better equipped in a real emergency. Drills for fires, earthquakes, and other types of disasters are practiced on a regular basis in many child care environments. Role playing is often recommended for other types of dangerous situations such as child abuse prevention, gun safety, and neighborhood safety.

Modification works well when applied to the factor of condition. The caregiver cannot change the time of day when injuries are most likely to happen. However, she can teach the children to avoid certain activities when they are tired. Caregivers can also modify activities at times that children are more prone to injuries, for example, making a climbing apparatus off limits during high injury times such as late morning. The caregiver might also make that a time when children gather together to relax over stories, instead of playing outside. If a mixed age group is present, while younger children nap, older children might play with toys that are not appropriate for the younger children. These would be put away once the younger children awaken (Blythe-Saucier, 2000). Role modeling and communicating about safety conditions offer children greater protection. Older children who are able to learn safety practices and understand certain conditions that can lead to injury can have a greater sense of safety and security.

Monitoring

Monitoring the physical environment of child care for accessories is an ongoing process. Change is a constant process. A caregiver should develop an intuition for the changes, but the monitoring process should be formalized. The use of checklists allows the caregiver to evaluate changes and check for hazards.

Monitoring the child care environment for behaviors includes observing whether or not safety practices have changed. This involves keeping track of whether injuries have decreased or increased and examining the behaviors present in the environment. Regularly scheduled weekly examination of injury reports is a good idea because it helps the caregiver to recall any incidence of lack of safety precautions in the environment while they are still fresh in mind. The child care environment should be reviewed for changes on a monthly basis. Changes can occur with the arrival of new children, in the developmental levels of the children in care, in the community, or in family situations. Monitoring helps to manage change by once again anticipating and modifying the environment.

Careful observation under conditions that lead to injury is the foremost activity of monitoring. Mishaps can be prevented through observation. Ongoing evaluation for conditions that lead to injury will help to find changes. Use of monitoring tools such as a convex mirror on corners to increase visibility and baby monitors to listen for safety might lessen risk (Aronson, 2001). If changes in conditions occur, this type of evaluation can lead to early intervention to prevent injury and protect the child. Evaluation of conditions is accomplished through observation, active listening, and communication.

KEY CONCEPT 1.4

Constructing a Safety Plan for Child Care

Constructing a safety plan for child care environments is a process that involves anticipation, modification, and monitoring. The three-step process considers the accessories, the behaviors, and the conditions that lead to injury or lack of safety and protection of the children in care. Some of the tools for the process include checklists, feedback, modeling, practice drills, education, and other promotional techniques. Other effective tools include careful observation, active listening, and communication.

1.5 Implications for Caregivers

The caregiver should use preventive and protective measures to prepare and maintain a safe child care environment. The risk management tools that will help the caregiver to provide a good measure of safety include role modeling, education, observation, and supervision.

Role Modeling

Children like to imitate the adults in their lives. Safety and protection of children from harm can be influenced by caregivers who role model good safety practices and create a safe, secure environment.

A safety policy for role modeling should reflect those behaviors the caregiver wishes to instill in the children. Some of the knowledge and practices the children should be able to observe the caregiver role model are listed in Table 1–6.

TABLE 1–6   Role Modeling Behaviors for Safety
• Verbalizing safety actions to the children
• Caregiver safety actions in the child care and community environments
• Presence of safety devices such as smoke alarms and electrical outlet plugs
• Caregiver being attuned to unsafe conditions
• Caregiver safety behaviors during practice drills and role playing
• Good caregiver/parent communication level about safety measures
• Daily routines for safety checklists
• Removal of hazards to ensure a safe physical environment
• Promotion and education on safety issues and practices
• Caregiver predictability and support given the importance of safety in the child care environment

A Child Care Safety Checklist for Parents

Children's safety can be increased by parents and caregivers using preventive and protective measures, but some parents think that nothing bad will happen to their children. It is imperative that a child's safety be a major consideration of parents and caregivers. The caregiver needs to provide a safe environment. Parents should protect their children by checking the child care environment for safety. The Child Care Action Campaign provides information guides for parents. Their guide, *Finding Good Child Care: The Essential Questions to Ask When Seeking Quality Care for Your Child* provides a checklist for parents seeking child care. A number of these items refer to children's safety and protection. The following is a listing of the items that pertain to safety, printed with permission of the Child Care Action Campaign (1996):

■ The staff to child ratio is at a safe level. The safest level includes:

For family child care: 1 adult per 5 children, including the caregiver's children. No more than two infants.

Child care centers: 1 adult per 4 infants and toddlers
1 adult per 4 to 6 two-year-olds
1 adult per 7 to 8 three-year-olds
1 adult per 8 to 9 four-year-olds
1 adult per 8 to 10 five-year-olds
1 adult per 10 to 12 school-age children

■ Caregivers have some training in child care. They continue to learn by reading books, taking courses, and belonging to professional organizations.

■ Caregivers pay attention to children and interact with them, rather than chatting with other caregivers or attending to personal things.

■ Caregivers change their style of supervision to suit the age and abilities of the child; very close supervision for infants and toddlers, more independence for three- and four-year-olds. Children are never left unsupervised.

■ Reasonable discipline is maintained through careful supervision, age-appropriate explanations, clear limits, use of "time out." No spanking or corporal punishment is ever used, nor is harsh discipline such as shouting, shaming, or withholding food.

■ Caregivers avoid conflicts between children by listening and watching carefully so that they can step in early, before the situation escalates.

■ Children, including babies and toddlers, have easy access to safe toys.

■ Safe and easy-to-use art materials, such as nontoxic crayons, paints, and play dough, are provided so that children can create their own work as soon as they are able.

■ There is enough safe crawling space for infants and toddlers that encourage exploration of the environment.

■ Challenging materials, such as scissors or toys with many pieces, are introduced, with supervision, as children are ready for them. A caregiver stays with the children as they use these materials.

■ Children play outdoors in a safe area every day, except in bad weather.

■ Electrical outlets and heaters are covered, and stairs have safety gates.

■ Equipment is maintained to ensure safety, and there is enough space for active physical play outdoors (and to some degree, indoors) for all age groups.

■ Cleaning fluids, medicines, and other harmful substances are stored in locked cabinets out of the reach of children.

■ The outdoor play area is fenced and cleared of debris and poisonous plants.

■ There are fire extinguishers in the building and an adequate number of working smoke detectors.

■ Emergency numbers for the fire station, rescue squad, police, poison control, and so forth, are posted near the telephone.

■ There is an emergency exit plan so that the caregiver can get all the children out quickly. Fire drills are held monthly, so that children and caregivers know what to do in case of an emergency.

(continued)

- Safety restraints and car seats are used every time a child is in a car, bus, van, or other moving vehicle.
- There is an "open door" policy for parents: you are welcome to visit your child and the child care at any time of day.
- The facility is registered or licensed, if required.

Caregivers should provide this list to prospective families interested in their child care center or family child care home. Complying with this list will offer the parents the knowledge that their children are in safe hands while in child care.

Education

Safety education should involve the child caregiver, the children, and the parents. To provide safety in child care, the caregiver must be aware of strategies and methods to reduce risk (Aronson, 2001). The caregiver must develop a keen awareness of the risks posed by the accessories, behaviors, and conditions of his particular child care environment.

Children can learn safe practices as they watch the caregiver model safe practices and behaviors. The caregiver can talk to the children about safety and share books and videos that promote safety and safe behaviors.

Educational materials provided for the parents may help them understand the importance of safe practices and behaviors for children in all environments. A parent who is aware of conditions or behaviors that may put a child at risk for safety is able to offer an extra measure of protection and prevention.

Observation

A child caregiver can use observation to protect children from risk and to prevent risk to safety. Observing for accessories, behaviors, and conditions keeps the caregiver aware of all areas of injury risk management. The caregiver should watch for safety from hazards and equipment. He should observe for the need for safety devices. Behaviors of both children and adults should be observed for safe practices and risk from injury. The caregiver should observe the conditions in the environment that are known to lead to risk of injury and reduction of safety.

Supervision

Using the ABCs of injury risk management helps the caregiver offer the greatest degree of constant supervision in order to maintain the safest child care environment possible. Supervision can also help ensure that all strategies and practices that promote safety, prevent risk, and offer protection are used.

KEY CONCEPT 1.5

Implications for Caregivers

The child caregiver needs to use all tools at her disposal to help promote safety, prevent injury, and offer protection. Role modeling, education, observation, and supervision provide the practices, strategies, and methods needed to provide these for the children in care.

CHAPTER SUMMARY

Safety policies that manage risk and prevent injury promote and protect the safety of the child care environment. Caregivers should be aware of the environmental hazards such as accessories, behaviors, and conditions in their particular child care. Children's developmental levels should be understood and addressed when considering safety. Caregivers should learn to anticipate, modify, and monitor child care for injury prevention. Role modeling is a key to promoting safe practices. Education and supervision also help the caregiver maintain a safer child care environment.

TO GO BEYOND

In this section you will find a number of activities that you can use to apply and improve your knowledge of this chapter. There are also thorough Online Resources™ that accompany this text that can be found at: http://www.early childed.delmar.com/resources/robertson/index.html. Included on this site are chapter practice quizzes, PowerPoint outlines, Web links, a discussion forum, and various other activities to help you better understand the material in this chapter. This site is updated regularly so check back often to receive the latest information about the subjects in this chapter.

Chapter Review Critical Thinking Applications

1. Discuss the interrelationship of accessories, behaviors, and conditions of safety applied to child care.
2. Describe how the anticipation, modification, and monitoring process occurs in a typical child care center. Compare that to a family child care home. Compare that to an in-home care situation. What are the commonalities? What are the differences? Select the five most important elements for any child care situation.

As an Individual

1. Interview a child caregiver in your community, preferably at the child care site. Ask the person how risk and injury prevention are managed in his/her particular child care. Was the caregiver aware of developmental levels? How were these applied to risk management? Were any modifications made to the child care environment in relation to developmental levels? How might you personally improve your own risk management in relation to child care?
2. Go to a local park and observe the community surrounding the park. Would you consider this a safe environment for children? Would there be any risk to a child care center or family child care home if the park were nearby? Record your observations and conclusions.
3. Find someone you know who is divorced, separated, or never married and has young preschool-aged children. Is there a child custody order

for the child(ren)? If not, find out why. What arrangements have been made for picking the child up at child care? Does the child care have a child custody policy? Compare his/her answers to the information in the Reality Check on Child Custody.

As a Group

1. Watch *Setting Up for Health and Safe Care,* an AAP video. What safety measures were observed? If you do not have access to this, go as a group to a child care site and observe for safety. Discuss two indoor and two outdoor risk management measures that were promoted. Compare those measures to the measures from other groups in your class. Have the entire class select the two most important indoor and outdoor safety measures that will lessen risk in child care.

2. In a small group of four to five people, create a safety checklist that would be used in a child care situation. Compare the lists. Select the 10 most important items.

3. Divide the class into three smaller groups. Have one group write a safety policy for indoor safety, one group write a policy for outdoor safety, and one group write a policy for child custody. Review the policies with the whole class and make any suggested changes.

4. Survey a local child care facility for the diversity of its population. Estimate the largest non-English speaking group at the site. Obtain three safety policies that the site considers the most important they have. Enlist the help of parents from that site that represent that population to help translate the three center safety policies. Present these translations to the child care site.

CHAPTER REFERENCES

American Academy of Pediatrics and American Public Health Association (APA & APHA). (2002). *Caring for our children: National health and safety performance standards: Guidelines for out-of-home care.* Washington, DC: American Public Health Association.

Aronson, S. (2001). Reducing the risk of injury in child care. *Child Care Information Exchange, 3,* 64–66.

Blythe-Saucier, S. (2000). Toy safety. *Healthy Child Care, 3*(1). Retrieved May 15, 2002, from http://www.healthychild.net/Issues3.html.

Centers for Disease Control (CDC). (1999). *Childhood injury fact sheet.* Atlanta, GA: Author. Retrieved May 15, 2002, from www.cdc.gov/ncipc/factsheets/childh.htm.

Child Care Action Campaign. *Finding good child care: Essential questions to ask when seeking quality care for your child* (CCAC Information Guide 19). New York: Author.

Consumer Product Safety Commission (CPSC). (1999). *Safety hazards in child care settings.* Washington, DC: Author.

Co-parenting.com. (2001). Joint custody vs. sole custody. Retrieved May 15, 2002, from http://www.co-parenting.com/cjc.html.

Deal, L., Gomby, D., Zipporli, L., & Berhman, R. (2000). Unintentional injuries in childhood: Analysis and recommendations. *The Future of Children, 10*(1), 4–22.

DivorceSource.com. (2001). State divorce information. Retrieved May 15, 2002, from http://www.divorcesource.com/index.html.

Earls, F., & Buka, S. (2000). Measurement of community characteristics. In S. Meisels & J. Shonkoff (Eds.), *Handbook of early childhood intervention,* (2nd ed., 309–324). New York: Cambridge University Press.

Eller, D. (1998, August). It's shocking how many people you know own a gun and how easy it is for kids to get their hands on one. *Parents Magazine,* 62–65.

Hatted, A. (1994) Safety and children: How schools can help. *Childhood Education, 70*(5), 283–286.

Jackman, G., Farah, M., Kellerman, A., & Simon, H. (2001). Seeing is believing: What do boys do when they find a real gun? *Pediatrics, 107*(6), 1247–1250.

Jones, M. (1998, May). Without a home. *Parenting Magazine,* 86–92.

Kelly, J. (1997). *Determination of child custody in the USA.* The World Wide Legal Information Association. Retrieved May 15, 2002, from http://wwlia.org/uscus5.htm.

Kendrick, A., Kaufmann, R., & Messenger, K. (1995). *Healthy young children: A manual for programs.* Washington, DC: NAEYC.

Levin, D. (1994). Building a peaceable classroom: Helping young children feel safe in violent times. *Childhood Education, 70*(5), 267–270.

Levin, D. (1999). Changing needs, changing responses: Rethinking how we teach children. *Child Care Information Exchange, 99*(7), 46–49.

Maslow, A. (1968). *Toward a psychology of being.* New York: Van Nordstrom.

National Center for Health Statistics (NCHS). (1991). Firearms mortality among children, youth and young adults, 1–34 years of age 1979–1988 [Supplement]. Washington, DC: U.S. Department of Health and Human Services.

National Conference of Commissioners of Uniform State Laws (NCCUSL). (1997). *Uniform child custody jurisdiction and enforcement act.* Chicago, IL: Author. Retrieved May 15, 2002, from http://www.law.upenn.edu/bll/ulc/uccjea/chldcus2.htm.

Nolo.com. (2001). Types of custody. Retrieved May 15, 2002, from http://www.nolo.com/encyclopedia/articles/div/pc18.html.

Shallcross, M. (1999). Family child care homes need health and safety training and an emergency rescue system. *Young Children, 54*(5), 70–73.

Smith, C. (2001). Safe spaces for infants and toddlers. *Healthy Child Care, 4*(4), 7–10. Retrieved May 15, 2002, from http://www.healthychild.net/Issues4.html.

SUGGESTIONS FOR READING

Ciccheti, D., & Lynch, M. (1993). Toward an ecological/transactional model of community violence and child maltreatment. *Psychiatry: Interpersonal and Biological Processes, 56*(1), 96–118.

Elders, J. (1994). Violence as a public health issue. *Childhood Education, 70*(5), 260–262.

Mickalaide, A. (1994). Creating safer environments for children. *Childhood Education, 70*(5), 263–266.

The quiet crisis. (1994). *Young Children, 49*(7), 60.

Sewell, K., & Gaines, S. (1994). A developmental approach to childhood safety education. *Pediatric Nursing, 19*(5), 464–466.

Smoke signals. (1995, June/July). *Healthy Kids,* 8.

Wood, S. (1996, July/August). How to protect your baby from SIDS. *Child Magazine,* 26–28.

For additional information on safety, nutrition, and health in early education, visit our Web site at **http://www.earlychilded.delmar.com**

Indoor Safety

After reading this chapter, you should be able to:

2.1 Indoor Safety Policies

Describe and discuss safety policies for indoor environments as tools for risk prevention, protection, and promotion.

2.2 Indoor Safety Guidelines

Indicate and discuss specific guidelines for making any indoor child care environment free from risk and protected for safety.

2.3 Indoor Equipment Safety

Relate and discuss the safety hazards of indoor equipment in child care situations.

2.4 Toy Safety

Describe and discuss the importance of safe, risk-free toys for infants, toddlers, and preschoolers.

2.5 Interpersonal Safety

Describe and discuss clear rules for consequences of behavior and appropriate methods of conflict resolution.

2.6 Poison Control

Indicate the methods and means of poison control and risk prevention in child care environments.

2.7 Fire and Burn Prevention

Describe and discuss methods of fire and burn prevention in child care.

2.8 Implications for Caregivers

Indicate the need for education, observation, and supervision to maintain a safe indoor environment.

2.1 Indoor Safety Policies

The safety risks of indoor and outdoor environments vary widely. Because the variation is so widespread, we will look at these environments separately. The indoor child care environment can include many physical hazards that pose risk through choking, interpersonal violence, poisoning, burns, lead poisoning, and others. The following factors indicate the need for policies to cover indoor safety:

- Twelve percent of child care centers were reported as unsafe in a study conducted in 400 centers throughout the United States (Chiara, 1995).
- Falls are the most common source of injury in the child care setting (Zavitkovsky & Thompson, 2000).
- Each year, 30,000 children are treated in emergency rooms for scald burns. Foods and hot liquids prepared in the kitchen account for over 25,000 of the burns. Another 4,000 children are burned in the bathroom by hot water. Approximately one-half of these victims are under the age of five (Mickalaide, 1994).
- Children four years of age and under account for more than 70,000 toy-related injuries and more than 75 percent of deaths related to toys (NSKC, 2001).

To ensure the safety of the children in their care, child caregivers must make sure toys are developmentally appropriate. This child is not at risk because playing with small blocks is appropriate for his age and developmental level.

■ Using violence to solve interpersonal problems has become common for children. Every two hours an American child loses his life to a gunshot wound ("Children's Defense Fund Reports," 1994).

■ "Biting causes more upset feeling than any other behavior in child care" (Oku, 1999).

The indoor environment includes a multitude of levels that can pose risk. Hazards come from household items, toys, animals, stoves and other kitchen equipment, children's furniture, foods, firearms, fireplaces, paint, ceramics, medications, plants, electrical outlets and cords, among others. Other indoor risks include unsafe caregiver practices, unmonitored conditions, and children's behavior based on developmental levels, physical abilities, and emotional health. The child caregiver must have an awareness of all accessories, behaviors, and conditions that may lead to an accident or injury. The caregiver must also be in compliance with all regulations affecting the safety in care such as those from licensing and fire boards.

Indoor environment risk management process should include:

1. *Indoor Child Care Environments:* understanding indoor safety practices and applications for risk management as they apply to specific child care environments

2. *Indoor Equipment Safety:* practices for preventing injuries and managing safety on indoor equipment

3. *Toy Safety:* practices for preventing injuries, removing unsafe toys, and managing selection of toys for children in care

4. *Interpersonal Safety:* strategies for developing guidelines for interpersonal safety and conflict management for the children in care

5. *Poison Control:* strategies for developing guidelines for poison prevention and protection in child care

6. *Fire and Burn Prevention:* educational and promotional strategies to model good fire and burn prevention behaviors and practices

7. *Implications for Caregiver:* methods and practices of conducting education, supervision, observation, and utilizing outside resources

KEY CONCEPT 2.1

Safety Policies

Safety policies should be planned as a tool for prevention of injuries, the protection of children, and the promotion of safe practices in the child care indoor environment. These policies should consider the specific environment and should be applicable to the accessories, behaviors, and conditions present indoor. Use of these policies minimizes risk to children and maximizes the child's care environment for safety.

2.2 Indoor Safety Guidelines

Some hazards are common to all child care environments. The most common indoor childhood accidents are related to

- falls
- choking
- burns
- drowning
- poisoning

Screening the environment for these risks to safety should be done in an organized fashion. In 1999, the Consumer Product Safety Commission conducted a national study of safety hazards in 200 licensed child care settings. They were looking for safety hazards in these product areas: cribs, soft bedding, playground surfaces, surface maintenance, window blind cords, drawstrings in children's clothing, and recalled children's products. This investigation found that two-thirds of these settings had at least one safety hazard present. Applying the ABCs of injury risk (see Table 2–4) allows the caregiver to anticipate, modify, and monitor the child care environment. This chapter will provide indoor safety checklists that can be used as a basis to help prepare to minimize risk.

REALITY CHECK

Sudden Infant Death Syndrome

Sudden Infant Death Syndrome (SIDS) claims more lives of children per year between the ages of one month and one year than childhood deaths from cancer, child abuse, AIDS, cystic fibrosis, muscular dystrophy, pneumonia, and heart diseases combined (SIDS Network, 1996). It is estimated that as many as 3,000 babies die every year from SIDS (Gorman, 2001). SIDS strikes without warning to children of all racial, ethnic, and economic levels.

The medical community still cannot explain what causes SIDS. Speculation includes a vulnerability period, a birth defect, stress caused by infection, and/or failure to develop (SIDS Network, 1996). Recently, several risk factors that contribute to SIDS deaths have been found. Although these risk factors are not the cause of SIDS, they can

have a negative effect and make children more prone to the cause.

These risk factors include:

- sleeping on the stomach in the prone position
- pre- and postnatal exposure to cigarette smoke
- sleeping on materials that are too soft
- overheating of the baby

A caregiver can help reduce risk by offering protective measures for each of these risks.

A major discovery has revolutionized how parents and caregivers should put babies down to sleep. Studies in Europe in the 1980s found that when babies were put to sleep on their stomachs in the prone position, they were twice as likely to

(continued)

die from SIDS as children placed on their sides. In 1992 the American Academy of Pediatrics recommended that all babies be put down to sleep on their backs or sides and not on their stomachs, which had been the preferable sleeping position for babies (AAP, 2000a). Today, only 24 percent of American infants sleep on their stomachs, which is down from 1992, when 70 percent of babies slept on their stomachs. The change in this position alone has contributed a 40 percent reduction of SIDS deaths from 5,000 per year to 3,000 per year (Gorman, 2001). This reduction applies to both full and preterm, as well as low birth weight babies (Malloy & Freeman, 2000). A public health campaign called Back to Sleep is partially responsible for this success.

Despite this success, it has been found that child care centers continue to place infants in the prone position for sleep (Moon & Bilitier, 2000). Of SIDS deaths, more than 20 percent occur in child care settings, where infants were more likely to be placed in the prone position (Moon et al., 2000). A reason cited for this discrepancy is that 43 percent of caregivers were unaware of the relationship between prone sleep and SIDS and 49 percent of caregivers were likely to place babies in the prone position to sleep (Moon & Bilitier, 2000). It is imperative that caregivers understand the relationship between sleep position and SIDS, and use this information to prevent risk to the children in their care.

Cigarette smoke is considered the second greatest risk factor for SIDS. It is believed that this risk factor may account for 20 to 40 percent of SIDS cases (DiFranza & Lew, 1995). *An infant exposed to cigarette smoke may be at a 200 percent increased risk for SIDS* (Wisborg et al., 2000). If babies are also exposed in utero they are three times more likely to be at risk for SIDS (Anderson & Cook, 1998; MacDorman et al., 1997).

Babies should sleep on firm, flat mattresses to lesson the risk of entrapment or heavy covering (Kemp et al, 2000; AAP, 2000a). Parents and caregivers should avoid placing infants on beanbags, sheepskins, synthetic pillows, and foam pads, either alone or covered with a comforter. All stuffed animals should be removed from the crib or sleeping area (Gorman, 2001).

The final contributing factor is overheating. Too much bedding, clothing that is too heavy, and an environment that is too warm can contribute to SIDS. Overheating my occur when babies have a cold and efforts are made to keep the child warm. Overheated babies exhibit sweating, damp hair, heat rash, rapid breathing, and fever. It is recommended that the indoor temperature be kept at 70°F or less (SIDS Network, 1996).

Several other factors may have a correlation with SIDS. Infants who used pacifiers were significantly less likely to succumb to SIDS and co-sleeping in the parents' bed was more likely to cause SIDS (Arnestad et al., 2001; Kemp et al., 2000). The American Academy of Pediatrics feels that when placing a child to sleep, using clean hands and checking for foreign objects by sweeping the mouth will also help lessen the SIDS risk (APHA & AAP, 2002).

Using preventive measures can reduce the risk, but there is no guarantee that SIDS will not strike. This should be remembered by both parents and caregivers.

Environmental Hazards

The indoor screening should include environmental hazards such as lead, asbestos, chemicals, and so on, that might also be found in the environment, but not necessarily at a child's reach. Other irritants to a child's air quality environment should also be thought through. Examples of irritants may include air fresheners, plug-in fresheners, and perfumes used by caregivers. All environmental hazard risks should be removed or modified wherever possible.

Ventilation.   Adequate ventilation is a safety risk that is considered an environmental hazard. Air needs to move sufficiently so there is no gathering of fumes, germs, or other safety risks to children. Children inhale two to three times more air than adults, so adequate ventilation is necessary (Rosenblum, 1993). APHA and AAP standards can be found in *Caring for Our Children: National Health and Safety Performance Standards: Guidelines for Out-of-Home Child Care Programs* published by the APHA.

Pets or Animals.   Pets or animals in the environment can also provide safety risks through injury, infection, and allergic reactions. Any animal that is present should be friendly and healthy. Puppies and kittens can carry infections that cause a variety of serious diseases in children. Dogs and cats should be fully immunized and under a veterinarian's care for flea, tick, and worm control. Never allow turtles, parrots, or lizards to be handled by children because these types of pets often carry diseases that are contracted by direct contact (French, 1999). Do not allow other wild or aggressive animals such as ferrets to be present in a child care environment (Zamani, 1999). If pets are present in child care, they should be kept in a supervised and confined area of the facility and regularly checked for disease by a veterinarian. Pet living quarters should be cleaned often and animal waste kept to a minimum. Children should always wash their hands immediately after handling pets. Follow the AAP/APHA guidelines for animals present in child care.

Another risk factor that pets may present is allergic reactions. Some children may be allergic to certain pet hair or dander. Parents may be unaware of the allergy if there are no pets in the home environment. The caregiver should observe children for any reactions to the pets in the child care environment.

Family pets, although vaccinated and clean, may still be a conceivable safety and health risk to children in family child care. Animals must be supervised and monitored regularly to avoid unpleasant incidents.

Figure 2–1
Caregivers should teach children the meaning of the poison sign.

Safety latches and electric outlet covers are just two of the numerous safety devices available. As with any device, these must be properly installed and utilized to be truly effective.

Cleaning and Other Supplies. Cleaning supplies are a risk to children whether or not they are poisonous. These items can cause burns or rashes and other possible problems. All cleaning supplies or chemicals that might present danger to children should be kept at a level where children cannot reach them. Paints and some craft supplies may present a risk if a child ingests them. Anything that might be poisonous should be kept at a high level in a locked cabinet. These items should be well labeled with the poison sign. The caregiver can teach the children about the danger present when they see the sign (see Figure 2–1). This may not help the toddler or crawling infant, but it will help the older children.

Safety Devices

Safety devices should be present wherever applicable in the indoor child care environment. All wall sockets should be covered with difficult-to-remove plastic plugs. All drawers that can be pulled out and fall onto a child's head or upper body should have safety latches in them that make them childproof. All doorways that might lead to danger should be shut and lockable. Safety gates should be installed for doorways without doors that may lead to danger or risk. All stairways where infants and toddlers are present should have safety gates to prevent the children from crawling up or falling down the stairs. The child caregiver should check local hardware stores and child care catalogs for safety devices.

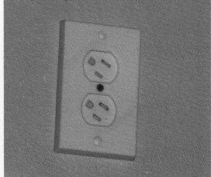

Developmental Level

Prevention is the single most significant factor in risk management for safety. The caregiver begins this process by defining the boundaries for indoor safety and screening the environment for hazards with the developmental levels of the children in care in mind (CDC, 1999). Safety hazards can be broken down by developmental age and vulnerabilities associated with that particular stage as shown in Table 2–1.

Infants. Young infants are relatively helpless and must be carefully watched to protect and prevent risks. Older, more mobile infants develop new motor skills at a rapid rate that lead them into an increasing number of hazardous

Most children under the age of three are not developmentally ready to use scissors. Even children who are three or older should be regularly monitored for safety reasons.

TABLE 2–1	Indoor Safety Hazards	
Age	**Hazards**	**Prevention Tips**
0–6 months	Scalds	Set hot water temperature to 120°F or less and always test bath water before immersing baby.
	Falls	Never leave infant alone on bed or table.
	Choking/Suffocation	Buy toys larger than two inches in diameter. Keep crib free of plastics or pillows. Crib slats should be less than 2⅜ inches apart and space between mattress and slats should be less than 2 fingers wide.
	Toys	Should be larger than 1½ inches in diameter and should have smooth round edges and be soft and flexible.
	Drowning	Never leave child in bath unattended
6 months–1 year	Burns and scalds	Check water temperature (see above). Keep hot foods and liquids out of reach. Put guards around hot pipes, radiators, and fireplaces.
	Poisons	Store household products, cosmetics, and medicines in high, preferably locked cabinets. Keep syrup of ipecac on hand. Post poison control number by phone.
	Choking	Check floors and reachable areas for small objects such as pins, coins, buttons. Avoid raw vegetables, nuts, hard candy, popcorn, and other foods that are difficult for child to properly chew and swallow.
	Toys	Should be large, unbreakable, and smooth.
	Drowning	Always carefully supervise when bathing.

(continued)

TABLE 2–1	Indoor Safety Hazards *(continued)*	
Age	**Hazards**	**Prevention Tips**
1–2 years	Falls	Put toddler gates on stairways and keep any doors to cellars, attics, and porches locked. Remove sharp-edged furniture from child's frequently used area. Show child proper way to climb up and down stairs using handrails.
	Burns	While cooking, turn pot handles to back of stove. Keep electric cords out of reach. Use shock stops to cover used and unused outlets. Teach child the meaning of the word *hot* and talk about different types of hot.
	Poisons	Keep poisons locked in high cabinets. Have child tested for lead poisoning during regular checkup.
	Drowning	Always supervise child's bath.
	Choking	Removes small objects.
2–3 years	Poisons	Teach child about the difference between food and nonfood and what is not good to eat. Watch child during art projects so he does not put art supplies in mouth. Keep poisons locked in high cabinets.
	Burns	Keep matches, lighter, and cigarettes out of reach and sight of children. Put screen around fireplaces and wood stoves. Reinforce the meaning of *hot*.
	Toys	Check for sharp edges, hinges, and small parts that could be swallowed. Remove toy chest lids,
	Drowning	Always supervise.
	Guns	Keep any firearms unloaded and locked away out of reach.
3 years and up	Burns	Teach child drop and roll to prepare for clothing catching fire. Practice fire drills with escape route meeting place and sound of smoke alarm. Train to bring found matches to adult.
	Tools and equipment	Teach child safe use of scissors. Keep sharp knives out of reach.
	Guns	Keep firearms unloaded and locked. Teach safety precautions about guns, by telling an adult immediately when they see a gun and not to touch! Discourage use of toy guns or violent play.

situations. Children at this stage are particularly at risk for choking on small objects that they can mouth. The environment should be constantly and carefully monitored for small objects if infants are present, and expanding hazards should be anticipated. The child care environment should frequently be updated and checked for any Consumer Product Safety Commission recalls of toys or infant equipment that might pose risk (CPSC, 1999).

Toddlers. Toddlers probably represent the developmental group with the most potential for unsafe practices. They are at a cognitive level that allows them new ways of thinking and solving problems, but they do not understand cause and effect. Toddlers try to stretch their limits and test their environment, which they now have the physical ability to accomplish. Toddlers like to explore places that may not be in view. Poisons and chemicals that are kept in cabinets, drawers, or on shelves are a major risk for this age group. Toddlers need careful, constant monitoring and potential hazards need to be constantly anticipated. Therefore, the environment should be modified as needed (see Figure 2–2).

The Preschooler. Preschool-aged children have more physical and cognitive abilities and are beginning to understand cause and effect. Indoor falls pose risk to these children. Although they know about cause and effect, physical mastery often takes precedence over thought processes. Besides monitoring the conditions and safety risks, the caregiver can teach a preschool child preventive measures and help them to anticipate hazards. Children of this age can be good helpers to monitor the indoor environment for hazards.

School Age. School-aged children are much less prone to indoor safety hazards than children who are younger. Firearms may be the greatest threat to school-aged children. This age group has intense curiosity about things they see in movies and on television. They may not understand the danger guns pose. It is important that if guns are present in a child care environment, such as a family child care home, that they be stored unloaded and locked up. Children of this age can learn preventive measures and can help the caregiver monitor the environment and younger children.

Figure 2–2
Common Indoor Hazards

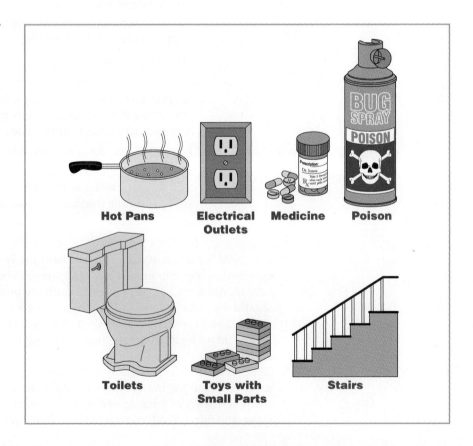

Hot Pans   Electrical Outlets   Medicine   Poison

Toilets   Toys with Small Parts   Stairs

Adequate floor space in a clear and organized environment will aid in the prevention of injury.

Space

Specific child care environments present unique conditions and circumstances that can lead to environmental hazards. There should be adequate space to move around the equipment and not have to compete for space with other children. Most child care centers, Head Start programs, and state preschools are licensed and do comply with spacing required by the licensing agencies.

Recommended indoor space is 35 square foot per child of play space, which does not include kitchen, bathroom, closet, laundry, or staff facilities (APHA & AAP, 2002). This space usually translates to 50 square feet per child when furnishings are included in this measurement. Family child care homes that are informed try to keep to this standard. Unlicensed or license-exempt sites also need to follow this standard for space.

Adequate floor space is essential. How the child caregiver sets up the environment in the space available is a critical factor in prevention of injury. Enough space should be provided for crawling, keeping separate play areas for infant/toddlers and older children. Caregivers should not have barriers that impair their ability to watch all the children at the same time. These considerations need to be remembered as the child care space is planned and organized. Child care space planning should include the arrangement of interest areas of the classroom with the interest of safety in mind (see Figure 2–3).

Shared Space

Another indoor environmental hazard for child care may be shared space. Some child care situations are located in areas that have multiple uses. These shared spaces may carry risks that the caregiver must anticipate, continually assess, and be prepared to eliminate (see Table 2–1).

Whenever spaces are shared, safety risks can occur. Multiple use facilities need thoughtful anticipation for possible hazards, and the environment should be carefully screened before resuming child care in a shared space that was used for another purpose.

Figure 2–3

How to Set Up an Environment—
Dos and Don'ts

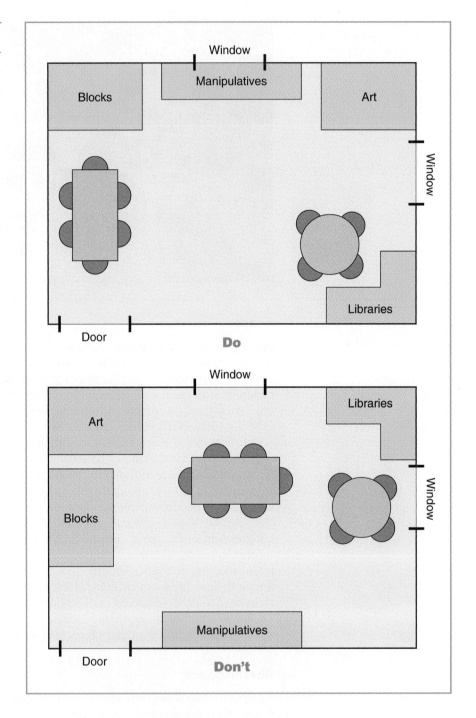

Screening a shared space may require coming to the site 15 to 30 minutes before the children arrive. Using a shared facility checklist created for the particular multiple uses helps organize and speed up this process. Table 2–2 contains a checklist for a family child care home's morning check that could also be used by a nanny upon arrival at a child's home.

It was Monday morning at the church preschool. Monica, the teacher, was pleased to see that someone had filled the juice pitchers for her and had them ready in the refrigerator. The children had come to school either tired or still excited from a busy summer weekend, so Monica really appreciated the extra help.

Lorraine, the director, had a habit of taking time to sit with the children at their morning snacks on Mondays to see how they were doing and to hear about their time on the weekends. She sat down after the snacks had been handed out and the juice had been poured. Lorraine took one sip of the juice and commented to the children, "You know this juice doesn't taste quite right, let's all throw it out and get some new juice." Lorraine had a very organized reaction to drinking punch with alcohol that had been left over from a wedding at the church over the weekend.

It turns out that the people cleaning up didn't want anything to go to waste, so they saved the punch in the only containers available—the preschool pitchers. Monica should have checked to see what it was first, and fortunately Lorraine had the presence of mind to solve the problem before anyone had a chance to take more than a sip of juice.

TABLE 2–2   6 A.M. Checklist

☑ *Check for:*

Remove:

☐ All food, beverages, and dirty dishes

☐ Scissors, knives, or other sharp items

☐ Pesticides, medications, or other products that might be poisonous

☐ Standing water left around in buckets or other containers

☐ All craft supplies, game pieces, and so forth

☐ All breakable objects

☐ All matches or flammable items

☐ Any small toys or other objects that could cause a child to choke

☐ Any object that attracts a child to climb, such as a stepladder or stool

Replace as needed:

☐ Safety latches

☐ Safety gates by stairways

☐ All other safety devices

☐ All doors, gates, and other openings that could cause safety hazards

It is also helpful to post signs in the shared facility about hazards so that others who use the facility are aware of safety risks to the child care environment (see Figure 2–4). Speaking with the person in charge of the other uses helps to keep the risks at a minimum. People who are responsible for the cleaning and care of the facility should be encouraged to cooperate and watch for the possible safety hazards that will keep the children from undue risks. Parents should also be trained and utilized as environmental scanners whose extra eyes can help check for risks when they drop off their children.

Figure 2–4
Sign for Shared Used Facility

> ## Please Remember
> ## Child Care Takes Place Here!
>
> • Pick up all small objects.
>
> • Put any dangerous objects out of reach.
>
> • Check electrical outlets for safety covers.
>
> • Lock all cabinets that contain nonchildproof objects.

KEY CONCEPT 2.2

Indoor Safety Guidelines

Examining the indoor environment for safety hazards allows the caregiver to provide protection for the children and may help prevent unnecessary accidents. Indoor environmental hazards include ventilation, cleaning and other supplies, and pets. Safety devices can be used to prevent risk. The environment should be screened to meet the risk due to the developmental levels of children. Adequate space and setup for indoor child care are factors that should be considered to prevent undue risk. Shared spaces pose many risks and need extra supervision to promote safety and prevent risk.

2.3 Indoor Equipment Safety

Equipment used in child care shall be sturdy and free of sharp points or corners, splinters, protruding nails or bolts, loose rusty parts, hazardous small parts, or paint that contains lead (APHA & AAP, 2002). Furniture should be durable, easy to clean, and where appropriate, child-sized. Equipment should be placed so that children have enough freedom of movement to prevent accidents and collisions with equipment and each other. Refer to Figure 2–3 for improper equipment placement and proper placement of the same equipment.

Some infant equipment is regularly tested and must comply with certain standards (APHA & AAP, 2002). Cribs, high chairs, strollers, and safety gates

Safety gates and latches should be routinely used.

fall into this category. For information regarding the specifications of the standards, the caregiver can write to:

> The American Society for Testing and Materials
> 1916 Race Street
> Philadelphia, PA 19103

Cribs should be made of wood, metal, or plastic, and should have non-lead-based paint. Cribs should also have

- slats that are no more than 2⅝ inches apart.
- a mattress that is fitted so that no more than two fingers can be wedged between the mattress and the crib side.
- a minimum height of 36 inches between the top of the mattress and the top of the crib.
- secure latches, which when dropping the sides shall hold the sides in the raised position. The latches should be inaccessible to the child in the crib.

Never leave a large stuffed toy in a crib. Children can use it to climb out of the crib. Never place a crib near a window because children can fall out of windows, hurt themselves on broken glass, or get caught up in cords from window shades or curtains. Bumper pads should be securely tied to the crib. There should be a minimum of six evenly placed tie strings that prevent children from crawling into an opening and suffocating. Make sure the tie strings are less than 12 inches so that children do not strangle in them.

When high chairs are used in child care, they should have a safety strap that goes between the legs and around the waist. The legs should have a wide enough base so the high chair will not tip over. If paint is used on the high chair, it should be lead-free. Strollers should clearly display the ASTM seal of compliance with the number F833. Safety gates should display the seal with the number F406 (APHA & AAP, 2002).

If the caregiver is using a changing table, it should have a lip around it that discourages a child from rolling off the changing table. The changing table should have a safety strap and the strap should always be used. The child should never be left unattended when being changed.

Preventing Falls

Falls are one of the most common injuries related to indoor equipment. Childhood falls account for more than two million emergency room visits per year (CDC, 2001d). A child's changing abilities to move about and manipulate the environment are major contributors to causing safety risks with indoor equipment. A tiny baby can wiggle and move and push. An older baby can roll over, crawl, and creep. Changing tables vary greatly and can be the cause of an infant's fall if the infant is left unattended, even if the safety strap is used. Although infant walkers are tested, they are the cause of more injuries than any other infant equipment, so the American Academy of Pediatrics recommends against their use.

Toddlers can climb to get to places that were formerly inaccessible. Discouraging climbing on furniture and other equipment will help prevent risk. Using safety devices such as window guards will help prevent falls if the toddler does try to climb.

Preschoolers are coordinated enough and fast enough to do almost any physical activity. Using only safe, sturdy equipment that is in good repair also helps protect children from falls. Table 2–3 presents a list for checking indoor equipment to help prevent falls.

Indoor Water Safety

Water safety is also a consideration in the use of indoor equipment. Drowning can occur in a relatively small amount of water; for example, a bucket of standing water that someone forgot to clean up and put away. A curious infant or toddler could look into the bucket, fall in, and drown. Toilets, tubs, and sinks also pose risk for drowning. Toilet lids should always be closed. Some child care environments do not have lids for toilets, in which case, the area should have a door that shuts and should be carefully monitored. Water should never be left standing in tubs or sinks.

Hot water faucets also pose risk. Hot water can cause burns by scalding. All hot water heaters should be set at 120°F (see Figure 2–5). Children should never be left unattended near hot water faucets. When turning on water for children, always turn on the cold water first.

TABLE 2–3   Checklist to Prevent Falls in the Indoor Environment

☑ *Check for:*

- ☐ Use infant and child equipment that is in good repair and inspected for safety.
- ☐ Use durable, balanced furniture that will not tip over easily.
- ☐ Do not allow climbing on furniture, stools, or ladders.
- ☐ Place safety gates at stairways.
- ☐ Remove all objects from stairs.
- ☐ Repair or remove frayed carpeting or other flooring.
- ☐ Install window guards on upstairs windows.
- ☐ Secure all window screens.
- ☐ Clean up spills quickly.
- ☐ Avoid highly waxed floors and stairways.
- ☐ Do not use loose throw rugs.
- ☐ Keep toys picked up as often as possible.
- ☐ Never leave a baby alone in a high place.

Figure 2–5
Hot water heaters should be set
to 120°F to prevent burns.

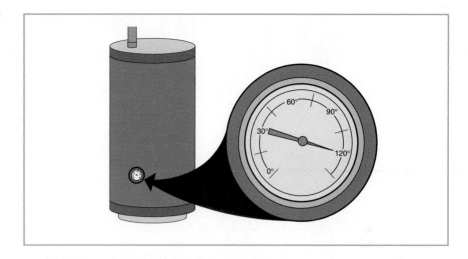

Toilets and water tables may also carry germs that put children at risk.
To promote indoor water safety, the basic rules in Table 2–4 should be followed.

TABLE 2–4   Indoor Water Safety Guidelines
• Any equipment that utilizes water such as toilets, sinks, tubs, and buckets should be carefully monitored and cleaned often. • Keep hot water temperature at 120°F. • Never leave standing water unattended. • No child should ever be left unattended in a tub or other device used to bathe a child. • Where toilet lids are present, when possible, keep them down. • In a family child care home keep the door to the bathroom closed when not in use, if very young children are present. Keep a set of jingle bells on the door to hear the door opening and closing. • Keep lid on diaper pail securely fastened. • Keep lid on water table when not in use.

Equipment that utilizes water,
such as toilets and sinks, should
be carefully monitored and
cleaned often, and children and
staff should be encouraged to
wash hands often.

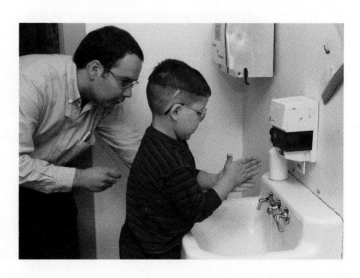

Indoor Equipment Safety

Using safe, sturdy indoor child care equipment can help eliminate some risk. Safety devices, safety practices, and good supervision will help the caregiver add a greater degree of protection for the children. Some indoor equipment that involves water poses risks. The risk of drowning and of burns from scalding water can be reduced through safe practices and supervision.

2.4 Toy Safety

Toy-related accidents cause more than 118,000 children to be injured each year. Approximately 70 percent of deaths for children three years of age and under were caused by toys and other children's products (CDC, 2001c). Other typical toy-related accidents involve inhaling balloons, toy chest lids falling on or pinching a child, projectile toys that pierce the body, and strangulation on toys with ropes or strings that may be inappropriately used. These accidents may be avoided if the toys are examined for **age appropriateness** of the children playing with them. Art supplies may also pose risk to children and should be checked for safety and age appropriateness.

Age appropriateness consideration of the development abilities of a particular age group in the selection of toys, materials, and equipment

Choking and Suffocation Hazards

Choking and suffocation are major hazards to very young children who still mouth things such as toys, foods, and small objects in their environment. The developmental level for that mouthing, along with new cognitive abilities to master the environment can lead children to risk their safety (Table 2–5).

Ensuring that small toys and other objects are too large for mouthing is an important criteria for finding choking and suffocation hazards (see Figure 2–6). As consumers, we are probably more conscious of foods and small

Children in the oral stage need to be carefully watched and provided with a safe environment free of small toys and objects.

TABLE 2–5   Choking and Suffocation Hazards for Young Children

Toys	
Marbles	Game tokens
Balloons	Game pieces
Dress-up jewelry	Jacks
Plastic bags	Toy chest with no air holes
Any toy less than 1½ inches in diameter	

Food	
Hot dogs	Peanuts
Grapes	Popcorn
Gum	Olives
Lollipops	Hard candy and cough drops
Carrots, celery, and other raw vegetables	

Small Objects	
Pins and safety pins	Crayons
Toothpicks	Nails
Tacks	Pencils and pens
Jewelry	Staples
Coins	

objects causing choking hazards than we are of toys. One purchases a toy and expects that toy to be safe. However, what is safe for a five-year-old may be very dangerous to a two-year-old. The Consumer Product Safety Commission has a small parts standard that prohibits manufacturers from marketing toys with small parts to children under the age of three years. Their toll free phone number is 1–800–638–2772.

Figure 2–6
Device for Measuring Small Parts to Prevent Choking. Notice that the domino gets caught in the tube, but the die passes through the tube, indicating a choking hazard.

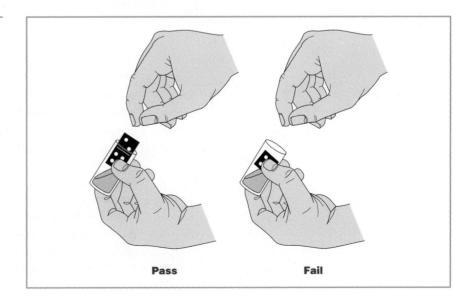

Pass   **Fail**

Marty had been a family child caregiver for about six months. She had children in care from four months old to five years old. The older children were very active and helpful. Diana, the older four-year-old, and Holly, the five-year-old, really liked to do things that were grown-up. They especially enjoyed helping Marty. Marty appreciated their help and liked to give them little tasks to do. One of those tasks was to help her go through the child care setting looking for any safety risks. The girls often caught things that Marty might have missed because they explored the environment from a child's level.

One day Ramsey, a toddler, was chewing something. Holly went to Marty and brought her to Ramsey right away. Even though they had all searched for hazards that morning they had missed a playing piece from a Monopoly game. The safety consciousness in this child care setting helped save Ramsey from a hazard that could have caused a real problem.

Age Appropriateness

The age group for which a toy is intended is often included on the package. However, contents of the package including small parts are not always listed, and safety precautions are often not included in the packaging or instructions. If a caregiver fails to see the package or if she does not understand other safety precautions that should be taken with a toy, she may put the children in care at risk for injury.

Consumer awareness of toy safety is imperative, especially in child care settings where there is a population of mixed age children. Age appropriateness is one of the most important tools for removing hazardous toys from the environment. Table 2–6 shows age-appropriate toy suggestions.

TABLE 2–6	Age-Appropriate Toys
Age	**Toys**
Up to 6 months:	squeeze toys, colorful mobiles, large pictures of faces or simple patterns, and nonbreakable mirrors
6 months to 1 year:	cradle gyms, sturdy books, drums, manipulative toys, toys that make noises and busy boards
1 year to 18 months:	stacking toys, balls, large blocks, pounding toys, push-pull toys, books, simple puzzles, and tapes with simple stories or music
18 months to 3 years:	large blocks, crayons, puzzles, trucks, dolls, dramatic play toys, musical instruments, outdoor climbing equipment, sandboxes, sand toys, and water toys
3 years to 6 years:	dramatic play toys, puppets, playhouses, art materials, chalkboards, tricycles, bicycles, balls, simple games, books, simple board games

The caregiver needs to check the environment for the age appropriateness of toys, because different developmental levels affect the way children play with toys. Table 2–7 gives the caregivers a checklist for toy safety.

Art Supplies

Art supplies present some potential hazards. The hazards may be from inhaling, lead, or other dangerous substances, and mouthing the various materials used for art. The Federal Arts Materials Labeling Act took effect in 1990. Hazard-free art products should be labeled CP or AP. Products that may be potentially toxic should carry a health label that indicates caution or warning. Table 2–8 will help the caregiver lessen risk to safety when using art supplies. If there is any question regarding art supplies, contact the manufacturer and ask for a copy of the Material Safety Data Sheet. This will give information about ingredients and toxicity.

Common household products are often used to make art materials. Examples of these are play dough, cornstarch clay, and goop. If these items are used in the child care environment, children should be instructed in how to use them. Children should not mouth these materials and toddlers should be well monitored when these materials are used.

TABLE 2–7   Toy Safety Checklist

✔ *Check for:*

☐ Age appropriate for the children playing with toy.

☐ Set safety rules for mixed age groups to keep toys for older children out of younger children's reach, and secure a place in the care environment where the older children can use these toys.

☐ No toys or toy parts smaller than 1½ inches.

☐ Check for sharp parts, points, rough edges, pinch points, and loose small parts.

☐ Check toys for durability—if it is easily broken, it is dangerous.

☐ Examine toys for construction, including stuffed animals that might have seams that would open easily or eyes that could be pulled off and swallowed.

☐ Throw out all pieces of broken toys, crayons, and games.

☐ Reguarly check pacifiers that children use for nipples that resist pulling and for guards that cannot fit inside a child's mouth.

☐ Check instructions for art and craft supplies and make sure that they are nontoxic, washable, and environmentally safe.

(continued)

TABLE 2–7   Toy Safety Checklist *(continued)*

✔ *Check for:*

☐ Check toys that are mouthed but too large to be swallowed to make sure they are washed after use.

☐ Check paint on toys to make sure it is lead-free.

☐ Toys with projective parts are not present.

☐ Toy chests with lids are not present.

☐ All toys are flame resistant.

☐ Mobiles and other hanging toys are not used when infants are able to sit up.

☐ Toys are cleared and put away when not in use.

☐ Toys with pull strings are restricted to use for when an adult is present.

☐ Play areas are away from electrical cords and other cords, such as telephone wires.

TABLE 2–8   Keeping Art Safe

- Avoid using any art supplies like tempera paint and clay that are dry and could be easily inhaled.
- Avoid using any materials that contain lead or other hazardous substances that can cause poisoning if ingested.
- Use poster paints, liquid paints, and water-based paints that are nontoxic.
- Do not use rubber cement, epoxy, or instant glue. Use glue sticks, double sided tape, paste, or school glue. These should have the AP or CP label. Use only water-based glues, glue sticks, and paste.
- Do not use permanent markers. Use only washable markers and avoid using scented markers that tempt children to put them in their mouths.
- Avoid using empty film canisters for art projects as lids can be mouthed and have the potential hazard for choking.
- When using small items such as beans, rice, or small Styrofoam shapes for projects, always keep special watch because children may mouth their art materials and might choke on them. It is better to use these items only with older children.
- Avoid the use of glitter, which is metallic and can cause eye damage if it gets into the eye.

Toy Safety

The child caregiver needs to supply toys and other play materials that are safe and as risk-free as possible. Toys should be examined for hazards. By using such tools as the choking hazard checklist and the toy safety checklist, the child caregiver can eliminate those toys that may present risk. Knowledge of age-appropriate toys will help the child caregiver select toys that are safe for the care environment. If the environment is mixed age, supervision and safety practices should be used to make certain younger children are not playing with toys that may present risk to them. Art materials may pose risk. The child caregiver should be aware of these risks and do whatever is necessary to minimize them.

2.5 Interpersonal Safety

Injuries to children by other children such as biting, kicking, scratching, and fighting are common in child care settings. Caregivers need to be prepared to intervene when behaviors that threaten interpersonal safety occur. They need to understand the background for such behavior and know strategies for eliminating that behavior and utilizing conflict resolution. The NAEYC's position statement on violence reflects this.

Of all these behaviors, biting is the most upsetting. It is also common for children under the age of three. There are a number of reasons why children bite. Among these are using their mouths to explore, not having language to express themselves, teething, and attention getting. Many caregivers ask parents if the child has had a biting problem before entering care. If so, they can be alert. When biting occurs, appropriate action should be taken (see Table 2–9).

Exposure to Violence

Violence as a means of handling conflict has filtered down into early childhood. Children are seeing violent behavior modeled on television, on the streets, in their neighborhoods, and even in their homes (Palmer, 2000). When children are angry, tired, or upset they may resort to behaviors that reflect their exposure to the violence in our society.

Interpersonal behaviors that threaten safety include biting, fighting, kicking, hitting, stealing, screaming, spitting, hard pushing, and threatening violence. These behaviors show aggression that may indicate a child has personal problems that may have to be addressed if the behavior continues.

Research has shown that children who have witnessed or been direct victims of violence can suffer from posttraumatic stress disorder. This disorder can be displayed by reliving the violence in play (Groves et al., 2000). Children who display especially violent behavior may need special help, including psychological referrals. A conscientious caregiver can often handle violent behavior by observation, communication, and redirection.

Even plastic toy guns pose a potential safety risk for children since they do not teach how dangerous guns are.

TABLE 2–9 Biting in Child Care

Develop a policy for biting and inform parents upon entry of child into care. Try to create an atmosphere that reinforces positive behaviors to avoid biting in the first place.

If biting does occur, find out:

- When (under what conditions) does it happen?
- Who is involved?
- Why did the child bite? (Is there a pattern?)
    —Teething
    —Exploring
    —Inability to express frustration or anger verbally
    —Overstimulation
    —Jealousy
    —Insecurity
    —Recent changes in child's life
    —Asserting independence

Immediately after biting occurs:

- Intervene
- Never bite the child back
- Talk to child who bit
    —Tell the child that biting is not okay
    —Explain that food is for biting, not friends
    —Encourage the child to help the child he bit
- Talk to the child who was bitten and give them reassurance
    —Encourage the child to tell the biter that "that hurt me"
- Give immediate first aid (see Chapter Four)

(continued)

TABLE 2–9   Biting in Child Care *(continued)*

Follow-up

- Alert the staff
- Fill out injury report
- Tell parents of both children what happened
- If it is not the first incident, sit down with the parents of the biter and work out a plan for changing the behavior
- Examine child care environment for any actions, behaviors, or conditions that might be modified to lessen risk

The amount of violence shown on television is increasing. It can be harmful to children and may cause children who watch it to be more aggressive with other children (Singer et al., 1999). The use of guns has escalated even among young children. Real firearms, not just toy guns, are a threat to many young children in their neighborhoods and their homes (Elders, 1994).

Strategies to Promote Positive Interaction

Caregiver awareness of unsafe behavior is the primary tool for safety promotion and prevention of injury in interpersonal relations among the children. Children learn best when appropriate behavior is modeled for them.

Strategies that the caregiver can use to promote positive social interaction and conflict resolution are listed in Table 2–10. The use of these strategies will be helpful to ensure a greater degree of interpersonal safety in the child care environment.

Kevin lived in a neighborhood where he saw much violence. His child care center was in an inner city area. Jacob, Kevin's primary caregiver, noticed that Kevin seemed to become more and more aggressive in his play. One day Jacob decided to track Kevin's behavior. He counted four physical confrontations with friends, two biting incidents, and several threats. Jacob did not know what might have occurred to change Kevin's usually good behavior. Jacob spoke to Kevin's mother, Mona, and found that Kevin's older brother had been beaten up and Kevin had witnessed it. Jacob decided to try several things to help Kevin deal with his emotions.

First, Jacob talked to Kevin about his brother and what had occurred. He explained to Kevin how violence did not solve problems and that talking out feelings was better than acting on them. Jacob knew that this was not always easy. He decided to bring in a punching bag and placed it in a corner of the child care center so that using it would not put children at risk.

Jacob showed Kevin how to use the bag and he instructed Kevin to come and use it whenever angry feelings started to grow. Kevin began using it the next day. In fact, he spent a lot of time punching the bag. After a week or so, Kevin's behavior was noticeably improved, as was the interpersonal safety of the other children. Jacob noticed an interesting result in helping Kevin. Without discussing it, many of the children began using the punching bag when they were angry.

Kids and Guns

Kids and guns cause a serious safety issue for this country. Approximately 1.2 million children over the age of six have access to guns in their homes. One in every four households contains a gun (NSKC, 2001). Forty-four million Americans own a total of 192 million guns. Approximately one-third of those are handguns (Eller, 1998). In the United States, 10 children die every day from gunshot wounds (CDF, 2002). In 1998, more children died from gunshot wounds than from a combination of HIV-AIDS, cancer, asthma, influenza, and pneumonia.

The majority of families that own guns feel their guns are hidden and stored safely. A study showed otherwise. As many as 80 percent of children whose families had guns knew where those guns were by the time they were in the first or second grade (NSKC, 2001). Even more revealing was a study whose subjects were 8–12-year-old boys. Findings showed that even though 90 percent of these boys had had gun safety training, when they found a handgun in a safe environment, all of them picked up the gun and played with it and many pulled the trigger (Jackman et al., 2001).

Children are witnessing violence in increasing numbers on the streets, in their homes, and on television. Even very young children who see a violent act are deeply affected by it (ACT, 2001). As children's minds develop rapidly in these early years, behavior learned in those years can affect development and adult personality (Palmer, 2000). Witnessing violence may threaten a child's basic sense of trust in people. Some children who witness violence may turn their feelings outward toward others (Groves et al., 2000).

Often the witnessing of violence occurs while viewing television. By the time a child completes elementary school, he has witnessed some 8,000 murders on television. Commercial television for children is 50 to 60 times more violent than adult prime-time television (Osofsky, 1999). Children may learn that handling violence with aggression is acceptable. Violence and the use of firearms are often treated humorously in cartoons. Some cartoons average 80 violent acts per hour.

Children need a sense of trust and safety so they can grow and develop to their potential. Children are witnessing the fact that they may not be safe or protected in many of their life situations.

> Children need to feel that they can direct part of their existence, but children who live with violence learn that they have little say in what happens to them. Beginning with the restrictions on autonomy when they are toddlers, this sense of helplessness continues as they reach school age. (Wallach, 1994)

As they grow up, many children exposed to violence may begin to carry guns in order to feel safe and protected.

Children's curiosity about guns and how they work is encouraged by the violence they see on television. They are also tempted by manufacturers of children's toys. Guns are everywhere. They are in poor neighborhoods as well as middle-class schools. The events at Columbine and other schools reinforce this (Eller, 1998). Many children are at risk for safety because of guns.

The child caregiver can do several things to protect children from guns. The best thing would be to have no guns in the environment so that no children are at risk (AAP, 2000b). However, some family child care homes and some child care centers in high-risk neighborhoods may have guns. The caregiver can ensure that any firearm present is kept out of sight, locked away, separate from the ammunition. Caregivers can provide children with alternative forms of handling disagreements in a prosocial manner by teaching children to resolve their conflicts (Levin, 1999). Caregivers can insist

(continued)

on a peaceable classroom, with no toy guns and no pretending other toys such as Legos or blocks are guns. Caregivers can also provide a sense of community in their child care so that children learn that contributing toward peace in a community is a valuable thing (Palmer, 2000). Caregivers can also educate parents about the dangers of guns and that no child is immune from playing with a firearm if it is around. If television is available in the child care situation, programs may be monitored and violent programs should be turned off. Caregivers should also model appropriate behaviors in how they handle conflict, anger, and stress (Massey, 1998).

TABLE 2–10 Strategies for Promoting Interpersonal Safety

- Help children recognize the difference between appropriate and inappropriate behaviors.
- Help children recognize that violence and antisocial behavior cause problems.
- Provide limits and consistent behavior.
- Acknowledge needs, fears, and wants of children.
- Realize negative behavior may indicate unmet needs of a child.
- Verbally redirect children's behavior.
- Model a full range of emotions in acceptable ways.
- Allow, identify, and react to a child's expression of emotion.
- Label expressions of emotions so children learn to identify those emotions.
- Use play, role playing, conversation, books, and pictures to explore and help the child express a range of feelings.
- Do not allow the use of toy guns.
- Avoid storing firearms in the child care environment, if possible. If present, the guns must be locked up and ammunition stored in a separate location.
- Support and encourage cooperation among the children during play.
- "Catch them being good" by acknowledging positive behaviors.
- Encourage those behaviors that promote conflict resolution.

KEY CONCEPT 2.5

Interpersonal Safety

The child care environment may have situations involving behaviors that put interpersonal safety of those present at risk. Biting, kicking, and other aggressive behaviors can pose threats to other children and the caregiver. The effect that television and other media may have on how children behave in relation to violence needs to be addressed. Some types of child care environments may have guns present that would pose great risk if children were to gain access to them. It is very important that the caregiver use all the strategies for positive social interaction in order to resolve conflict and protect the interpersonal safety of those present in the child care environment.

2.6 Poison Control

The most common emergency involving children is accidental poisoning. Ninety percent of poisonings occur in the home, and of these more than one-half involve children under the age of six (CDC, 2001b). Children under the age of two are especially at risk. Family child care and nanny care operate out of a home environment, so they are more likely to be at risk than center-based care. Regardless of the child care type, the caregiver must employ prevention as the primary means of poison control.

The first order of prevention is vigilance in monitoring the children in care. This is only effective if the environment has been modified for safety. Removing all hazards and risks for exposure to poisons provides a protected environment.

Examining the Environment

Poisoning occurs from many common items found in a household or child care environment. Cleaners, medicines, laundry supplies, cosmetics, plants, pesticides, garden supplies, automobile fluids, and certain foods can poison a child who ingests them. The caregiver should make a room-by-room inspection for poisons in the child care environment. If the child care is performed in a home, special care should be taken to inspect the entire environment. Bathrooms, bedrooms, kitchens, and garages are full of poisonous substances that may go unnoticed in daily life, if children are not present. Table 2–11 gives the caregiver a list of common substances that are poisonous to children that are found in the home.

Medications and poisonous substances should be either kept out of reach of small children or securely locked in cabinets with safety latches.

TABLE 2–11 Common Hazardous Substances Found in the Home

Bathrooms

Prescription drugs	Antacids
Over-the-counter medicines, creams, and lotions	Hair care products
Peroxide, alcohol, mercurochrome, and other medications for injuries	Makeup and skin care products
Vitamins, iron pills, and other dietary supplements	Nail products such as polish and polish remover
Cleaning solutions	Hair removal products
	Electric blow dryers, curling irons, and radios

Bedroom

Birth control pills, foams, and so forth	Hair care products
Body lotions	Makeup and skin care products

Kitchen

All-purpose cleaning products	Alcoholic beverages
Detergents	Bleach
Polishes for silver, brass, chrome, and so forth	Oven cleaning products
Baking sprays and oils	Waxes and other appliance care products
Insecticides	Floor care products

Garage

Gasoline	Laundry products
Motor oil, lubricants, and other engine care products	Solvents
Waxes, detergents, and other car care products	Paint and paint removal products
Insecticides and pesticides	Glue

Strategies for Removal of Risk from Poison and Toxins in Child Care

The caregiver who anticipates, modifies the environment, and monitors children carefully should be able to avoid risk due to poisoning. Poisonings can occur in five ways

1. ingestion
2. contact
3. inhalation
4. animal, insect, or reptile bites
5. injection

Ingestion is swallowing the poison. Children are attracted to bright colorful packages, pills, and odd shapes. They often encounter containers that have been used for food or drink that now contain poisonous substances.

Contact occurs when poisonous substances or plants come in contact with the skin. This type of poisoning is indirect; the poison is absorbed through

Some common indoor plants such as the philodendron are poisonous. To protect the children in their care, caregivers need to know which plants are poisonous and keep them out of the children's reach. *(Courtesy of Interior Plantscape division of ACLA)*

the skin into the bloodstream. *Inhalation* occurs when children breathe fumes from pesticides, certain types of art materials, or dust that may contain lead. The exchange of air in the lungs allows the poison to come in direct contact with the lungs, after which it then enters the bloodstream.

Animal and insect bites can cause allergies in children. Some allergic reactions are very toxic and can lead to death. Certain insect bites can cause health and safety risks. These include ticks, which cause Lyme disease or Rocky Mountain spotted fever. Reptiles such as rattlesnakes and copperhead snakes can bite children and cause the poison to enter the bloodstream. Other safety hazards such as cat scratch fever, rabies, and salmonella can come from bites or other types of direct contact with animals.

Injection occurs when there is a puncture wound. The danger may come from the substance that was injected or remnants of tetanus on the item that caused the puncture. Today there is an extra threat of children finding needles that have been used to inject drugs. An accident like this can cause the child to be exposed to HIV.

Table 2–12 includes caregiver strategies for promoting poison control protection in the child care environment.

Plants that Pose Risk

Plants are another poisonous hazard found in the indoor environment. The caregiver should be familiar with the types of plants that may be present. All plants should be out of reach of children. Any plants that are potentially hazardous to children should be removed from the child care environment. Table 2–13 lists indoor plants that pose risk for poisoning.

TABLE 2–12 Strategies for Promoting Poison Control
• Always supervise children in your care.
• Keep poisons out of sight and reach of children and in a locked cabinet.
• Keep medicines, household cleaners, and laundry products in their original containers. Never store nonfood items in food containers.
• Use childproof safety caps.
• Use safety latches or locks on all storage cupboards.
• Never call medicine candy and do not take medicine in front of children—they love to imitate.
• Inspect your child care location from a child's eye view—on your hands and knees—to check the environment for poison risks.
• Determine that all the plants in your environment are nonpoisonous (see Table 2–13).
• Keep pets in a regulated environment.
• Keep the environment free of insects.
• Teach poison prevention to the children and child care providers who are in the child care facility.
• Keep the local poison control center number on your phone.
• Keep parents informed about poison control.
• Keep a bottle of syrup of ipecac at your facility.
• When prevention fails, learn to act immediately in an educated manner.

TABLE 2–13 Common Indoor Plants that Pose Risk for Poisoning	
Plant	**Reaction**
Philodendra Schefflera Pothos	Burning and irritation of the lining of the mouth, tongue, and lips. Can be fatal. May also cause skin reaction.
Diffenbachia Elephant ear	Intense burning and irritation of the lining of the mouth and tongue. If tongue swells it may cause blockage to air passage and result in death.
Hyacinth Narcissus Daffodil	These bulbs are often found indoors in late winter and early spring. Nausea, diarrhea, and vomiting. Can be fatal.
Castor bean Rosary pea	Fatal. A single pea or bean is enough to kill a child.
Poinsettia	Nausea, skin reactions

KEY CONCEPT 2.6

Poison Control

Poison control is an essential task of the caregiver. The environment should be examined for poisons. Safety risks from poisons in the child care environment can be reduced through removal, proper storage, supervision, and using as few poisonous products as possible. Good safety practices and supervision help prevent accidents involving poisoning. Plants in the environment should be nonpoisonous and should be kept away from children.

2.7 Fire and Burn Prevention

Children are very susceptible to fires and burns because they are so curious and do not yet recognize dangers. Injuries from these accidents are the third leading cause of death among American children (CDC, 2001a). Thirty-five percent of all burn injuries happen to children; scalding is the chief cause of burns to children of preschool age. Fires caused by playing with matches and lighters are the number one cause of fire-related deaths among young children (see Figure 2–7). The concept of cause and effect is not operational enough to help children protect themselves unless they are repeatedly taught fire and burn prevention and safety.

Environmental Hazards

The caregiver must be aware of all the things in the child care environment that can present hazards and present fire and burn risks. Table 2–14 gives an overview of typical environmental hazards that may be present.

First, second, and third degree burns. In second degree burns, such as shown here, the outer and inner skin layers are burned and usually blister. If nerve endings are exposed to air or are affected by swelling, the injury may be very painful.

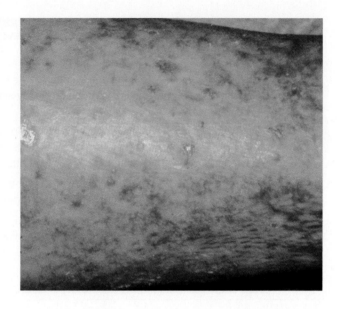

TABLE 2–14 Environmental Hazards for Burns

Scalding

- Boiling liquids or food on or off stove
- Steam
- Hot coffee or cocoa
- Hot bath water or water out of tap more than 120°F

Electrical

- Sticking a foreign object into an electrical outlet
- Touching a live wire
- Water contact with an electrical appliance

Contact

- Hot pan on stove
- Touching fire in fireplace
- Candles or candle wax
- Cigarettes, cigars, or pipes
- Matches, lighters
- Flammable clothing or sleeping materials

Chemical

- Strong household chemicals
- Automobile chemicals
- Lawn and garden chemicals

Figure 2–7

First, second, and third degree burns.

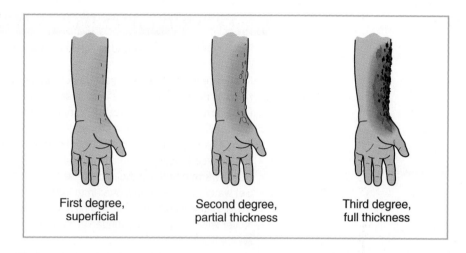

First degree, superficial

Second degree, partial thickness

Third degree, full thickness

Strategies for Fire and Burn Prevention

It is up to the caregiver to help the children be aware of hazards that can cause fires or burns. Children should regularly be taught to avoid matches and lighters. These items should be stored out of sight and not used unless necessary. Children should also have regular practice drills for fire evacuation and should know how to "Stop, Drop, Roll, Cool, and Call." Safety devices such as fire extinguishers and smoke alarms should be present and in working condition. As with any safety hazard, the caregiver is ultimately responsible for keeping children safe. Modeling preventive behaviors will reinforce fire and burn accident prevention. Table 2–15 gives the caregiver some strategies that will help prevent fires and burns in the child care environment.

TABLE 2–15 Strategies for Fire and Burn Prevention
• Use only correct size fuses in the fuse box.
• Install and regularly check smoke detectors. Change batteries frequently.
• Teach children to Stop, Drop, Roll, Cool, and Call. Be sure to include keeping their faces covered with their hands during the Roll portion.
• Keep a fire extinguisher on hand, know how to use it, and refill it immediately upon use.
• Place and maintain barriers around fireplaces, heaters, radiators, and hot pipes.
• Try not to use matches or lighters around children. If present, store out of sight in a locked cabinet or drawer.
• Teach children to bring you any matches they find. If they find a lighter have them immediately tell you so that you can pick it up.
• Use safety devices to cover electrical outlets.
• Inspect and clean heating systems including stoves and fireplaces once a year.
• Make sure there are sufficient outlets for all appliances to prevent overloading electrical wiring.

(continued)

TABLE 2–15 Strategies for Fire and Burn Prevention *(continued)*

- Place smoke alarms around the child care and check the batteries on a regular basis.
- Keep extension cords exposed; do not run them under furniture or rugs.
- Keep all flammable liquids stored in safety cans and out of reach of children.
- Keep furnaces, heating equipment, and chimneys and flues cleaned regularly.
- Never allow children in food preparation area without supervision.
- Do not drink or carry anything hot when close to a child.
- Test hot food before giving it to a child.
- Never warm a bottle in the microwave.
- Set water heaters to no higher than 120°F
- Never bathe a child in water you have not tested.
- Never leave children unattended in the bath or near a faucet. They might turn on the hot water.
- Turn pot handles in toward center or rear of stove and only cook on rear burners when possible.
- Never use portable, open-flame, or space heaters.
- Never smoke around children.
- Never store flammable liquids such as gasoline near the child care environment.

KEY CONCEPT 2.7

Fire and Burn Prevention

The caregiver should actively practice fire and burn prevention. Burn hazards to children come from many areas. Children can be burned from scalding hazards, electrical hazards, hazards that are directly contacted with heat or fire, and by chemical hazards. The child caregiver needs to use all strategies available to protect the children in child care from any hazards that might cause fires or burns.

2.8 Implications for Caregivers

The child caregiver should use observation, supervision, and education to provide a safe indoor environment. These risk management tools provide preventive and protective measures for the child care environment.

Table 2–16 shows a safety policy for the child caregiver to prevent choking and suffocation. This measure uses all of the risk management tools previously mentioned.

Observation

Observation for accessories, behaviors, and conditions offers the caregiver the awareness needed to prevent risk in the indoor environment. Knowledge of hazards in equipment, toys and craft supplies, and poisons helps the caregiver

TABLE 2–16 Preventing Choking and Suffocation in Child Care

- Remove loose parts from toys.
- Use a choke testing device on small toys. Always do this before adding a questionable toy to the environment.
- Keep diaper and other pins, toothpicks, and nails out of your mouth.
- Do not wear dangle-type jewelry like necklaces and earrings.
- Check toys, games, and art supplies for broken pieces and throw away.
- Teach children not to run with anything in their mouths.
- Teach children to chew well and not allow playing when eating.
- Never prop a baby bottle.
- Never use Styrofoam cups—children like to chew them.
- Regularly hand out consumer toy alerts as you find them. Newspapers and magazines carry this information, particularly around Christmas.

remove these items and reduce risk. Observation adds another layer of protection. The caregiver needs to also be aware of unsafe interpersonal behavior practices. This may help the caregiver to stop or redirect action before it causes injury. The child care environment should also be inspected for fire and burn hazards. Children should be carefully observed to avoid burns or fires.

Supervision

The greatest concern for supervision is the constant monitoring of children for safety in all situations. In addition, all safe practices, methods of prevention, and means of promotion should be monitored by the caregiver (Aronson, 2001). This will ensure that every measure possible is being used to provide a safe environment. Checking for compliance with licensing standards, local fire safety guidelines, and other safety related ordinances is another way to monitor the environment for safety. Communication is a tool that the caregiver can use to make sure safe practices are being used by all adults in the child care environment.

Education

Prevention of safety risks is promoted through education of child caregivers, children, and their parents. The more tools everyone has for becoming aware of hazards, developmental limitations, and the child care environment, the greater the opportunities that are available to prevent accidents and injuries.

Children can be taught many safe behaviors through a number of methods and curriculum. Visitors such as firefighters and police officers can show children how to keep safe. Caregivers can be role models of safe behaviors every day. They can read books and provide videotapes that will help children become aware of the need for safe practices. Caregivers can conduct regular drills for fire and other safety threats. They can practice "Stop, Drop, Roll, Cool, and Call" with children on a regular basis. Caregivers can talk with children about appropriate and inappropriate interpersonal behaviors.

Caregivers can provide parents with information about safety by handing out information sheets or handouts supplied by agencies such as fire departments, poison control, and police departments. They can request parents and children to practice fire drills at home on a regular basis.

KEY CONCEPT 2.8

Implications for Caregivers

The child caregiver should use all measures possible to protect the children and prevent injury. Tools such as observation, supervision, and education can provide practices for the caregiver to ensure safety through promotion, prevention, and protection.

CHAPTER SUMMARY

There are a number of threats to indoor safety, including indoor equipment, toys, interpersonal behaviors, poisons, and fires and burns. Safety policies are necessary for the caregiver to monitor and protect the environment. An understanding of the developmental level of the children present is essential. The caregiver should use checklists to monitor and modify the child care environment. All items, including cleaning supplies, pets, plants, and art supplies, should be examined for safety, and should be removed if they present risk. Caregivers should promote and practice safe behaviors by using observation, supervision, and education.

TO GO BEYOND

In this section you will find a number of activities that you can use to apply and improve your knowledge of this chapter. There is also a thorough Online Resource that accompanies this text that can be found at http://www.early childed.delmar.com/resources/robertson/index.html. Included on this site are chapter practice quizzes, PowerPoint outlines, Web links, a discussion forum, and various other activities to help you better understand the material in this chapter. This site is updated regularly so check back often to receive the latest information about the subjects in this chapter.

Chapter Review Critical Thinking Applications

1. Compare and contrast the safety policies for the indoor environment found in a child care center and a family child care. How are these policies affected by the ages of children?
2. Discuss the need for safe, risk-free toys.
3. Relate how age appropriateness affects toy selection for child care. What are some of the potential risks if inappropriate toys are selected?
4. Discuss the importance of conflict resolution for interpersonal safety in child care.

As an Individual

1. Visit a child care center and survey it for indoor safety. Write down the risks observed and bring it back to class to share. Compare it to what others observed.

2. Take the list of indoor plants found in this chapter to a local nursery or flower shop and identify poisonous indoor plants that you find there. Have you seen any of these plants in a household that has children in it? Share your results in a discussion in class.

3. Search the World Wide Web for two sites that directly relate to kids and guns. Write a synopsis of the sites. Share these sites with your classmates in class.

As a Group

1. List the developmental level risks for an 18-month-old toddler in an indoor environment at a day care center, then a family child care home. Compare and contrast the two lists.

2. In groups of four or five students design a child care center room for two-year-olds that includes all the amenities, while being at low risk.

3. In groups of four or five students have the group choose among the following and design a safety policy
   - fire safety
   - play dough
   - art projects
   - interpersonal safety
   - poison control
   - indoor water safety

4. As a class, discuss Sudden Infant Death Syndrome. List the major risk factors. Design a safety policy that would work for child care from this list.

5. Visit a fire station and have the firemen give the class the same demonstrations that they would give to preschoolers. Assess the presentation for developmental appropriateness. Have students discuss what they learned from this demonstration.

CHAPTER REFERENCES

Adults and Children Together (ACT). (2001). *Violence prevention for teachers of young children.* Retrieved May 15, 2002, from http://www.actagainstviolence.org/class.html.

American Academy of Pediatrics (AAP). (2000a). Changing concepts of sudden infant death syndrome: Implications for infant sleeping environment and sleep position. *Pediatrics, 105*(3), 650–656.

American Academy of Pediatrics (AAP). (2000b). Firearm-related injuries affecting the pediatric population. *Pediatrics, 105*(4), 888–895.

American Public Health Association & American Academy of Pediatrics (APHA & AAP). (2002). *Caring for our children: National health and safety performance standards: Guidelines for out-of-home care*. Washington, DC: American Public Health Association.

Anderson, H., & Cook, D. (1998). Review: Maternal smoking associated with an increase risk for SIDS. *Evidence-Based Medicine*. Retrieved May 15, 2002, from http://www.acponline.org/journals/ebm/julaug98/maternal.htm.

Arnestad, M., Andersen, M., Vege, A., & Rognum, T. (2001). Changes in the epidemiological pattern of sudden infant death syndrome in southeast Norway, 1984–1998: Implications for future prevention and research. *Archives of Disease in Childhood, 85,* 108–115.

Aronson, S. (2001). Reducing the risk of injury in child care. *Child Care Information Exchange, 101*(3), 64–66.

Centers for Disease Control (CDC). (1999). *Childhood injury fact sheet.* Atlanta, GA: Author. Retrieved May 15, 2002, from www.cdc.gov/ncipc/factsheets/childh.htm.

Centers for Disease Control (CDC). (2001a). *Fire safety.* Atlanta, GA: Author. Retrieved May 15, 2002, from http://www.cdc.gov/safeusa/fire/firesafe.htm.

Centers for Disease Control (CDC). (2001b). *Poisoning prevention.* Atlanta, GA: Author. Retrieved May 15, 2002, from http://www.cdc.gov/safeusa/poison.htm.

Centers for Disease Control (CDC). (2001c). *Preventing choking among infants and young children.* Atlanta, GA: Author. Retrieved May 15, 2002, from http://www.cdc.gove/safusa/home/chok.htm.

Centers for Disease Control (CDC). (2001d). *Preventing falls among young children.* Atlanta, GA: Author. Retrieved May 15, 2002, from http://www.cdc.gove/safusa/home/falls.htm.

Chiara, S. (1995, Feb. 2). American child care called unfit. *San Diego Union Tribune,* A-10, 11.

Children's Defense Fund Reports. (1994). Violence: Every two hours a gun kills a child. Washington, DC: Children's Defense Fund.

Children's Defense Fund. (2002). *Violence touches the lives of too many children.* Washington, DC: Author.

Consumer Product Safety Commission (CPSC). (1999). *Safety hazards in child care settings.* Washington, DC: Author.

DiFranza, J., & Lew, R. (1995). Effect of maternal cigarette smoking on pregnancy complications and sudden infant deaths. *Journal of Family Practice, 40*(4), 385–394.

Elders, J. (1994). Violence as a public health issue. *Childhood Education, 70*(5), 260–262.

Eller, D. (1998, August). It's shocking how many people you know own a gun and how easy it is for kids to get their hands on one. *Parents Magazine,* 62–65.

French, L. (1999). Children and pets in childcare. *Healthy Child Care, 2*(5). Retrieved May 15, 2002, from http://www.healthchild.net/Articles.

Gorman, C. (2001, June 24). Prevent crib death. *Time Magazine.*

Groves, B., Lieberman, A., Osofsky, J., & Fenichel, E. (2000, April/May). Protecting young children in violent environments: A framework to build on. *Zero to Three, 5,* 9–13.

Jackman, G., Farah, M., Kellerman, A., & Simon, H. (2001). Seeing is believing: What do boys do when they find a real gun? *Pediatrics, 107*(6), 1247–1250.

Kemp, J., Unger, B., Wilkins, D., Psara, R., Ledbetter, T., Graham, M., Case, M., & Thach, B. (2000). Unsafe sleep practices and an analysis of bedsharing among infants dying suddenly and unexpectedly: Results of a four-year, population based, death-scene investigation study of sudden infant death syndrome and related deaths. *Pediatrics, 106*(3), 41.

Levin, D. (1999). Changing needs, changing responses: Rethinking how we teach children. *Child Care Information Exchange, 99*(7), 46–49.

MacDorman, M., Cnattingius, S., Hoffman, H., Kramer, M., & Haglund, B. (1997). Sudden infant death syndrome and smoking in the United States and Sweden. *American Journal of Epidemiology, 146,* 249–257.

Malloy, M., & Freeman, D. (2000). Birth weight- and gestational age-specific Sudden Infant Death Syndrome mortality: United States, 1999 versus 1995. *Pediatrics, 105*(6), 1227–1231.

Massey, M. (1998). *Early childhood violence prevention.* ERIC Digest. Champaign, IL: Eric Clearinghouse on Elementary and Early Childhood Education.

Mickalaide, A. (1994). Creating safer environments for children. *Childhood Education, 70*(5), 263–266.

Moon, R., & Bilitier, W. (2000). Infant sleep position policies in licensed child care centers after back to sleep campaign. *Pediatrics, 106*(3), 576–580.

Moon, R., Patel, K., & McDermott-Shaefer, S. (2000). Sudden infant death syndrome in child care settings. *Pediatrics, 106*(2), 295–300.

Oku, C. (1999). *Biting in the child care setting.* California Child Care Health Program. Health and Safety Notes. Retrieved May 15, 2002, from http://www.childcare health.org.

Osofsky, J. (1999). The impact of violence on children. *The Future of Children, 9*(3), 33–49.

National Safe Kids Campaign (NSKC). (2001). *Why kids are at risk.* Retrieved May 15, 2002, from www.safekids.org.

Palmer, D. (2000). Violence prevention: What childcare providers can-must!-do about it. *Healthy Child Care, 3*(6). Retrieved May 15, 2002, from http://www.healthchild. net/Articles.

Rosenblum, G. (1993, November). Is your house making your children sick? *Sesame Street Parents,* 68–72.

SIDS Network. (1996). *Reducing the risks for SIDS: Some steps parents can take.* Retrieved May 15, 2002, from http://SIDS-Network. Org:80//Risk.htm.

Singer, M., Miller, D., Shenyang, G., Flannery, D., Frierson, T., & Slovak, K. (1999). Contributors to violent behavior among elementary and middle school children. *Pediatrics, 104*(4), 787–884.

Wallach, D. (1994). *Violence and young children's development.* ERIC Digest. Champaign, IL: Eric Clearinghouse on Elementary and Early Childhood Education.

Wisborg, K., Kesmodel, U., Henriksen, T., Olsen, S., & Secher, N. (2000). A prospective study of prenatal smoking and SIDS. *Archives of Diseases in Childhood, 83,* 203–206.

Zamani, R. (1999). *Pets in the child care setting.* California Child Care Health Program. Health and Safety Notes. Retrieved May 15, 2002, from http://www.childcare health.org.

Zavitkovsky, A., & Thompson, D. (2000). Preventing injuries to children: Interventions that really work. *Child Care Information Exchange, 100*(1), 54–56.

SUGGESTIONS FOR READING

Chiara, S. (1994). Television in the lives of children and their families. *Childhood Education, 70*(2), 103–104.

Latona, V. (1996, August/September). What on earth? *Healthy Kids,* 43–46.

Protecting your baby from environmental hazards. (1994, February). *Child Magazine,* 75–79.

Violence threatens our youth. (1993/94, Winter). *Childhood Education,* 96-E.

For additional information on safety, nutrition, and health in early education, visit our Web site at **http://www.earlychilded.delmar.com**

Outdoor Safety

After reading this chapter, you should be able to:

3.1 Safety Policies for the Outdoor Environment

Describe and discuss safety policies for outdoor environments as tools for risk prevention, safety protection, and safety promotion.

3.2 Examining Child Care Environments for Outdoor Hazards

Indicate and discuss specific guidelines for making the child care playground environment free from risk and protected for safety.

3.3 Playground Equipment Safety

Relate and discuss the safety hazards of outdoor equipment as they relate to child care situations and general safety.

3.4 Traffic and Transportation Safety

Relate the guidelines for safe transportation and traffic involved in child care situations.

3.5 Water Safety

Describe and discuss the water safety hazards in outdoor child care.

3.6 Implications for Caregivers

Indicate the need for education, observation, and supervision to maintain a safe outdoor environment.

3.1 Safety Policies for the Outdoor Environment

Unintentional accidents and risks to safety are more likely to occur in the outdoor environment than indoors. Some risks may be similar, such as drowning, falling, choking, and poisons. Other hazards, such as automobiles and bicycles, are responsible for a large number of childhood injuries and deaths each year. The following factors indicate a need for outdoor safety policies:

- More than half of the injuries in child care centers result from falls. Falls from playground equipment account for almost half of the serious injuries (Thompson, Hudson, & Mack, 1999).

- Playgrounds should provide both play value and safety for health development (Frost, 1994).

- Approximately 3 million thefts and violent crimes occur near public schools each year (Levin, 1994). Many child care centers and family child care homes are close to schools; thus, they are at risk for safety.

- Motor vehicles cause most accidental deaths of children (CDC, 1999). The majority of these fatalities could be prevented with the use of a safety seat restraint (Berg et al., 2000).

- Nearly 400,000 children each year are treated in an emergency room for bicycle related injuries (Berg et al., 2000).

Safety policies for the outdoor environment need to cover a wide range of areas. Not all the policies in this chapter will apply to all child care environments. Vulnerability to safety will come from a number of risks. These risks may come from playground equipment, travel, traffic, bicycles, bodies of water, and the nearby neighborhood. Some of the hazards are related to accessories such as improper equipment or lack of proper cushioning under equipment. Behaviors such as lack of attention or a child trying a physical act he is not

Even something as common as duct tape covering a damaged slide is a potential safety risk for the children using this piece of playground equipment.

capable of performing may present risks. Conditions such as the child being tired or the caregiver talking to another adult can cause risk.

Policies should cover monitoring accessories, conditions, and behaviors. They should comply with local licensing regulations and suggestions for accreditation, if applicable. Planning and promoting safe practices should be based on children's physical and developmental abilities as well as their emotional needs. Safety policies should include:

1. *Outdoor Child Care Environments:* understanding outdoor safety practices for the child care environment and applications for risk management as they apply to the type of outdoor environment

2. *Playground Equipment Safety:* practices for preventing injuries and managing safety on playground equipment

3. *Travel and Traffic Safety:* practices for preventing injury, promoting safety, and strategies for developing guidelines for travel and traffic as it applies to child care

4. *Water Safety:* practices for removing hazards, promoting safety, and preventing injury as it applies to water in the child care environment

5. *Implications for Caregivers:* methods and practices for conducting education, supervision, and observation and using outside resources for safety in the outdoor environment

KEY CONCEPT 3.1

Outdoor Safety Policies

The outdoor environment offers a large degree of risk for child care. Outdoor safety policies should begin with examining the child care environment. Policies should be created for playground equipment, traffic and travel safety, water safety, and implications for the caregivers.

3.2 Examining Child Care Environments for Outdoor Hazards

Outdoor environments may vary greatly from one child care situation to the next, but they all have common features that contribute to outdoor childhood accidents. These relate to

■ falls

■ motor vehicle and other transportation accidents

■ poisons

■ equipment

The environmental screening for safety should address the ABCs of injury risk (refer back to Table 1–5). The caregiver must anticipate problems, modify the environment, and monitor the children in care for unsafe practices. The caregiver must also be aware of conditions and behaviors that lead to injury in the outdoor environment.

Outdoor Environmental Hazards

The child care outdoor site should be free of hazards. Protective measures and preventive practices can help reduce the risk that accessories may provide in the outdoor environment of the child care site. General environment hazards include lack of barriers, poisons, insects, and extremes of temperature. Other considerations may also present risk to the outdoor environment.

Barriers. The play area should have a fence or other barrier that surrounds it and be at least four feet high. A fence should separate the play area from all automobile traffic and any hidden corners of the outdoor area that may go unobserved if a child wanders into that corner. Fences should be constructed of safe materials and kept intact and in working order. Gates should fasten securely and should have latches high enough to be out of the reach of children or should have a safety latch that is childproof.

Poison Control. Poison control in the outdoor environment is essential. Toxic plants are the most common hazard for poison in the outdoors. Table 3–1 has a comprehensive listing of toxic outdoor plants.

Other poison hazards include pesticides, insecticides, other gardening materials, and barbecue supplies. If these are in the environment, they should be placed up high and in a locked cabinet (Haupt, 1999). If a garage or workshop is present on the site where automobile repair fluids or gasoline are present, this area should be off limits and fenced off or have a locked door as a barrier to this area.

Keep the outdoor area as free from pollutants as possible. Use insect sprays sparingly and only when children are not present. If lawns are sprayed with weed killers or fertilizers, wait several days before allowing children to play on them (KidsHealth.org, 1999). Also, keep the environment free of poison ivy, poison oak, and sumac, which can cause rashes that may spread on contact. Remove these plants from the environment but do not burn them as the fumes can damage the lining of a child's lung.

Insects. Insect safety is important. Although bites and stings do not usually seriously harm a child, some children may be especially sensitive. To avoid stings, do not use scented soaps or lotions and make sure children wear shoes. Children in bright colors seem to attract insects, so remind parents of this during high insect season. Do not let children in areas where insects gather or where food is left uncovered.

Teach children what beehives and wasp's nests look like. The outdoor environment should be inspected and rid of insect infestation and ant hills. No standing water that allows insect breeding should be present in the child care environment.

Some areas of the country have problems with ticks that can cause Lyme disease in children. In these areas children should be dressed in high socks and their clothing should be checked for ticks before coming indoors. Remind parents to check children during bath time. If pets are in the child care environment, inspect them daily and remove any ticks that are found.

TABLE 3–I Common Outdoor Poisonous Plants	
Flowers	
Azaleas	Hyacinth
Bleeding heart	Iris
Calla lily	Jonquil
Daffodil	Larkspur
Delphinium	Lily-of-the-valley
Foxglove	Lobelia
Four o'clock	Rhododendron
Shrubs and Trees	
Black locust	Oak
China berry	Oleander
Elderberry	Poison hemlock
Holly berries	Pencil tree
Jerusalem cherry	Wild cherry
Mistletoe	Wisteria
Night blooming jasmine	Yellow jasmine
Nightshade	
Vines	
Boston ivy	English ivy
Devil's ivy	Morning glory
Vegetable Plants	
Potato sprouts and leaves	Rhubarb leaf
Tomato vines	

Temperature.   Extremes of temperature are potential hazards for children. Protection from heat stroke or heat exhaustion is a major consideration for outdoor play areas. Shade should be present in the outdoor area (Buller & Farina, 1999). If it is not naturally available, provide a shade structure. Children need the relief from the sun and heat to prevent overheating. All facilities should also have a safe outdoor source of drinking water to protect children from overheating or becoming dehydrated.

Freezing temperatures and snow on outdoor equipment may result in slippery surfaces that cause children to fall more easily. Before going outdoors in these conditions, check equipment surfaces to make sure they are safe and not slippery. Children should be dressed warmly when playing outdoors in the cold.

Other Considerations.   Other backyard safety considerations for the outdoor area include keeping bushes and trees trimmed so children do not run into branches and injure themselves. Trimming trees will also discourage or prevent climbing. If there is dirt in the environment, make sure it is not so fine

Sun Safety

Skin cancer from sun exposure begins in early childhood. Scientists believe that two things can predispose a person to skin cancer: (1) a lifetime exposure and (2) severe sunburns (AMC, 2001). It may only take one severe sunburn as a child to cause melanoma in adulthood. Because children do play so much outdoors, and the outdoor environment in child care is so important to children's development, it is critical that children be kept sun safe.

Protecting children from the hazards of the sun on hot and sunny or very sunny days is very important. It is recommended that the child caregiver should access the climate prediction center and find out the degree of ultraviolet exposure for that day at: http://www.cpc.ncep.noaa.gov/products/stratosphere/uv_index/ (EPA, 2001). On days where the ultraviolet exposure is highest, plan activities that keep you out of the sun.

Other suggestions to help keep ultraviolet exposure for children at a minimum include:

- Keep infants out of direct sunlight (AAP, 1999).
- Avoid exposure to the sun between 10 A.M. and 2 P.M., if possible (Skin Cancer Foundation, 2001).
- If that is not possible, make sure children play in a shady area, such as under a tree, a permanent shade structure, or cloth canopy. Teach children how to seek out these areas for themselves (EPA, 2001).
- Make sure children wear protective clothing if going out into the sun, such as hats and long-sleeved shirts, pants, and socks. Teachers should model this (Buller & Farina, 1999). Explain to parents that on hot sunny days, dressing children in lightweight clothing that will cover their body offers more protection.
- When taking children out into the sun, use a sunscreen of SPF 15 or higher for children over the age of 6 months, 30 minutes before going outside (Skin Cancer Foundation, 2001). Staff should also do this. The AAP has recommended if there is no shade for infants under 6 months, a sunscreen could be used (AAP, 1999). You may want to ask parents to provide the sunscreen for their child or children.
- Plan field trips for sunny days where shade is available. (Buller & Farina, 1999).
- Educate parents and children about sun safety.

that it will cause breathing problems for some children. Always check the outdoor environment after storms, high winds, and heavy rains.

Some family child care backyards or shared facilities may have barbecues present. This implies potential for harm from lighter fluid, barbecue utensils, and the barbecue itself. Other common hazards in these two environments are gardening tools and equipment. All of these hazards should be kept in a garage, barn, or out of the reach of children.

Items such as toxic fumes, gases, and air conditioner units should not impact the outdoor environment. Child care environments should not be less than 30 feet from high-voltage power stations, railroad tracks, and electrical substations. The facility should be maintained in a safe condition by removing any sharp rocks, building supplies, or dilapidated structures. The outdoor area should be free of unprotected ditches, cesspools, wells, and utility equipment (APHA & AAP, 2002). Abandoned appliances should not be present in the child care environment.

Limit children going barefoot to areas where the surfaces are safe. Confine pets to certain areas during child care and remove animal feces often. Treat the feces as you would disposing of a diaper, following the same procedure as in Table 10–6 on page 347.

Developmental Level

The impact that behavior has on risk for safety is especially crucial in an outdoor environment. The majority of accidents happen outdoors. Children's developmental behaviors such as lack of fear, curiosity, inattention, and going beyond physical capabilities can easily put them at risk for injury. Caregivers may not be paying adequate attention or may not properly communicate the risk of certain outdoor hazards.

Using developmental levels to define the boundaries of the outdoor environment will help the caregiver screen for accessories, behaviors, and conditions that lead to injuries. Prevention is the key to risk management. Planning and evaluating the environment based on the vulnerabilities of the children in care will help increase protection. Developmental levels of the children in care should be used as the starting point for screening the outdoor environment for hazards. Table 3–2 indicates the relationship of outdoor safety hazards to the developmental levels by age. This chart also indicates the greatest threats to safety at particular ages.

TABLE 3–2	Outdoor Safety Hazards by Developmental Levels of Age	
Age	**Hazards**	**Prevention Tips**
0–6 months	Motor Vehicle	Infant should always be in rear-facing infant safety seat in backseat.
6 months–1 year	Motor Vehicle	Continue using safety seat; switch to toddler seat when able to sit up by self; keep child in backseat.
	Poisons	Watch child for mouthing of objects. Check area for poisonous plants.
	Choking	Watch child for mouthing of objects.
	Drowning	Keep pool covered, fenced, and lock gate.
1–2 years	Motor Vehicle	Continue using safety seat; keep child in backseat.
	Falls	Carefully watch while climbing on outdoor equipment. Teach child safe play practices.
	Equipment	Check playground equipment for rough edges, rust, loose parts. Wood chips or soft sand are best ground coverings under play equipment.
	Poisons	Place all outdoor chemicals, and so forth, in high place, preferably locked. Check area for poisonous plants.

(continued)

TABLE 3–2	Outdoor Safety Hazards by Developmental Levels of Age *(continued)*	
Age	**Hazards**	**Prevention Tips**
	Drowning	Cover, fence, and lock gate to pool. Always supervise child when playing near pool or any body of water.
2–3 years	Motor Vehicle	Keep child away from streets and driveways using supervision, fences, and firm discipline.
		Role model pedestrian behavior such as crossing street.
		Role model wearing seat belt; use safety seat for child; keep child in backseat.
	Falls	Carefully supervise when on equipment.
		Reinforce safe behavior on equipment.
	Poisons	Keep poisons up high and locked.
		Check for poisonous plants.
	Drowning	Always supervise when near any body of water.
		Begin to teach water safety, including role modeling.
		Cover, fence, and lock gate to pool.
	Equipment	Check equipment for hazards.
		Supervise and role model safety.
3 years and up	Motor Vehicle	Use safety seat or seat belt; keep child in backseat.
		Teach pedestrian and traffic safety rules. Role model this behavior.
	Equipment	Reinforce safe play habits.
		Supervise when using tools.
		Check equipment for hazards.
	Drowning	Children should have swimming lessons if they are in care near a body of water.
		Teach water safety.
	Violence	Teach children neighborhood safety, including safe houses and familiarity with law enforcement.

When the caregiver realizes the hazards that make children at risk by age level, it will be much easier to carry out safe practices, appraise risks, and avoid potential dangerous situations.

As the caregiver inspects the outdoor environment, age appropriateness should be kept in mind. If there are children of different ages and they play at the same time, the caregiver will need to provide low barriers that prevent

To avoid collisions, there should be a separate tricycle path on the playground and traffic on the path should be one-way only.

infants and toddlers from using equipment intended for older children. These barriers provide the caregiver more time to watch the children for safety and less time for worry.

Infants and Toddlers. The outdoor play area for infants and toddlers should consist of flexible materials that offer no hazards due to the common "mouthing" of children of this age. The emphasis for this age group is sensory motor activity, so the outdoor equipment for this age group should reflect that need. These children will be exploring and mastering their environment so it is imperative that there be a safe place for them to investigate.

Preschool. As the caregiver looks at the environment with preschool children in mind, the task is to see if enough space has been provided for the children to be as active as this age group is likely to be. Are there areas for exercise play, construction play, and dramatic play, as well as solitary play? Are the climbers and swings at appropriate heights or are they too high or too low? Does this inappropriate height level provide risk? The APHA & AAP standard for children six years old and under is that no structure shall be more than 5½ feet tall. When structures are more than that, research indicates that injuries are more serious. Do the climbers, swings, and slides have appropriate cushioning materials under them? Are these structures free of loose or rusty parts? A complete checklist for these pieces of equipment is found in Table 3–3 on page 112. The caregiver should ensure that the children have been given guidelines for the use of swings, slides, and climbing equipment and should remind them on a constant basis of proper use.

School Age. Children of this age have good coordination and are physically capable of most activities. The caregiver should provide equipment that will offer children the ability to use their skills. Is there enough equipment available so that children do not become bored and find inappropriate activities to engage in that may pose risks? Does the equipment provide options for degree of difficulty for children of different ability levels? For example, does the climbing structure provide different heights, a number of exits, and areas that challenge skills yet does not threaten the safety of a child with less physical abilities? Managing risks by age appropriateness will minimize the risk and provide greater protection.

Space

Child care facilities vary greatly. Each facility's outdoor area will be unique and present conditions that may be unsafe or lead to risk. Adequate outdoor space is important to prevent crowding of children and equipment. Space must also be provided to allow safety zones around large equipment so there is no encroachment by other equipment or potential for collision with other children playing in the area. The rule of thumb is a clearance of 9 feet around stationary equipment and 15 feet around equipment with moving parts, such as swings.

The outdoor play area should provide 50 square feet of space for each child. If equipment areas are figured in, this generally translates to about 75 square feet per child (APHA & AAP, 2002). If this is not possible in the child care environment, but there is a large indoor activity area such as a gym available, then that area can be used for some outdoor types of activities and space is less likely to be a risk factor.

The total outdoor play area may not be utilized by all the children at once, so the total area need not reflect space for all children present. The general standard in that situation is that there be enough space for one-third of the children in care to play at any one time and that the outdoor scheduling accommodate all children over a period of time without space being an issue. If the entire play area is utilized at the same time then space becomes a more critical issue.

This playgrond provides children with a safe environment: children are visible to the caregiver at all times, swings are not in a walking area, and the entire playground is fenced to keep strangers out while protecting children from wandering.

The outdoor space should be arranged so that all play areas are visible to the caregiver at all times. This allows for prevention of injury and abuse and gives children a more secure feeling. Bathrooms should be close enough to the outdoor play area so that the caregiver can keep an eye on the children in the outdoor area and the child who is using the toilet facilities.

Shared Space

A shared space facility can present a distinctive set of dangers that need to be managed for risk. The outdoor environment of these facilities may not meet child care safety standards. Close inspection and constant observation are vital to the children in care under these situations.

Using a list similar to Table 2–2 on page 71, the outdoor environment should be inspected every morning before it is used. Remove all debris, trash, and anything else that may have been discarded in the play area. Inspect the area for animal droppings.

For public multiuse facilities in inner city areas, particular caution should be taken to inspect for sharp objects such as broken glass, razors, and needles from syringes. Also inspect the area for discarded condoms, clothing, and so on that may pose risk for infectious diseases.

In cases where the facility includes a swimming pool or other body of water, particular care should be taken to make sure that all safety devices are in place, including shutting the gate to this area of the facility before children are allowed outside to play.

When the multiuse facility is a family home in the evenings and on the weekends, the caregiver should routinely inspect the outside for hazards he knows might remain after normal family use. For example, if there are pets, a check for animal feces should be a regular morning event, or if someone barbecued the night before, a check for matches and lighter fluid might be necessary.

Time of Day

Many outdoor accidents can occur at any time of day. Poisoning, choking, drowning, and burns occur because of the potential hazards in the environment. Many accidents and injuries occur because children cannot understand cause and effect. This may relate to developmental level.

Maureen and Sara were two child caregivers at an inner city child care center. One Monday morning they decided to take the children to the park next door. Several of the children were excited and really wanted to get on the slide, the swings, and the climbing structure. The children had seen their caregivers go through an inspection process before, but they rarely found any hazards. Several of the children voiced displeasure about the inspection but Maureen and Sara insisted the children wait. On this morning they were very surprised to find razor blades placed on the slide. The caregivers showed the children this hazard and explained what might have happened. The children never complained about the safety inspection again.

Some accidents seem to occur at particular times of day, when children are tired or hungry and are not concentrating on what they are doing. The caregiver should be aware of the times in the child care environment that a child appears to be tired or indicates that she is hungry. For example, more active play injuries occur in summer and fall during midmorning and midafternoon (Aronson, 2001). Monitoring can help prevent risk. The caregiver can modify the environment by changing the schedule to avoid the outdoor environment at the times of day that seem to pose a higher risk.

The Neighborhood

The neighborhood contributes to the child care environment. It may offer conditions that support child care or it may offer risks to child care. The caregiver needs to be aware of the neighborhood and plan for safety for the child care accordingly.

A supportive environment is one that has little traffic, no noise pollution, and poses little risk for the safety of children. It may be a neighborhood where people know and support each other and the safety of the area. There may be community resources such as a park or recreation center that pose no risk for violence or injury.

Many neighborhoods do not offer an environment that supports safety (Shonkoff, Phillips, & Keilty, 2000). A number of risks may come from a neighborhood where the child care is situated. There may be traffic, people who do not belong coming in and out of the area, and noise pollution. There may be community resources that are not safe areas for children. It is up to the caregiver to determine what the risks are in the neighborhood. Once these risks are determined, the caregiver should do everything possible to minimize the risk to the children in care.

Figure 3–1

Continuum of Violence in Children's Lives. *Reprinted with permission from* Teaching Young Children in Violent Times: Building a Peaceable Classroom *by Diane E. Levin ©1994. Published by Educators for Social Responsibility. For more information, call (800) 370-2515.*

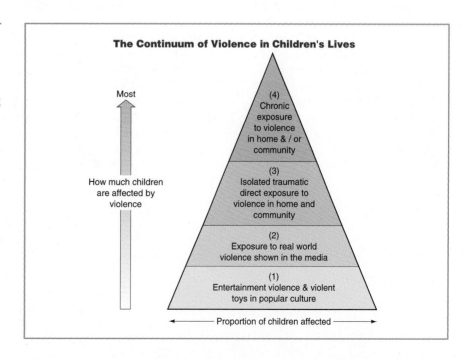

Neighborhood Violence

Someone is raped, murdered, assaulted, or robbed every 16 seconds in the United States (Moyers, 1995). Children are often victims of violence and may react by being instruments for violent behaviors themselves (Osofsky, 1999). Many children are finding that the world is no longer a safe place. It is dangerous and people use violence to hurt other people (Groves, 2001). Poor neighborhoods, where violence may be a way of life, can have severe impacts on a child's and family's well-being (Shonkoff, Phillips, & Keilty, 2000). Exposure to neighborhood violence is particularly common in low-income inner-city areas. In New Orleans, it was found that 90 percent of elementary children surveyed had witnessed violence in their community and 40 percent of those children had seen a dead body. It is estimated that 10–20 percent of homicides in Los Angeles are witnessed by children (Groves, 2001).

Exposure to neighborhood violence can put children at risk for safety as well as for good mental health. Neighborhood violence may have indirect effects on development, if mothers feel they need to restrict their children's ability to interact with their environment (Shonkoff & Phillips, 2000). Some children may be exposed to so much violence that they become desensitized to it (Linares, 2001). Children may lose perspective on what is right and what is wrong. When neighborhood violence may be the norm children may be at risk for performing violent crimes themselves, later in life (Groves et al., 2000).

Violence is becoming a standard in our society (Figure 3–1). Although known to permeate neighborhoods in the inner cities, it has reached the suburbs and rural areas as well. Neighborhood violence is severely affecting the children in this country (CDC, 2000b). More children than ever before are reported to have posttraumatic stress disorder (Groves et al., 2000). Many of the victims and perpetrators of violence may be the parents of young children (Osofsky, 1999). If a child perceives a threat from the people around them, they are less likely to interact with them (Haberman, 1994)

Children's ability to cope with violence and the resulting trauma may depend on several factors: (1) age, (2) developmental stage, (3) the availability of resources to help them, and (4) the ability of the children to use those resources (Groves et al., 2000).

Caregivers can offer children a safe haven from neighborhood violence (Osofsky, 1999). They can monitor their neighborhood environment for safety on a constant basis. They can access resources such as police and public help to offer children a greater degree of protection. Caregivers can encourage children to become less violent and more gentle (Levin, 1999; Haberman, 1994). A good caregiver can help children recognize and acknowledge their feelings. When children become angry, caregivers can show them appropriate ways to express their anger (Massey, 1998). Caregivers can offer children a person they can trust and relate to (Osofsky, 1999; Linares, 2001). For a part of every day, neighborhood violence can be eliminated from children's lives.

KEY CONCEPT 3.2

Examining the Outdoor Environment for Safety

The outdoor environment should be examined for safety on a regular basis. Hazards that pose risk may be items such as lack of barriers, poisons, insects, temperature, and others. Developmental behaviors and mixed age play may pose risk. Lack of space or space not properly organized can pose risk through collision and falls. Shared space allows certain conditions such as debris or trash that may cause danger to children. The neighborhood may pose risk for outdoor safety and should be carefully monitored.

3.3 Playground Equipment Safety

Playground equipment is a major source of childhood injury and accident. Falls are responsible for two out of three playground injuries (Shallcross, 1999). The greatest number of these injuries are results of falls to the ground, onto other children, or onto other equipment. Play equipment that is properly designed, well maintained, and correctly placed can help minimize risk and provide greater protection from serious injury.

Using a general inspection list is a good idea for the caregiver to review the safety of the playground equipment. The list in Table 3–3 is suggested as a tool for regular inspection.

Climbing Equipment, Slides, and Swings

In addition to inspecting equipment for general hazards, climbing equipment, slides, and swings must meet standards set by the U.S. Consumer Product Safety Commission. Figure 3–2 shows areas to check on the playground.

In addition to these quick safety inspection checks, there are other considerations for minimizing risk in the outdoor environment. All playground equipment should have energy absorbing resilient surfaces under and around them to cushion falls and prevent serious injury. Materials such as soft, loose sand, pine or bark mulch, or pea gravel are **shock absorbers**, and should have a minimum depth of 12 inches. Asphalt, grass, and dirt are more dangerous and should not be used around play equipment. The surface material should be raked every several days to keep it from getting compacted and therefore losing some of its shock absorbency.

Shock absorbers
materials that lessen the force of a fall

Riding Toys

Toys that children ride should be sturdy, have a low center of gravity, and be well balanced. These toys should also be age-appropriate. There should be no sharp edges and pedal and hand grips should be in good condition. The area for riding should have a flat, smooth surface and not be slippery. There should be barriers protecting this space from other play areas as well as from traffic and walkways.

TABLE 3–3 General Inspection for Outdoor Equipment

✓ *Check for the presence of the following hazards:*

- ☐ Inadequate fall zone
- ☐ Protrusion and entanglement hazards
- ☐ Insufficient equipment spacing
- ☐ Age-inappropriate activities
- ☐ Platforms with no guardrails
- ☐ Equipment, such as swinging exercise rings and trapeze bars, not recommended for public playgrounds
- ☐ Broken, cracked, bent, or warped surfaces
- ☐ Sharp parts or edges
- ☐ Squeaky parts in need of lubrication
- ☐ Loose nuts and bolts
- ☐ Rotting wood, splinters
- ☐ Defects in moving parts
- ☐ Broken or missing parts
- ☐ Peeling paint, rust
- ☐ Tripping hazards
- ☐ Hard surfaces under equipment
- ☐ Worn out parts
- ☐ Open tubes or pipes that need to be capped

Adapted from U.S. Consumer Product Safety Commission, Handbook for Public Playground Safety, *1997, publication #35.*

Sandboxes

Sandboxes should be kept clean and raked at least once a week. If the sandbox is in a shared use facility, it should be carefully checked and raked daily for broken glass and other sharp objects. Where possible, the sandbox should have a cover in place when the sandbox is not being used. A sandbox also tends to attract cats that may use it as a litter box. Cats' feces can pose risk. Surfaces around the sandbox should be swept often to prevent falls. If standing water remains in sandbox after a rain, it should be removed as soon as the rain stops.

Other Equipment

Seesaws and trampolines are not recommended as regular equipment in child care. If a seesaw is present, it should be designed so children are protected from parts that can pinch. If a trampoline is present, it should have a protective surface underneath and surrounding it just like other large equipment. Only

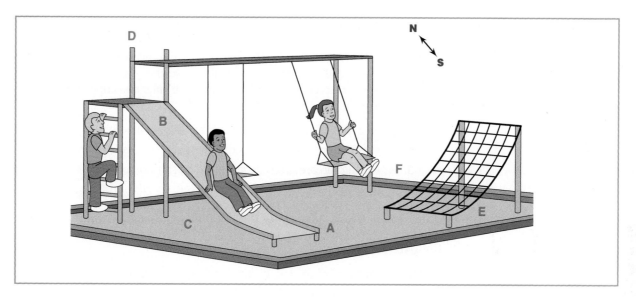

Figure 3–2

Potentially Harmful Areas on a Playground

A. The end of the slide is too close to the border.

B. The slide faces south and will get hot during the warm months. Locating the slide in a shaded area will minimize the risk of burns for children wearing shorts.

C. The structure is built on asphalt, whereas rubber, sand, pea gravel, wood chips, bark, or turf cushions falls.

D. Decks above 3 feet need a safety barrier to prevent falls.

E. The climbing net and posts are too close to the main structure and maximize the risks of collisions and injury during accidental falls.

F. The border is too close to the swing area; children jumping from the swings are likely to fall against the border.

one child should use the trampoline at a time and only when there is an adult observer present who is dedicated to that one task.

All equipment, including equipment assembled or made at home, must meet the basic criteria of the standards set for manufactured equipment. Close inspection and adaptation to U.S. Consumer Product Safety Commission standards will lessen risk. If someone donates equipment to a child care facility, follow the same procedure. Proceed with caution because one can never assume that playground equipment is always safe.

KEY CONCEPT 3.3

Playground Equipment Safety

Playground equipment safety is essential in the child care environment. Risk is posed to the environment because the equipment may not have met national safety standards. Climbing equipment, swings, and slides should be properly placed to prevent accidents. There should be shock absorbing material beneath this equipment. Riding toys should be sturdy and not tip over easily. If seesaws and trampolines are in the environment they should be closely observed and have rules for use. All equipment should be regularly inspected to keep the playground safe.

3.4 Traffic and Transportation Safety

In 1999, 242,000 children under the age of 14 were involved in motor vehicle accidents (NSKC, 2001). Of those, 1,765 died from their injuries. In the United States, motor vehicle accidents are the number one killer and crippler of children under four years of age. Motor vehicle injuries to children occur in three ways.

1. when children are pedestrians and are hit by an automobile
2. when children are riding in a car that stops suddenly or crashes
3. when children are riding bicycles and crash into or are run into by a car

To protect the children in care, safety policies should be developed for each case.

Pedestrian Safety

Children being let off at and picked up from school account for the great majority of pedestrian accidents. There should be a plan devised for safe dropping off and picking up of children. Pick-up and drop-off points for children should be located in an off-street area or directly at a curb near the child care facility under an adult's supervision. In the majority of cases this adult would be the parent bringing the child to school or taking him home. Parents should be reminded of the importance of close supervision of their children in a traffic situation. The outdoor play area should be as far away from traffic as possible and should be fenced.

Motor Vehicle Safety

Car travel and field trips are likely to be special events and not common occurrences in most child care situations. Planning for these events should be well organized and use accessories, behaviors, and conditions as the guidelines for safety. Developmental level of the children you are transporting should also be considered (Healthy Child Care, 1999).

The Vehicle. The accessories in motor vehicle travel are the vehicle itself and the safety seats utilized. Vehicles should be in good working order, and be cleaned and inspected inside and out on a regular basis. Special care should be taken to see that brakes, lights, and other safety features of the car are working properly.

Vehicles should have heating and air conditioning features working in locations where temperatures go below 50°F and over 75°F. Children are susceptible to cold and heat and need to have the vehicle climate controlled.

Safety Seats. Safety seats are very important to the prevention of serious injury in motor vehicles. Although there are laws in every state that require a child riding in a car to be safely restrained, many drivers still do not follow the "buckle up" rule. As many as 59 percent of toddlers involved in motor vehicle accidents were not in car seats at the time of the accident ("Please Be Car-Seated," 1994). As many as nine out of ten safety seats are not properly used even when the driver makes sure a child is buckled up (Mickalaide, 1994).

The safest place for children in a motor vehicle is riding in the backseat and in an approved, secured car seat.

Drivers should become familiar with the manufacturer's installation instructions for the safety seat used by the child.

Each child should be in an appropriate safety seat, harness, or seat belt that corresponds to the child's weight and age. These features shall be approved in accordance with federal safety seat standards and used in compliance with the manufacturers' directions. If a small bus or van is used, seat belts shall be provided for all children. The caregiver should always model safety by using a seat belt.

Pretravel Guidelines. Safety behaviors are necessary in the preplanning stage as well as in actual travel in the motor vehicle. Begin pretravel planning by using the guidelines in Table 3–4.

TABLE 3–4 Pretravel Safety Guidelines

Caregiver:
- Obtain authorization slips for all children participating in travel. Check your insurance coverage.
- Make sure driver is licensed, is familiar with vehicle, and knows how to drive defensively.
- Carefully plan out route, including placement of emergency care facilities along the way.
- Explain route to children and point out highlights.
- Prepare children for travel by explaining why buckling up and safe passenger behavior are important.
- Arrange for backup vehicle in case of car emergency.
- Understand safety precautions and child supervision for travel.

(continued)

TABLE 3–4 Pretravel Safety Guidelines *(continued)*

Caregiver:

- Know how to handle emergency situations, and be certified in pediatric first aid and CPR.
- Make sure the vehicle is in good working condition. This check should include checking the gas, oil, and tires.

Children:

- Understand the importance of travel safety, including buckling up.
- Practice safe travel behaviors, including hands inside the car.
- Understand rules for play in car, including no yelling or screaming.

Travel Guidelines. If the pretravel guidelines have been met, the next step is to follow the travel guidelines in Table 3–5. These guidelines are to help the caregiver be prepared for all contingencies and offer a greater degree of protection for a safe journey for the children in care.

Travel Conditions. Try to plan any travel with the children for a time when the conditions are optimal. Avoid high traffic times or times when children will be most tired or hungry and less alert. If the weather is bad, it is best to postpone the trip until it improves. Prepare a backup activity that will excite the children to lessen the disappointment if the trip is postponed.

Make sure children are constantly under supervision during travel. At a minimum, keep to the proper adult–child ratio, but it is a good idea to ask for volunteers to accompany the caregiver. If travel is by walking and away from the neighborhood or across streets, the ideal ratio would be one adult for three to five children, depending upon age. The caregiver must prepare any volunteers with rules of supervision by giving them handouts and talking to them several days before the trip so that they understand what is expected of them. It is also helpful to remind them of basic travel safety before leaving so it is fresh in their minds when the trip begins.

TABLE 3–5 Child Care Travel Safety Guidelines

Caregiver:

- Have trip authorization forms in your possession for all children present.
- Provide the proper ratio of adult to child and assign specific children to each adult.
- Do not allow loud music or tapes.
- Stop and pull off road to calm children down, if they are unruly and noisy.
- Do not be under the influence of drugs or alcohol, including prescription or over-the-counter medications that can make you drowsy.
- Provide soft books or toys and conversation and songs for children so driver can concentrate on traffic safety.
- Provide a first aid kit to carry in each vehicle.
- Make sure everybody buckles up, and never allow children out of seat restraints while car is moving.

(continued)

TABLE 3–5	**Child Care Travel Safety Guidelines** *(continued)*

- Pay special attention to traffic and the children when exiting and entering the vehicle.
- If the trip is more than a few minutes, have juices and snacks for children allowing them to keep their focus on safety and not on being hungry or thirsty.
- Do not allow children to ride up front in vehicles that have passenger airbags.

Children:

- Observe car safety rules.
- Buckle up.
- Ride quietly, keeping hands to yourself.
- Be extra alert for traffic when exiting and entering vehicle.

Travel information sheet
check-off sheet that monitors all conditions for travel safety

The caregiver should always leave a travel information sheet with a responsible person left at the child care site. This sheet should include the following:

- date and time of trip, including approximate return time
- destination, including address, telephone number, and contact person
- planned route; be specific: "Main Street to Laurel Ave., left on Center Circle, right on Pine two miles to Fourth"
- names of children participating
- names of caregivers and parents providing supervision

Bicycle Safety

School-aged children in family home child care, nanny care, or after school care should be taught about bicycle safety. Every year 300 children are killed in bicycle-related crashes (NCHS, 1991). Nearly one-half million other children are injured. The majority of these crashes involve head trauma. Using bike helmets can reduce the risk of injury by 85 percent and the risk of brain injury by 88 percent (CDC, 2000a). Unfortunately, it is estimated that only 25 percent of children between five and fourteen years of age wear helmets.

Figure 3–3
Helmets Are Available in Different Sizes

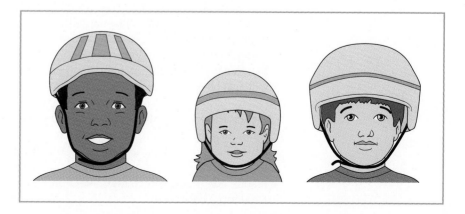

One important and necessary element of bicycle safety is to wear a helmet properly.

Helmets. Practicing safety by using bike helmets for children riding tricycles and small bicycles in child care can reduce risk while riding the vehicles in the outdoor environment (Figure 3–3). It can also help prepare them for a future of greater safety by being in the habit of wearing a helmet. The Consumer Product Safety Commission sets mandatory standards for helmets so the caregiver must make sure the helmets provided meet these standards.

Riding Safety. Helping children learn proper tricycle behaviors can begin in the child care environment, using the same rules as for the riding toys. The skills and precautions in Table 3–6 will help the caregiver set guidelines for teaching children bicycle riding safety.

The riding safety guidelines will help the caregiver set up the child care environment to minimize risk. If children all ride in the same direction the number of crashes or collisions with other riders will be reduced. Keeping nonriders out of the area also reduces the number of collisions. A caregiver who observes the children for speed, reckless riding, and two hands on the handlebar can prevent accidents and ensure a safer experience for them. Risk will also be reduced by checking the riding toys for proper working order.

Other Riding Conditions. Optimizing the conditions in the outdoor environment should not be too difficult. Creating a riding area in which riders have a nice, flat, nonslick surface is important. Enforcing the rule that riders only go in one direction will be a matter of changing habits and most children will readily adapt and will change direction when reminded, whereas others may need more effort.

TABLE 3–6 **Guidelines for Safe Bicycle Riding**
• Always ride in the same direction so all traffic goes the same way and not against each other.
• Always be careful of other people and other traffic in the riding area.
• Keep hands free to hold handlebars with both hands. Never carry anything with your hands.
• Never show off, fool around, or ride recklessly.
• Do not ride too fast, so if you do see someone or other traffic you can slow down or stop to avoid colliding with them.
• The tricycle, bicycle, or other riding vehicle is appropriate for the age of the rider.
• The riding vehicle is in good working order.
• Stay clear of pedestrians.

Setting the time of day when children are most alert for outdoor riding activity decreases risk. Providing necessary and active supervision will also help offer greater protection to the children in the outdoor environment.

KEY CONCEPT 3.4

Traffic and Travel

Traffic and travel pose risk for children in and out of care. Children should be protected and learn good travel safety practices. Pedestrian, motor vehicle, and bicycles are the three areas where there should be safety promotion and prevention from risk. Checklists, guidelines, use of safety devices, travel information sheets, and using optimum conditions will help the caregiver set up the environment for travel and traffic safety.

3.5 Water Safety

Water safety presents its own set of challenges to the child care environment. Bathtubs pose the biggest drowning hazard to infants and pools are the greatest drowning hazard to toddlers, preschoolers, and school-age children (Zavitkovsky & Thompson, 2000). Two-thirds of all drownings occur in the outdoor environment in standing bodies of water such as swimming pools, wading pools, hot tubs, ponds, and ditches. Covers for these items that are left with standing water after a rain become potential drowning hazards even though they may have originally been meant to protect. Popular belief is that a child in danger of drowning screams for help. In reality, drowning can be a silent event, which means constant adult supervision is necessary whenever there is any body of water around children. These bodies of water also have the potential for spreading disease.

Gates that enclose a pool should be self-closing and have locks that are at least 55 inches high.

Water Hazards

Safety precautions must be taken to keep the water in the child care environment as risk-free as possible. Any body of water poses a threat so screening the outdoor environment for hazards that may lead to the risk of drowning should be thorough. Young children can drown in as little as one inch of water.

Water hazards in the outdoor environment must be secured to prevent children from reaching them. Drownings occur in surprisingly short periods of time. Children have been seen playing indoors or outdoors away from a water source, and adults have been present nearby, yet these children have still drowned. Table 3–7 lists ways to childproof the child care environment from the hazards that may lead to drowning.

Children's Behavior Around Water

Children themselves pose a threat when a body of water is present in the outdoor environment. They move fast, are curious, and do not understand cause and effect. They may lack fear or overestimate their physical abilities. Adults may underestimate children's abilities to manipulate their environment and therefore get into trouble. The majority of drownings occur within a very short period of time after a caregiver has seen a child. It is imperative that the caregiver *never* leave a child alone, even for a moment, when there is a body of water in the outdoor environment.

The children should be taught safe practices for swimming and playing in the water to further protect them if they will be using the pool or wading pool. Table 3–8 offers guidelines for teaching safe behavior around and in the water.

TABLE 3–7 Water Safety Guidelines

- Any hazard should be enclosed with a fence that is at least five feet tall and that is not easy to climb. A door or sliding glass door is not a safe substitute for a fence.
- Gates should have locks that are at least 55 inches high and should be self-closing. Keep gate keys in a safe place away from children.
- Remove chairs and objects children can use to climb over fences or gates or into spas.
- All bodies of water that are man made, such as swimming pools, hot tubs, and cesspools, should have rigid covers to protect children from falling in, if they get past the gate.
- If an inground pool is present in the child care environment, it should have a nonskid surface that surrounds the pool to prevent slipping and falling.
- Always drain standing water from pool or spa covers.
- Do not use floating spa or pool covers. Children can slip underneath and out of sight.
- Avoid the use of floating devices that can give children a false sense of safety.
- Remove all toys from pool after children are out of pool.
- If a portable wading pool is used in child care, it should be filled with water, used immediately, and drained and put away as soon as children leave the pool.
- Always carefully supervise children if there is a body of water present in the outdoor environment. *Never leave children without adult supervision, even for a few seconds.* Maintain visual contact with children.
- Keep a rescue device such as a long pole right next to the pool.
- Have telephone access to pool for emergencies.

Reprinted with permission of Children's Hospital of San Diego.

When outdoors and near the water, always reinforce safety for the children. If the children are allowed to play in water, plan the time of day for this activity for when they are least tired and most alert. Always be sure there is adequate supervision and maintain sufficient ratios of adult to children. *Anyone attending children in the water should know how to swim and be competent in pediatric cardiopulmonary resuscitation.*

TABLE 3–8 Water Safety Behaviors for Children

- Do not run, push, or play around swimming areas.
- Do not swim with anything in your mouth.
- Be on the lookout for other children who may be having difficulty.
- Do not swim in very cold water. It increases risk of drowning.
- Never go near pool unless supervised.
- Never run around a pool.
- Wait at least an hour after eating before entering water.
- Do not roughhouse or fool around in water.
- Do not scream for help unless you mean it.
- Never swim alone, always have a buddy with you.

Water Safety

Water in many forms poses risk for children in the outdoor environment. Swimming pools, ponds, or any type of standing water may cause safety to be endangered. The caregiver needs to understand water hazards and how to eliminate them, if possible. Children's behavior poses risk and caregivers should be prepared to promote and teach children water safety behaviors.

3.6 Implications for Caregivers

Outdoor safety poses a number of risks to children in child care. The risks may come from different areas of hazards, such as environmental hazards, playground equipment, traffic and travel, and water. The risk may come from specific hazards, behaviors, and conditions. The caregiver should provide observation, supervision, and education that promote safe behaviors and prevent risks.

Observation

There are many areas of outdoor safety for which observation is the best method of prevention of accident and injury. Learning to use the ABCs of safety as it applies to outdoor accessories, behaviors, and conditions can help the caregiver. A child caregiver who understands specific risks can be on guard for those risks.

Supervision

Children need to be constantly supervised in the outdoor environment. The child caregiver should supervise all aspects of the environment for risk posed by accessories, behaviors, and conditions. These are effective tools for managing outdoor risk to children.

Supervision also supplies the caregiver with methods and practices that provide a checks and balances system in environments where there is more than one caregiver. Communication about outdoor safety should be a regular occurrence between the caregivers. Constant supervision can also reinforce that outdoor safety training and promotion take place on a regular basis.

Education

The caregiver, children, and parents can be educated for outdoor safety. The caregiver should access training that will provide the knowledge and awareness needed. The caregiver who has a knowledge base of outdoor safety can maximize the environment to protect the children.

Children can be taught safe behaviors and items or conditions to look for that may pose risk. The children can be encouraged to use safety devices that will protect them. Communicating with children on a regular basis and reminding them about outdoor safety can offer a greater degree of protection both in and out of child care. The caregiver can use educational methods such as reading books, showing videos, and circle time to reinforce safety measures and methods.

Parents can be educated to help promote and provide for greater protection from outdoor safety risk. Methods such as an outdoor safety awareness week with handouts, videos to borrow, and a parent group meeting can help the caregiver provide the educational support needed.

KEY CONCEPT 3.6

Implications for Caregivers

The child caregiver can promote and protect for outdoor safety in a number of ways. Observation for safety risks can prevent injury. Supervision for making sure safe practices are followed can promote safety and provide protection. Education for caregivers, children, and parents can provide extra measures of protection.

CHAPTER SUMMARY

Risks for accidents are greater in the outdoor environment. These risks can occur on playgrounds, backyards, bicycles, streets, in water, and in automobiles. Caregivers should monitor the children and the outdoor environment and make modifications using safety checklists. Safety devices such as helmets and safety car seats should always be used. Caregivers should use observation, supervision, and education to protect their environment and to promote safe behaviors.

TO GO BEYOND

In this section you will find a number of activities that you can use to apply and improve your knowledge of this chapter. There is also a thorough Online Resource that accompanies this text that can be found at http://www.early-childed.delmar.com/ resources/robertson/index.html. Included on this site are chapter practice quizzes, PowerPoint outlines, Web links, a discussion forum, and various other activities to help you better understand the material in this chapter. This site is updated regularly so check back often to receive the latest information about the subjects in this chapter.

Chapter Review Critical Thinking Applications

1. Discuss the relationship between outdoor activities and risk to safety.
2. Describe some of the safety hazards that might be found in a shared space environment. How do these differ from child care that does not share space. Compare and contrast the two types.

As an Individual

1. Find a child care setting in the local area that reflects shared space, such as a church preschool, a child care at a gym, or a community center. Observe the environment and record your observations.
2. Visit an elementary school playground. Observe the equipment and the surface under it. Do these meet the safety standards discussed in the text?

3. Locate a park in your area. Assess it for the degree of shade it would permit for children on a hot day. What might you do to improve it?

As a Group

1. In groups of four to five people, make a safety checklist for a shared space environment at a church preschool. Use the information collected as individuals to compile this list. Compare the lists of the whole class.

2. Collect handouts from community resources that deal with outdoor safety. These might include an auto club, poison control, and the American Red Cross.

3. Think of a local neighborhood that is often in the news for the violence that occurs in it. What are the characteristics of that neighborhood? Research what might be done to make the neighborhood safer for children. List the local agencies that might be enlisted to help with this project.

CHAPTER REFERENCES

AMC Cancer Research Center. (2001). Sun safety: Work, rest or play in a sun safe way. Retrieved May 15, 2002, from http://www.amc.org/ssafety.htm.

American Academy of Pediatrics (AAP). (1999). Ultraviolet light: A hazard to children. *Pediatrics, 104*(2), 328–333.

American Public Health Association & American Academy of Pediatrics (APHA & APA). (2002). *Caring for our children: National health and safety performance standards: Guidelines for out-of-home care.* Washington, DC: American Public Health Association.

Aronson, S. (2001). Reducing the risk of injury in child care. *Child Care Information Exchange, 101*(3), 64–66.

Berg, M, Cook, L., Corneli, H., Vernon, D., & Dean, J. (2000). Effect of seating position and restraint use on injuries to children in motor vehicle crashes. *Pediatrics, 105* (4), 831–835.

Buller, M., & Farina, A. (1999). Becoming a sun-safe child care center. *Child Care Information Exchange, 99*(5), 69–71.

Centers for Disease Control (CDC). (1999). *Childhood injury fact sheet.* Atlanta, GA: Author. Retrieved May 15, 2002, from http://www.cdc.gov/ncipc/factsheets/childh.htm.

Centers for Disease Control, (CDC). (2000a). Preventing bicycle-related head injuries. Retrieved May 15, 2002, from http://www.cdc.gov/ncipc/factsheets/yvfacts.htm.

Centers for Disease Control, (CDC). (2000b). Youth violence in the United States. Retrieved May 15, 2002, from http://www.cdc.gov/ncipc/factsheets/yvfacts.htm.

Frost, J. (1994, April). Preventing playground injuries and litigation. *Parks and Recreation,* 53–60.

Groves, B. (2001). *Children who witness violence.* Family Communcations. Retrieved May 15, 2002, from http://www.fci.org/early_care/violence_witness_article.asp.

Groves, B., Lieberman, A., Osofsky, J., & Fenichel, E. (2000, April/May). Protecting young children in violent environments: A framework to build on. *Zero to Three, 5.*

Haberman, M. (1994, Spring). Gentle teaching in a violent society. *Educational Horizons,* 131–135.

Haupt, D. (1999, April). Poison prevention: What every parent must know. *Parenting Magazine,* 49–50.

Healthy Child Care. (1999). Safety and fieldtrips. *Healthy Childcare, 1*(3), 3–4. Retrieved May 15, 2002, from http://www.healthychild.net/Articles/Fieldtrip.html.

KidsHealth.org. (1999). Environmental health issues. Retrieved May 15, 2002, from http://kidshealth.org/parent/safety/environ.html.

Levin, D. (1994). Building a peaceable classroom—Helping young children feel safe in violent times. *Childhood Education, 70*(5), 267–270.

Levin, D., (1999, July). Changing needs, changing responses: Rethinking how we teach children. *Child Care Information Exchange, 99*(1), 46–49.

Linares, L. (2001). Community violence and its effects on children. Retrieved May 15, 2002, from http://www.aboutourkids.org/articles/communityviolence.html#how.

Massey, M. (1998). *Early childhood violence prevention.* ERIC Digest. Champaign, IL: Eric Clearinghouse on Elementary and Early Childhood Education.

Mickalaide, A. (1994). Creating safer environments for children. *Childhood Education, 70*(5), 263–266.

Moyers, B. (1995, January 8). There is so much we can do. *Parade Magazine,* 4–6.

National Center for Health Statistics (NCHS). (1991). *Vital statistics of the United States.* Washington, DC: Public Health Services.

National Safe Kids Campaign (NSKC). (2001). *Car.* Retrieved May 15, 2002, from http://safekids.org.

Osofsky, J. (1999). The impact of violence on children. *The Future of Children, 9*(3), 33–49.

Please be car-seated. (1994, Winter). *Scholastic Parent and Child,* 6.

Shallcross, M. (1999). Family child care homes need health and safety training and an emergency rescue system. *Young Children, 54*(5), 70–73.

Shonkoff, J., Phillips, J. (Eds.), & The Committee on Integrating the Science of Early Childhood Development. (2000). *Neurons to neighborhoods.* Committee on Integrating the Science of Early Childhood Development, Board of Children, Youth and Families. Washington, DC: National Academy Press. Retrieved May 15, 2002, from http://www.nap.edu.

Shonkoff, J., Phillips, D., & Keilty, B. (Eds.). (2000). *Early childhood intervention: Views from the field: A report of a workshop.* Committee on Integrating the Science of Early Childhood Development. Washington, DC: National Academy Press. Retrieved May 15, 2002, from http://www.nap.edu.

The Skin Cancer Foundation. (2001). The Skin Cancer Foundation Children's Page. Retrieved May 15, 2002, from http://www.skincancer.org/children/index.html.

Thompson, D., Hudson, S., & Mack, M. (1999). Who should supervise the children? *Child Care Information Exchange, 99*(5), 74–77.

U.S. Consumer Product Safety Commission (CPSC). (1997). *Handbook for public playground safety.* Pub. #35. Washington, DC: Author.

U.S. Environmental Protection Agency (EPA). (2001). *SunWise.* Washington, DC: Author. Retrieved May 15, 2002, from http://www.epa.gov/sunwise/actionsteps.html.

Zavitkovsky, A., & Thompson, D. (2000). Preventing injuries to children: Interventions that really work. *Child Care Information Exchange, 100*(1), 54–56.

SUGGESTIONS FOR READING

Crist, D. (1995, October/November). Car seat Q & A: Everything you need to know about car seats—but forgot to ask. *Healthy Kids,* 44–52.

Frost, J. (1994, April). Preventing playground injuries and litigation. *Parks and Recreation,* 53–60.

Groves, B. (1991). In *Can they hope to feel safe again? The impact of community violence on infants, toddlers, their parents and practitioners* (pp. 19–27). A report from the Seventh Biennial National Training Institute.

Munson, M. (1994). Simple ways to safeguard your kids. *Prevention, 46*(10), 60–64.

For additional information on safety, nutrition, and health in early education, visit our Web site at **http://www.earlychilded.delmar.com**

Emergency Response Procedures for Child Care

After reading this chapter, you should be able to:

4.1 Safety Policies for Emergency Response

Describe and discuss safety policies for response to childhood accidents and injuries.

4.2 Identifying an Emergency

Define and discuss the differences between what constitutes an emergency and what necessitates only basic first aid.

4.3 Basic Emergency Response Procedures

Indicate the steps to go through in addressing the proper responses to a real emergency and how it is to be performed.

4.4 Basic CPR and First Aid

Define, discuss, and summarize the methods of basic cardiopulmonary resuscitation, and first aid to infants and chlidren.

4.5 Emergency Planning for Children with Special Needs

Discuss methods and practices for emergency care of children with special needs.

4.6 Disaster Preparedness

Define, discuss, and summarize the basic methods of disaster preparedness for child care.

4.7 Implications for Caregivers

Indicate the need for supervision, observation, and education for basic response procedures for childhood injuries and accidents.

4.1 Safety Policies for Emergency Response

Emergencies occur in many situations. Automobiles, playground equipment, and natural disasters all pose risk for accidental injury that might be classified as an emergency. A chronic illness or a childhood disease might manifest as an emergency situation. It is important that the caregiver in any child care situation be prepared to handle emergencies. The following show the need for preparedness for emergency response in child care:

■ In a survey of over 400 child care centers, 12 percent were found to be unsafe (Chiara, 1995).

■ The most common types of childhood injury that may constitute an emergency are pedestrian injuries, motor vehicle passenger injuries, burns, firearm injuries, and drowning ("American Red Cross," 2001a).

■ When emergencies do happen in child care it is necessary to know how to take proper action (Palmer, 1998).

■ It is essential that at least one caregiver in child care be trained for emergency, life-threatening situations such as breathing difficulties, head injury, or poisoning (Sokol-Gutierrez, 1999).

■ Child care environments should be prepared for emergencies with a code blue emergency plan (Copeland, 1996).

Child caregivers need to avoid emergencies by providing prevention and protection in the care environment. They do this with constant supervision and by anticipating, modifying, and monitoring for accessories, behaviors, and conditions that pose risk. These proactive behaviors reduce risk.

To provide the maximum protection in the child care environment, the caregiver needs to be prepared for the possibility that an emergency may occur. The caregiver needs to plan for emergencies, be prepared to handle emergencies, and be equipped with the training necessary to deal with life-threatening emergencies as they occur.

In order to carry this out, the caregiver needs to plan for policies in the following areas:

1. *Defining an Emergency:* understanding what constitutes an emergency situation

2. *Basic Emergency Response Procedures:* understanding of methods and practices for response to emergencies in child care

3. *Basic CPR and First Aid:* understanding when and how to use basic CPR and first aid to handle emergencies in child care

4. *Emergency Planning for Children with Special Needs:* methods, practices, and understanding of how to handle emergencies for children in care with special needs

5. *Disaster Preparedness:* methods and practices for preparing for disasters such as fire, weather, and earthquakes

6. *Implications for Caregivers:* methods and practices for preparing the child care environment to deal with emergencies through education, observation, and supervision

4.2 Identifying an Emergency

In order to understand how to prepare for an emergency, the caregiver must first understand what constitutes an emergency. There are common factors that indicate an emergency exists. The child caregiver needs to be able to identify these factors to help determine if an emergency is occurring. Three major factors have been used to indicate that an emergency is taking place.

Bleeding, Breathing, and Poison

The three basic factors that always indicate an emergency exists are bleeding, breathing, and poison. These emergencies are fairly easy to recognize. They are also rapidly life threatening and must be acted upon quickly. There may not even be time to call 911 right away if there is only one person present besides the victim. Any of these three factors could occur in child care and the caregiver should be prepared to recognize them and act immediately and appropriately (see Figure 4–1).

A person who is bleeding profusely may die if the bleeding is not stopped. Stopping the bleeding is of foremost importance, and first aid is needed immediately. If someone else is present, that person can call the emergency number (usually 911).

If a person has difficulty breathing, brain damage can occur in a matter of a few minutes and the heart may stop and death will follow. Anything that interferes with a child's breathing is life threatening (Aronson, 2001). Offering rescue breathing may be the only alternative. Calling an emergency number is also vital, if possible.

When someone has ingested or has contacted poison directly through the skin, or has inhaled it, emergency procedures should begin immediately. Call the local poison control number to get help for the victim. In most cases, the person who answers will walk the rescuer through the exact method of treating the particular poison.

Profusely
pouring forth freely or abundantly

Rescue breathing
the process of steps to help a person who is not breathing resume normal breathing

Figure 4–1

In an emergency situation, there may not be time to call for help; the caregiver may have to take action.

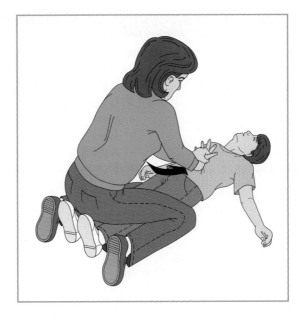

Other Emergency Indicators

There are a number of other indicators that show when an emergency may be present. The American Red Cross suggests that using one's senses is a good tool to help recognize when an emergency may exist. Hearing, seeing, smelling, and feeling can all be tools of recognition as listed in Table 4–1.

When any of the conditions in Table 4–1 are present in child care, an emergency may exist and the child caregiver should act promptly (Figure 4–2). The caregiver should follow through with any unusual sights, sounds, smells, and sense of touch. The follow-up may prove that nothing was out of order; on the other hand, it may establish that an emergency is taking place. The child caregiver needs to remain calm, act quickly, and follow emergency procedures.

Emergency numbers such as the local poison control number should be located next to the phone for immediate use.

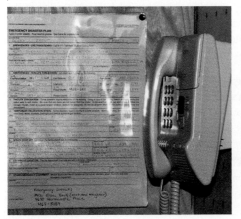

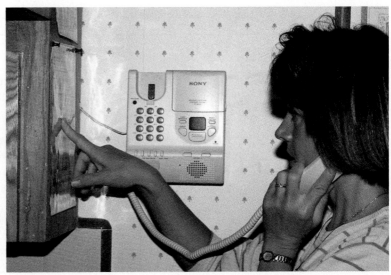

TABLE 4–1 Indicators of Emergencies

Sight

Unusual Appearances or Behaviors
- Difficulty breathing
- Unusual skin color
- Clutching the throat or chest
- Unexplained drowsiness or confusion
- Sweating for no apparent reason
- Slurred, confused, or hesitant speech

- A bone protruding from skin
- Unconsciousness
- Uneven pupils after a fall
- A rash of hives or welts that quickly appear
- A child having a seizure with no history of seizures
- Bleeding from a deep cut

Unusual Sights
- A spilled medicine container
- Broken glass
- Smoke or fire

- Downed electrical wires
- An overturned pot or pan

Hearing

Unusual Noises
- Screams, yells, moans, or calls for help
- Sudden, loud voices
- Breaking glass, crashing metal, or screeching tires
- Changes in equipment or machinery noises

- A loud crack, pop, or bang
- An explosion nearby
- A choking, gasping, or high-pitched sound from inability to get breath

Smelling

Unusual Odors
- Odors that are stronger than usual
- Unrecognizable odors

- Smoke or a burning electrical odor
- Chemical odors

Feeling

Unusual Conditions
- Cold, clammy skin
- High fever

- Skin more moist than usual, possible sweating
- A bone that feels broken

Courtesy of the American Red Cross. All Rights Reserved in All Countries.

There are a number of risks that regularly contribute to childhood injuries. These risks can be found in Table 4–2.

TABLE 4–2 Contributors to Child Care Emergencies

- Garage door injuries (family child care)
- Choking from toys and other hazards
- Falls from playground equipment
- Firearms, poisons, and bodies of water
- Burns from fires, scalding, or electric wires
- Natural disasters such as floods, earthquakes, hurricanes, and tornadoes

Figure 4–2
Illustration of Indicators of
Emergencies

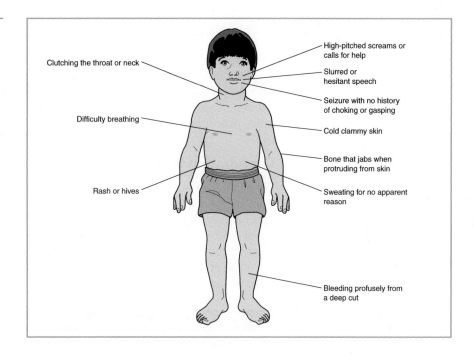

KEY CONCEPT 4.2

Identifying an Emergency

The child caregiver needs to identify what constitutes an emergency. Profuse bleeding, difficulty breathing, and ingestion or direct contact with poison always present emergency conditions that need prompt action. Other emergency indicators may be observed through the use of the senses of sight, hearing, smell, and touch. Once the caregiver has observed a questionable condition, follow-up can eliminate or determine the need for emergency response procedures.

Several dangerous items exist in this garage. How many can you find?

4.3 Basic Emergency Response Procedures

The child caregiver should be prepared for an emergency at all times. In order to lessen risk as an emergency occurs, the child caregiver should be prepared with proper planning, organizing, and responses based on knowledge and training. Copeland (1996) suggested the child caregiver establish an emergency plan similar to the medical plan "Code Blue."

Organization for Emergency

When an emergency occurs, the caregiver should remain calm and act immediately. This is hard enough to do under normal conditions, but is even more difficult in emergencies if one is not prepared to follow emergency procedures. There are a number of ways to prepare for the possibilities of emergencies and organize the child care environment to cope with them.

The procedures in Table 4–3 should be followed to prepare the environment for emergencies.

TABLE 4–3   Emergency Preparedness Procedures
• All child caregivers should have basic training and certification for first aid for children, including how to offer help to a choking victim. There should be one caregiver on site in child care who is certified in basic CPR and all other caregivers should be trained in rescue breathing.
• All emergency information forms and health records should be readily available for each child present in child care.
• Emergency numbers should be posted next to each phone. In addition, a list of vital information that the emergency operator will need should be posted.
• Have a list of backup helpers in case the caregiver must accompany a child to the hospital, away from child care.
• In case of fire, natural disasters, or other major emergencies, an evacuation plan should be prepared.
• Have available a first aid kit that is comprehensive enough for most emergencies.

Basic Training.   All child caregivers should have basic training for and certification in first aid for children, including how to offer help to a choking victim. This training should be updated as required by certification and the follow-up should be recorded to keep track. Any new caregivers should have this training before they start. One caregiver at the child care site at all times should be trained in basic CPR and should renew that certification yearly. All other caregivers should know how to perform basic rescue breathing.

All child caregivers should be familiar with the procedures to be followed for first aid and rescue breathing. Keep reminders of this training available in a notebook or on the wall where it is readily available. Posting pictures that depict emergency responses are helpful as reminders. These reminders can be invaluable in a real emergency. Reference books for this training should also be available for the caregiver to look at on a regular basis to help keep current.

Emergency Response Plan Posted at a Child Care Site

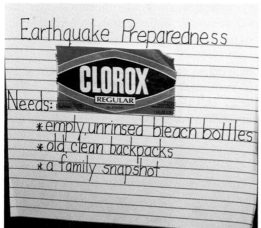

Emergency Information. All emergency information forms and health records should be readily available for each child present in child care. These forms include:

- emergency information forms filled out by parents including health information, the parents' work and home phone numbers, emergency phone numbers of other people listed by the parents in case of an emergency, the physician's phone number, the name of the hospital that has a treatment release on file, and any allergic reaction information
- a parental release form to treat the child in case of an emergency
- all "ouch" or injury reports filled out for the child
- all health records, including immunizations
- a master log of injuries that occurred in the child care environment

Emergency Numbers. Emergency numbers should be posted next to each phone. In addition, a list of vital information that the emergency operator will need should be posted as a reminder of what the caregiver needs to provide. This emergency information includes:

- caregiver's name and address
- type of emergency (e.g., burn, fall)
- where and how accident occurred
- child(ren)'s name, sex, age, and condition
- directions to child care site
- assistance already given to child
- always stay on the line until the emergency operator hangs up

The child caregiver should be informed about the local area emergency system. Knowing where the emergency care is coming from, how it is dispatched, and the location of the nearest hospital emergency room are helpful bits of information that may come in handy in an actual emergency.

A list of emergency contact numbers for all children in care should also be posted by each phone. These will be readily available and can be grabbed if an evacuation takes place or a field trip is planned.

Emergency Backup. A list of backup helpers should be available in case the caregiver must accompany a child to the hospital, away from child care. The backup person could be an off-duty child caregiver, a substitute, a friend, neighbor, or volunteer to the child care environment. It is essential that these people be familiar with the child care environment and have been introduced to the children. A familiar person adds a sense of protection to the children who may already be very upset. Leaving the children with a stranger would be more upsetting. If the caregiver must leave with an injured or ill child, she should have the peace of mind that the children are in familiar good hands.

Rescue Registration. Another part of organizing for an emergency would be to submit a "Rescue Registration Form" (see Figure 4–3) to the local fire/ rescue department, so when an emergency does occur they have adequate information that may help them in arriving as quickly as possible. It would also help them to have knowledge of the child care situation (Shallcross, 1999). Although these forms are intended for family child care, they would work equally well for centers and shared space care facilities.

Evacuation Plan. In case of fire, natural disasters, or other major emergencies, an evacuation plan should be prepared. This is a major topic and will be dealt with later in this chapter.

First Aid Kit. A first aid kit that is comprehensive enough for most emergencies should be available. The kit should be easy to access and at the same time should be out of reach of the children. It should include the items found in Table 4–4. The first aid kit should accompany the caregiver and children on any outings (walking) or any field trips (automobile). In addition to the kit, there should be ice or bags of frozen vegetables available for fast ice packs.

FAMILY CHILD CARE RESCUE REGISTRATION FORM

(Send one copy to your nearest fire/rescue station. Keep one copy for your files.)

Date of Registration _____

Provider's Name _____

Street Address _____

City/Town_____ State _____ Zip Code _____

Phone _____

Licensed Family Child Care Home?   Yes _____   No _____

License # (if Applicable) _____

Hours of Operation _____

Maximum Number of Children (Including Own Children) in Home at Any Time _____

Age Range of Children in Child Care _____

Employee(s)/Assistant(s) Present: Yes _____ No _____ If Yes, What Are Their Hours? _____

Language Commonly Spoken in Home _____

Describe where exactly in your home you provide child care. Include as much information as possible, including the type of home (single, multifamily, etc.), which floors and rooms you use. Describe entrance to child care and any additional entrances, etc. _____

_____

_____

_____

_____

Other important information, such as special needs children/adults, animals, etc.

_____

_____

_____

DESIGNED AND PREPARED BY DR. MARY ANN SHALLCROSS-SMITH, CEO
25 BLACKSTONE VALLEY PLACE
LINCOLN, RI 02865
PHONE NUMBER 401-727-8982
WWW.CHILDCARECONNECT.COM

Figure 4–3

Family Child Care Rescue Registration Form. Courtesy of Mary Ann Shallcross Smith, Ed.D. Child Care Connection.

 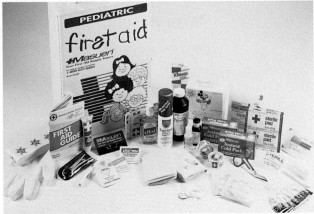

A first aid kid should accompany the caregiver and children on any outings or field trips. *(Courtesy of Masuen)*

TABLE 4–4   **First Aid Kit Checklist**
✓ *Check for:*
☐ American Red Cross first aid guide
☐ Cellular phone
☐ Emergency phone numbers for all children and adults
☐ Adhesive bandages, assorted sizes
☐ Sterile gauze pads
☐ Adhesive bandage tape
☐ Stretch gauze
☐ Eye pads
☐ Scissors
☐ Tweezers
☐ Triangular bandage with pins
☐ Nonglass thermometer
☐ Disposable latex-free gloves
☐ Syrup of ipecac
☐ Instant ice cold packs
☐ Insect sting preparation and bee sting kit for allergic reactions
☐ Items for children with special needs such as an inhaler for an asthmatic child

(continued)

	TABLE 4–4 First Aid Kit Checklist *(continued)*
☐	Liquid antibacterial hand soap
☐	Bottled water
☐	Large plastic trash bag for disposal of contaminated items
☐	Coins for pay phone, for field trip
☐	Finger splints
☐	Leather work gloves
☐	Safety goggles
☐	Duct tape
☐	Emergency management plan for children with special needs

Courtesy of the American Red Cross. All Rights Reserved in All Countries.

Order of Response

The child care environment that is organized for possibilities of an emergency situation will be better prepared to respond to an emergency when it actually occurs. When an emergency does occur, the following responses are recommended by the National Association for the Education of Young Children for the caregiver to attend to the emergency:

1. Act immediately and remain calm.
2. Stay at the scene, giving help and reassurance to the victim and other children present. If another caregiver is present, assign him the task of keeping the other children calm.
3. Assess the child with a head-to-toe check as if using Figure 4–2 and the senses check in Table 4–1.
4. Do not move a seriously injured child unless in a life-threatening situation, such as immediate danger from fire.
5. If necessary, call for emergency help. In most areas of the country this is accessed by dialing 911. The emergency numbers will be posted by the phone. If for some reason the child care environment's phone is out, send someone to the nearest pay phone, car phone, or cellular phone. A portable or cellular phone serves as an extra precaution for emergencies in a child care environment.
6. Notify parents and agree on a plan of action. If the agreement is to meet at the emergency care site because it is closer, call for backup help for the child care site. If the parent is unavailable call other emergency contacts and let the child's physician know what has happened. Call for backup child caregiver.
7. Give medication only if authorized by the local poison control. This might be **syrup of ipecac**, which will help the child vomit the poison. *This is used only in certain poisoning cases.*

Syrup of ipecac
a liquid substance used to induce vomiting

Shock

an imbalance of the circulatory system as a result of injury that includes a decrease in blood pressure, a rapid pulse, and possible unconsciousness

8. Treat child for shock, if indicated. Cover with blanket and keep warm.

9. Stay with the child until parents or emergency help arrives. Accompany child if parents are to meet the child at the emergency care site. Have backup caregiver stay with children. If parents have not arrived and there is no other caregiver present and the backup caregiver is unavailable, the caregiver must stay with the children who remain in child care. Try to reassure the child that he will be taken care of by the emergency technicians. If the caregiver knows that a parent or other emergency contact is going to be at the emergency care site let the child know that someone will be with her soon.

10. After the incident is over, fill out a report. Study it carefully to see if the incident could have been avoided through better safety practices or greater compliance with health practices.

These procedures are easy to follow if they have been reviewed frequently and are posted in several places throughout the child care site. Good planning and preparation will help the emergency situation go more smoothly.

KEY CONCEPT 4.3

Basic Emergency Response Procedures

Knowledge of and training in basic emergency response procedures are essential for the child caregiver. All caregivers should have training in basic first aid and rescue breathing and at least one caregiver per site must be certified in CPR. The caregiver should organize for emergencies and plan accordingly. Emergency numbers and information should be posted and be easily accessible. Every child care situation should have a comprehensive first aid kit that travels with the group if they leave the site for an outing or field trip. Every child caregiver should have an understanding of the 10 steps for emergency response and be able to respond in the right order.

4.4 Basic CPR and First Aid

Breathing emergencies are always life threatening. Regular breathing is effortless and comfortable. When breathing becomes an effort, causes pain, or makes unfamiliar noises these are indicators that a breathing emergency may be occurring. If a child is found unconscious it probably indicates a breathing problem. Every caregiver should be able to recognize the symptoms and be able to perform rescue breathing.

Basic CPR or Rescue Breathing

If a child is found unconscious, the caregiver should check the victim (Figure 4–4) and emergency assistance should be called. Figure 4–5 shows a caregiver administering rescue breathing.

Figure 4–4
Check the victim.

If a child appears to be choking, the airway for breathing may be partially or totally blocked. Choking in children can happen during eating or when a child puts an object in his mouth that is small enough to swallow and get caught. The usual recognized sign that a child is choking is when he grasps his throat with one or both hands. Another sign of a choking child is coughing. Forceful coughing usually indicates partial blockage. This means that the child still is able to get air in the lungs. The best procedure for the moment is to encourage the child to continue coughing and try to cough up the object. The child should be attended by a caregiver. If nothing comes out in a short time call for emergency assistance.

Figure 4–5
Give rescue breathing.

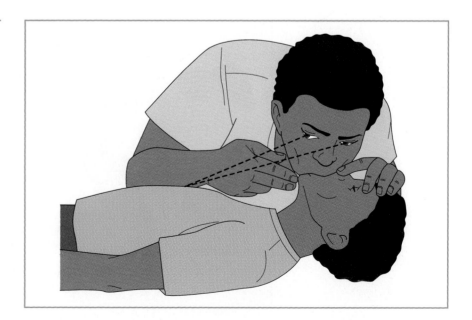

Figure 4–6
Give abdominal thrusts.

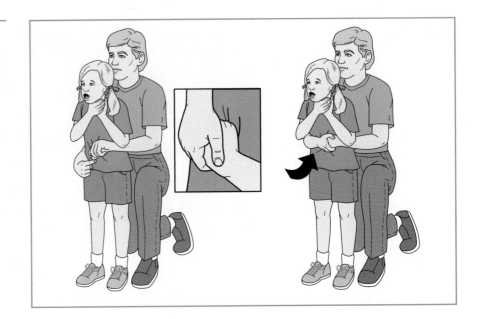

Weak coughing usually indicates the blockage is more complete. A choking child can stop breathing and lose consciousness rapidly. The caregiver should give abdominal thrusts until the object is coughed up or the child becomes unconscious (see Figure 4–6). Have someone call for emergency assistance.

If a breathing emergency exists and none of the other methods work, then the caregiver qualified in CPR should begin performing CPR (see Figure 4–7) while someone calls for emergency assistance.

Figure 4–7
Give CPR.

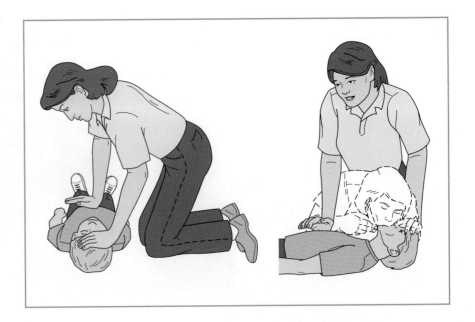

First Aid Procedures

There are many minor emergencies such as scraping a knee or bumping a head that can be taken care of easily by first aid. Other emergencies, such as a broken bone, a cut that needs stitches, or a burn that is beyond first degree, will need prompt first aid and then have the parent take the child to his own physician for further treatment. It is essential that the caregiver know how to perform basic pediatric first aid procedures. The American Red Cross and other organizations perform a service to the community by providing this training. The following are reminders for the caregiver of signs, symptoms, and responses.

Bites.   There are a number of common ways that a child can suffer bites in a child care environment. These include bites from insects and other children or animals. Insects may bite or sting a child. These commonly come from bees, wasps, ants, and ticks. Some of these bites may cause an allergic reaction in some children. When the caregiver observes those signs, the emergency medical services should be called immediately. Table 4–5 reflects those signs.

TABLE 4–5 Signs of Allergic Reaction to Insect Bites or Stings	
• Pain	• Swelling of the throat
• Itching	• Difficulty breathing
• Hives or red rash	• Partial loss of consciousness

If a child is stung and the stinger remains, the caregiver should try to remove it with tweezers. The area around the stinger must not be scraped or squeezed after removing the stinger; the caregiver must wash the area with soap and water and apply an ice pack. The same procedure is followed with an insect bite. If the child care is located in areas of the United States where ticks, scorpions, black widow spiders, and brown recluse spiders live, the caregiver should have first aid information regarding them.

For a bite from another child or an animal, the caregiver should wash the wound immediately with soap and water. If the bite breaks the skin, the child should be taken to his physician for a follow-up. The wound should be covered with a sterile gauze bandage. If heavy bleeding is caused by the wound, emergency assistance must be called.

Cuts and Other Injuries to the Skin.   Cuts and other injuries to the skin occur when children play, collide with objects, or take risks. The type of cut or degree of injury to the skin determines whether emergency assistance is necessary. If the cut is bleeding profusely or is jagged, torn, or deep, emergency assistance will be needed. Table 4–6 indicates the type of cut and the degree of injury.

Cuts and wounds not needing emergency medical treatment should be washed with soap and water and covered with a bandage. Cuts that are over an inch long or involve a large or deep wound that may cause scarring may require stitches. If there is an indication for stitches, the child should be sent to his own physician as soon as possible.

TABLE 4–6	Types of Cuts and Wounds

Abrasion. A scrape caused by contact with hard surface such as pavement or carpet. Common childhood cut.

Incision. A sharp, even cut caused by glass, knives, and other sharp objects. The depth or length of wound will determine the blood flow and the degree of seriousness.

Laceration. A jagged or torn cut caused by objects with uneven edges or by force. Tissue damage may be great.

Puncture. A hole in the skin caused by sharp objects such as a nail, thorn, or splinter.

Bruise. A discolored area of the skin caused by contact with an object, usually by force such as falling, or colliding with another object.

Adapted from American Red Cross.

Injuries Involving the Head, Mouth, and Nose. Injuries involving the head are common in child care because of falls from outdoor equipment and collisions with objects or other children. Head injuries may be minor or they may be more serious. Sometimes it is difficult to tell immediately if the injury is serious when the child remains conscious. Table 4–7 lists the symptoms of a serious head injury.

For many children, the result of a fall will be a bruise and swelling where contact was made. Have the child lie down for a while with an ice pack. Carefully observe the child's behavior for at least one hour.

Injuries to the mouth and nose can happen easily. Injuries to the mouth can be to the gums, teeth, tongue, or lips. If there is unusually heavy bleeding, emergency assistance must be summoned. Otherwise bleeding is controlled by direct pressure by holding a sterile piece of gauze where the injury has occurred. Once the bleeding has stopped for a while have the child rinse out the mouth with water. If the injury is outside the mouth, wash with soap and

Some cuts and wounds require stitches.

TABLE 4–7	Symptoms of Serious Head Injury
• Vomiting	• Change in breathing rate
• Shock	• Change in pulse rate
• Confused behavior	• Cold, clammy skin
• Unevenly dilated pupils	• Loss of consciousness

Head injuries should be carefully evaluated before they are determined serious.

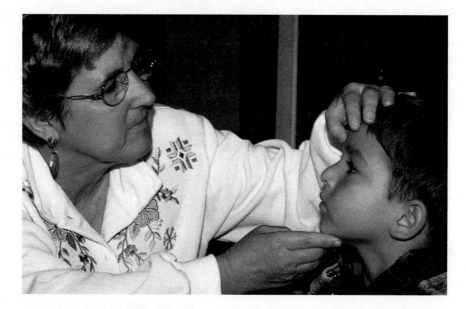

water. In case of swelling, apply an ice pack. If a child loses a tooth, find the tooth and clean it off with water. Place the tooth in a jar of milk and have the parents take the child to his dentist immediately.

Nose injuries most commonly involve nosebleeds. This is usually handled by pinching the child's nostrils together between the caregiver's thumb and forefinger. Do not tilt the head back. Have the child sit quietly. Talk quietly to the child while this is being done. Explain the procedure and ask the child if he has any questions. It normally takes approximately ten minutes for a nosebleed to stop. If it does not stop after ten minutes, the child's physician should be consulted. Some children may have a history of nosebleeds that may take longer to stop. The physician can offer further advice.

Burns. Burns come from a number of sources, such as heat, steam, chemicals, or electrical sources. The different degrees of burns are listed in Figure 4–8.

If the burn is a third degree burn, emergency medical assistance must be called immediately. There are three basic steps to care for burns. First, the burning must stop, which may entail putting out a fire and removal from the area. Never pull off clothes that are stuck to the skin. Second, cool the burn by flushing it with water. Do not use ice unless it is a very minor burn, because it may damage the tissue. Flush the skin or layer cool, wet cloths on the burn. Third, when the burn has cooled down, cover with a dry, clean, and sterile dressing. If the burn appears to be more serious than a first degree burn, have the parents take the child to his physician.

Figure 4–8
Burn Institute Burn Depth
Categories *(Courtesy of the
Burn Institute)*

BURN DEPTH CATEGORIES

DEGREE	APPEARANCE	PAIN LEVEL
1st	Pink Red	Uncomfortable
2nd	Pink - Pale May blister Moist	Marked discomfort
3rd	Pale - White Charred Dry	Painless Some pain

WHEN TO CALL FOR MEDICAL HELP:

✓ If the burn is on the face, hands or feet.

✓ If the victim is an infant, child, sick or elderly person.

✓ If swelling or infection develops.

✓ If there is marked discomfort or the burn is painless.

✓ If a third degree burn is suspected.

✓ If there is any doubt about how serious the burn is.
Burns are often more serious than they first appear.

FOR BURN EMERGENCIES
(619) 543-6503

UCSD Regional Burn Center, 24 hours a day

or 911

Burn Institute

3702 Ruffin Rd, Ste.101, San Diego, CA 92123 (619) 541-2277
© 1996

Temperature. Both extremes of temperature can have an effect on children in a child care environment. Children can get easily overheated. They may get cramps from the heat or heat exhaustion. The cramps occur in the leg muscles and the stomach. These are usually the first warning signs of trouble with heat.

Figure 4–9

Heat exhaustion results from fluid loss through perspiration; heat stroke results after sweating stops and the body's temperature continues to rise until vital organs start to fail.

Heat exhaustion involves nausea, headache, dizziness, and flushed skin. Both conditions are treated by placing the child in a cool place and having him drink lots of liquids. Sometimes applying a cool cloth to the face makes the child think he feels cooler (see Figure 4–9).

Exposure to cold may involve frostbite, but the normal conditions of child care would preclude this from occurring. However, if the caregiver observes the signs, he or she should act accordingly. Frostbite is indicated by a lack of feeling in an area where the skin is cold and may appear discolored or look waxy (see Figure 4–10). To render first aid, warm the area by soaking in warm

Figure 4–10

Frostbite results when cold temperatures freeze body cells. Hypothermia results when, over time, the body's temperature drops.

(not hot) water. Keep in warm water until it appears red and feels warm. Bandage the area with a light sterile dressing. Have the parents take the child to her physician.

Poisoning. Poisoning can occur in four ways: by ingestion, by inhalation, by absorption, and by injection such as snake venom. Under any poisoning circumstance, the first step in first aid is to call the **poison control center** in your area. Closely follow the instructions given. These instructions will include the age of child and the evidence of poisoning that has been observed. As indicated by poison control, call for emergency assistance where applicable. Table 4–8 indicates the symptoms of poisoning by ingestion, inhalation, and absorption. The symptoms in Table 4–5, on page 141, are the same symptoms that may appear after injected poisoning.

The child must not have anything to eat or drink unless instructed. If the poison has been absorbed through the skin, flush the skin with water until help arrives. If the child appears to have inhaled a poison, provide fresh air or put the child in a well-ventilated room with an open window.

Poison control center
a resource available through a phone call in case of poisoning

TABLE 4–8	**Symptoms of Poisoning**
Ingested	
• Nausea and/or vomiting	• Change in breathing
• Diarrhea	• Unconsciousness
Inhaled	
• Headache	• Difficulty breathing
• Dizziness	• Unconsciousness
Absorbed	
• Irregular breathing	• Abnormal pulse
• Headache	• Skin or eye irritations

KEY CONCEPT 4.4

Basic CPR and First Aid

It is important for the child caregiver to know basic CPR and first aid techniques because they may help save a child's life. Knowing what an emergency is and when to call for help are vital. There may be other situations where some basic first aid techniques will satisfactorily solve the situation and enable the caregiver to take care of the child's injury. Having information about illness or injury due to bites, cuts, head injuries, temperature, burns, and poisons will allow the caregiver to provide a greater degree of protection for the children in care.

4.5 Emergency Planning for Children with Special Needs

Many child care situations today include one or more children with special needs such as a chronic medical condition or allergy that may call for emergency response. The caregiver should be very familiar with what emergency might arise for each child that has special needs.

Every child with special needs should have a written emergency management plan that includes the child's diagnosis, routine measures that keep that child healthy and at less risk (Sokol-Gutierrez, 1999). It should also include emergency signs to watch for, emergency procedures that should be followed, and who should be contacted when this occurs. A duplicate copy of this plan should be kept in the first aid kit.

This information should be updated regularly (AAP, 1999).

If medication is part of the emergency response, it should also be included in a separate first aid kit. This might include inhalers for children with asthma, epinephrine for children with peanut or other allergies, and insulin for a diabetic child. It would be helpful for the caregiver to speak to the physicians of children with special needs in order to better understand how to protect and be prepared to handle emergency situations that can arise when children with special needs are in care. Parents will need to authorize the release of this information.

KEY CONCEPT 4.5

Emergency Planning for Children with Special Needs

It is essential for a caregiver to be prepared to handle emergency responses for children with special needs. An emergency management plan should be written for each child in care that has special needs. The caregiver should be prepared to respond in the proper manner. These responses may include the administering of special medications that will help a child to recover from the emergency.

4.6 Disaster Preparedness

Disaster preparedness is an essential element in addressing emergency response procedures. No caregiver ever expects a disaster to occur. However, for the safety of the children in care, it should be planned for and the environment should be organized to cope with a disaster, should it occur.

Disasters have normally been associated with acts of nature such as tornadoes, floods, and earthquakes or fires. Fires may also be caused by human carelessness. Other potential disasters might include a gas leak or noxious fumes from a chemical spill. Procedures for a chemical emergency spill or release should be prepared and posted (CDC, 1997). Another potential for a disaster might be blackouts of electricity, whether they are rolling or otherwise. Lack of electricity could affect heating, air conditioning, and refrigeration. These may be critical factors for some children with special needs. An example might be a child who needs to be on a nebulizer for which electricity is needed. Lack of refrigeration could put the food that is stored in the freezer or refrigerator at risk for growing bacteria that could cause illness. A plan for dealing with blackouts should be discussed if you live in an area where they are an issue.

We have recently observed that child care may also be impacted by an intentional human act of violence, meant to harm. The recent destruction of the World Trade Center Twin Towers in New York City greatly impacted the on-site child care. Quick action and an evacuation plan by caregivers at that child care center allowed all children in care to escape safely. The bombing of the Federal Building in Oklahoma City included an on-site child care center and there was much loss of life, including children. Child care centers have also been threatened with violence involving guns. For example, an incident in the late 1990s in Granada Hills, California, occurred when a man invaded a child care site and shot a number of children.

A planned response to violence should be talked about and agreed upon before it occurs. A code phrase such as "Ground Hog Day" should be known to all caregivers so that they could be put on the alert of danger without causing fear to the children (Sailors, 2000). If you are a family home caregiver who may be all alone with no one to assist you, you should respond by calling 911 or the rescue number in the local area.

Just as it has been suggested to all Americans that we be vigilant in our awareness of our surroundings for terrorists, the same should hold true for a child care situation. As child caregivers we are protectors of children and should do our utmost to keep their environment safe from any type of violent act, including terrorism.

The disaster most likely to occur is fire because it is more common than all of the other disasters combined. Fire can happen any time, any where, and under a number of circumstances. Because it is a common disaster, all child caregivers should prepare the environment to deal with a fire should it take place.

The location of the child care has an impact on the type of natural disaster that may occur. Tornadoes are more likely to occur in the mid-America sector, while hurricanes are more likely to occur on the southern coastal areas. Earthquakes are more apt to happen in California. Floods occur near rivers, lakes, dams, and other bodies of water. Snow, with blizzard potential, occurs throughout the country. Knowledge of the particular disasters that are likely to occur in the location of the child care is a good way to begin preparations.

Evacuation Procedures

Evacuation
removal of persons from a site where a disaster or emergency exists

Survival procedures
preparation and steps to follow to stay in place in case of disaster or weather emergency

Most disasters can be divided into two categories. The first is a disaster that requires **evacuation** and the second type of disaster calls for **survival procedures**. Many types of disaster such as fires, floods, tornadoes, and hurricanes may require evacuation. Evacuation procedures are basic. Since evacuation may be necessary in the case of fire, all caregivers should be prepared with evacuation procedures and policies that help to reinforce them.

Every child care environment should have a written plan that includes a diagram about emergency evacuation. Figure 4–11 shows a diagram of a typical child care center. Included on the diagram are the exit doors and windows,

Figure 4–11

A diagram of the child care center is an important tool to have during emergencies, particularly if the center must be evacuated.

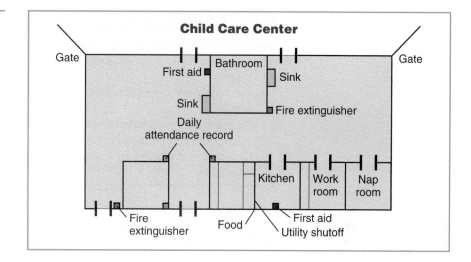

location of first aid kits, daily attendance records and fire extinguishers, utility shutoff, and location of food, clothing, and tools. Each of these items may need to be accessed.

It is essential that there be an evacuation plan that everyone concerned with the child care understands. This includes caregivers, children, and their parents. Caregivers will need to know what emergency records might have to be accessed. It is a good idea to keep copies of all children's emergency information in a fireproof, portable file because this allows the caregiver access to information about emergency contacts and so forth. If a child has a specific health challenge such as an allergy or other special needs, his records should be copied and placed in the portable file. A caregiver should be designated in charge of this file, including keeping the information current and updated.

A caregiver should be responsible for keeping daily attendance checklists for the children in care. The checklist should be frequently checked throughout the day for accuracy. This information may be needed if evacuation occurs and confusion ensues. Having a checklist will help to bring order. The child caregiver should also be familiar with emergency phone numbers and should follow the organization for emergencies.

The child caregiver should plan for emergency evacuation using several proactive strategies. These are included on Table 4–9.

TABLE 4–9   Proactive Strategies for Evacuation
• Plan two exit routes from the building. Post these throughout the building.
• Test smoke and fire alarms once a month.
• Plan a fire drill once per month.
• Plan exit strategies for removing infants and toddlers. These may be using a wagon, crib, and so forth, that can carry several children at a time and will go through a door.
• Be familiar with and post information concerning the shut-off switches for gas, water, electricity, and other utilities that may pose a safety risk.

(continued)

TABLE 4–9   Proactive Strategies for Evacuation *(continued)*

- Know how and when to use a fire extinguisher.
- Prepare children to handle emergencies by drills, discussion, and use of diagram.
- Teach children "Stop, Drop, Roll, Cool, and Call" techniques and practice with them.
- Keep a fireproof, portable file with emergency and health information for special needs of children in care.
- Choose a safe emergency shelter spot and prearrange for its use during an emergency.

The caregiver should discuss emergency procedures with parents so they are familiar with the practice and drills the children are performing. Inform parents of the emergency evacuation plans. The caregiver should let the families know where the children will be taken in case of an emergency. Having a safe emergency shelter is important and it is equally important that the parents know the location.

The caregiver should prepare the children for an evacuation emergency by having them practice fire drills, using and understanding exits. They should participate in group discussions about what to do and should understand about a meeting point outside if the building does have to be evacuated. These drills should be held once a month.

The caregiver should practice drills with infants and toddlers who may not walk or not walk well yet. These exit drills would take place in a wagon or

Caregivers and teachers should conduct practice fire drills once a month.

Figure 4–12
Stop, Drop, Roll, Cool, and Call
(Courtesy of the Burn Institute;
Note: new graphic not available
at time of this printing)

crib, just as it would under emergency conditions. Children should also be taught the "Stop, Drop, Roll, Cool, and Call" fire procedure (see Figure 4–12). They should practice it regularly on the day of a fire drill.

Survival Mode Procedures

Other disasters such as an earthquake or blizzard may call for everyone to remain in the child care environment. This isolation may last a few hours or several days. The survival mode may need to be applied in this instance. If the caregiver lives in a location that has potential for the need for survival, then he

Children should regularly practice the "Stop, drop, roll, cool, and call" procedure.

or she must be organized and properly prepared. Another reason for survival mode might be a countywide school lockdown due to gunfire or an intruder in the local area (ARC, 2001b). Certo (1995) suggests that a "pretend" emergency day be held so that children and staff are prepared to function should that emergency occur. Table 4–10 shows a sample schedule explaining the functions that can take place when simulating an emergency due to an earthquake.

TABLE 4–10 Sample Schedule for an Earthquake Emergency

Time	Activity
8:15 A.M.	Pretend quake. Children get under tables. Staff supervises then gets in doorways. Staff then simulates damage and blocks off some areas. Staff tries to keep children calm and quiet.
8:25 A.M.	Go to center of room. Count children, check attendance list. Discuss plan and assign every child a partner. Give first aid with masking tape. Simulate shutoffs of gas, electricity, and water.
8:35 A.M.	Gather emergency survival kit (see Table 4–11) and emergency information. Pretend cleanup with children helping with smaller items.
8:45 A.M.	Try to resume normalcy by having children play in small groups away from windows. Simulate aftershock. Children go under tables, staff into doorways. Try to calm and quiet children again.
9:00 A.M.	Children wash up (simulate, using very little water). Have snack bar from emergency survival kit. Drink juice. Talk about quake and plans for further survival mode.
9:15 A.M.	End of drill.

Adapted from "Helping Children and Staff Cope with Earthquakes," by D. Certo, March 1995, Child Care Information Exchange.

Table 4–11 shows an emergency survival supplies list that should be kept on hand in case of a survival mode emergency.

In case of an earthquake, it may be safer if the caregiver carries out the survival mode outdoors. The supplies kept on hand might just be moved outside. It is important to have a designated area in which care will take place.

Helping Children Cope with Disaster

The first rule of any disaster is for the caregiver to behave in a calm manner. If the caregiver is in a total panic, the children's behavior will reflect this (ARC, 2001b). Therefore, although the caregiver may feel upset or panicky, he or she should try not to show it. When disasters are planned for and practiced, physical safety is easier to cope with and handle.

Adults often tend to ignore the emotional needs of a child, once safety has been established. Children often have emotional consequences as a result of being in an emergency situation. Children are often very afraid and may not be able to verbalize it. This may be especially true in situations like earthquakes

Creating an Emergency Natural Disaster Plan for Your Child Care

Natural disasters are more widespread than one might think. In 2000, there were 44 major disasters in 32 states in this country. These disasters included tornadoes, tropical storms, severe winter and spring storms, hurricanes, floods, and wildfires. Each area has liabilities for certain natural disasters. Floods, wildfires, severe thunderstorms, and earthquakes have occurred in every state (ARC, 2001c). Hurricanes occur from Texas to Maine on the gulf and eastern seaboard. Several hailstorms happened in the midwest and tornadoes take place in 38 states. Weather-related disasters seem to be increasing due to changes in the weather pattern and ozone layer.

Mitigation is the preparation to protect people and structures from risk for natural disasters (DTI, 2001). This should occur in child care, since risk is everywhere and children may be more vulnerable to injury. Lack of adequate preparation for disaster could cause the need to replace equipment or repair buildings, requiring a program to be shut down for a time. It could also mean injury or loss of life to children or caregivers.

An example of child care using mitigation measures took place in Washington State, when Federal Emergency Management Agency (FEMA) officials helped Little Church on the Prairie Learning Center prepare for earthquakes since it was in a seismic zone. The measures, such as bolting cribs to walls and strapping water heaters in place, prevented any children from getting injured on February 28, 2001, when a quake hit (FEMA, 2001a). The project was funded in part by FEMA Hazard Mitigation funds and the rest was funded by local businesses.

To adequately prepare for a natural disaster in your local area, there are certain steps to consider. The first step would be to identify the hazards that are typical in your area (ARC, 2001b). There are several ways to do this. You could talk with emergency management people in the local area to find out the possible hazards they have dealt with, or you could look at the history of weather for the past 100 years for that area. The American Red Cross has a place on their Web site that identifies the typical disaster state by state: http://www.redcross.org/services/disaster/keepsafe/map.html. FEMA's Web site, http://www.fema.gov/, has storm watches and other information to help determine risk in your area. The national weather bureau's site, http://www.noaa.gov/, includes a large amount of information on weather, as well as forecasts for hurricanes and tropical storms.

The next step would be to develop an outline for each hazard you have found to be present in your area.

- How often does this hazard occur?
- How bad might it get?
- Where is it likely to happen?
- How long might it last?
- Is it seasonal?
- How fast might it occur?
- Will there be a warning?

You may live in an area where an earthquake has occurred once in 50 years, so it would not be a hazard for which you might develop a disaster plan. On the other hand, if you live in an area where there are severe snowstorms or tropical storms on a regular seasonal basis, you might need to be better prepared for them than you have been.

The third step would be to put together the information you have gathered as to risk for each hazard and then look to your center or family child care home for answers to possible consequences should that hazard occur. For example, if your center or family child care home is in a valley near a river and the most potential risk you found was flooding, your location points to greater degree of risk than if you were located on a hillside. To fully

(continued)

examine this step you should ask the following questions:

- ■ What are the geographical features that might put you at risk (DTI, 2001)?

- ■ Are there any features of your property that might cause risk or offer protection? For example, are there telephone or electrical wires directly above your building?

- ■ What are the available communication systems between your facility and the parents? Do you have a cell phone, and which parents have cell phones or pagers?

- ■ How many children are in care, and what are their developmental levels, i.e., can they walk or do they have to be carried?

- ■ What local resources do you have that could help in an emergency and help you plan for one?

As those questions are answered, the information will be combined with the information gathered in the first two steps and used to prioritize risk for the local area and specifically to the center or family child care home.

The last step is to think about possible scenarios for the risks that you found. What would the impact of each hazard be and how would you deal with it? At this point, you would list the needed actions and resources that would be available to help you mitigate your center or child care home to prepare for disaster. This might be a complex preparation or it could be simple. For example, if earthquakes were a great risk, then mitigation similar to the one done in Washington State would have to be performed. You would also talk about earthquakes, conduct earthquake drills for "stop, drop, and hold" with children, and find the "safe place" in every room. Adequate preparation for survival mode should take place (Copeland, 1996).

However, if the greatest risk in your area was thunder and lightning storms, the mitigation would be to be aware that a storm might be coming and to take the necessary precautions. Lightning kills approximately 100 people a year and another 300 are injured by it (Lay, 2001). You could talk to the children about lightning and read books about how it occurs (FEMA, 2000b). You could also look at the FEMA Web site for kids: http://www.fema.gov/kids (FEMA, 2001c). You will know that when you hear thunder, you need to move children inside immediately, even before it rains (Lay, 2001).

As you create a plan or plans for the natural disasters in your area, remember that children learn a lot by seeing and talking about events. You can better prepare them to deal with natural disasters if you talk about them, read books about them, look at Web sites, and discuss how to keep safe. Do not scare the children, but treat these disasters as the natural occurrences that they are and help the children to understand them before they happen.

when aftershocks occur, or tornadoes, when the wind might still be blowing. The University of Illinois Cooperative Extension has a helpful pamphlet *Children, Stress and Natural Disasters* that may help you to help the children as they try to cope with any type of disaster that has occurred (UIE, 1998).

Because children need reassurance, the caregiver must explain as clearly as possible what has occurred and the facts that are known about it. The caregiver should encourage the children to talk and express their concerns and fears. Listening to what they say about their fears and about how they feel and think about what has happened can help the children realize that this shared experience affected everyone. When things settle down, it is important for the caregiver to establish a routine. Routines give children a sense of comfort and some predictability.

TABLE 4–11   Emergency Survival Supplies Checklist

☑ *Check for:*

☐ Fire extinguisher

☐ First aid kit

☐ Flashlights and extra batteries

☐ Crescent or pipe wrench to turn off gas/water, if needed

☐ Shovel, screwdriver, 20 foot length of rope

☐ 1 gallon of water per child, 2 gallons per adult, and iodine tablets

☐ Duct tape and one package plastic sheeting

☐ Portable radio and batteries for emergency broadcasts

☐ Three- to four-day supply of dry or canned food per person, hand (nonelectric) can opener; include energy bars and juice boxes

☐ Paper plates, plastic utensils, paper cups, and paper towels

☐ Alternate cooking source, matches

☐ Blankets and extra clothing (Most child care sites already keep extra clothing for children.)

☐ Extra newspapers to wrap waste and trash

☐ Large plastic trash bags for trash and waste

☐ Three- to four-day supply of toilet paper

☐ Infant supplies—diapers, formula, food—for three to four days

☐ Three- to four-day supply of food and water for any pets present

☐ Essential medication needed for children with special needs (inhaler for asthmatic, and so forth)

☐ Safe alternate heat source (nonelectric) and fuel for it; this might be wood for a fireplace or kerosene for a room heater

It is important for the caregiver to understand that children may go through stages similar to the bereavement process in dealing with *any* disaster. The first stage occurs during and immediately after the disaster and can bring anxiety and disbelief. The second stage can appear several days or several weeks after disaster strikes. This is when the most disturbing behavior may occur and children may need the most reassurance. Boys are more likely to take a longer time to recover and display more aggressive behaviors, while girls are more distressed and are more verbal about how they feel (Saylor, Swenson, &

Fire extinguishers should be visible and all emergency exits should be clearly marked.

Stokes, 1994). The last stage may occur months later and this is the time where the children come to terms with the disaster. It is important for caregivers to understand that they may feel extra stress and strain in dealing with distressed children and need to take care of themselves, as well as the children in care (UIE, 1998).

Some children may act more clingy or revert to an earlier stage of behavior. Often children are afraid of being left alone, and this may escalate because they are not with their families. Continued reassurance will help. In most disasters help arrives quickly and the children are likely to be reunited with families in a short period of time.

If the disaster that the children are reacting to is as a result of an act of violence or terrorism, it is especially important that they get extra help in trying to cope with this disaster. There are crisis counselors available through both public and private agencies who are trained to deal with this type of traumatic event, both for children and adults. You may be having difficulty yourself, coping with your own reactions. Do not try to do this alone. Both you and the children in your care may need professional help, so do not be afraid to seek this outside support.

Fire is just one of the destructive natural disasters that can occur in any region of the country. *(Courtesy of Palm Harbor Fire Dept.)*

KEY CONCEPT 4.6

Disaster Preparedness

Child caregivers should be prepared to handle a disaster. Although chances for disasters are slim, preparation will allow for the physical safety of the children to be carried out in an organized manner. Disasters come in many forms and may be natural or man made. Regardless of the source, disasters can be prepared for by defining what type of disaster might be likely to occur in the child care location. All child caregivers should prepare for evacuation, because fire is the most likely disaster to occur. Children should practice fire drills and know all exits. Caregivers in locations where the survival mode might be needed should be prepared to handle taking care of children for several days. Caregivers should also be prepared to help children with their emotions through the disaster as well as protect their physical safety.

4.7 Implications for Caregivers

Providing prevention and protection should be a part of everyday child care. The caregivers should be prepared as best as possible to handle emergencies as they arise. In order to promote protection and prevention in the child care environment, the caregiver can act in several ways.

Education

The beginning step for the caregiver is training and education to be prepared to handle an emergency. All caregivers should know basic pediatric first aid and response breathing. At least one caregiver per child care site should have basic CPR training for infants and children. The caregiver should know how to organize for and respond to an emergency, including disasters.

The parents should be educated in prevention and emergency responses as well. The caregiver should provide written information to parents, explaining evacuation procedures, a safe place to meet, and basically how the child care environment will respond. Fire safety information can also be provided to parents. Families should create their own evacuation plans for their homes.

Children should be educated in evacuation procedures, should understand exit routes, and should know how to respond. The caregiver should arrange for the fire department to visit several times a year and explain about fires and the procedures to respond to them.

Fire drills should be given monthly to prepare and practice. The drill should be so routine that all children and caregivers are evacuated within two minutes. Children should also be taught about falls and collisions and how to avoid them. They can also be informed about how to avoid poisons in any environment. Children in areas where survival mode may be a possibility should be given practice drills in survival mode emergency situations.

Supervision

Supervision plays a major role in keeping the environment prepared to respond to emergency situations. The emergency forms should be accurate, current, copied, and ready for fast response by being in a fireproof file. Emergency information should be posted by each phone. The caregiver should make sure that everyone in the child care environment is prepared to make a call if necessary. Everyone should understand the information needed in an emergency. The caregiver should make sure that the backup list for people to help in emergencies is updated and kept current. These backup caregivers should be contacted on a monthly basis to maintain the currency of the list.

The first aid kit should be checked regularly to make sure that it is kept up-to-date. As items are used, they should be replaced. If there is a supervising caregiver, he or she should make sure all caregivers have the basic first aid and response breathing procedure training, and follow up to make sure everyone is kept current in their training. The caregiver should be prepared for evacuation or survival mode disasters. The evacuation plan should be regularly reviewed. The survival mode supplies should be periodically checked and replaced if needed.

Cultural Competence

Emergencies are unsettling to everyone. Emergencies need understanding and adequate preparation. The caregiver should provide families of children whose first language is not English with all the written emergency information in their native language whenever possible. The caregiver may need to find someone who can translate by using resources such as the local chapter of the

NAEYC or the National Family Child Care Association. Arming people with knowledge can prevent panic in emergency situations. The families can reinforce the information that the caregiver has given the children by discussing it at home.

If there are families who are recent immigrants or refugees, they may have left their home environments in emergency situations. Because of the trauma they suffered, these children may need extra support during emergencies.

KEY CONCEPT 4.7

Implications for Caregivers

Caregivers need to be prepared to handle emergencies in the child care environment. This requires education, supervision, and cultural competence. Education takes place by preparing the caregiver to be trained in basic first aid, response breathing, and organization for and response to emergencies. The caregiver needs to provide written information to families and to train children through fire drills and practice techniques for responding to emergencies.

Supervision should be provided to keep updated and current the emergency information, the backup caregiver list, the first aid kit, the evacuation plan, and the survival mode supplies. Cultural competence should be practiced by having emergency information translated into native languages so that all families are prepared to help their children respond to emergencies.

CHAPTER SUMMARY

An important part of being a caregiver is knowing how to respond in an emergency. To be prepared to respond, the caregiver defines what constitutes an emergency and what injuries necessitate first aid. The steps for taking proper action and how they are performed are established. Basic CPR and first aid are summarized. The steps for disaster preparedness are given and the difference between evacuation procedures and survival mode procedures are defined. Strategies for supervision, observation, and education are discussed.

TO GO BEYOND

In this section you will find a number of activities that you can use to apply and improve your knowledge of this chapter. There is also a thorough Online Resource that accompanies this text that can be found at http://www.early childed.delmar.com/resources/robertson/index.html. Included on this site are chapter practice quizzes, PowerPoint outlines, Web links, a discussion forum, and various other activities to help you better understand the material in this chapter. This site is updated regularly so check back often to receive the latest information about the subjects in this chapter.

Chapter Review Critical Thinking Applications

1. Describe the three factors that always indicate an emergency. Relate these to other indicators that an emergency is present.

2. Discuss the importance of preparing for an emergency. How might this preparation have helped the caregivers at the World Trade Towers on-site child care?

3. Compare the evacuation and survival modes of disaster preparedness.

As an Individual

1. Assemble a list of emergency numbers for your local area.

2. Create an emergency contact form for child care.

3. List the items that you would have in an emergency survival mode kit for the type of natural emergency most likely to occur in your local area.

As a Group

1. Discuss the items that should be kept in child care to prepare for disaster.

2. Break into smaller groups and identify and list at least five things that should be done in child care to prepare children for an emergency.

3. Role play different emergency situations, taking turns being the injured and the teacher who finds them. Have the group evaluate the actions of the teacher during the exercise.

4. Formulate a plan and safety policy that would help you deal with the gun-carrying irate ex-husband of one of your caregivers. Compare and contrast that plan to one you might have for the gun-carrying upset parent in a child custody suit.

5. What might be done for a child care environment to help children and families who do not speak English prepare for an emergency?

CHAPTER REFERENCES

American Academy of Pediatrics (AAP). (1999). Emergency preparedness for children with special health care needs. *Pediatrics, 104*(4), 53.

American Red Cross (ARC). (2001a). *Community first aid and safety.* Boston: Stay Well Publishers.

American Red Cross (ARC). (2001b). *Children and disasters.* Washington, DC: Author. Retrieved May 15, 2002, from http://redcross.org/services/disaster/beprepared/forchildren.html.

American Red Cross (ARC). (2001c). *Recommended emergency supplies for schools.* Washington, DC: Author. Retrieved May 15, 2002, from http://www.redcross.org/disaster/masters/.

American Red Cross (ARC). (2001d). What types of disaster do you need to prepare for? Retrieved May 15, 2002, from http://www.redcross.org/services/disaster/keepsafe/map.html.

Aronson, S. (2001). Reducing the risk of injury in child care. *Child Care Information Exchange, 101*(3), 64–66.

Centers for Disease Control (CDC). (1997). Evacuation plan and drills for fires, chemical emergencies and other disasters. Retrieved May 15, 2002, from http://www.cdc.gov/ncidod/hip/abc/facilit3.htm.

Certo, D. (1995, March). Helping children and staff cope with earthquakes. *Child Care Information Exchange, 95*(3), 9–12.

Chiara, S. (1995, February 2). American child care called unfit. *San Diego Union-Tribune,* A-1, 10.

Copeland, M. (1996). Code blue! Establishing a child care emergency plan. *Child Care Information Exchange, 96*(7), 17–21.

Disaster Training International (DTI). (2001). Emergency plans for centers. Retrieved May 15, 2002, from http://www.disastertraining.org/EmergPlanCenters.htm.

Federal Emergency Management Agency (FEMA). (2001a, May/June). Taking earthquake mitigation steps in Washington state keep youngsters safe. *FEMA Impact, 4*(1), 8. Retrieved May 15, 2002, from http://www.fema.gov/about/hqnltr/downloads/may01.pdf.

Federal Emergency Management Agency (FEMA). (2001b). Helping children cope with disaster. Retrieved May 15, 2002, from http://www.fema.gov/pte/children.htm.

Federal Emergency Management Agency (FEMA) (2001c). FEMA for kids. Retrieved May 15, 2002, from http://www.fema.gov/kids/.

Lay, K. (2001). Natural disasters: Are you prepared? *Healthy Child Care, 4*(1). Retrieved May 15, 2002, from http://www.healthychild.net/Articles.

Palmer, D. (1998). Prevention, preparedness, performance: What do I do and when do I do it? *Healthy Child Care, 1*(5). Retrieved May 15, 2002, from http://www.healthychild.net/Articles.

Sailors, J. (2000). Preparing for emergencies: Information and training. *Healthy Child Care, 3*(2). Retrieved May 15, 2002, from http://wwwhealthychild.net/Articles.

Saylor, C., Swenson, C., & Stokes, S. (1994). *Psychosocial issues for children and families in disasters: A guide for the primary care physician.* Elk Grove Village, IL.: American Academy of Pediatrics.

Shallcross, M. (1999). Family child care homes need health and safety training and an emergency rescue system. *Young Children, 54*(5), 70–73.

Sokol-Gutierrez, K. (1999). Being prepared: The first aid kit. *Healthy Child Care, 2*(6). Retrieved May 15, 2002, from http://www.healthychild.net/Articles.

University of Illinois Cooperative Extension (UIE). (1998). *Children, stress and natural disasters: A guide for teachers.* Urbana-Champaign, IL: Author. Retrieved May 15, 2002, from http://www.ag.uiuc.edu/~disaster/teacher/csndres2.html.

SUGGESTIONS FOR READING

Aronson, S. (1993, September). Early childhood safety checklist #1: Emergency preparedness. *Child Care Information Exchange,* 73–74.

For additional information on safety, nutrition, and health in early education, visit our Web site at **http://www.earlychilded.delmar.com**

Nutrition in Child Care

II

In this section we will discuss nutrition and how it impacts children:

5. Promoting Good Nutrition in Child Care

6. Providing Good Nutrition in Child Care

7. Menu Planning and Food Safety in Child Care

These topics will relate nutritional needs to health promotion and risk management tools that will enable the student to design nutritional policies that work well in child care settings.

Promoting Good Nutrition in Child Care

After reading this chapter, you should be able to:

5.1 Nutrition Policies

Define and discuss nutrition policies and their use as tools for the nutritional well-being of children.

5.2 Understanding Nutritional Guidelines

Describe the importance of the Dietary Guidelines for Americans, the USDA Food Guide Pyramid, the Recommended Daily Allowances, and other measures that provide guidelines for nutritional well-being.

5.3 Basic Nutrients

Define the six basic nutrients in the diet and discuss their importance to overall well-being.

5.4 Childhood Nutritional Challenges

Discuss childhood nutrition in regard to the challenges of malnutrition, undernutrition, and overnutrition.

5.5 Implications for Caregivers

Indicate the need for education, supervision, and role modeling for proper nutrition to promote health and well-being.

5.1 Nutrition Policies

Policies that ensure proper nutrition for child care are important to the overall well-being and development of children in care. Children are at risk for poor nutrition under most circumstances. Indicators of the need for nutrition policies are:

- There are 13 million children in child care every day and of those, 46 percent are infants and toddlers. All of these children will get a significant part of their weekday nutrition from child care (Briley & Roberts-Gray, 1999).

- Parents should consider the nutritional program of a center before choosing child care. This includes meals and snacks as well as the environment for eating and the nutrition education program. (Nicklas, 2001).

- Many children fail to consume enough vegetables, bread, cereal, pasta, and rice while in child care (Bruening, Gilbride, Passannante, & McClowry, 1999).

- The low degree of staff nutritional knowledge has a direct effect on menu planning, food selection, and role modeling (Briley, Roberts-Gray, & Simpson, 1994).

- Only 2 percent of children actually eat according to the Food Guide Pyramid and 16 percent fail to meet any of the number of servings required at any level (Aronson, 2000).

- Child care programs have difficulty achieving nutrition standards (Briley & Roberts-Gray, 1999; Rolls, Engell, & Birch, 2000).

All caregivers should have a basic knowledge of nutrition. This information may be used to model proper food selection, create menus to serve the children, or teach nutrition to children and their parents. Food and nutrition should be an integral part of the promotion of health.

Caregivers need to create nutritional policies that will support the growth, health, and well-being of the children in their care. The four major goals for nutritional policies are similar to the policies for health and safety. They include:

1. maximizing nutritional status
2. minimizing nutritional risk
3. using nutritional education as a tool
4. recognizing the importance of nutritional guidelines

Nutritional policies may include menu planning guidelines, food selection, and preparation practices. These policies should be clearly written and should reflect nutrition as part of the promotion of health.

Nutritional policies should encompass the following:

- *Nutritional Guidelines:* understanding nutritional guidelines for optimum nutritional well-being

- *Basic Nutrients:* understanding the basic **nutrients**, their sources, and the problems related to deficiencies

- *Nutritional Challenges:* awareness of specific nutritional challenges present in early childhood and how these challenges put children at risk

Nutrients

substances found in foods that provide for the growth, development, maintenance, and repair of the body

■ *Implications for Caregivers:* methods and practices for promoting good nutrition through education, role modeling, and supervision to provide minimum nutritional risk and maximum health

KEY CONCEPT 5.1

Nutrition Policy

Nutritional policies should be created for child care. These policies should use nutritional guidelines, apply basic nutrition, and address specific challenges of childhood nutrition. These policies should assist the caregiver with nutrition education, role modeling, supervision, and observation.

5.2 Understanding Nutritional Guidelines

Adequate nutrition during childhood is necessary to maintain overall health and to provide for growth. A number of nutritional guidelines or strategies for good health have been established to help accomplish this task. In the past, the responsibility for following these recommendations fell to the parents because young children ate most of their meals at home. The past 20 years have presented major societal shifts in the number of working mothers and the number of single parent families. The resulting numbers of children in child care has risen dramatically. In the United States, child caregivers are helping to meet at least part of the nutritional needs of 60 percent of children under five years and millions of school-aged children (Briley & Roberts-Gray, 1999).

Although some families of school-aged children depend on the children caring for themselves, the majority of these children are in some form of care. It is essential that the caregiver understand nutrition regardless of whether the care is center based, school based, family child care, or nanny care. Since so many children are cared for by others, the transfer of responsibility for adequate nutrition has at least partially shifted from the home to child care. The more hours the child is in care, the greater the caregiver's responsibility for providing adequate nutrition for growth and maintenance of health. Established nutritional guidelines help the caregiver plan for adequate nutrition in menu selection. These guidelines and good nutritional practices can be shared with the children and their parents.

Dietary Guidelines for Americans

Dietary Guidelines for Americans forms the basis for nutrition policies in the United States. It is considered an important part of the standard for any federal program that deals with food and nutrition. The guidelines were completely revised in 2000. Table 5–1 highlights the basic guidelines.

The Food Guide Pyramid for Young Children

The U.S. Department of Agriculture introduced a Food Guide for children between the ages of two and six years of age. This guide for children supplements the general guide already available (see Appendix D). This pictorial format establishes easy to understand good daily nutritional habits based on the dietary guidelines (see Table 5–1, Figure 5–1) (Mydlenski, 2000).

TABLE 5–1	**Dietary Guidelines for Americans**
	The ABC's of Nutritional Recommendations

Aim for fitness
- Aim for a healthy weight
- Be physically active

Build a healthy base
- Let the Pyramid guide your food choices
- Eat a variety of grains daily, especially whole grains
- Eat a variety of fruits and vegetables daily
- Keep foods safe to eat

Choose sensibly
- Choose a diet that is low in saturated fat and cholesterol and moderate in total fat
- Choose beverages and foods to moderate your intake of sugar
- Choose and prepare foods with less salt

Overnutrition

excess intake of foods that provide more than adequate amounts of the substances needed for growth, development, maintenance, and repair of the body, often resulting in overweight

Undernutrition

less than adequate intake of foods that provide the substances needed for growth, development, maintenance, and repair of the body

Malnutrition

inadequate nutrition as a result of improper diet or lack of food

The Food Guide Pyramid focuses on the total diet and addresses the aspect of overnutrition as well as undernutrition. These are both forms of malnutrition. The Food Guide Pyramid supports the dietary guidelines by keying in on moderation of fats and sugars as well as supporting a varied diet consisting of a higher proportion of fruits, vegetables, and grains (Johnson & Kennedy, 2000).

The information in the pyramid is organized by food choice levels from bottom to top. The levels of choices relate to the number of servings needed for

Figure 5–1

Food Guide Pyramid for Young Children *(Courtesy of the U.S. Department of Agriculture)*

Nutrition education includes teaching children about the basic food groups. Graphic representations of these groups using flannelboards or posters are good tools for teaching the importance of proper nutrition. What are some other ways to teach children about nutrition?

adequate nutrition. The Food Guide Pyramid helps people of all ages and educational levels compare their food intake with the pyramid and make necessary changes at any level to improve their diet and nutritional well-being. This is probably the easiest overall guideline to proper nutrition.

Level One. The bread, cereal, rice, and pasta group includes whole grain breads, bagels, muffins, and cereals, as well as pastas, tortillas, pita, a variety of rice, and other ethnic breads and grains. This group is the major source of carbohydrates in our diet. Six servings should be consumed daily.

Typical Level One Foods
(Courtesy of the U.S. Department of Agriculture)

Level Two. Level Two consists of two subgroups: the vegetable group and the fruit group. The vegetable group includes a wide variety of vegetable choices, from alfalfa sprouts to zucchini. Three servings per day are encouraged. Soups and stews can be counted as part of the daily vegetable servings.

Fruits, fruit juices, fruit leathers, and dried fruits such as banana chips and cranraisins comprise the fruit group. Fruits contain many of the vitamins and minerals we need in our diet. Two servings of fruit are needed daily.

Typical Level Two Foods
(Courtesy of the U.S. Department of Agriculture)

Level Three.   Level Three consists of two subgroups: the milk, yogurt, and cheese group and the meat, poultry, fish, dry beans, eggs, and nuts group. The milk, yogurt, and cheese group is the major source of calcium in our diet. Selection of low-fat varieties of milk, yogurts, and cheeses is encouraged. Ice cream, custard, and pudding are included in the milk, yogurt, and cheese group.

The meat, poultry, fish, dry beans, eggs, and nuts group is the major source of protein in our diet. Low-fat selections of meat, poultry, and fish are encouraged. The number of eggs per week should be limited to four and dry beans and nuts should be used occasionally as an alternative to meats. Both subgroups at Level Four are also sources of fats in our diet.

Typical Level Three Foods
(Courtesy of the U.S. Department of Agriculture)

Level Four.   Level Four consists of fats, oils, and sweets, including margarine, butter, and liquid oils; jams, jellies, and candy; and reduced fat candy bars. This group should be used in moderation to cut down on fats and sugar consumption that add nothing but empty calories to the diet.

Typical Level Four Foods
(Courtesy of the U.S. Department of Agriculture)

Reference Daily Intake

The U.S. Reference Daily Intake (U.S. RDI) are the suggested amounts of essential nutrients such as protein, vitamins, and minerals that should be consumed in foods daily to ensure good health. The Daily Reference Values (DRV) have been established for **macronutrients**, cholesterol, sodium, and potassium.

RDIs are most commonly found on food labels (Figure 5–2) on packaged products where manufacturers are required to list nutrition facts. The information is broken down on a per serving basis. Calories and amounts of fat, cholesterol, carbohydrates, protein, vitamin A, vitamin B (thiamine, riboflavin, and niacin), vitamin C, vitamin D, sodium, and other essential minerals such as calcium and iron are listed.

Macronutrients

major nutrients needed for the body, such as fats, protein, and carbohydrates

Figure 5–2

Food Label *(Courtesy of U.S. Food and Drug Administration)*

Nutrition Facts

Serving Size 1/2 cup (114g)
Servings Per Container 4

Amount Per Serving

Calories 90	Calories from Fat 30

	% Daily Value*
Total Fat 3g	**5%**
Saturated Fat 0g	**0%**
Cholesterol 0mg	**0%**
Sodium 300mg	**13%**
Total Carbohydrate 13g	**4%**
Dietary Fiber 3g	**12%**
Sugars 3g	
Protein 3g	

Vitamin A	80%	•	Vitamin C	60%
Calcium	4%	•	Iron	4%

*Percent Daily Values are based on a 2,000 calorie diet. Your daily values may be higher or lower depending on your calorie needs:

	Calories	2,000	2,500
Total Fat	Less than	65g	80g
Sat Fat	Less than	20g	25g
Cholesterol	Less than	300mg	300mg
Sodium	Less than	2,400mg	2,400mg
Total Carbohydrate		300g	375g
Dietary Fiber		25g	30g

Calories per gram:
Fat 9 • Carbohydrate 4 • Protein 4

Healthy People 2010

Many of the objectives included in Healthy People 2010 are aimed at decreasing the prevalence of overweight in both adults and children, increasing intake of fruits and vegetables, and decreasing intake of sodium, sugar, and fat. It also addresses reducing growth retardation and iron deficiency in children (Tate & Patrick, 2000).

Child and Adult Care Food Program

The Child and Adult Care Food Program (CACFP) of the U.S. Department of Agriculture enables family child care homes as well as nonprofit child care centers to be reimbursed for creating menus and serving meals that meet dietary guidelines established by this program. These dietary guidelines are based on the RDIs and the Dietary Guidelines for Americans. Recommended meal patterns are provided by CACFP.

Child care centers or regulated family child care homes that participate in the CACFP are required to follow meal pattern guidelines (see Table 7-1, page 240), engage in some training, and utilize food and nutrition handbooks. Investigations in the past have shown that as many as 90 percent of observed

Television has become a major challenge to healthy lifestyles. Television use in the preschool and home care setting should be kept to a minimum.

participating centers fell short of the recommended CACFP standards (Briley, Roberts-Gray, & Rowe, 1993). The American Dietetic Association has stated that no extensive evaluations have been done to assess the effectiveness of CACFP.

KEY CONCEPT 5.2

Nutritional Guidelines

An increasing number of children rely on child care to provide a good portion of their nutritional needs. Caregivers should be knowledgeable about nutritional guidelines as they plan menus and provide food to the children in care. The Food Guide Pyramid is the easiest to understand and will help the child caregiver educate children and their parents about nutrition. Dietary Guidelines for Americans, the Reference Daily Intake, Healthy People 2010, and the Child and Adult Care Food Program also provide helpful information for the caregiver.

5.3 Basic Nutrients

The basic nutrients found in food perform all the functions needed to help the body grow, repair, regulate, and maintain itself. There are six sources of nutrients: carbohydrates, fats, protein, vitamins, minerals, and water. Each source of nutrients performs specific functions. The two major functions by which nutrients can be categorized are the energy nutrients and the supporting nutrients. Energy nutrients are fats, carbohydrates, and protein; supporting nutrients are vitamins, minerals, and water.

Energy Nutrients

Energy is needed to maintain life, support growth, regulate body processes, and perform voluntary activities. We measure the energy needs of our bodies

Calories

the unit of measurement for the energy found in foods

Basal metabolism

the amount of energy used by the body while at rest

Metabolism

chemical changes that take place as nutrients are taken into the blood, processed and absorbed by the blood, or eliminated from the body

in terms of **calories**. The number of calories each body needs depends on the **basal metabolism**, **metabolism** of food, growth and physical activity, and age of that body. Calories are supplied to the body from three major nutrients:

■ fats supply 9 calories per gram
■ carbohydrates supply 4 calories per gram
■ proteins supply 4 calories per gram

Carbohydrates, fats, and protein provide the energy needed to run the body and provide the materials to help the body grow and maintain its functions. These energy providers are often referred to as macronutrients.

Carbohydrates. Carbohydrates are the first source of energy the body uses and are the major source of energy for the central nervous system. Carbohydrates are made up of carbon, hydrogen, and oxygen. Carbohydrates, protein, and fats provide energy to the body in the form of calories. If our bodies do not have carbohydrates we cannot properly use the other energy sources of protein and fat. Carbohydrates provide a slow, steady source of energy necessary for utilization of other nutrients in the body. An example would be that carbohydrates supply energy so that protein can be used for growth and maintenance of body cells.

Carbohydrates come in two forms, simple and complex. Simple carbohydrates include the sugars, while complex carbohydrates are made up of strings of sugars in the form of starch or fiber. Simple carbohydrates are found in various forms including lactose, which is found in milk. Lactose from breast milk or formula supplies the major source of carbohydrates for infants. Complex carbohydrates are generally found in Level Two foods such as grains, cereals, and pasta. They are also found in fruits, vegetables, and beans. The majority of our diet should come from this source.

A diet with insufficient amounts of carbohydrates causes the body to use fats or proteins for the energy it needs, thus robbing it of the functions these two nutrients provide. Growth and maintenance of the body will be at risk. A child needs carbohydrates to fuel the work of muscles. If a child appears list-

Foods high in fat but low in nutritional value, such as fast food, should be limited in a child's diet. It is important to remember, however, that adequate amounts of fat are important for children's normal growth and development, particularly for infants and children under the age of two.

less and tired, it may be that the carbohydrate level is low. This fuel is especially important to get the day started, so a breakfast that includes complex carbohydrates is a good source to start the day with energy.

Fats. Fats are considered to be the body's second source of energy. Fat also supplies essential fatty acids that are critical for proper growth of children. Other functions include cushioning of organs, maintaining body temperature, promoting healthy skin, and helping fat-soluble vitamins be carried throughout the body. Fat is in the membrane of every cell in the body. Fats also help regulate the metabolism of **cholesterol** in the body. Body fat also provides a good energy reserve.

Cholesterol

a steroid or fatty alcohol found in animal fats that is produced by the liver of the animal

Intake of fat is an important part of every child's diet. However, it should be carefully monitored not to exceed 30 percent of the diet as recommended in the Dietary Guidelines and the Reference Daily Intake. Fat is an essential part of promoting brain development and growth in infants and young children. Infants and children under the age of two need greater amounts of fat than the guidelines recommend. The American Academy of Pediatrics and the Dietary Guidelines for Americans both advise against the restriction of fat in the diet for the first two years of life (AAP, 1998; Johnson & Kennedy, 2000).

The major source of fats come from Level Three and Level Four foods. Sources are both plant and animal. Primary animal sources include red meats, fish, poultry, eggs, and milk products, which account for about 58 percent of the fat in our diets. Plant sources such as corn, safflower, canola, palm, and coconut oils provide the remaining 42 percent of the fat found in a typical diet. Table 5–2 lists the different types of fats.

The Reference Daily Intake for fat consumption takes into consideration the risk of excess fat. Saturated fats are of particular concern because they contribute to high blood cholesterol, which influences the development of coronary heart disease. All animal fats are saturated; most vegetable sources of fat are either polyunsaturated or monounsaturated. To help lower the fat in the diet, it is important to choose vegetable sources of fat more often than animal fats (see Figures 5–3 and 5–4).

TABLE 5–2   Types of Fats

- Polyunsaturated fats
  Function: Lowers blood cholesterol, decreases tendency of blood to clot
  Sources: Plants and plant oils (sunflower, corn, canola) and fish
  RDI: 10 percent or less of total calories
- Monounsaturated fats
  Function: Neutral—neither raises nor lowers blood cholesterol
  Sources: Olives, peanuts, nuts, avocado
  RDI: 10 percent of total calories
- Saturated fats
  Function: Raises blood cholesterol, increases tendency of blood to clot
  Sources: Animals, animal fats, butter, shortening, nuts, cheese, coconut, coconut and palm oil, ice cream
  RDI: 10 percent or less of total calories

Figure 5–3

Chart of Fats (Comparison) *(Data from Proctor & Gamble and Reeves, J. B., & Weibrauch, J. L., [1979]. Composition of foods, agriculture handbook no. 8-4. Washington, DC: U.S. Department of Agriculture)*

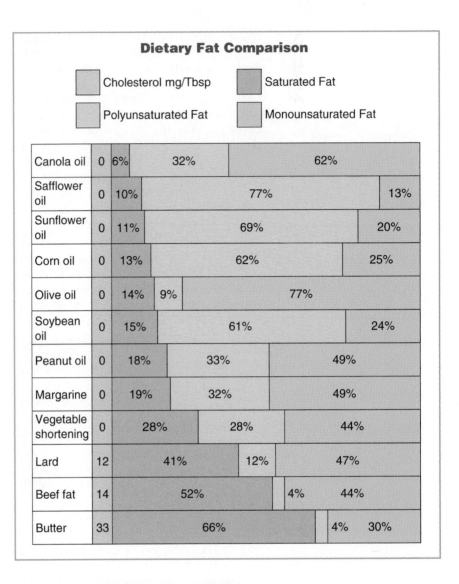

Dietary Fat Comparison

Legend:
- Cholesterol mg/Tbsp
- Saturated Fat
- Polyunsaturated Fat
- Monounsaturated Fat

	Cholesterol	Saturated	Polyunsaturated	Monounsaturated
Canola oil	0	6%	32%	62%
Safflower oil	0	10%	77%	13%
Sunflower oil	0	11%	69%	20%
Corn oil	0	13%	62%	25%
Olive oil	0	14%	9%	77%
Soybean oil	0	15%	61%	24%
Peanut oil	0	18%	33%	49%
Margarine	0	19%	32%	49%
Vegetable shortening	0	28%	28%	44%
Lard	12	41%	12%	47%
Beef fat	14	52%	4%	44%
Butter	33	66%	4%	30%

Figure 5–4

Saturated vs. Unsaturated Fats *(From Hubbard, M., & Robertson, C. [1989]. Cholesterol countdown. San Diego, CA: Pegasus Press)*

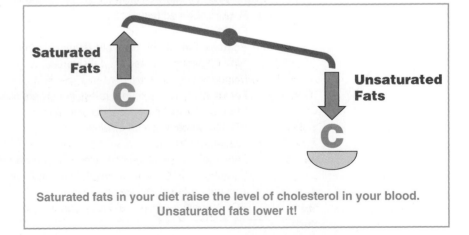

Saturated Fats

Unsaturated Fats

Saturated fats in your diet raise the level of cholesterol in your blood. Unsaturated fats lower it!

Enzymes

organic substances produced in body cells that can cause changes in other substances through catalytic reaction

Hormones

chemical substances formed in one organ of the body and carried to another organ or tissue where they have specific effects

Antibodies

proteins produced in the body to react with antigens in order to neutralize or react with the antigen to protect the body

Amino acids

organic compounds containing carbon, hydrogen, oxygen, and nitrogen; the key components of proteins

Complete protein

protein that contains all essential amino acids

Micronutrients

supporting nutrients, such as vitamins, minerals, and water, needed by the body

Protein.   Protein, the third source of energy, is the major building block in our bodies. It is found in every cell and is necessary for growth and maintenance. Any new tissue is put together from proteins. Any growth or regeneration needs proteins to accomplish the task. Protein builds new cells and aids in the repair of damaged tissue. It is used to form enzymes that aid in digestion and provides hormones and antibodies that increase resistance to infection. Enzymes, some hormones, and antibodies are all types of proteins. Enzymes promote certain chemical reactions in the body, such as breaking down starches to aid in digestion. Hormones such as thyroxin help the body to regulate itself. Antibodies aid the immune system to prevent invasion of bacteria and other threats.

Protein is made of amino acids, nine of which are essential for tissue growth, repair, and maintenance. There are 21 different types of amino acids present. For a food to be considered complete protein, it must provide all of the nine essential amino acids. Foods from animal sources are the only complete protein foods by themselves.

To obtain adequate protein with the essential amino acids in a vegetarian diet, foods can be combined to provide complete protein. For example, a grain food would be combined with a legume food. Additions of egg or milk products help to provide complete protein in a vegetarian diet. Vegetarian diets should be carefully monitored to ensure adequate intake of nutrients.

A diet that is deficient in protein causes stunted growth in children and makes them easily fatigued and irritable. Lack of protein also makes children susceptible to infection and slow to recover or repair a wound. It is recommended that diets have 12 percent protein to be sufficient.

Helper Nutrients

The energy nutrients depend on the helper nutrients, or micronutrients, to perform their functions and to regulate the body's metabolism. Micronutrients, which are classified as vitamins, minerals, and water, must be present in sufficient quantities for the energy nutrients to perform properly. Micronutrients do not contain calories. They each perform specific functions and are found in many foods.

Vitamins.   Vitamins are essential nutrients needed by the body in small amounts and are categorized into two groups. Fat soluble vitamins attach to fats to travel throughout the body and can be stored in the body. Water soluble vitamins travel easily through the body with water and cannot be stored in the body, so they must be replaced daily (see Figure 5–5).

The fat soluble vitamins are vitamin A, vitamin D, vitamin E, and vitamin K. These are stored in the body in the liver and build up over time, so too much can produce toxic effects.

Vitamin A

- ▪ is important for good vision, healthy skin and membranes in the body, and strong bones
- ▪ lack of vitamin A can cause poor bones and tooth enamel growth, rough skin, and night blindness
- ▪ is most commonly found in foods in the form of retinol and carotene

Figure 5–5
Fat and Water Soluble Vitamins

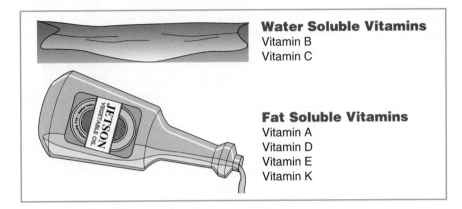

Water Soluble Vitamins
Vitamin B
Vitamin C

Fat Soluble Vitamins
Vitamin A
Vitamin D
Vitamin E
Vitamin K

- ■ retinol is most commonly found in the fat of animal products such as fish, milk, eggs, and liver
- ■ carotene is most commonly found in yellow, orange, and green leafy vegetables, and yellow and orange fruits
- ■ carotene, also known as beta-carotene, is considered an antioxidant that strengthens the immune system and might be a deterrent to cancer

Vitamin D

- ■ is needed to help calcium make strong bones and teeth
- ■ is produced naturally in the skin when it gets sunshine and is often referred to as the "sunshine" vitamin
- ■ is produced by a reaction of the ultraviolet rays with cholesterol in the skin
- ■ to ensure vitamin D consumption is adequate in all parts of the country at all times of the year, vitamin D is added to most milk
- ■ is also found in fatty fish, liver, eggs, and butter
- ■ insufficient amounts of vitamin D can lead to rickets, a disease in children that stunts bone growth

Vitamin E

- ■ helps preserve cell tissues
- ■ protects red blood cells and the lungs
- ■ is considered an antioxidant
- ■ can be found in whole grain cereals, vegetable oils, and a wide variety of foods so most people get enough
- ■ there are no known effects of vitamin E deficiency

Vitamin K

- ■ is needed for normal blood clotting.
- ■ lack of vitamin K has been known to cause hemorrhaging
- ■ is found in dark green leafy vegetables and whole grains, and is also made in our bodies

Water soluble vitamins include the B vitamins and vitamin C. There are numerous B vitamins, but the most important for children are thiamin (B_1), riboflavin (B_2), niacin and folicin, more commonly known as folic acid. These B vitamins work with the enzymes in the body to release the energy from food.

Thiamin

- is essential for carbohydrate metabolism so that energy can be released and used
- contributes to the normal functioning of the nervous system
- good sources are lean pork, nuts, grains, and green leafy vegetables
- fatigue and irritability may be signs of a lack of thiamin in the diet

Riboflavin

- is essential for the metabolism of all the energy sources
- promotes healthy skin and eyes, and clear vision
- good sources of riboflavin include milk products, eggs, legumes, liver, and leafy vegetables
- lack of riboflavin can cause skin and digestive disturbances, as well as sensitivity to light

Niacin

- is needed for release of energy from all the energy sources, as well as helping fat synthesis and tissue respiration
- helps promote healthy nerves and skin and aids in digestion
- meat, poultry, fish, peanuts, liver, whole grains, enriched cereals, and green leafy vegetables are good sources of niacin
- insufficient amounts of niacin can cause conditions known as pellagra or the Four Ds: dermatitis, diarrhea, dementia, and death

Folic Acid

- is required for normal growth, helps prevent anemia, and is an important factor in reproduction
- helps to form red and white blood cells and is necessary for proper cell division
- during pregnancy, infancy, and early childhood when rapid cell division is occurring, sufficient amounts of folic acid is crucial. In pregnant women it can help to prevent neural tube defects or damage to the fetus.
- good sources of folacin include dark green leafy vegetables, legumes, liver, and nuts
- anemia might be the result if there is insufficient folic acid in the diet

Vitamin C

- is an antioxidant that helps fight disease and protect the body by preventing oxidation of molecules that could help create free radicals

- assists with the formation and maintenance of collagen that gives support and shape to the body
- helps in healing wounds and maintaining healthy blood vessels
- prevents scurvy in humans
- stimulates the immune system to prevent infections
- good sources are citrus fruits, cabbage, kale, brussels sprouts, broccoli, bell peppers, black currants, and turnip greens

Minerals. Minerals help the metabolic process and regulate body fluids. There are 25 minerals that help the body to perform. The minerals that are especially important for children are calcium, phosphorous, iron, sodium, magnesium, potassium, fluoride, and zinc.

Calcium

- is the most important mineral because it is present in all bones and teeth. Since the childhood years are also the bone-forming years, it is critical to have enough calcium.
- helps to regulate the body systems, promotes normal nerve transmission, and functions in normal muscle contraction and relaxation
- major sources of calcium are milk and dairy products and dark green, leafy vegetables

Phosphorous

- is combined with calcium in the bones and teeth
- helps to transport fat and provides enzymes for energy metabolism
- is found in milk products, meat, poultry, fish, whole grain cereals, and legumes

Iron

- combines with protein to form red blood cells and carry oxygen to the blood
- helps the immune system resist infection and helps enzymes release energy to the body
- liver, green leafy vegetables, whole grains, legumes, meats, and dried fruits are good sources of iron
- a deficiency of iron causes anemia and fatigue
- anemia among children is one of the major health problems in the United States

Sodium

- is important for fluid balance in the body. This balance occurs between the inside and outside of the body's cells.
- contributes to the stimulation of nerves and muscle contraction
- sources are salt, baking soda, celery, milk, eggs, meats, poultry, and fish. Canned foods are another source. Even if we never used salt on our foods, our diets would have sufficient amounts of sodium from all the foods that have it.

Magnesium

- is present in bones and teeth
- is important for the release of energy from the energy nutrients
- helps transmit nerve impulses and helps muscles contract
- is found in milk, meat, green leafy vegetables, whole grain cereals, nuts, seafood, and legumes

Potassium

- is important for the metabolism of protein and carbohydrates
- helps maintain water balance in the body and transmits nerve impulses
- is the critical factor in maintaining heartbeat
- during exercise or in hot weather, when sweating occurs, potassium loss can result, so it should be replaced through food or drink
- sources are vegetables, fruit juices, and fruits, especially bananas and tomatoes, and is also found in meats and cereals

Fluoride

- helps to promote strength of bone and tooth structure and is important in preventing tooth decay
- is found in fish and fluoridated water. Many water systems in the United States add fluoride to the water to help prevent tooth decay.
- some fluoridated water is too high in fluoride for many young children. Overfluoridation can cause pitting and discoloration of teeth.

Zinc

- is necessary for healing of wounds, fetal development, proper growth, and helps the body properly use vitamin A
- can be found in whole grains and meats and meat products
- seems to be one of the RDIs that child care has a difficult time providing in sufficient amounts (Skinner et al., 1999)

Milk is a primary source of calcium, an important mineral for bone and teeth development.

Encourage children to drink water when they are thirsty. This will make them more likely to turn to water instead of sugary fruit drinks.

Water. Water is necessary to sustain life and is the most indispensable nutrient we have. It comprises about 70 percent of the body and transports nutrients and oxygen. Water also protects organs, regulates temperature, and helps to eliminate waste products. How much water a body needs on a daily basis depends on body metabolism, age, and outside temperature.

Most of the water loss in the body is due to urination or evaporation from the skin or respiratory tract. A small amount of water is lost through fecal elimination. Larger than normal losses such as may occur with increased sweating from exercise or heat may be dangerous. This is especially important for infants and young children. Loss of water from fever, diarrhea, or vomiting can occur quickly and cause the infant or child to become dehydrated. This condition can turn serious very quickly, so children should be monitored for their water intake. Early signs of fluid loss include fewer wet diapers, less urination, or dark urine. The tongue may also be coated with a film instead of looking moist. There may also be nausea, clammy skin, and muscle cramping. If these occur, medical attention should be sought.

Water is present in most foods found in nature. Fruits and vegetables have it in large amounts. Fruit juices can be a major source of water for older infants and young children. Fruit juice intake should be limited to four to six ounces per day for children under six and between eight and twelve ounces for older children (AAP, 2001). Children should be encouraged to drink water on a regular basis. Children who learn to drink water at an early age are more likely to turn to water to quench their thirst instead of sugary drinks.

KEY CONCEPT 5.3

Basic Nutrients

Foods provide the basic nutrients needed by the body to grow, repair, regulate, and maintain itself. There are six sources of nutrients, which are divided into two categories. The energy nutrients—carbohydrates, fats, and protein—provide the calories needed to run the body and the materials needed for growth and maintenance. Protein is the major building block for the body. The helper nutrients—vitamins, minerals, and water—help the energy nutrients perform their functions and help regulate the body's metabolism. A diet that follows the Food Guide Pyramid and considers the RDI should provide all the basic nutrients in sufficient quantities.

5.4 Childhood Nutritional Challenges

Social changes such as increases in one-parent families, dual-career families, poverty, and homelessness have a negative impact on the food selection and nutrition of children in this country ("Position of the American Dietetic Association," 1993). Nutritional challenges that pose risks to children's health can be related to malnutrition, which can be either overnutrition or undernutrition. These risks may appear in the form of growth retardation, hunger, obesity, dental disease, and iron deficiency anemia (Splett & Story, 1991). In addition, diets high in sodium and fat can lead to the development of hypertension and high levels of cholesterol later in life. Another risk factor is food allergies.

Some of the societal changes affecting the family relate to the lack of environmental support needed for proper growth. More than one-fourth of the children in the United States live in a single parent household. There are 500,000 children born to teenage mothers every year, of whom 70 percent are unmarried. More than half of the children in single parent families are living at the poverty level (Children's Defense Fund, 2001).

Other children may be at the poverty level or even homeless due to unemployment or underemployment. Families with children represent the fastest growing portion of the homeless population. It is estimated that more than 100,000 children are homeless every day. Half of these are reported to be under six years of age (Taylor & Koblinsky, 1994).

During the past two decades the number of working mothers has greatly increased. More than 13 million children under the age of six have mothers who work outside the home. These families are turning to child care for their children in increasing numbers. Child care often fails to meet the nutritional needs of children (Briley, Roberts-Gray, & Rowe, 1993).

Hunger and Malnutrition and Their Effects

Hunger is defined as a chronic shortage of necessary nutrients. According to that definition, four million children are experiencing hunger. (Evers, 2000). Another 8 percent of children may be experiencing food insecurity, which means that they do not always have access to enough food to meet basic needs. The prevalence of food insecurity and hunger varies through the United States. It is most common in the eleven states that make up the west coast and southern border of this country, as well as the District of Columbia (Nord, Jemison & Bickel, 1999).

Hunger can disrupt the healthy development of children. It can lead to weigh loss, growth retardation, weakened resistance to disease, and cognitive difficulties. Malnutrition from hunger or food insecurity can be especially harmful to children in the first years of life when their bodies and brains are developing rapidly (Brown & Marcotte, 1999). Recent findings have shown that malnutrition's effects on brain development of very young children can be reversed (Brown & Pollitt, 1996). These studies have also found that healthy children over two years of age can be adversely affected if they become malnourished. This reverses the former theory that malnourishment to children under two is always permanent and that these are the only years to be concerned about.

Starvation and malnutrition is not something that happens only in other parts of the world. Children in U.S. cities are especially at risk, as the number of single parent families below the poverty level continues to rise.

Children with chronic health conditions, physical handicaps, and developmental delays may be at increased risk for hunger and growth retardation due to inadequate nutrition. These children may have physical feeding difficulties, alterations in bodily functions, or poor feeding behavior. Nutrition expectations and growth patterns must be carefully monitored for these children to prevent malnutrition.

Malnutrition may occur because some parents or caregivers may lack the time, knowledge of nutrition, or ability to prepare nutritious meals. They may rely on fast foods and convenience foods to feed their children (Briley et al., 1999). These may give children an upside down pyramid effect, and proper nutrition would not be present. These children are likely not to have adequate amounts of vitamins and minerals in their diets. Children who are poorly nourished are more vulnerable to infection and disease, including frequent colds, ear infections, anemia, tuberculosis, and environmental toxins such as lead poisoning.

Prevention strategies for malnutrition and undernutrition include nutrition education, a balanced diet with a selection of healthy foods, and healthy food preparation methods. Since many children eat twice a day in child care, the caregiver should examine the menus and compare them to the Food Guide Pyramid to see how the selections meet the standards. Children who eat well and see good food in care may change their outlook on food selection as well as influence their nutritional status. Children who understand that food is the fuel that makes their bodies work properly may make better food choices when offered the opportunity, especially if the food is enjoyable and appetizing.

Ruth, a nanny, went to work for a family when the child, Mark, was two months old. She had no problems with Mark's diet until he was eleven months old and ready to begin eating a regular diet without baby food. His parents ate all their meals away from home and were not used to keeping regular food at home. The only thing they normally had in the refrigerator were salad dressing, olives, and leftovers from their latest take-out meals.

Fortunately, Ruth was a trained nanny who had taken a child's nutrition class and was therefore aware of what Mark needed in his diet. She was able to educate the parents as to the importance of Mark's diet. They asked her to provide them with a shopping list and they bought the foods she requested. The nicest reward for Ruth was that the entire family began eating better and the parents started preparing family meals at home to share with Mark. They were grateful to Ruth for making them realize how their habits may have caused Mark problems.

Obesity

Childhood obesity is now the most prevalent nutritional disease of children 18 years of age and under (Dietz, 1999). The percentage of children who are obese (13 percent) has doubled in the last 20 years (CDC, 2001). It is considered to be an epidemic that relates to both the health of these children today as well as to increased risk for adult morbidity and mortality (Dwyer et al., 2000). Obesity is especially prevalent among Hispanic, African American, and Native American children (Freedman et al., 1999). This condition has been recently linked to television viewing (Anderson et al., 1998), sugary soft drinks, and portion size (Ludwig et al., 2001). There are a number of other reasons for childhood obesity as shown in Table 5–3. It is likely that childhood obesity results from a combination of familial, nutritional, physical, and psychological facts. One of the major nutritional factors is the fast food consumed away from home, including at restaurants, schools, and even day care centers.

TABLE 5–3   **Common Reasons for Obesity in Children**
• Dietary excesses in foods containing fats, cholesterol, and sugar
• Poor infant or child feeding practices
• Lack of sufficient exercise
• Watching too much television
• Family genetic predisposition
• Using food as a comforting device or for emotional support
• Weight gain during critical developmental periods

Excess weight is basically a problem created by energy imbalance. The amount of energy taken in through foods is metabolized and then released through the body's work, including involuntary bodily functions such as breath and voluntary functions such as movement and exercise. If more energy is taken in than is put out, then an imbalance results and that excess energy is stored in the body as fat.

A child who weighs more than 10 percent above the normal weight shown on the growth chart (see Appendix B) is considered overweight. A child who weighs more than 20 percent over the normal weight for corresponding height on the growth chart is considered obese.

Childhood obesity can cause pediatric hypertension and diabetes mellitus. Stress on the weight-bearing joints is one physical problem that may result. Mentally and emotionally, obesity lowers self-esteem (Strauss, 2000) and has a powerful effect on peer relationships and social acceptance.

Prevention is the key to curbing childhood obesity. However, a problem in perception may result in difficulty to initiate preventive measures. Many mothers of preschool children who were obese did not perceive their children as obese (Baughcum et al., 2000). Many mothers believe that if they are overweight, their children will be too, regardless of preventive measures (Jain et al., 2001).

The problem of childhood obesity can be improved by an increase in physical activity, diet management, and behavior modification. Physical activity alone does not seem to be effective, but the addition of diet and behavior modification contributes to successful weight loss in obese children.

Diet management should include both a doctor-recommended modified caloric intake and nutrition education. Modifying caloric intake reduces dietary fat intake and nutrition education encourages children to make better choices in food selection. Parents should be included in the behavior modification process, which should include problem-solving techniques. Early intervention

Serving a balanced variety of child-size foods makes eating a pleasant and comfortable experience for young children. Color variety has also been shown to stimulate children's interest in food. What other ways can a caregiver make meals appealing to children?

that utilizes the whole child approach has been especially effective in helping obese children lose weight and increase their level of self-esteem. The best way to help prevent childhood obesity is good parent education.

Caregivers can help obese children by providing a well-balanced diet that is not high in fat. They can provide nutritional information for parents, including referrals for help if needed. Caregivers should provide children with plenty of activity and exercise throughout the day so they have adequate opportunities to burn calories.

Dental Caries

Dental caries, or cavities as they are commonly known, affect almost everyone in the population. Low-income African American and Hispanic mothers see dental caries as one of three major health problems affecting their children (Pestano-Binghay, Reis, & Walters, 1993).

Foods that are high in carbohydrates and sugar promote the formation of cavities. Carbohydrates in the form of starches break down as sugars, which change rapidly to acid when mixed with the microorganisms commonly found in the plaque present in the mouth. The acids produced break through the natural barrier and form cavities. When sugar is ingested, the acid formation process lasts for about 25 minutes. Sticky items that contain sugar, such as honey, soft drinks, raisins, and bananas, lengthen the acid formation process. This is also true of sugars found in milk and fruit juices (Kidsource.com, 2000).

Fluoride use is the most effective method of preventing dental caries. Fluoride is added to many water supplies in the United States. If the caregiver lives in an area that has fluoridated water, she should encourage children to drink the water. If fluoride is not in the water supply, then the family dentist should prescribe fluoride supplements. Many family doctors include fluoride in the vitamin and mineral supplements given to babies. Other prevention methods include brushing teeth after eating meals and using only water in a baby bottle at bedtime. Baby bottle tooth decay is a leading cause of dental caries for children under the age of three years (Kidsource.com, 2000). This can come from either milk or juice in the bottle. When milk or juice is given in a bottle at bedtime, the fluid pools in the child's mouth and increases the incidence of cavities. If a baby needs a bottle to go to sleep, the baby should be fed

Teeth brushing can be a fun and informative activity that caregivers can add to their nutrition education program. Giving children the opportunity to brush after meals is another way to encourage good dental hygiene.

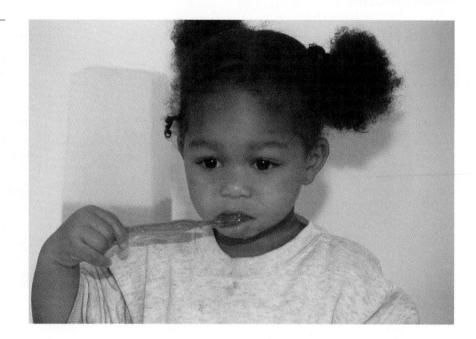

a bottle of formula or should be nursed before going to bed, thus allowing for adequate nutrition. Introducing a child to a cup around the age of one year can help support the prevention of baby bottle tooth decay.

Twenty-five percent of U.S. children account for 75 percent of dental carries. Children who live in areas without fluoridated water, or live in rural areas, or are a minority are more likely to have dental caries (Skinner et al., 1999).

Caregivers can make sure that child care is using good practices to prevent dental caries by providing diets low in sugar and offering children the opportunity to brush their teeth.

Iron Deficiency Anemia

Iron deficiency anemia is the most prevalent nutritional problem in childhood. It is two times more likely to occur among poor children than among those whose families are not poor. Older infants and young children are more likely to become at risk for iron deficiency as the iron stored in their bodies when they were born diminishes over time. Anemia due to iron deficiency may cause a shortened attention span, irritability, and fatigue. Children with iron deficiency anemia may have trouble concentrating, which may later affect their cognitive development and IQ (Evers, 2000).

The only way to avoid iron deficiency and the anemia that results from it is to get adequate supplies of iron in the diet or to supplement the diet with a doctor-recommended vitamin compound containing iron.

Infants receive most of their nutrients from formulas or breast milk. Most formulas provide the necessary iron (PageWise, 2001). Breast milk provides iron also, but after about four to five months of age, infants need more iron than their mothers can provide. Therefore, doctors recommend vitamin supplements that include iron to prevent iron deficiency. Baby cereals are fortified with iron to help provide the necessary iron in the diet.

Adequate supplies of iron must be provided in a growing child's diet but frequently are not. Caregivers should provide iron-rich meals to ensure that children get enough of this essential mineral.

As a child grows, more sources of iron, such as is in meats, fish, poultry, green leafy vegetables, and whole grains, are necessary to prevent iron deficiency. However, many children do not eat balanced diets. When quality of diets was investigated, Stanek, Abbott, and Cramer (1990) found that one-fourth of the children's diets studied were iron deficient. Menus at child care centers were found to be lacking in foods that could help children meet their need for iron (Briley, Roberts-Gray, & Rowe, 1993). Iron deficiency in poor children has been linked to poor compliance with feeding practices due possibly to inadequate funds or lack of parental understanding of the importance of diet.

The best way to prevent iron deficiency and the resulting anemia is through education of the parents, the caregivers, and the children themselves. Caregivers who are aware of the importance of iron can provide more balanced diets with better food selections. In cases where supplementation is necessary, iron-fortified breads and cereals should be used.

Cardiovascular Disease and Hypertension

Cardiovascular disease
disease resulting from impaired function of the heart and/or surrounding arteries

Coronary atherosclerosis
disease of the heart resulting in the walls of arteries degenerating due to fat buildup

Coronary heart disease
disease of the arteries feeding the heart muscle

The diet of many Americans contains too many calories, too much fat, and too much cholesterol. It is also high in sodium. The Bogalusa Heart Study is an ongoing research project focusing on **cardiovascular disease** risk factors present in children's lives (TCCH, 2001). The National Cholesterol Education Program (NCEP) sponsored by the U.S. Department of Health and Human Services is also concerned with the issue of children's diet and cardiovascular risk.

Early elevated levels of cholesterol can lead to the development of early **coronary atherosclerosis**. The combination of diet and genetic risk factors can trigger a higher incidence of this disease than in the normal population. Higher blood cholesterol levels can also lead to **coronary heart disease (CHD)**, which is the number one cause of death in this country. Children who eat diets with excess calories and too much fat tend to be overweight. This is another risk factor in coronary heart disease (see Figure 5–6).

Children base their food interests on what tastes good, not nutritional value. Many of children's favorite foods contain too much salt and sugar.

Hypertension

very high blood pressure

Risk Factors

High cholesterol
Being male
Diabetes mellitus
High blood pressure
Obesity
Cigarette smoking
Vascular (blood
  vessel) disease
Family members with
  CHD before age 60

Figure 5–6
Risk Factors for Cardiovascular Disease

Excess weight and high sodium intake contribute to hypertension. The Bogalusa Heart Study found that nearly all children under ten years of age consume more than the RDA levels of sodium. High sodium intake can be linked to the later development of high blood pressure. Convenience foods and fast foods are high in sodium. Some of children's favorite foods contain too much salt, including chips, hot dogs, lunch meats, canned soups, and store bought breads. Menus at child care centers often feature these foods. The average daily intake of sodium for preschoolers was found to exceed the RDI (Briley et al., 1999).

The best way to improve the risk factors for cardiovascular diseases and hypertension is to modify the diet. Following the recommendations of the Dietary Guidelines for Americans, children's fat intake should be decreased to no more than 30 percent of total calories, saturated fat should be decreased to less than 10 percent of total calories, and sodium intake should be decreased.

Children should also eat diets higher in carbohydrates, which means more fruits, vegetables, and grain products (Briley & Roberts-Gray, 1999). Helpful guidelines for following these recommendations are found in Table 5–4.

Child caregivers can help children decrease the amount of cholesterol, fat, and sodium intake by following Table 5–4.

TABLE 5–4   Guidelines to Decrease Fat and Sodium Intake

- Provide plenty of fresh fruits and vegetables.
- Serve whole grain breads and cereals.
- Use only lean meats, poultry, and fish.
- Choose low-fat dairy products.
- Choose fats from vegetable sources such as margarine and canola oil. Limit the intake of these fat products.
- Select cooking methods that are lower fat alternatives to frying such as grilling or baking.

(continued)

TABLE 5–4 Guidelines to Decrease Fat and Sodium Intake *(continued)*

- Avoid high-sodium foods such as hot dogs, lunch meats, and chips; if these foods are occasionally used, do so in moderation.
- Carefully select menu items that are lower in fat and sodium at fast food restaurants.
- Moderate the use of frozen, packaged, and canned foods.
- Use margarine products made with unsaturated vegetable oils instead of saturated vegetable oils like coconut and palm kernel.
- Set a good example by eating healthy foods.

Food Allergies

If a child cannot eat or properly metabolize a food with important nutrients, he may be at risk for malnutrition and undernutrition. The response to food allergies may range from skin rashes and difficulty breathing to gastrointestinal difficulties. Foods that commonly bring on allergic reactions are milk, peanuts, orange juice, wheat, pork, and eggs.

Allergic reaction to milk is most often apparent as lactose intolerance. Lactose is the simple sugar found in milk. When someone is unable to metabolize lactose properly, she experiences gastric distress such as diarrhea or vomiting. Infants who exhibit lactose intolerance are put on soy-based or other lactose-free formulas.

If a child is suspected to have an allergic reaction to a food, use of that food should be halted immediately and that child should be taken to a physician for diagnosis. The family and caregiver can use proper means prescribed to treat the allergy. Consulting a dietician for recommendations to compensate for any possible nutrient loss is also helpful. Parents should inform caregivers and caregivers should ask if a child suffers from a food allergy. It is necessary to post reminders of food allergies of the children in care on the refrigerator or other obvious places seen during food preparation.

Lactose intolerance

inability of body to process lactose found in milk and milk products

Lactose intolerance is a common allergic reaction to lactose, the simple sugar found in milk. Good communication between caregivers and parents regarding a child's food allergies should be maintained.

Peanut Allergy

Anaphylaxis
sensitivity to an allergen that causes an attack that can result in collapse or death

In recent years, more media focus and more information has been available on the allergy to peanuts. It is an important issue for child care for three reasons. The first reason is that the most common time for food allergies is between infancy and age three. This occurs in approximately 5 percent of that age group. In fact, the allergy to peanuts represents 28 percent of food allergies, occurs under one year of age in 46 percent of cases, and under 15 years of age in 93 percent of cases (Moneret-Vautrin et al., 1998). The second reason is that many child care centers often rely on peanut butter and peanut products to provide a less expensive form of protein in snacks and lunches. Other products used in daily food preparation may contain peanut oil or other peanut derivatives. The third reason is that allergy to peanuts seems to be increasing in frequency (Sicherer et al., 1999; Sampson, 2000) and exposure to peanut dust or skin contact with someone who has been handling a peanut product can bring on a reaction.

Peanut allergies bring about more severe symptoms than all other food allergies. Approximately one-third of all emergency room visits for anaphylaxis are due to the allergic reaction to peanuts. It is also more likely to cause death than many other food allergies. A recent study found that a peanut allergy was responsible for 55 percent of deaths due to food anaphylaxis (Bock et al., 2001). Anaphylactic shock occurs when one is hypersensitive to a substance and when exposed to the substance, the result is an attack that sometimes causes collapse and death. Often this type of shock includes the constriction of the ability to breathe.

Parents of children with a peanut allergy should inform you immediately upon entering their child into care (Salmon, 1999). If child care has a child with this allergy, a plan for preventing exposure and follow-up if exposure does occur should be carefully organized and adopted, including:

- work with the child's parent to develop a plan for that child that would include information as to the severity of the allergy
- inform everyone on staff, including volunteers, that this child has an allergy to peanuts and educate them as to what they are to do in case of emergency
- post this child's name and allergy wherever food is prepared, served, or in any way a child could be in contact with foods, to remind staff, so there is always the precaution reminder
- understand how to read food labels, so as to avoid products that include peanuts and their derivatives so they are not served
- if this is too difficult an issue, you may wish to ask the child's parents to provide the child's lunch or snack. You would still read labels, and would try to keep exposure down as much as possible
- have the food handler wash hands after food preparation and handling
- as a safety precaution, have all staff and children wash their hands immediately after eating to avoid skin contact possibilities
- after snacks and meals, wash the tables with warm soapy water so any residue might be removed
- notify all parents in child care, so that if they provide lunch or snacks, they can attempt to cut down on the peanut products they include in lunches. You might want to include a list of "safe" foods and snacks that they might include that do not contain peanuts or peanut products. This list may need to be updated periodically, as ingredients do change.
- a written emergency action plan, provided by the child's physician should be on file

(continued)

- an epinephrine auto-injector should be readily available and there should be someone on staff at all times who understands how to administer it

- if a field trip is planned, be aware of any possible exposure in the surroundings. Make sure the allergic child brings his or her own snack. Have the epinephrine auto-injector available, just in case

- guidelines about developing a food allergy plan for a child in school can be found at The Food Allergy Network http://www.food allergy.org/school.html#guidelines

It is important to also understand this allergy and be prepared to act on it, even if you do not know if there are any children in care that have it. Many reactions to peanuts and their derivatives comes on first exposure to them (Sicherer et al., 2001).

KEY CONCEPT 5.4

Nutritional Challenge

Childhood nutritional challenges result from lack of balanced diets. Hunger, growth retardation, and iron deficiency anemia may result from undernutrition or malnutrition. Too many of the wrong kind of nutrients can result in dental caries, obesity, cardiovascular problems, and hypertension. Food allergies may result in a nutritional imbalance. Risk management measures such as monitoring children for growth, providing well-balanced diets with healthy food selections, and nutrition education will help prevent nutritional challenges for children.

5.5 Implications for Caregivers

Nutrition education of children and their parents is one of the most powerful tools that a child caregiver has to promote and protect the health and well-being of children. Good nutrition can help a child maintain health and fight off infections, colds, and other communicable diseases. It allows children to grow adequately and develop to the best of their potential. Nutrition information shared with parents and other family members can lead to a healthier, more protective environment for the families.

Education

Many families are unaware of the importance of an adequate diet. Because of the pace of life in this country, regular family meal times are losing ground as part of a daily routine. Use of convenience foods, fast foods, and take-out meals is increasing and taking a toll on the general diet of Americans. Children in urban areas may obtain more than half of their calories outside the home.

Parents play a major role in the prevention of inadequate nutrition or obesity in their children. If parents have the knowledge of some prevention methods, then children are more likely to follow good dietary practices. Some preventive practices for nutrition are listed in Table 5–5 and will help the caregiver educate parents about their role in providing children good nutrition.

Carol had a part-time job and did not rely much on child care for her daughter Jessamyn, age two-and-one-half years. Carol had the opportunity to be promoted into the job of her dreams and she took it. Early every morning, she dropped Jessie off at the family child care home. In the evening when she returned to pick Jessie up, Carol was exhausted. Carol fell into the habit of feeding Jessie cold cereal almost every night, or picking up hamburgers, fries, and soft drinks. In the mornings, cold cereal was breakfast because it was easy and quick. Aleta, the family child caregiver, noticed how Jessie seemed to be coming down with more colds and seemed to lack the healthy glow she had had when she first arrived. Aleta spoke with Carol about Jessie's diet and Carol admitted that she knew it should be different but she didn't know what she should do and had very little time to figure it out. Aleta shared some nutritional information, gave Carol a few suggestions, and provided Carol with some tips that would improve the whole family's diet. Carol was willing to make changes because of Aleta's support and the nutritional information and tips for organizing food selection and menu planning. The entire family made it their project and it benefited the health of everyone in the family.

TABLE 5–5 **Good Nutrition Practices for Parent Education**

- Monitor your child's growth in height and weight.
- Help children understand the difference between hunger and other needs.
- Provide only good, nutritious food choices that will lead to a well-balanced diet.
- Observe the amount and type of food consumed.
- Do not use food as a reward—choose other methods of rewarding a child.
- Help children learn to interact with others.
- Role model exercise and encourage children to exercise.
- If a child's nutritional health seems to be at risk, seek nutritional counseling.

Parents should be involved in planning menus in child care and should work at home to complement what children have to eat in child care (Briley & Roberts-Gray, 1999; Briley et al., 1999).

Children can learn about nutrition and food selection early. Nutrition education activities should be prepared with the children's developmental level in mind (Plum et al., 1998). Good role modeling, providing healthy food selections, and discussions about the Food Guide Pyramid can send children positive messages about good nutrition. Children can learn that they play a role in their nutritional well-being.

Children may be bombarded by messages about food through visits to fast food restaurants, watching television ads, and looking at food labels in the supermarkets. The messages carried by these foods make it hard for children to understand that good nutrition is not present in all foods. Children may see poor food selections at home or in child care due to convenience and the time crush. It is important to talk about food and nutrition with children often. Child care has an impact on children's developing food habits (Fuhr & Barclay, 1998).

Children learn the most about nutrition from the adults in their life. Good role modeling by caregivers is therefore extremely important. This pregnant caregiver has an additional teaching opportunity, in that she can tell the children how good nutrution is helping the baby inside her grow.

Looking at labels and discussing the nutrition of the food being eaten should occur regularly so children begin to understand the importance of good food in their diets.

Role Modeling

Nutrition and food selection are integral to achieving good health and well-being. This is an area where many centers and family care homes fall short. Nutrition is often disregarded as an important part of child care. Recent studies have shown a majority of child care facilities do not meet the nutritional needs of the children they serve (Briley et al., 1999; Briley, Roberts-Gray, & Simpson, 1994). Some common practices that role model poor nutrition and food selection are included in Table 5–6.

TABLE 5–6   Observed Practices for Role Modeling Poor Nutrition
• There was little variety in the food presented; the same foods and menus were repeated often.
• Vegetables were generally ignored.
• Foods that were high in fats and low in fiber were served often.
• Sweets such as sugar, jelly, and honey were used moderately to liberally.
• Teachers encouraged children to eat, but rarely discussed the importance of a food and why the child should eat it.
• There was not enough food served to meet the RDI requirements for energy during the time the children were in child care.
• Menus did not reflect the cultural diversity of the groups they served.
• Food served did not provide adequate amounts of niacin, iron, zinc, and vitamin B_6 needed in a child's diet.
• Convenience seemed to drive menu planning and included using a majority of foods that were canned or frozen.
• Staff in some centers ordered fast food instead of eating the same foods prepared for the children.

These poor role modeling practices show a need for nutrition education and training in menu planning and food selection. A good background in basic nutrition and nutritional guidelines provides the knowledge for good role modeling strategies and practices. Some of the basic role modeling for good nutritional practice is included in Table 5–7.

TABLE 5–7   Basic Practices for Role Modeling Good Nutrition

- Provide menus and food selections that follow USDA, RDI, and CACFP guidelines, taking into consideration the number of meals and snacks a child will consume while in care. Match this consideration to the percentage of daily diet that the caregiver provides for the child. Plan the menus accordingly.
- Select a variety of foods for snacks and meals while planning menus.
- Use a large number of fresh fruits and vegetables to provide more vitamins, minerals, and fiber.
- Select low-fat foods and preparations.
- Eat with the children, eating the same foods and discussing the importance of individual foods in the children's diet. This is a good place to use the Food Guide Pyramid.
- Plan menus that take into consideration the regional and cultural diversity of the population at the child care site. This includes children, teachers, and parents.
- Establish good communication with parents about nutrition and why it is an integral part of overall health and well-being.
- Promote and provide nutrition education for children, their parents, and staff.
- Provide parents sack lunch guidelines for the children who bring their lunch from home. The guidelines should include acceptable food selections and suggestions for meeting the child's nutritional needs. Combined with healthy snacks provided by the caregiver, the child will have an adequate diet while in care.

Marylou, a center director, has a basic knowledge of nutrition. When the center was small, Marylou planned the menus, but as it grew she got further away from menu planning and food selection. Several years ago the center became involved with the Child and Adult Care Food Program (CACFP), which allowed it to be reimbursed for providing meals that met CACFP program guidelines. CACFP provided training and technical assistance and gave the center a handbook to help in menu planning and food selection. With staff turnover, menus changed only gradually and the same foods appeared over and over—sometimes two or three times a week. When a local college dietetics class evaluating menus at several centers and family child care homes in the area asked Marylou's center to participate in their study, Marylou accepted because the staff felt they were doing an adequate job.

They were surprised to learn that not only was their menu not well balanced, but it did not even comply with the directives of the CACFP. In addition,

(continued)

Marylou's staff had not considered the cultural diversity of the children now attending the center when planning menus. The staff looked carefully at the problems and decided to hold inservice nutrition workshops periodically and to put into practice the suggestions made by the college class. Marylou and her staff also took greater advantage of the CACFP handbook and technical assistance. The staff involved the parents in menu planning and asked for recipes that reflected the cultures present in their center.

When the center participated in the same college study the following year, the staff got a glowing report and the center was cited in the local press as being a good example of healthy nutritional practices in child care.

Supervision

Supervision ensures that the process of parent education, child education, and role modeling occurs. It is also helpful in examining whether the child care facility, family child care home, or in-home site is practicing good nutrition habits and offering healthy food choices.

CHAPTER SUMMARY

An increasing number of children will rely on child care to provide a good portion of their nutritional needs. Nutritional policies that include the use of nutritional guidelines and that provide awareness of nutritional challenges should be created for child care. Caregivers should have an understanding of the basic nutrients and use the Food Guide Pyramid to plan menus. They can monitor children for growth and provide nutrition education to avoid nutritional challenges. Caregivers can use education, role modeling, and supervision to manage risk and practice good nutrition.

TO GO BEYOND

In this section you will find a number of activities that you can use to apply and improve your knowledge of this chapter. There are also thorough Online Resources that accompany this text that can be found at http://www.early childed.delmar.com/resources/robertson/index.html. Included on this site are chapter practice quizzes, PowerPoint outlines, Web links, a discussion forum, and various other activities to help you better understand the material in this chapter. This site is updated regularly so check back often to receive the latest information about the subjects in this chapter.

Chapter Review Critical Thinking Applications

1. Discuss the interrelationship between nutrition and health.
2. Assess how nutritional challenges impact the caregiver.

3. Examine why the caregiver needs to be so concerned that the children in her care get enough liquids, including water. How does a caregiver make sure that children are drinking enough liquids?

4. As a caregiver, why would you have to be careful to meet the needs of a vegetarian child in your care?

As an Individual

1. Record and chart your diet for three days, including one weekend day. Analyze by comparing it to the Food Guide Pyramid (see Appendix D). What could you do to improve your overall diet? What steps should you take?

2. Find a local day care that serves all the meals to children. Ask to look at their menus and evaluate them. How well do they do? What might you do to improve those menus, if you worked at the child care center?

3. How does hunger affect the children in your local area? Research the issue and relate the special programs that help these children. What agencies might you contact if this involved children at your child care?

As a Group

1. Examine and discuss practical ways to encourage children to try different kinds of foods.

2. Gather nutritional information available in your local community. Make sure that there are enough copies for your entire class, and compile into a portfolio for each class member to keep.

3. Evaluate the impact that a child with a peanut allergy might have on the entire child care environment.

4. Separate into smaller groups and discuss childhood obesity. Each group should make five suggestions to help an obese child improve his/her weight. Compare these with the entire class and list the seven most important strategies.

5. Hold a class potluck with students bringing foods from diverse cultures that represent people in your local area. Compare the tastes and share ideas for cultural food awareness for the children in care.

CHAPTER REFERENCES

American Academy of Pediatrics (AAP). (1998). Cholesterol in children. *Pediatrics, 101*(1), 141–147.

American Academy of Pediatrics Policy Statement (AAP). (2001).The use and misuse of fruit juice in pediatrics. *Pediatrics, 107*(5), 1210–1213.

Anderson, R., Crespo, C., Bartlett, S., Cheskin, L., & Pratt, M. (1998). Relationship of physical activity and television watching with body weight and level of fatness among children. *Journal of the American Medical Association, 279*(12), 938–942.

Aronson, S. (2000, July). Updates on healthy eating and walkers. *Child Care Information Exchange,* 30.

Baughcum, A., Chamberlin, L., Deeks, C., Powers, S., & Whitaker, R. (2000). Maternal perceptions of overweight preschool children. *Pediatrics, 106*(6), 1380–1386.

Bock, S., Munoz-Furlong, A., & Sampson, H. (2001). Fatalities due to anaphylactic reactions to foods. *Journal of Clinical Immunology, 107*(1), 191–193.

Briley, M., Jastrow, S., Vickers, J., & Roberts-Gray, C. (1998). Dietary intake at child-care centers and away: Are parents and care providers working as partners or at cross-purposes? *Journal of the American Dietetics Association, 99*(8), 950–954.

Briley, M., Jastrow, S., Vickers, J., & Roberts-Gray, C. (1999). Can ready to eat cereal solve common nutritional problems in child care menus? *Journal of the American Dietetic Association, 1999, 99*(2), 341–342.

Briley, M., & Roberts-Gray, C. (1999). Nutrition standards for child care programs—Position of ADA. *Journal of American Dietetic Association, 99*(6), 981–988.

Briley, M., Roberts-Gray, C., & Rowe, S. (1993). What can children learn from the menu at the child care center? *Journal of Community Health, 18*(6), 363–377.

Briley, M., Roberts-Gray, C., & Simpson, D. (1994). Identification of factors that influence the menu at child care centers: A grounded theory approach. *Journal of the American Dietetic Association, 94*(3), 276–281.

Brown, J., & Marcotte, L. (1999, January/February). Nutrition and cognitive development in children. *Early Childhood News.*

Brown, J., & Pollitt, E. (1996, February). Hunger in the U.S. *Scientific American,* 38–43.

Bruening, K., Gilbride, J., Passannante, M., & McClowry, S. (1999). Dietary intake and health outcomes among young children attending two urban day-care centers. *Journal of the American Dietetic Association, 99*(12), 1529–1535.

Centers for Disease Control (CDC). (2001). More American children and teens are overweight. Retrieved May 15, 2002, from http://www.cdc.gov/od/oc/media/pressrel/r010312b.htm.

Children's Defense Fund. (2001). *The state of America's children: Yearbook 1996.* Washington, DC: Author.

Dietz, W. (1999). Childhood obesity: Causes and prevention. *Feeding Kids Newsletter, 22.* Retrieved May 15, 2002, from http://nutritionforkids.com/emlnews.

Dwyer, J., Stone, E., Yang, M., Webber, L., Must, A., Feldman, H., Nader, P., Perry, C., & Parcel, G. (2000). Prevalence of marked overweight and obesity in a multiethnic pediatric population: Findings for the Child and Adolescent Trial for Cardiovascular Health (CATCH) study. *Journal of the American Dietetic Association, 100,*(10), 1149–1154.

Evers, C. (2000, January/February). Teaching kids about hunger. *Feeding Kids Newsletter, 28.* Retrieved May 15, 2002, from http://nutritionforkids.com/emlnews.

Freedman, D., Dietz, W., Srinivasan, S., & Berenson, G. (1999). The relationship of overweight to cardiovascular risk factors among children and adolescents: The Bogalusa Heart Study. *Pediatrics, 103*(6), 1175–1182.

Fuhr, J., & Barclay, K. (1998). The importance of appropriate nutrition and nutrition education. *Young Children, 53*(1), 74–80.

Jain, A., Sherman, S., Chamberlin, L., Carter, Y., Powers, S., & Whitaker, R. (2001). Why don't low-income mothers worry about their preschoolers' weight? *Pediatrics, 104*(5), 1138–1146.

Johnson, R, & Kennedy, E. (2000). The 2000 Dietary Guidelines for Americans: What are the changes and why were they made? *Journal of the American Dietetic Association, 100*(7), 769–774.

Kidsource.com. (2000). Baby bottle tooth decay and oral health in the child care setting. Retrieved May 15, 2002, from http://kidsource.com/health/babybottle.html.

Ludwig, D., Peterson, K., & Gortmaker, S. (2001). Relationship between consumption of sugar-sweetened drinks and childhood obesity: A perspective observational analysis. *Lancet, 357*(9255), 505–508.

Moneret-Vautrin, D., Kanny, F., Rance, G., Olsewski, A., Gueant, J., & Dutaul, G. (1998). Food allergy to peanuts in France—evaluation of 142 observations. *Clinical and Experimental Allergy, 28*(9), 1113–1119.

Mydlenski, P. (2000). New eating right food pyramid. *Healthy Child Care, 3*(4). Retrieved May 15, 2002, from http://healthychild.net/Articles.

Nicklas, T. (2001). Consider nutrition when choosing day care. *Nutrition and Your Child, 2,* 1, 3.

Nord, M., Jemison, K., & Bickel, G. (1999). *Prevalence of food insecurity and hunger, by state, 1996–1998.* Economic Research Service, U.S. Department of Agriculture, Food Assistance and Research Report, 2. Retrieved May 15, 2002, from http://www.ers.usda.gov/publications/fanrr2/index.htm.

PageWise. (2001). Iron deficiency anemia in infants and young children. Retrieved May 15, 2002, from http://www.allsands.com/Kids/Health/anemiainchild_bsy_gn.htm.

Pestano-Binghay, E., Reis, J., & Walters, M. (1993). Nutrition education issues for minority parents: A needs assessment. *Journal of Nutrition Education, 25*(3), 144.

Plum, J., Hertzler, A., Brochetti, D., & Steward, D. (1998) Games to assess nutrition concepts of preschool children. *Journal of the American Dietetic Association, 98*(7), 1168–1171.

Position of the American Dietetic Association: Child nutrition services. (1993). *Journal of the American Dietetic Association, 93*(3), 334–336.

Rolls, B., Engell, D., & Birch, L.(2000). Serving portion size influences 5-year-old but not 3-year-old children's food intakes. *Journal of the American Dietetic Association, 100*(2), 232–236.

Salmon, D. (1999, April). Living with a food allergy. *Child Magazine,* 60–63.

Sampson, H. (2000). What should we be doing for children with a peanut allergy? *Journal of Pediatrics, 137*(6), 741.

Sicherer, S., Munoz-Furlong, A., Burks, A., & Sampson, H. (1999). Prevalence of peanut and tree nut allergy in the United States determined by a random digit dial telephone survey. *Journal of Allergy and Clinical Immunology, 103*(3), 559–562.

Sicherer, S., Munoz-Furlong, A., Burks, A., & Sampson, H. (2001). A voluntary registry for peanut and tree nut allergy: Characteristics of the first 5149 registrants. *Journal of Allergy and Clinical Immunology, 108*(1), 128–132.

Sicherer, S., & Sampson, H. (1998). The role of food allergy in childhood asthma. *Immunology Allergy Clinician of North America, 18*(1), 49–60.

Skinner, J., Carruth, B., Houck, D., Bounds, W., Morris, M., Cox, D., Moran, J. III, & Coletta, F. (1999). Longitudinal study of nutrient and food intakes of white preschool children aged 24 to 60 months. *Journal of the American Dietetic Association, 99*(12), 1514–1521.

Splett, P., & Story, M. (1991). Child nutrition: Objectives for the decade. *Journal of the American Dietetic Association, 91*(6), 665–668.

Stanek, K., Abbott, D., & Cramer, S. (1990). Diet quality and the eating environment of preschool children. *Journal of the American Dietetic Association, 90*(11), 1582–1584.

Strauss, R. (2000). Childhood obesity and self-esteem. *Pediatrics, 105*(1), e15.

Tate, M., & Patrick, S. (2000). Healthy People 2010 targets healthy diet and healthy weight as critical goals. *Journal of the American Dietetic Association, 100*(3), 300.

Taylor, M., & Koblinksy, S. (1994). Food consumption and eating behavior of homeless preschool children. *Journal of Nutrition Education, 26,* 20.

Tulane Center for Cardiovascular Health (TCCH). (2001). The history of the Bogalusa Heart Study. New Orleans, LA: Author. Retrieved May 15, 2002, from http://www.som.tulane.edu/cardiohealth/bog.htm.

U.S. Department of Agriculture. (1992). *Food guide pyramid, A guide to daily food choices.* Hyattsville, MD: Human Nutrition Service.

U.S. Food and Drug Administration. (1999). *The Food Label.* Retrieved August 16, 2001, from http://www.fda.gov/opacom/backgrounders/foodlabel/newlabel.html.

SUGGESTIONS FOR READING

Basch, C., Zybert, P., & Shea, S. (1994). Five-a-day: Dietary behavior and the fruit and vegetable intake of Latino children. *The American Journal of Public Health, 84,* 814.

Dietz, W. (1994). Critical periods in childhood for the development of obesity. *American Journal of Clinical Nutrition, 59*(5), 955–959.

Fox, M., Glanz, F., Endahl, J., & Wilde, J. (1997). *Early childhood and care study.* Alexandria, VA: U.S. Department of Agriculture.

Hunter, B. T. (1994, March). The importance of breakfast. *Consumer's Research Magazine, 3,* 8.

Meltsner, S. (1996, September). The new skinny on overweight. *Parents Magazine,* 64–66.

Romero-Gwynn, E., Gwynn, D., Grivetti, L., McDonald, R., Stanford, G., Turner, B., West, E., & Williamson, E. (1993). Dietary acculturation among Latinos of Mexican descent. *Nutrition Today, 28*(8), 6.

Satter, E. (1987). *How to get your kid to eat . . . But not too much.* Palo Alto, CA: Bull Publishing Co.

Satter, E. (1989). *Feeding with love and good sense.* Palo Alto, CA: Bull Publishing Co.

Werner, P., Timms, S., & Almond, L. (1996). Health stops: Practical ideas for health related exercise in preschool and primary classrooms. *Young Children, 51*(6), 48–55.

For additional information on safety, nutrition, and health in early education, visit our Web site at http://www.earlychilded.delmar.com

Providing Good Nutrition in Child Care

After reading this chapter, you should be able to:

6.1 Specific Nutritional Policies

Define and discuss the need for nutrition policies that address growth and development to prevent risk, provide protection, and promote nutritional well-being.

6.2 Early Feeding and the Infant in Care

Discuss breast-feeding, bottle feeding, and the introduction of solids into the infant's diet including the developmental implications and practices for the caregiver.

6.3 Feeding the Toddler

Discuss the impact of development on the feeding behavior of the toddler and describe strategies for the caregiver to redirect that behavior.

6.4 Food and the Preschooler

Discuss the food behaviors of the preschooler and the strategies for the caregiver to guide the child to behaviors that foster well-being.

6.5 School-Age Nutrition

Discuss the nutritional needs of the school-aged child and the strategies for the caregiver to meet these needs that may be compromised by outside influences.

6.6 Nutrition and the Child with Special Needs

Explain how special needs might affect the nutrition and feeding of a child and discuss specific strategies to meet the child's nutritional challenges.

6.7 Exercise as a Part of Diet

Discuss the impact of exercise on the diet and overall well-being of children and strategies to promote exercise.

6.8 Implications for Caregivers

Describe and discuss methods for education, supervision, and role modeling to ensure good nutrition for children in care.

6.1 Specific Nutritional Policies

The importance of providing good nutrition in child care cannot be stressed enough. Greater numbers of children are relying on their caregivers to provide a significant portion of their nutritional needs. Child caregivers play a significant role in the nutritional well-being of children. Creating policies to meet the changing nutritional needs of the children in care is a vital risk management tool that can affect the way children grow and learn. The following indicators reveal the need for those policies:

■ Children in day care for eight hours should receive at least one meal and two snacks. Food should be available at least every three hours (Nicklas, 2001).

■ Caregivers are being asked to take on the role of nutritional gatekeeper for children (Briley, McBride, & Roberts-Gray, 1997).

■ Only 2 percent of children are eating according to the Food Guide Pyramid, and 16 percent of children don't meet any recommendations of the guide (Aronson, 2000).

■ Children in day care for eight hours or more should receive foods that provide 50–67 percent of their nutritional needs (Nicklas, 2001; Briley & Roberts-Gray, 1999).

■ Providing a pleasant eating environment helps set the stage for good nutritional habits (Fletcher & Branen, 1999; Kendrick, Kaufmann, & Messenger, 1995).

Many children are in child care for more than eight hours a day, yet their nutritional needs may not be met by the caregiver. The caregiver may be unaware of nutritional standards or may not know how to plan menus to meet those standards (Briley & Roberts-Gray, 1999). The caregiver's perceptions about what a child will or will not eat may also influence food choices. For example, some caregivers may believe that children do not like vegetables and prefer foods that are like fast foods, so they may create menus that they think children will like and eat. These factors can have a negative effect on menu planning choices for food and the balance of the nutrition provided by that food.

Cost is always a factor when trying to balance care with the business of caregiving. Many caregivers watch for sales, buy in bulk, and look for other opportunities to cut back on cost. Saving should never be so important as to sacrifice the children's well-being. Child care centers and family child care homes may be eligible to participate in funded food programs that will help to defray the costs for children from low-income families.

Convenience may also be a factor in food selection in child care. Menus in child care have typically been in use a long time with few updates and are limited by lack of nutritional knowledge on the part of the staff (Briley, Roberts-Gray, & Simpson, 1994). If the effort is not made to change menus or to learn more about nutrition, then choices may be limited.

Culture may also affect food choices in child care. The caregiver may have a cultural background that influences cooking and menu selection and may even limit choices available (Story et al., 2000; Johnson & Nicklas, 1999). Children may or may not eat foods from cultural backgrounds that are different from their own. Children may have family cultural influences that may limit what they will eat. Television and fast food commercials may have an effect on what the caregiver fixes and what children will eat.

The caregiver who serves the family in their home may have an added difficulty providing proper nutrition. Many families who hire nannies are so busy and have their focus elsewhere that food for themselves and their children may be more of an irritant than an issue. Some parents may eat all of their meals away from home and only provide what they consider are the necessities for the child or what they think the child will eat, with no regard to nutritional value. Parents may have no knowledge about nutrition and how it can affect the growth and development of a child. This can make caring for the nutritional needs of a child a challenge to a nanny.

Another factor that should be considered is the purpose of the child care. Briley, Roberts-Gray, and Simpson (1994) pointed out that there were three perspectives on the purpose of child care: *(1) to promote the well-being of the child, (2) to provide a service to the community, or (3) to provide a living for the provider.* If the child caregiver is focused on the second or third perspective, the nutritional well-being of the child may be at risk.

Children have specific nutritional needs at each stage of their growth and development. It is essential that the caregiver be aware of these nutritional needs and create policies that will help to meet the specific needs of the children as they grow and develop.

Nutritional policies that will help the caregiver meet the specific needs of the children in care are:

- *Early Feeding and the Infant:* understanding the changing need of infants including breast-feeding, bottle feeding, and the introduction of solid foods
- *Establishing the Feeding Behavior of the Toddler:* understanding the impact of development and changing needs on the behavior of the toddler regarding food and eating
- *Food and the Preschool Child:* understanding the food behaviors and changing needs of the preschooler

Family style meals that allow children to serve themselves and be served by the caregiver work well in combination for feeding young children.

- *School-Age Nutrition:* understanding nutritional needs and how these needs are threatened by outside influence, including school food programs
- *Nutrition and the Child with Special Needs:* understanding how special needs might affect the diet and feeding of a child
- *Exercise as Part of Diet:* understanding the impact of exercise on the diet and well-being of children
- *Implications for Caregivers:* understanding the need for education, supervision, support, and role modeling to ensure good nutrition

KEY CONCEPT 6.1

Nutritional Policies

Every caregiver should practice good nutrition in child care. Many caregivers are not meeting the nutritional needs of children in their care. Nutrition for child care is approached by each caregiver with that person's own perspective based on background, food practices, culture, and what the children eat or will not eat. The caregiver should have nutritional policies that cover early infant feeding, food and the toddler, the preschool child, school-age children, special needs, and nutrition and exercise as part of nutrition. The implications for the child caregiver include education, role modeling, and supervision.

6.2 Early Feeding and the Infant in Care

The birth weight of a healthy baby will double in the first four months of life and nutritional needs will change as a child grows and develops. An infant grows faster during the first year than at any other time of her life. This growth rate is due to the growth patterns of all the internal organs. An infant's nutrition should be able to supply the nutrients including energy for this rapid growth.

The growth and development of an infant is directly related to nutrition. In the first four to six months of life, the only form of food an infant's body can accommodate is liquid breast milk or formula that provides the necessary nutrients. The changes in the organs provide the ability to digest and assimilate solid foods as the infant grows.

At birth, newborns cannot chew or use their tongues to push food. Their kidneys are too immature to handle the wastes of solid food. Digestive systems are not yet mature enough to handle the nutrients from solid foods. Allergic reactions, cramping, and crying are common results of introducing solid foods before the baby can assimilate it into the body.

Breast-Feeding

Historically, infants were breast-fed. This changed when technology was developed to provide sanitation for bottle feeding and formulas on which babies could survive and thrive were created for the bottle. Doctors saw bottle

Breast milk contains all the nutrients that babies need during the first six months of life. Caregivers should work to accommodate the mother who wants to continue breast-feeding while the child is in care.

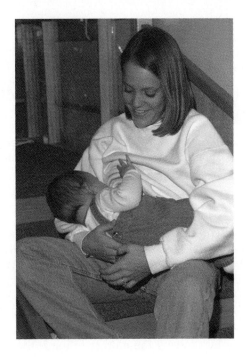

feeding as a way to measure the amount of milk a baby was drinking. The trend for bottle feeding infants increased until the early 1970s when research showed that breast-feeding offered more nutrition and immunity than bottle feeding. Today, the American Academy of Pediatricians is involved in an effort to increase the number of babies who are breast-fed, and to have those babies breast-fed for the first 12 months of life (AAP, 2000).

Current knowledge shows that breast-feeding is the preferable form to provide infants proper nutrition, protection from bacteria, and give them immunity from diseases. There is also good cause to believe that breast-feeding actually optimizes cognitive development (AAP, 2000). See Table 6–1 for the benefits of breast-feeding.

The caregiver may be called upon to help the breast-feeding mother with quality support (HHS, 2001; AAP, 2000). This offers advantages to everyone concerned. The baby will benefit as Table 6–1 indicates, and the mother and the caregiver will both benefit because a breast-fed baby is less likely to become

TABLE 6–1   Benefits of Breast-Feeding
• Protein is suited to baby's metabolism.
• Provides antibodies to combat bacteria.
• Provides immunological protection from illness and disease.
• Fat and iron in breast milk are easily absorbed and digested by the baby.
• Convenient—right temperature, sterile, and changes composition as baby's needs change.
• Psychological advantages—bonding with mother, tactile stimulation.
• Fosters optimum cognitive development.

Figure 6–1

Types of Nipples

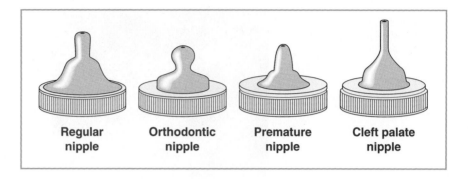

Regular nipple Orthodontic nipple Premature nipple Cleft palate nipple

sick when left in care than a bottle-fed baby (Jones & Matheny, 1993). Increasing breast-feeding is also a goal of the Special Supplemental Food Program for Women, Infants and Children (WIC) because babies receive so many health benefits from it (Carmichael et al., 2001; Ahluwalia et al., 2000).

Mothers can help the caregiver by collecting and storing breast milk to use while they are not with the baby. Breast milk will last up to 48 hours in the refrigerator or can be frozen for two weeks. The caregiver can help the nursing mother by allowing the mother to nurse the baby at the child care site. This may occur as the baby is dropped off, picked up, and even at lunch time if the mother is close enough to visit her child during the lunch break. This type of support will help mothers continue to breast-feed for the recommended time for optimum health and well-being for the infant. A mother should be discouraged from breast-feeding if: (1) the mother has a communicable or chronic disease such as AIDS; (2) she is taking medication that is harmful to the baby; or (3) she is a drug or alcohol abuser.

Breast-fed babies usually need to be fed every two to three hours. Breast-fed babies may have more trouble accepting the bottle because they are used to sucking the breast. Using a breast-shaped nipple or a soft nipple may help the baby get more milk (see Figure 6–1). It may take several tries before the right nipple is found. The caregiver should not give up!

The caregiver should apply good sanitary practices and food safety procedures when using breast milk as listed in Table 6–2.

TABLE 6–2   Safe and Sanitary Practices for Breast-Feeding
• Breast milk that has been stored unfrozen should be thrown away if not used within three days.
• Expressed milk should be stored in single portion feedings with date and child's name clearly labeled.
• Thaw frozen milk in the refrigerator or under cold running water. Never heat in the microwave.
• Shake refrigerator thawed milk to mix cream into all the milk.
• Do not refreeze thawed breast milk.
• Dispose of any unused milk left in the bottle immediately after feeding.

Bottle Feeding

Although breast-feeding is the preferable form, many children are fed formula from the beginning or are switched to formula for a variety of reasons. Mothers may find this is easier when they work, and it allows anyone, including fathers, to participate in the feeding of the baby. A child may also be on a combination of breast and bottle feeding; for example, breast milk may be fed in the morning and at night and bottled formula may be fed during the day.

Formulas are easy to prepare and come in several forms. Powdered and liquid concentrate formulas are meant to have sterile water added to the exact directions on the can. This is very important because when incorrectly mixed the formula may be harmful to the infant. The other kind of formula is ready-to-feed and merely needs to be put into the bottle.

Many manufacturers make soy-protein formulas for infants born with lactose intolerance. These infants may suffer from diarrhea, gas, and bloating. An infant may also be allergic to the soy formula, in which case there is a formula available with the proteins already broken down by enzyme action to prevent the allergic reaction.

Formulas try to copy breast milk as closely as possible. Formula manufacturers start with nonfat cow's milk as a base, then add vegetable oil, lactose, vitamins, and minerals to approximate energy and nutrients from human milk. Commercially prepared formulas are heavily regulated to keep infants safe from harm.

For proper food safety and sanitation, the measures in Table 6–3 should be commonly practiced in bottle preparation using formula.

Feeding Pattern. Whether the baby is being breast-fed or bottle fed, there is an important factor to keep in mind. Even at this young age, the child should be able to control his own eating pattern. To accomplish this, the caregiver must be aware of the cues the baby gives when a break is needed or when he

TABLE 6–3   Safe and Sanitary Practices for Bottle Feeding

- Wash hands with liquid soap and hot water before beginning the sterilization process.
- Wash bottles, nipples, and caps in hot, soapy water, using a bottle brush for hard-to-reach places. Rinse thoroughly in hot, clean water.
- Sterilize all bottle parts in a pan of water. Boil for 5 to 6 minutes. Remove from pan with tongs and fill immediately.
- Always buy cans of formula that are intact and have current use dates.
- Wash the tops of formula cans before opening them.
- Prepare formula exactly to manufacturers' instructions. If formula is diluted too much, malnutrition may result. If an insufficient amount of water is added, the child's digestive system may be strained.
- Use clean, sterile bottled water rather than tap water because some tap water may cause digestive upsets in some infants.
- Pour formula into sterilized bottles and top with nipples, caps, and rings if the bottle is being stored in the refrigerator. Use up all the prepared formula. Prepared bottles should be stored no longer than 24 hours.

Babies should be held in a slightly elevated, reclined position when feeding to avoid choking and ear infections. These early feedings contribute significantly to the basis of the child's later eating habits.

is full. These cues include drawing the head away from the nipple, releasing it, spitting it out, or biting it. The infant may also stop sucking or shut his mouth tightly. Changing posture or being attentive to the surroundings and not the feeding are also cues that the child may not need any more breast or bottle feeding. A baby should be fed according to his own body's schedule of food energy needs instead of an imposed routine.

Infant controlled feeding requires the caregiver to be attentive to the infant's behavior and to allow the quantity eaten to vary depending on the infant's needs. The caregiver can identify the infant's cues by allowing time for pauses. This may be a good time to see if the baby needs to be held upright to pass a gas bubble. If the baby is fussy during a feeding, it is wise to find the source of the discomfort instead of interpreting the fussiness as a sign that the baby is done eating.

Introducing Solid Foods

Solid foods should not be introduced into a baby's diet until the baby is at least four months old and not until six months if she does not show signs of readiness. This is about the time it takes for the fine, gross, and oral motor skills to develop so that the child is ready to eat solid food. The normal pattern of development and ability of the body to accept solid food and the nutrients they supply are listed in Table 6–4.

Feeding Patterns.   When the infant is demonstrating developmental readiness, then solid foods should be introduced. Until this point, the protein needed for brain growth has been provided by the breast milk or formula. There is a common pattern for the introduction of this type of food and the pattern has been developed with good reasons. The caregiver should start the introduction of solid food slowly, serving only one or two servings of the food at the beginning. One new food is introduced at a time and the caregiver

TABLE 6–4	**Pattern of Developmental Skills for Eating Solid Foods**

- Birth: Baby is only capable of sucking.
- 6 weeks: Baby can smile and has the ability to extrude or push things out of the mouth with the tongue.
- 8 weeks: Baby can use the tongue against the palate and can swallow semisoft food, but cannot digest the food itself.
- 3 months: Baby's gastrointestinal system is sufficiently developed for digesting starch.
- 4 months: Baby shows signs of being ready for solid foods: drinks 40 or more ounces of milk, can swallow instead of suck, and drools, indicating teeth will soon appear. Should be double his birth weight. If formula fed, iron stores may be depleted and baby will need iron from other food sources.
- 4 to 6 months: Baby can control head movements and can keep food in the mouth instead of pushing it out with the tongue.
- 5 months: Baby is a social creature and may be more interested in people and surroundings than in eating. May demonstrate interest in other people's food and open the mouth to show this interest.
- 6 months: Baby can sit up in a high chair and can be easily spoon fed. If breast-fed, iron stores may be depleted and baby will need iron from other food sources.
- 8 months: Baby can grasp soft finger foods with hands and put them in the mouth.
- 10 months: Baby should be able to grasp cup with both hands.
- 12 months: Baby should be able to hold an age-appropriate spoon.

should wait five to seven days before introducing another new food. This waiting period allows the caregiver to identify if the food causes allergies or digestive complications such as diarrhea, gas, rashes, vomiting, or unusual fussiness. If this does not occur, move on to the next new food.

As the caregiver starts the solid food routine, there are several things to keep in mind that will help the baby learn how to eat in a safe way. Utensils used to feed the baby should be small and age appropriate (Briley & Roberts-Gray, 1999). To begin with, only small amounts of food should be offered on the tip of the spoon. As the baby progresses, the amount should be increased to two or three tablespoons at a feeding. The food the caregiver serves should be placed in a small bowl or custard cup with only enough for one serving, and any unfinished food should be discarded. Returning food to the jar might contaminate the food remaining in the jar and make it unsafe for the baby to eat. Table 6–5 contains the introduction pattern for solid foods.

TABLE 6–5	**Solid Food Introduction Pattern**	
Age	**Include**	**Exclude**
0 to 4 months	Formula or breast milk	Solid foods, cow's milk
4 to 6 months	Add iron-fortified cereals	Honey, meat, eggs, sugar, powdered sweetened drink mix, cow's milk

(continued)

TABLE 6–5	Solid Food Introduction Pattern *(continued)*	
Age	**Include**	**Exclude**
6 to 9 months	Add vegetables, fruits, soft finger foods, yogurt, cheese, unsweetened fruit juices	Same as above plus soft drinks
9 to 12 months	Add meats, egg yolks, breads, crackers, cottage cheese, pasta, rice	Egg whites, all sugared products, honey, peanuts, popcorn, low- or nonfat milk, hot dogs, high sodium meat products

Cereals.   The first food normally introduced is iron-fortified rice cereal. Rice is a good food to begin the introduction pattern because it is easily digested. The caregiver should mix the cereal with some formula until it is somewhat runny. It will be easier for infant to assimilate this experience if it is not totally dissimilar from her liquid diet. This food should be fed to the child on a spoon, not from a bottle. It is common practice among certain cultures, including Hispanics, to introduce this food mixed with formula in a bottle in which the nipple has been cut to allow the cereal to come out. Developmentally, this puts the child back to sucking and swallowing rather than using the developing oral skills that will be needed later.

Cereals are normally fed for the first month or two of the introduction of solid foods. The child should not be fed mixed cereals or wheat-based cereal because of possible allergic reactions. It is difficult to tell which ingredient in mixed cereal may be the culprit and wheat is often the basis for allergy among infants.

Beginning around 4–6 months, babies can be fed a rice-fortified cereal. Remember to discard any uneaten food after the feeding, as the food may have been contaminated and should not be reused.

Vegetables.   The next food to introduce is vegetables, one at a time. Infants may show preference for flavors and may totally reject a food. This is one reason vegetables are introduced before fruits, since sweet flavors are preferred to savory flavors. This gives the child the opportunity to learn to enjoy vegetables before being introduced to fruits. It is a good idea to stick with dark green and yellow vegetables because they are good sources of vitamin A. Spinach and beets may cause allergic reactions, so the caregiver may want to avoid these in the beginning.

If the child rejects a food several days in a row, the caregiver should respect this dislike and discontinue it. The caregiver may try it again in a few months. Vegetables should be strained or pureed at this stage. The caregiver may use commercially prepared baby food or make it. Remember that infants do not need salt, spices, or other enhancements to make their food palatable. It is a good habit to get a child to accept food in its natural form so that the particular food will be acceptable later on in many forms. Infants cannot digest spices, and sweetening foods or adding salt may cause food preferences that may make it difficult for the child to follow the Food Guide Pyramid when he is older.

Fruits.   Fruits are introduced next, one at a time. Many fresh fruits can be easily mashed. This is a good time to introduce soft finger food such as bananas. Most infants respond well to the majority of fruits, but certain textures such as those in pears may cause the child to reject trying a particular food. If the child rejects a food, the caregiver can add the food to the list of things to try again later. When exposed to a food 8 to 10 times, children may develop an increase in preference for that food. By exposing them to new and different foods, caregivers can provide opportunities for children to learn to like a variety of nutritious foods (Johnson & Nicklas, 1999).

Yellow fruits such as apricots and peaches are good sources of vitamin A. The caregiver must be watchful when introducing items such as fresh strawberries and citrus fruits, because although they are excellent sources of vitamin

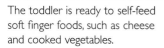
The toddler is ready to self-feed soft finger foods, such as cheese and cooked vegetables.

C, they also may cause allergic reactions. Fruit juices are another good source of vitamins, but the caregiver should use unsweetened juices. This is the perfect time to introduce a cup to a baby. It is preferable to feed a child juice from a cup, not from a bottle. Fruit juice in a bottle can lead to baby bottle tooth decay.

When choosing a cup, the caregiver should find one that is unbreakable and weighted at the bottom. It is better when first trying a cup to use one with at least one handle so the baby has something to grasp. These cups usually come with a lid, but if the baby seems to have difficulty with the sipping action, the lid may be removed. Try a sip at a time beginning with a small amount using a bib to protect baby from spills.

Other Foods. At this time most children will have enough teeth to be able to do some chewing. Soft finger foods such as cheese are good beginner foods to help the child learn to feed himself. Cheese and yogurt are good sources of calcium and protein and both are easily digestible by now.

At nine months meat such as chicken, beef, lamb, and fish can be added. Wait awhile for pork, because it may cause allergic reactions. If the child has enough teeth, the meat can be chopped into very small pieces so she can pick up the pieces and feed herself. Egg yolks can also be added now, but it is best to avoid egg whites and whole eggs until the child is at least one year old. Cottage cheese is another addition that will offer a good source of calcium and protein.

This is the time when other finger foods such as toast and crackers can be added. They are good sources of carbohydrates, as are rice and pasta. These items can be chewed and easily digested by now. The pasta and rice should be fairly plain, not highly seasoned. The caregiver should avoid serving finger foods that are not soft or will not soften in the mouth, such as carrots or celery.

Caregiver Guidelines

There are some guidelines for infant feeding as shown in Table 6–6. As the caregiver helps to establish the eating behavior of an infant as he or she goes from breast or bottle feeding to solid foods these guidelines may assist in successful infant feeding.

TABLE 6–6 Guidelines for Successful Infant Feeding

- Use a small spoon and age-appropriate cup.
- Watch for cues that baby is full.
- Never use food as bribery, diversion, or reward.
- Offer an assortment of healthy foods.
- Try new foods at baby's best time of day.
- Respect the child's food likes and dislikes.
- Infants may not be able to eat a great deal at a time, so serve smaller meals throughout the day.
- Make mealtime pleasant, not distracting.
- Avoid serving foods that may choke an infant.
- Only serve foods that are soft or will become soft in the mouth.

KEY CONCEPT 6.2

Early Feeding and the Infant in Care

Infancy is a critical time for forming the pattern to meet the nutritional needs of a child. Whether the baby is fed by breast milk or formula, a caregiver can manage health risk by using food safety behaviors. Being aware of the cues that an infant will give when he is full will help the caregiver allow the infant to gain control of his own feeding behavior. The introduction of solid foods brings nutritional challenges that can be easily met if the caregiver is knowledgeable about the pattern of introducing these foods. Understanding how to accommodate the infant's physical and psychological needs will allow the caregiver to encourage the infant to go at her own pace. The caregiver plays an important role in helping the infant and his family to establish good nutrition and providing the groundwork for good feeding behaviors.

6.3 Feeding the Toddler

The transition from infant to toddler is most apparent in a child's eating behavior. This is the first place a child will begin to show his independence and need for autonomy. Good nutrition allows a child to grow, learn, and play. The challenge for this period is to maintain good nutrition while helping the child establish good food habits with her independence intact. Creating a framework for forming good food habits is one of the most important things the caregiver can do for a child to ensure good health and well-being. To help the child establish good eating behaviors, the caregiver must understand how growth patterns and developmental changes affect a toddler's actions (see Table 6–7).

The caregiver and the parent should work together in communicating the child's eating habits at school and at home, and decide how best to meet the child's nutritional needs.

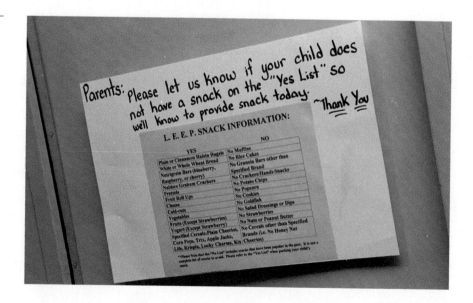

TABLE 6–7   Common Patterns of Toddler's Growth and Development That Affect Eating Actions

- Child wants and needs to be independent; child wants to control his own eating.
- Child learns to say "no" even to favorite foods.
- Appetite is sporadic as growth slows.
- Child learns by doing—wants to feed self.
- Child has food likes and dislikes. Child may develop food jags for favorite foods.
- Child is gaining more control over large motor skills, and can lift food to mouth. Because large muscle control is still developing, the child will sometimes drop or spill food.
- Child is gaining more control over fine motor skills, and is able to use a spoon.
- Child is learning to manipulate objects, and likes to touch and play with food.
- Child may be teething and have difficulty chewing, and will spit out or remove food from mouth.
- Child wants to master the job of eating and be successful, even if it means hiding food under plate or in a pocket to show he is done.
- Child is learning to be a social creature, and may entertain others with food antics.

Food as an Issue of Control

Adults feel responsible for a child's eating habits. If the child is not eating right, we may cajole, coerce, bribe, or beg the child to eat. Without realizing it, adults have just drawn the line for the battle over food being used as an issue of control between a well-meaning adult and an independence seeking toddler. As a child recognizes the adult's concern over the consumption of food, the child may figure out creative ways to utilize food as a weapon in the quest for independence.

Ellyn Satter, dietitian and author of several books (1987, 2000) on the subject of feeding behavior problems, has offered some specific guidelines to help alleviate the struggle for control between the adult and the child concerning food.

■ The adult is responsible for controlling what food comes into the house and how it is presented to the child.

■ The adult is also responsible for making sure the child is at a meal, keeping the child on task, making sure the child behaves well, and regulating the time for meals and snacks.

■ The child is responsible for how much he eats, whether he eats, and how his body turns out.

Careful examination of these areas of responsibility will change the battle into a cooperative venture.

Eating can often become a power struggle between the adult and child. Keeping the child on task and making mealtime enjoyable are ways that the adult can help to regulate the child's food consumption without causing undue stress.

The way that an adult treats a child at the table may very well be a reflection of how the adult treats the child elsewhere. The adult can help regulate the food consumption behavior in numerous ways. Training the child to be on task in the eating of satisfying and well-prepared foods is a good first step. When a child realizes that food can be enjoyable he is more likely to be agreeable with the idea of eating and will be less likely to balk at the task at hand. If the child does not eat, the adult should learn to relax and stay calm. Erratic food intake is normal and it will support the child's growth because over time the proper balance will be achieved. Branen, Fletcher, & Myers (1997) found that when children in child care were allowed select foods, the consumption pattern was not significantly different from being served preselected foods. The one difference they found is that children did not waste more food, but in some cases they tended to eat more because they were able to regulate their own intake. A conclusion of their study was that self-selection may help to regulate dietary intake in child care and may offer a more healthy alternative to preselection.

Another strategy for helping a child develop good eating habits is to make mealtimes significant for the child. Understanding the temperament of the child, his capabilities, and his tempo will help the caregiver prepare for mealtime. The caregiver should give the child time, attention, and awareness when meals are served. Sitting and talking with children while they are eating makes this time special. The caregiver should reinforce desirable behavior by paying attention, recognizing, and acknowledging good behavior.

The caregiver can contribute to regulating eating habits by managing the eating environment. Setting limits makes eating more important and worthwhile. When feeding a child a snack or a meal, the caregiver must make sure that is the only activity going on. The caregiver should also limit eating to one or two appropriate places. That may be in a kitchen or patio in a home situation, not in front of a television. In center-based care, eating may occur in the classroom or on tables near the playground. The caregiver should spend some

Judith always sits with her two-year-old child care group at lunch time. Teresa, the cook, serves the food family-style in large bowls and helps each child select foods. During this process Judith keeps the children who have their food on task, and talks with the children who have not been served yet. When everyone is served, the group discusses the food and talks about how things taste. Judith also talks with the children about the morning activities and explains some of the things Roberta, the afternoon teacher, has planned for them. This helps the children prepare for the transition and helps them remember what they have done that day. Another significant thing Judith does daily is to eat the same food for lunch that the children are eating. She is role modeling that the food served is just as acceptable to her as it is for the children. Judith's pet peeve is teachers who bring in fast food to eat in front of children and who do not practice what they are trying to enforce—good eating habits.

time getting the child ready to eat. The transition time from another activity should be quiet and calming to prepare children for eating time.

A child should come to the table at mealtime ready to eat. If the child is disinterested or not hungry, the caregiver should not force the issue, but should have the child stay at the table a few minutes before excusing him. This removes the temptation for the child to entertain or act out. If the child complains about being hungry a few minutes later, the caregiver can remind him that snack time is just a few hours away. The child made the choice not to participate and maybe next time will make a different choice. This reinforces the fact that the child made the decision and the caregiver supported it. The caregiver should not change the eating pattern for meals and snacks to accommodate whims.

The caregiver should keep food out of sight when eating is not the activity. Seeing food can make children think they need to eat when they are not really hungry. Age-appropriate foods and utensils should be chosen. Finger

The caregiver can promote good eating habits by managing the eating environment. The caregiver should also limit eating to one or two appropriate places.

foods and foods that are easy to eat should help toddlers to learn to manipulate more successfully. Foods such as popcorn, grapes, carrots, and celery that may cause the child to choke should be avoided. The caregiver must use utensils that a toddler can grasp easily, and small plates and cups that look as though they are full when the serving of food is placed on them.

Although it may be difficult to accommodate in some center schedules, child care homes and nannies can tailor the serving of food around when children need to eat. The caregiver should try to be as reliable and regular as possible in feeding the children, and not wait until they are really hungry and have behavior difficulties because of it. The caregiver should not feed children if they do not feel hungry at the moment.

These actions allow the caregiver to establish trust in relationship to food and children. Children will act more responsibly when they can trust their caregiver to provide the food and atmosphere that make them successful eaters.

Table 6–8 lists some key points about using food as nutrition and not as a battleground.

Nutritional Considerations

Whether it is served as a meal or a snack, food should be satisfying and meet the children's nutritional needs. The ideal meal or snack would include a protein food, a carbohydrate food, and some fat. When planning meals or snacks, the caregiver must treat empty nutrient, high-calorie foods that have too much sugar or fat, with respect. Snacks should be taken seriously and used as part of the day's nutrition. If someone has a birthday and brings cupcakes, enjoy them. The caregiver should model how the food should be savored and serve it with milk or some other nutritious food so all is not lost.

The caregiver should recognize that there will be a variation in food consumption. A child may refuse to eat foods from a particular food group or may eat only one food to the exclusion of others. This is referred to as a food jag and is common. If it continues for more than a short period of time, like a week, this food should be offered only at snack time and the caregiver must make sure other foods are served at regular mealtimes.

TABLE 6–8 Food as Nutrition, Not Control

- The modeling of your actions and attitudes toward food will affect how the children feel about food.
- Stay calm; do not react to negative behavior.
- Realize pressure does not work—forcing or withholding are ineffective.
- Do not use food as a punishment or as a reward.
- Outside influences, including cultural influences, can affect your good intentions about children and their food behavior.
- Respect cultural eating differences. Expose children to foods from many cultures.
- Children learn from feeding, their first attempt at independence, what to expect from the world.
- If they are successful, the world is a beautiful place. If they fail, they may withdraw or act out.

Milk is a food and should have its proper place. Children over the age of six months should not drink formula to the exclusion of other foods. Toddlers should not drink so much milk that they lose their appetite for other foods. Toddlers who use milk as the main source of energy and nutrients may have a condition called milk anemia, which is an iron deficiency due to lack of proper food and too much milk. A toddler should drink no more than 24 ounces of milk a day. Children over the age of one year can have cow's milk, but they should never be served nonfat milk, because they need the fat content for growth and development. Some children may not want to drink milk alone at this stage. The caregiver will need to substitute yogurt, cheese, and other dairy products to be sure the child receives the necessary amounts of calcium and other minerals.

According to recent studies, overconsumption of juice may cause a child to not keep pace with the growth and development of children of the same age (Aby-Valestrino, 2001). When juice was not served, all of the children observed began putting on weight again. As previously stated, the caregiver should serve juice only in a cup and should use it to enhance a meal but not to replace other foods. If a child is thirsty, water is the best alternative. Some guidelines for the caregiver to maximize the eating and nutritional needs of the toddler are listed in Table 6–9.

The caregiver should use whatever methods are available to encourage the toddlers in care to eat good food and be well-nourished.

TABLE 6–9   Guidelines for Forming Good Food Habits for Toddlers

- Make food easy to eat.
- Cut finger food in bite-size pieces.
- Make sure some of the foods served are soft and moist.
- Serve food at room temperature. Toddlers shy away from foods that are too cold or too hot.
- Toddlers are sensitive to texture and may not eat foods that are lumpy or stringy. Try these foods and if they will not eat them, try again later.
- Toddlers like colorful foods and often prefer vegetables that are raw or under-cooked because they are brighter in color and crisp.
- A typical toddler may like his food in different or specific shapes. Carrots may need to be cut in coins before cooking so the toddler will eat them.
- Toddlers like fun foods such as faces on pancakes or sandwiches or other foods cut into unusual shapes.

KEY CONCEPT 6.3

Feeding Behavior of the Toddler

The toddler is growing and developing in many ways. A number of these growth characteristics have an impact on the toddler's food behavior. If the caregiver understands this, food is less likely to be an issue of control. There are a number of strategies a caregiver can employ to help make mealtimes pleasant and encourage the child to eat, thus meeting the toddler's nutritional needs.

The toddler and preschooler are growing and developing, becoming more active and autonomous. The toddler's behavior at the table also reflects these changes and when identified can aid the caregiver in helping the child develop good eating habits.

6.4 Food and the Preschooler

As children reach the preschool stage, a number of developmental changes have occurred that make feeding and nourishing a much easier task. A child of three knows that he is a separate person and understands acceptable and appropriate behavior. He is capable of being patient and can control impulses. If the preschooler whines, complains, or begs for food not on the table, he is capable of understanding that this behavior is unacceptable and he may be asked to get down from the table.

Outside Influences

Preschoolers are social beings who like eating with others. Preschool children are ready to learn and are willing to change and try new things when they are together, so they are probably more likely to eat more servings of the basic food groups (Levy & Cooper, 1999). The preschooler learns much from observation

Encouraging children to accept new foods can be a difficult task. Serving new foods with familiar foods or having other children introduce the new foods are some methods for encouraging this exploration.

and role play. She is likely to feel good about herself and enjoys cooperating. The preschooler probably has food preferences that may have been influenced by others. Messages children receive at home from their parents and television have a great deal of influence on their attitude about food (Borzekowski & Robinson, 2001).

Preschoolers can also be influenced by teachers and friends at school. They feel secure eating familiar foods, but if encouraged to explore, they may try new foods. Often a preschooler may eat a food at school that she would not eat at home. This willingness to eat at school and not at home may be a result of negative messages or reinforcement about the particular food. A child whose parent says squash is "icky" or makes the comment, "Jerry won't eat squash," may be keeping that behavior a fact at home.

Children of this age are easily influenced by television advertising of food products that are poor nutritional choices (Borzekowski & Robinson, 2001). Over one-half of all the ads on television are for food products and the majority of these are for heavily sugared products. The cereal aisle of the grocery store contains an abundance of these foods. A parent may find it difficult to get through this aisle without a confrontation or without giving in to the child's demands. The cereal aisle is one of the best examples of **positive reinforcement** of negative behavior for young children. An adult who gives in to the demands for a certain sugared cereal seen on television allows the child to feel that television is right about the claims made. A better alternative for the adult, be it parent or caregiver, is to make positive use of the television ads and have the child help investigate the claim by reading the label.

Positive reinforcement
reward given in response to a particular behavior that increases the chance of that behavior occurring again

---

Dawn is a teacher of older four-year-olds in a community college preschool. The majority of children in her class have parents in the college. There is a real mixture of family types and income range. The children bring their lunches from home and Dawn spends time every day with each child investigating the lunches.

Kristin had a juice box that was full of sugar but not much juice. After reading the label with Dawn, Kristin informed her mother that it was not really juice and enlisted her help in finding a better drink for her lunch.

Zarli's dad was new to the lunch making business and the first few weeks were a struggle. But after Dawn helped Zarli investigate her lunches, Zarli became aware enough to encourage her dad to read the labels and learn about good food. Her lunches became more interesting and encouraged both child and parent to try to understand more about healthier eating. Her father often asked Dawn for advice on new ideas for lunches. He got to be very creative.

Rashid was from a different cultural background and often had foods that Dawn did not recognize. She did recognize the drink in his lunches as a highly advertised sugared drink and helped Rashid investigate the label. Dawn explained it to Rashid and he in turn helped explain it to his mother who spoke limited English. This exchange led to a wonderful dialogue between Rashid, his mother, and Dawn discussing the foods that Rashid brought. Dawn learned how the foods were prepared and what healthy ingredients they had in them. Rashid and his mother learned not to believe everything one sees on television.

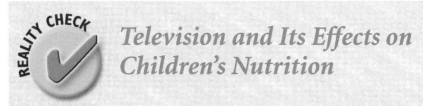

Television and Its Effects on Children's Nutrition

Television has a great impact on the health and nutritional status of young children in this country. Hunger/malnutrition, obesity, dental cavities, iron deficiency anemia, cardiovascular diseases, and food allergies are the basic nutritional challenges facing children. All but food allergies may be affected by television viewing.

Children between the ages of two and five years watch about 25 hours of television per week (Time in a Box, 1999). For that many hours viewing television, children would be watching about three hours of advertising. Children from the ages of two to twelve years are said to have watched 200,000 television ads. Of those, 45 percent are ads for food. Eighty percent of Saturday morning television ads are for low-nutritional quality foods (Consumers International, 2001). More than 50 percent of these ads were for sweets, breakfast cereals, and fast foods.

This is a concern to many health professionals and nutritionists. The food that is advertised is not healthy food. Struempler (2001) reported that 44 percent of ads were for the top of the pyramid, while there were no fruits and vegetables represented at all. Only 4 percent of the ads were for milk and yogurt, 2.5 percent for the meat group, and 37 percent were for breads and grains (Kotz & Story, 1994). Of the breads and grains, the majority of the ads were for sugared cereals. The ads for fast foods (10.8 percent) were mostly for hamburger and pizza restaurants, which are known to serve foods high in fat, sodium, and sugar.

The representative Saturday Morning Food Guide Pyramid (Kotz & Story 1994) shows the upside-down pyramid effect. Aronson (2000) reported that 16 percent of children were not meeting any needs in any category of the Food Guide Pyramid (see Figure 6–2).

Advertising usually has a particular "hook" or appeal that makes people want to purchase a product. Children's ads have an identifiable character to relate to more often than do adult ads (Brown, 1997). These characters may be cartoon or real-life heroes. Children's advertising often has jingles or corporate logos that help children associate with those ads (Borzekowski & Robinson, 2001). The number of times children request things seen on television may be an indicator of the effect of these ads. In a recent study, parents reported that after watching television ads, almost half requested a food item and 57 percent requested to go to a restaurant or store advertised (Borzekowski & Robinson, 2001).

Much of the advertising for breakfast cereals may include the phrase "part of a balanced breakfast," but this may be erroneous, considering the amount of sugar present in the cereal. Young children do not have knowledge or sophistication to be discerning consumers. The appearance of the hooks of happiness, being cool, or getting good taste or a toy may cause the children watching these ads to desire many items of low nutritional quality.

One major effect that television viewing has on children is a risk to both nutrition and health. It discourages exercise, so children may become "couch potatoes." Body metabolism for watching television is actually 14.5 percent less than lying down in bed (Time in a Box, 1999). Some children eat their meals in front of television, which increases intake of pizza, salty snacks, and sodas, and decreases intake of fruits, vegetables, and juices (Coon et al., 2001). The consumption of soft drinks has increased 500 percent in the last 50 years and much of this may be due to television advertising. All of these dietary habits may lead to obesity, and television viewing has been directly related to increased obesity in this country (Anderson et al., 1998).

Caregivers can promote good nutrition by using the Food Guide Pyramid to make healthier choices (Briley & Roberts-Gray, 1999). They can also talk about food advertisements and help children understand that while they are appealing, the food is not healthy and should be limited in their diets. Caregivers can also help children by reading food labels so that they can become more discriminating in their food choices (Johnson, 2000). Another effort to help children would be to teach them how to read their own internal cues as to when they are hungry and not to eat just because television is on (Johnson & Kennedy, 2000).

Figure 6–2

The Food Guide Pyramid Compared to the Saturday Morning Pyramid *(From Kotz, K., & Story, M. [1994]. Journal of the American Dietetic Association, 94, 1296.)*

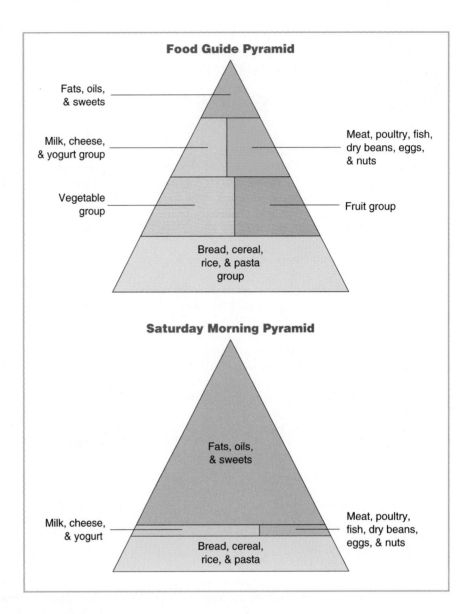

Participation

The caregiver can foster good nutrition by involving preschoolers with the selection of foods and helping with food preparation. Encouraging preschool children to be part of the process can empower them with the knowledge and awareness necessary to make better nutritional choices. Activities that are enjoyable give children confidence to try new foods and different ways of preparation. Children should have the opportunity to learn about food, nutrition, and food preparation and how they are linked to health. Reading books about new foods can pave the way for greater understanding. Letting preschoolers help prepare foods and experiment with new foods helps children develop skills that will widen their food horizons. Mealtime offers genuine opportunities for conversations about food and eating behavior. This is a good time to discuss, practice, and model good nutrition and correct eating behavior (Satter, 2000; Levy & Cooper, 1999). These strategies will help the caregiver positively impact the preschooler's nutritional well-being.

KEY CONCEPT 6.4

Food and the Preschooler

A preschooler is likely to be influenced by others, including television, as to his or her food choices. These choices have a direct effect on the health and well-being of the preschooler. A caregiver can use participatory activities to bring an awareness to the preschooler about what the best nutritional choices are. Encouraging a child to be involved in food selection, preparation, and mealtime activities will give the child the confidence to make better choices.

6.5 School-Age Nutrition

Caregivers from child care centers may not be involved with school-age care. Some centers do offer before and after school care to these children. Family child caregivers and nannies are commonly involved with school-aged children before and after school and during school vacations. The needs of school-aged children, ages five to eleven years, vary greatly from the infant, toddler, and preschooler.

Growth is slower during this period and is not as observable as the earlier infant-toddler growth spurt or the adolescent growth spurt that will occur later. However, the vigorous activity level that most school-aged children experience makes the need for adequate nutrition important. In addition, good nutrition will help the school-aged child maintain resistance to infection and help ensure adequate stores for the building materials and nutrition needed for the adolescent growth spurt.

Breakfast is a very imporant meal for children and has been proven to improve cognitive skills. Many schools and centers now provide this meal, which should be high in protein.

Children of this age are not totally capable of planning a well-balanced diet each day. They may eat for social reasons, such as television viewing, when they are not really hungry. Children of this age may have fluctuating appetites and may become finicky in their eating habits. These changes may be attributed to the consumption of more and more foods that are low in nutrients and high in calories.

Snacking is easier because school-aged children are capable of preparing a variety of snacks. High-fat or sweetened foods or beverages are easy to prepare and serve. If these are available, children will probably eat them.

Fast food has a tremendous influence on the school-aged child. These children are more mobile and they may have their own money that allows these purchases. Many school lunch programs serve fast type foods in order to get the children to eat what is served and cut down on waste. Most fast foods are high in calories or low in nutrients.

Good dietary habits should be focused on and practiced. Caregivers can perform a number of functions that will help school-aged children practice better nutritional habits. The first thing the caregiver can do is provide healthy, nutritious foods for the children to eat. If children have choices that are good foods, the choices will be limited and good nutrition will be more readily available.

Supervising school-aged children in planning their own menus and preparing good food will show children that they can affect their own nutritional well-being. If the child care includes breakfast, the caregiver can give children a good start by preparing a meal that includes some protein. Children who have a good breakfast are better at performing cognitive skills.

If the caregiver's job includes preparing or helping the child prepare a sack lunch, there are several important considerations. Children who help prepare their own lunches are more likely to eat the lunch. Typical brown bag lunches contain more sugar, sweets, and sweetened beverages and less meat, poultry, or fish than do school lunches prepared by cafeteria staff (Gordon & McKinney, 1995). Sack lunches usually do not contain enough fruits and vegetables and have too many convenience type foods. Packing good food may be a challenge, especially if food safety is taken into consideration. The caregiver should use imagination and safe food practices. Some suggestions are found in Table 6–10.

Snacks are likely to be the main foods that a caregiver will provide for most school-aged children. It is important that these foods are readily available when the child arrives at the site. Children are usually very hungry after a long school day. Offering foods prepared by the caregiver as well as items that are simple for the child to prepare will help the child appease hunger and build self-confidence.

TABLE 6–10 Packing Healthy Foods for Brown Bag Lunches

- Pre-cut fruits and vegetables can be stored in the refrigerator and packed in the morning.
- Sandwiches can be prepared the afternoon before so they get thoroughly chilled in the refrigerator and will last longer in the lunches.
- Choose low-fat cuts of meat. Cut the sandwiches into interesting shapes.
- Leftovers can be frozen in small containers and packed in the morning.
- Use only 100 percent fruit juices or have the parent provide money to purchase milk.

(continued)

TABLE 6–10 Packing Healthy Foods for Brown Bag Lunches *(continued)*

- Forego chips and other high-calorie, low-nutrient foods; substitute pretzels or other low-fat snack foods.
- Provide fruits that are in season and have the child select the fruit.
- Use "blue ice" or other devices that will help keep the lunches cool.

KEY CONCEPT 6.5

School-Age Nutrition

Many care situations do not have school-aged children. Those caregivers who do care for school-aged children face nutritional challenges that are different from infants, toddlers, or preschoolers. The caregiver needs to keep in mind the school-aged children's activity levels in order to provide them with adequate nutrition. The caregiver is practicing nutritional risk management by purchasing healthy foods, preparing them, and supervising the child in meal or snack preparation.

6.6 Nutrition and the Child with Special Needs

Developmental disabilities

physical or mental incapacities that interfere with normal progress of development

Some caregivers care for children who have special needs. Many of these children have **developmental disabilities** or chronic illnesses that affect feeding skills, nutritional needs, or equipment needed. Some children require special feeding procedures and some require special foods or diets.

Children who have cerebral palsy, Down's syndrome, a cleft lip or palate, or other developmental abnormalities may have physical difficulties eating or feeding themselves. Children with metabolic disorders such as cystic fibrosis, diabetes, PKU, and maple syrup urine syndrome have special dietary limitations that prevent them from eating certain types of food that make the Food Guide Pyramid less useful. Some children may have conditions that require modifying their intake of sodium, protein, carbohydrates, or fats. Others may have allergies or food intolerances. Certain medical conditions may call for dietary restrictions or requirements (HCC, 1998).

The Individuals with Disabilities Act (1990) requires certain child care centers and child care homes to accommodate children with special needs as best they can. That act also has a provision that requires states to provide early intervention services to infants and toddlers. Nutrition services were included in this early intervention (Yadrick & Sneed, 1994).

There are many children with special needs who can be accommodated easily and whose nutritional needs may not be difficult to meet. Chairs, tables, and eating utensils may need to be modified for some children. These accommodations can be made by the caregiver without great expense or effort.

Other children offer challenges that the caregiver really is not prepared or trained to accommodate. The nutritional needs of some children with chronic illness or developmental disabilities are complicated and may be

Feeding practice may have to be altered for children with special needs. In this picture, the child is reclined in her chair instead of being cradled. Caregivers need to be accommodating and sensitive to these needs.

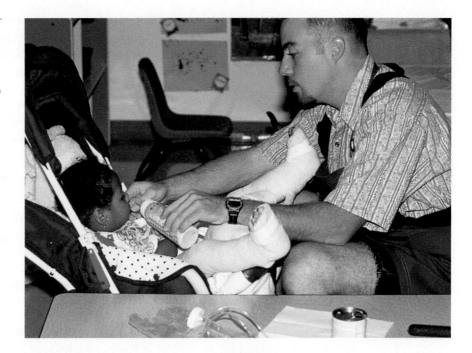

compounded by eating difficulties. The average caregiver should not be expected to provide this type of accommodation without outside assessment, intervention, and help. The disabilities act provides the vehicle for the nutrition services the caregiver may need. Contacting the state child nutrition staff is a good place to begin. Local school districts may be involved in early intervention assessment, and local regional centers may also provide some of this assessment. The American Dietetic Association supports the participation of its members in providing nutrition services to child care programs that include children with disabilities and chronic illnesses. Parents of these children may be good sources of information and may be able to help the caregiver to link up with the community services needed to support the care of these children.

Access to these services may not provide a caregiver with the skills and special handling that some children with special needs require. A referral for the child to a special care program or regional center may be all that the child caregiver is able to do to help the families of these children.

KEY CONCEPT 6.6

Children with Special Needs

The Individuals with Disabilities Act may require that some child care programs and some family child care homes accommodate children with special needs as best they can. Some children with disabilities or chronic illnesses may be easily accommodated in their nutritional needs and feeding levels. Others may require special early intervention nutritional services. Those services may not be adequate to provide the level of care some children with special needs may require.

6.7 Exercise as a Part of Diet

A new guideline has been added to the Dietary Guidelines for Americans that reflects the fact that physical activity is needed to balance food intake (Johnson & Kennedy, 2000). Healthy People 2010 has included increased physical activity as one of its top 10 priorities (Tate & Patrick, 2000). Even though they may not think their children are overweight, mothers generally understand that their children need to be physically active (Jain et al., 2001).

Preschool children and school-aged children are active on a daily basis. Large motor activities offer them the exercise that they need. The preschool years are especially important for motor development (Poole, 2000). Running, throwing, catching, kicking, climbing, and jumping are motor activities that come naturally to young children. They enjoy accomplishing these new abilities.

If the children in care are active, the caregiver should encourage them to remain that way. Free play is best for those active children. If some of the children are interested only in sedentary activities such as quiet play with dolls or puzzles, these children should be encouraged to be more active by providing interesting activities. Music and movement are wonderful ways to get children involved. Playing games together on the playground is another good way to get these sedentary children involved.

Encouraging children to take an active part in playground play is a good way for a caregiver to ensure children are getting enough exercise. Children should have 15 to 20 minutes of structured activity per day (Poole, 2000). Taking a daily walk or having game time would be using a structure for exercise. Both free and structured activities should be a part of the daily routine.

If the weather is inclement, indoor play should be planned for and used as a way for children to get exercise. If adequate room is not available and there is a nearby school, gym, or community center available for use, this would be a good alternative. Checking out a simple exercise video from the library and having the children try to perform the exercises on the video may be another fun way to exercise indoors on occasion (Brooks, 1996). If there are school-aged children in care, the caregiver can have them help lead the exercises. School-aged children might really enjoy demonstrating exercises they have learned in school.

A good amount of physical activity should be worked into every child care program. An evaluation of the general activity level of the class and of specific children, can help the caregiver identify what activities are best.

The caregiver can also remove temptations to inactivity such as television. This may enhance greater exercise and movement for the children in care. Children who watch a lot of television are more likely to be less physically fit, more overweight, and have a distorted knowledge of nutrition. Use the television sparingly and only for educational viewing.

KEY CONCEPT 6.7

Exercise as Part of Diet

Daily large motor activities are a necessary component of a child care program. A caregiver who encourages exercise in the child care daily program provides a broad base for nutritional risk management. Encouraging all children to be physically active and providing daily large motor activities to ensure this allows the caregiver to promote good health and well-being.

6.8 Implications for Caregivers

Nutrition education is an important tool for the caregiver to help parents and children better understand their role in proper nutrition for good health and well-being. Education can break down barriers, provide awareness of the effects of growth and development on feeding habits, and offer strategies to parents who want to make sure their children are getting a healthy start. Education can make children aware of their food selection and how their behavior has an effect on health and well-being. It can empower them to make better choices and participate in their own nutritional well-being. Role modeling can help the caregiver carry out educational strategies. Cultural sensitivity may be essential for the caregiver who has a diverse group in care. Supervision helps the caregiver to carry out good nutritional practices.

Education and Role Modeling

Caregivers and parents have a great influence on what children learn to eat. Modeling healthy eating to children of all ages can help children develop healthy eating habits themselves (Briley & Roberts-Gray, 1999). The type and kinds of food that are provided for children help to determine how the child will eat and grow. Parents and caregivers model food selection and acceptability to the children in their lives. If these selections are healthy choices, a child will have a positive perspective about good foods. If the selections are poor choices, this sends a negative message about good nutrition.

For Parents. Parents and caregivers have the power to establish positive, supportive environments that allow children to develop good feeding behaviors and attitudes toward food. The caregiver can help the parent understand this by providing good role modeling and some positive nutrition information. The caregiver needs to be aware that there may be some barriers to accepting this information (Briley, Jastrow, Vickers, & Roberts-Gray, 1998). There may be environmental constraints to good nutrition for some of the families. Cost of food, access and availability of good food, and storage space are factors that may limit the family's ability to make a wide range of good food choices.

Poverty or low income may prohibit the selection of many foods including fresh fruits and vegetables and dairy products. These families may need help in accessing food programs that help families meet their food needs. The caregiver may also be able to provide the parents with information on food selections as well as recipes that use low-cost fresh foods. Consequently, the caregiver may find there is great interest on the part of the family to help improve their nutritional intake.

Another influence on food selection may be convenience of preparation of some foods. Some adults may find it easier to open a can or a box than to prepare fresh foods. Other adults might select fast foods as a further measure of convenience. These behaviors are an enormous barrier with middle and upper income families who can afford the convenience of packaged or fast foods. Having the children help prepare foods may help interest the parents in preparing more fresh food. Role modeling and providing recipes as well as activities for the families to do together may encourage this behavior.

Another perceived barrier may be related to the role the adult plays as a parent. The parent may not understand the stages and phases of growth and development as well as the caregiver does. This may make a parent unsure as to how to proceed. It may also influence the parent to feed the child as she

When four-year-old Amy came to Head Start, her mother reported that Amy did not like and would not eat most foods. Tanya, Amy's teacher, observed Amy at snack and lunch time for several weeks. She watched as Amy refused to try new things for the first two weeks. The foods that she was most vocal about were vegetables and fruits. Of the fruits and vegetables offered to her, Amy would eat only canned applesauce and corn. Other children were eating most of the foods that Amy was refusing. One day Joelle, another four-year-old, encouraged Amy to try some green beans. Amy tried them and ended up eating all of her beans and asked for more. Several days later the preschoolers picked some carrots and cherry tomatoes at a cooperative garden they toured near their school. The vegetables were brought back to school and the children helped wash them and prepare them for a snack. Amy ate both the carrots and tomatoes. She loved the carrots and was mildly interested in the tomatoes.

Tanya reported these breakthroughs to Amy's mother, who had a hard time believing Amy was eating vegetables. She explained that Amy's father, who was no longer living with them, had hated vegetables and did not even want them in the house. Amy's mother got used to serving only applesauce and canned corn. Her budget was also tight so this wasn't a sacrifice on her part. Tanya spent some time explaining the Food Guide Pyramid and why a balanced diet was important. She also pointed out that there were some plots available in the community garden, so it did not have to cost too much money to increase the variety of fresh produce in the family's diet. Once Amy's mother realized the importance of a balanced diet, she signed up for a plot in the nearby cooperative garden and she started trying to add more variety to the menu at home.

Children learn many of their behaviors by watching the adults in their lives. For this reason, one of the most effective ways to teach children about good eating habits is for the caregiver to model these behaviors by sitting with the children and eating with them. In what other ways can caregivers model good nutrition habits?

was fed. Childhood food memories may influence selection or rejection of certain foods or food behaviors. A parent may model behaviors that are not productive to helping the child widen his food selections.

Adults may not realize that the social environment that is provided at mealtimes has a direct relationship to the dietary quality of their children. Children need a positive atmosphere, companionship, and the opportunity to view appropriate adult food-related behaviors to achieve good nutrition. The children in care may be the best educators for this barrier (Briley & Roberts-Gray, 1999). The caregiver can help parents by explaining the different stages of growth and development and encouraging parents to observe their child's behavior. Parents may then try different ways to support their children's eating behavior.

The results of companionship at mealtimes and the positive social atmosphere that can be created will be apparent through food selections and observation of behavior. Modeling these behaviors with the children in care will help the caregiver provide this information to the families.

The level of written nutritional information may be another barrier for the caregiver and the parent. Not all adults are literate. Approximately 60 million adults in the United States have not completed high school. Those who have completed high school may not read at the 12th grade level. In order to be effective, the nutritional information provided to the parent should be at the level that he is capable of understanding (Busselman & Holcomb, 1994).

With Children.   One of the greatest contributors to good health is good food habits. A child is capable of learning this through practice and observation from a very young age. Children are strongly influenced by what they see and hear. Parents and caregivers are sources of behavior and information that children model and remember. Children have an influence on the shopping habits of parents. Children's food preferences appear to mirror the television

This caregiver uses a flannel-board story to discuss with children the benefits of good eating habits and the risks of making poor food choices.

advertising that they see (Borzekowski & Robinson, 2001). Children have a large influence over parents' purchasing habits (Time in a Box, 1999).

The child caregiver should take time out, on a regular basis, to go over the Food Guide Pyramid with the children in care. The nutritional information about what each person should be eating in a day can be assimilated over time. Regular intervals of repetition help the children to understand and remember. This practice also helps the caregiver keep good nutritional information in action.

Enlisting children's help with food selection and preparation encourages them to try new foods and new ways of food preparation. Preparing children to help can be accomplished in several ways. The educational experience can be enhanced by reading books on certain foods, watching a video about foods, having circle time about what is going to be prepared, or telling a flannelboard story about the food or activity.

Cultural Competence

Cultural influences may present an obstacle to proper nutritional balance. The caregiver may face a challenge in helping parents select good food choices. Providing food and nutrition for children from diverse backgrounds can be a real task, but it can also be rewarding. Culture influences how food is prepared, seasoned, and even how or when it is eaten. There may be taboos or certain cultural traits to consider, such as the high percentage of lactose intolerance among the Asian population.

Understanding the cultural influence on food is important if the caregiver is going to help the families provide optimum nutrition for their children when they are not in care. Asking parents to share their culture's foods and food habits with the children in care is a good way for the caregiver to find out the extent of this obstacle. Adapting food selections to cultural influences may help increase the selection of foods available to the family. As the caregiver understands the dietary or food limitations of a family, he may need to call on outside help, such as a nutritionist.

Another issue in cultural competence may be the caregiver's own cultural perspective on the selection of foods. Not all children like foods that are different from the ones they are used to eating. These differences may be in the manner in which the foods are prepared or in the way they are seasoned. It is important for the caregiver to be sensitive to the needs of the children. The caregiver needs to present a balance of foods that represent the food selections of children from a number of other cultures.

Supervision

A caregiver is likely to serve one or more meals per day to the children in care. Supervision of mealtime requires a number of skills. If the caregiver provides meals to the children, the first area of supervision needed will be for the selection of healthy food choices. Regardless of whether the food is prepared by the caregiver or someone else, planning the meals should focus on healthy food choices and preparation forms. Food safety and sanitary practices should be used.

If the child brings meals from home, the caregiver may have to supervise what are acceptable food selections and what are not. She may also need to determine proper storage so the food remains safe. Sending a sheet of acceptable food choices for the child care situation may help remind the parents that the caregiver is there to provide optimum care for their children. If a child brings unacceptable foods, these foods can be set aside to eat only after the good choices have been finished. Reading labels with children can help make them aware of what foods contain. This can be a powerful tool to help influence the parents to make better food selections.

Direction or redirection of mealtime behaviors helps to establish good eating habits and feeding behaviors. Observing the behaviors of children will be made easier when growth and developmental levels are understood. Good role modeling of mealtime practices is essential. The caregiver has a great deal of influence on how the children in her care behave. Understanding the caregiver's level of responsibility and the child's responsibility about eating will help alleviate any issue of control over food. This helps the caregiver to provide a foundation of good feeding behaviors and eating practices.

KEY CONCEPT 6.8

Implications for Caregivers

The caregiver has an opportunity to provide positive food practices, good food selections, and an atmosphere conducive to eating. Application of information, strategies, and practices found in this chapter and the previous chapter enables the caregiver to do this. Opportunities to educate the children about nutrition will occur on a daily basis. Every time there is a meal or snack, the caregiver can sit with the children and role model good eating practices and have a dialogue about the food. Practicing cultural sensitivity can help remove any barriers about food selection and choices. Acknowledging diverse food habits and preparing foods to reflect this can help break down barriers. Supervision provides the caregiver with the tools needed to make sure that proper nutritional habits are being formed and practiced in the child care environment.

CHAPTER SUMMARY

Every caregiver should practice good nutrition in child care. Many caregivers are not meeting the nutritional needs of children in their care. Caregivers may approach nutrition with their own perspective based on background, food practices, culture, and what the children eat or will not eat. Caregivers should have nutritional policies that cover early infant feeding, food and the toddler, the preschool child, school-aged children, special needs, and nutrition and exercise as part of nutrition.

The caregiver who understands how to accommodate the infant's physical and psychological needs will encourage the infant to go at his own pace. A caregiver who understands that the developmental characteristics of a toddler influences how she deals with food is less likely to make food an issue of control. A caregiver should use participatory activities to help the preschooler develop an awareness about the best nutritional choices. The caregiver can provide adequate nutrition for school-aged children by keeping in mind their activity levels.

Some children with disabilities or chronic illnesses may be easily accommodated in their nutritional needs and feeding levels. Others may require special early intervention nutritional services or may not be able to be in the child care situation. Including exercise in the child care daily program helps the caregiver provide a broad base for nutritional risk management.

The implications for the child caregiver include education, role modeling, and supervision. Opportunities to educate and role model good nutrition to the children and adults occur on a daily basis. Cultural sensitivity can break down barriers to food selection. Supervision provides the caregiver with the tools needed to make sure that proper nutritional habits are being formed and practiced in the child care environment.

TO GO BEYOND

In this section you will find a number of activities that you can use to apply and improve your knowledge of this chapter. There are also thorough Online Resources that accompany this text that can be found at http://www.early childed.delmar.com/resources/robertson/index.html. Included on this site are chapter practice quizzes, PowerPoint outlines, Web links, a discussion forum, and various other activities to help you better understand the material in this chapter. This site is updated regularly so check back often to receive the latest information about the subjects in this chapter.

Chapter Review Critical Thinking Applications

1. Discuss how developmental levels relate to nutritional needs of children of different age levels. How do the developmental levels affect the eating process for children?

2. Examine the benefits of breast-feeding. Compare and contrast these benefits to those of bottle feeding. List suggestions as to how a breast-feeding mother might be supported to continue to breast-feed her baby.

3. Describe how you would introduce solid foods to an infant.

4. Analyze how food is used as an issue of control by toddlers and their parents. How would you avoid this in a day care situation?

As an Individual

1. Using "Rate Your Plate" found in Chapter 7 on page 246, rate your own diet. How does this differ from the three-day charting you did the previous week? Compare and contrast the two nutritional evaluations of your diet.

2. Observe children and their parents in a grocery store. How do they act in the cereal aisle? How do these interactions reflect positive rewards for negative behavior? How might food be an issue of control in these situations?

3. Observe Saturday morning television for one hour. Count the number of food commercials. How many of those commercials are for "junk foods?" Choose two commercials and list the methods those commercials use to convince the child to buy/eat their product.

As a Group

1. During a weeklong period, observe patterns of people eating, including children and cultural patterns. Discuss these patterns in class. List the patterns observed by all students in class. How would you use this information to talk to children about eating and food? How might you use this information to adapt to the different cultures in your local area?

2. Collect menus from child care centers, family care homes, and elementary schools in your area. Evaluate them and determine if they meet the nutritional needs of children. How might these menus be changed to better meet the needs described in the Food Guide Pyramid?

3. Break up into small groups and each group write three general policies for nutrition in child care. Come back as a large group and discuss. Choose the three most important policies. Discuss why these three policies were chosen.

4. Discuss the importance of exercise in child care. List 10 different ways exercise could be included in a daily child care program.

CHAPTER REFERENCES

Aby-Valestrino, M. (2001). Too much juice? *Healthy Child Care, 4*(4), 201. Retrieved May 15, 2002, from http://healthychild.net/Articles.

Ahluwalia, I., Tesssaro, I., Grummer-Strawn, L., MacGowan, C., & Benton-Davis, S. (2000). Georgia's breastfeeding promotion program for low-income women. *Pediatrics, 105*(6), e85.

American Academy of Pediatrics (AAP). (2000,Spring/Summer). Breastfeeding saves lives, reduces illness and fosters optimum child development and parenting. *Breastfeeding: Best for Baby and Mother Newsletter,* 2.

Anderson, R. Crespo, C., Bartlett, S., Cheskin, L., & Pratt, M. (1998). Relationship of physical activity and television watching with body weight and level of fatness among children. *Journal of the American Medical Association, 279*(12), 938–942.

Aronson, S. (2000, July). Updates on healthy eating and walkers. *Child Care Information Exchange,* 30.

Borzekowski, D., & Robinson, T. (2001). The 30-second effect: An experiment Revealing the impact of television commercials on the food preferences of preschoolers. *Journal of the American Dietetic Association, 101*(1), 42–46.

Branen, L., Fletcher, J., & Myers, S. (1997). Effects of pre-plated and family style food service on preschool children's food intake and waste at snacktime. *Journal of Research in Childhood Education 12,* 88–95.

Briley, M., Jastrow, S., Vickers, J., & Roberts-Gray, C. (1998). Dietary intake at child-care centers and away: Are parents and care providers working as partners or at cross-purposes? *Journal of the American Dietetics Association, 99*(8), 950–954.

Briley, M., Jastrow, S., Vickers, J., & Roberts-Gray, C. (1999). Can ready to eat cereal solve common nutritional problems in child care menus? *Journal of the American Dietetic Association, 99*(2), 341–342.

Briley, M., McBride, A., & Roberts-Gray, C. (1997). Banking on nutrition. *Texas Child Care, 21*(3), 2–5.

Briley, M., & Roberts-Gray, C. (1999). Nutrition standards for child care programs—Position of ADA. *Journal of American Dietetic Association, 99*(6), 981–988.

Briley, M., Roberts-Gray, C., & Simpson, D. (1994). Identification of factors that influence the menu at child care centers: A grounded theory approach. *Journal of the American Dietetic Association 94*(3), 276–281.

Brooks, M. (1996, January 6). Get a move on: Teaching kids to exercise should be a family affair—one that's fun. *San Diego Union Tribune,* E-1, 4

Brown, M. (1997). A comparison between adult and children advertising on television. Unpublished master's thesis, Western Connecticut State University, Connecticut. Retrieved May 15, 2002, from http://www.wscu.ed.

Busselman, D., & Holcomb, C. (1994). Reading skill and comprehension of Dietary Guidelines by WIC participants. *Journal of the American Dietetics Association, 94*(6), 622–625.

Carmichael, S., Prince, C., Burr, R., Nakamoto, F., & Vogt, R. (2001). Breast-feeding practices among WIC participants in Hawaii. *Journal of the American Dietetic Association, 101*(1), 7–62.

Consumers International. (2001). A spoonful of sugar: Television food advertising aimed at children: An international comparative study. Retrieved May 15, 2002, from http://www.consumerinternatin.org/campaign/tvads.

Coon, K., Goldberg, J., Rogers, B., & Tucker, K. (2001). Relationships between use of television during meals and children's food consumption patterns. *Pediatrics, 107*(1), e7.

Fletcher, J., & Branen, L. (1999). Feeding young children in group settings: Using scenarios for staff development. *Journal of Nutrition Education, 31*(6), 360B.

Gordon, A., & McKinney, R. (1995). Sources of nutrients for students. *Journal of Clinical Nutrition, 61*(1), 232–240.

Health and Human Services (HHS). (2001). *Blueprint for action on breastfeeding.* Department of Health and Human Services, Office on Women's Health. Rockville, MD: Author.

Healthy Child Care (HCC). (1998). Special dietary concerns in the childcare setting. *Healthy Child Care, 1*(4). Retrieved May 15, 2002, from http://www.healthychild.net/Articles/Diet4.html.

Jain, A., Sherman, S., Chamberlin, L., Carter, Y., Powers, S., & Whitaker, R. (2001). Why don't low-income mothers worry about their preschoolers weight? *Pediatrics, 104*(5), 1138–1146.

Johnson, R., & Kennedy, E. (2000). The 2000 Dietary Guidelines for Americans: What are the changes and why were they made? *Journal of the American Dietetic Association, 100*(7), 769–774.

Johnson, R., & Nicklas, T. (1999). Dietary guidance for healthy children aged 2 to 11 years: Position of ADA. *Journal of the American Dietetic Association, 99*(1), 93–101.

Johnson, S. (2000). Improving preschoolers' self-regulation of energy intake. *Pediatrics, 106*(6), 1429–1435.

Jones, E., & Matheny, R. (1993). Relationship between infant feeding and exclusion from child care. *Journal of the American Dietetic Association, 48*(5), 809–811.

Kendrick, A., Kaufman, R., & Messenger, K. (1995). *Healthy young children.* Washington, DC: NAEYC.

Kotz, K., & Story, M. (1994). Food advertisements during children's Saturday morning television programming: Are they consistent with dietary recommendations? *Journal of the American Dietetic Association, 94*(11), 1296–1300.

Levy, P., & Cooper, J. (1999). Five a day, let's eat and play: A nutrition education program for preschool children. *Journal of Nutrition Education, 31*(4), 235B.

Nicklas, T. (2001). Consider nutrition when choosing day care. *Nutrition and Your Child, 2,* 1, 3.

Poole, J. (2000, January). Fitness and the young child. *Childcare Information Exchange,* 49–50.

Reicks, M., Randall, J., & Haynes, B. (1994). Factors affecting consumption of fruits and vegetables by low-income families. *Journal of the American Dietetic Association, 94*(11), 1309.

Satter, E. (1987). *How to get your kid to eat . . . But not too much.* Palo Alto, CA: Bull Publishing Company.

Satter, E. (2000). *Feeding with love and good sense.* Palo Alto, CA: Bull Publishing Company.

Story, M., Holt, K., & Sofka, D. (Eds.). (2000). *Bright futures in practice: Nutrition.* Arlington, VA: National Center for Education in Maternal and Child Health.

Struempler, B. (2001). Saturday morning television shows may encourage poor eating habits. Alabama Cooperative Extension System. Retrieved May 15, 2002, from http://www.aces.edu/dept/extcomm/newspaper/sattv.html.

Tate, M., & Patrick, S. (2000). Healthy People 2010 targets healthy diet and healthy weight as critical goals. *Journal of the American Dietetic Association, 100*(3), 300.

Time in a Box. (1999). Statistical information on television and its impact on society. Retrieved May 15, 2002, from http://www.cnc-zone.com/time/states.htm#tele.

Yadrick, K., & Sneed, J. (1994). Nutrition services for children with developmental disabilities and chronic illness in education programs. *Journal of the American Dietetic Association 94*(10), 1122–1128.

SUGGESTIONS FOR READING

Branen, L., & Fletcher, J. (1994). Effects of restrictive and self-selected feeding on preschool children's food intake and waste at snacktime. *Journal of Nutrition Education, 26*(6), 273–277.

Diriga, O., Olgesby, A., & Bassoff, B. (1991). Assessment of the nutrition education needs of day care providers. *Journal of the American Dietetics Association, 91*(6), 714–715.

Gans, K., Sundaram, S., McPhillips, J., Hixson, M., Linnan, L., & Carleton, R. (1993). Rate your plate: An eating pattern assessment and educational tool used at cholesterol screening and education program. *Journal of Nutrition Education, 25*(1), 29–35.

Kendall, P. (1995). *Health impacts of Saturday morning t.v.* Colorado State University Cooperative Extension via Penn State Nutrition Center. Retrieved May 15, 2002, from http://countrystore.org:80/webpages/health/direct175.htm. Internet document number: 121011628.

Singleton, J., Achterberg, C., & Shannon, B. (1992). Role of food and nutrition in the health perceptions of young children. *Journal of the American Dietetic Association, 92*(1), 67–70.

For additional information on safety, nutrition, and health in early education, visit our Web site at **http://www.earlychilded.delmar.com**

Menu Planning and Food Safety in Child Care

After reading this chapter, you should be able to:

7.1 Nutritional Policies

Define and discuss nutritional policies in relation to menu planning and food safety in the child care environment.

7.2 Guidelines for Food Programs

Discuss the guidelines for subsidized food programs available for child care environments.

7.3 Menu Planning for Child Care

Indicate the importance of proper menu planning for children's well-being, including strategies for planning healthy breakfasts, snacks, and lunches.

7.4 Food Safety in Child Care

Summarize the need for food sanitation and safety and practice strategies for providing it in the child care environment.

7.5 Implications for Caregivers

Relate the strategies for providing safe and healthy meals in child care through education, observation, cultural sensitivity, and supervision.

7.1 Nutritional Policies

An increasing number of children are being cared for in a child care environment. Child care appears to be the place where many children are learning their food habits since they are spending much of their day in care. In order to meet the nutritional needs of the children in care, caregivers must be prepared to plan healthy menus that children will enjoy and eat. Caregivers must also be prepared to protect the children from disease by practicing food safety. The following are indicators of the need for sound nutritional policies for menu planning and food safety:

■ A CACFP study showed very few of the day care facilities met the guidelines for food portion size or food quality 100 percent of the time. It also found that only the meat standard for lunch and the milk standard for breakfast were consistently served (Kuratko et al., 2000).

■ Child care professionals need to understand the importance of nutrition in healthy child development (Mydlenski, 2000). Many child caregivers have never had any nutritional training and do not feel adequate in the planning of menus (Bomba, Oakley, & Knight, 1996). Research has shown that only one-half of caregivers knew food sources of nutrients and portion size for children (Briley & Roberts-Gray, 1999).

■ Seventy percent of children consume more than the RDI of total and saturated fats (Nicklas et al., 2001). The Dietary Guidelines for fat are rarely met at child care facilities (Spark et al., 1998).

■ It is recommended that caregivers provide two-thirds of the recommended daily intake for children who are in care for long hours (Briley & Roberts-Gray, 1999).

Many family child caregivers and in-home caregivers are also responsbile for menu planning and food preparation in addition to child care responsibilities.

Proper nutrition needs to be taught and reinforced at all levels.

■ Child care centers should have good food safety and sanitation practices, provide staff training, and promote healthy eating patterns (Nicklas, 2001).

■ Keeping food safe to eat is one of the Dietary Guidelines for Americans (Johnson & Kennedy, 2000).

Child care centers have a number of caregivers on staff. In some centers one of these may double as the food preparer and menu planner. The director may plan the menus, while a food preparation person is hired specifically for the job of cooking. In some cases, there may be a centrally located kitchen or food is catered and pre-prepared food is distributed to several child care centers. These menus may be provided by a dietician hired exclusively for that task.

The family child caregiver and the in-home caregiver are probably the menu planner and food preparer. This task, in addition to caring for children, may appear to be burdensome. With proper training in menu planning and food safety, the caregiver may find that awareness and knowledge often make a job easier to perform.

Recently, child care has been examined for its ability to provide good nutritional practices and safe food handling techniques. This can be improved through a more thorough understanding of the meals provided in care and the necessity for good menu planning as well as proper food sanitation and safety practices. Caregivers will need to use education, cultural sensitivity, observation, and supervision to carry out this task.

It is recommended that policies be created for the following areas:

■ *Guidelines for Food Programs:* understanding how the subsidized food programs guidelines should impact the food selection in child care

■ *Menu Planning:* understanding how to plan menus that meet children's tastes and nutritional needs, as well as being cost effective and easy to prepare

■ *Food Sanitation and Safety:* understanding the methods and practices for food sanitation and safety in child care

■ *Implications for Caregivers:* understanding how education, cultural sensitivity, and supervision can help the caregiver plan for adequate nutrition and food safety in child care

KEY CONCEPT 7.1

Nutritional Policies

More than five million children are eating meals in child care on a daily basis. Nutrition and food safety have been found to be inadequate in many child care environments. It is up to the caregiver who plans and/or prepares meals for children to be adequately trained. The caregiver needs to have an understanding of how breakfast, snacks, and lunches impact a child's nutritional needs. The caregiver should know how to select healthy foods, plan adequate menus, and prepare food that is safe. By using education, cultural sensitivity, observation, and supervision the caregiver ensures a child care environment that is providing for the nutritional needs of the children in care.

7.2 Guidelines for Food Programs

There are a number of food programs that caregivers and families can use to meet the nutritional needs of children. Several of these impact the child care program directly. The Child and Adult Care Food Program (CACFP), the Food Distribution Program, and the Summer Food Service Program for Children (SFSPC) help to provide foods for child care environments that meet the criteria. The CACFP, the Nutrition Education and Training Program (NET), and the Expanded Food and Nutrition Education Program (EFNEP) all provide nutrition information and training for teachers, food service personnel, and children.

Programs that help families include the Special Supplemental Food Program for Women, Infants, and Children (WIC), the USDA's Food Stamp Program, the National School Lunch Program, and the School Breakfast program. WIC provides formula and other foods to families with children under age three. The Food Stamp Program provides more food to children and their families than any other source. A great majority of the people who receive food stamp monies are families with children (Greenstein, 1992). Child caregivers should be informed about these resources should they need to make referrals to families to help them provide adequate nutrition to their children when not in care.

The Child and Adult Care Food Program

The Child and Adult Care Food Program provides funding for children to age twelve years. To be eligible to participate in this program and receive funds, the child care center or home must be a

1. nonprofit licensed or approved public or private child care center
2. family child care home that belongs to a sponsoring agency
3. for-profit private program that receives funding for more than one-fourth of the children present in care through Title Twenty (Title XX) of the Social Security Act

In 2000, 2.695 million children were served more than 896 million meals in child care centers and more than 738 million meals in family child care (FNS, 2001).

Funding for the CACFP is made possible through the U.S. Department of Agriculture's Food and Nutrition Service. Eligible child care sites may be funded for up to two meals and one snack per day or two snacks and one meal. A sliding scale is applied at the child care site that indicates how much to charge a family for meals depending upon their income. Many children receive free meals as a result of the application of the scale.

The family child care home must have a sponsoring agency that administers the program. This may be a local child care resource and referral agency, a public agency such as a USDA cooperative extension service, or other local agencies willing to provide financial administration. The state child care licensing agency can provide the caregiver with this information.

The CACFP provides funding for meals and nutritional training and menu planning for the child caregivers. In return, the child caregiver must meet the nutritional guidelines set by the CACFP. These are included in Table 7–1.

The main goal of organized food programs is to provide nutritious foods for children in need.

TABLE 7–1   CACFP Nutritional Guidelines

INFANTS

Birth to three months

Breakfast, Lunch, and Snack

    4–6 oz. formula

Four to Seven Months

Breakfast, Lunch, and Snack

    4–6 oz. formula

    0–3 Tbs. iron-fortified infant cereal (not snack)

    0–3 Tbs. vegetables or fruits (not snack)

Eight to Eleven Months

Breakfast and Lunch

    6–8 oz. formula

    2–4 Tbs. iron-fortified infant cereal

    1–4 Tbs. fruit or vegetables

Lunch

    1–4 Tbs. meat, fish, poultry, egg yolk, or dried beans *or*

        1–4 oz. cottage cheese, cheese spread, or cheese food *or*

        ½–2 oz. cheese

Snack

    2–4 oz. formula or milk or full strength fruit juice

    2 crackers or ½ slice bread

CHILDREN

One to Two Years

Breakfast

    ½ cup milk

    ¼ cup fruit juice, fruit, or vegetable

    Bread and/or cereal (¼ cup cereal, ½ slice bread)

Lunch

    ½ cup milk

    Meat or meat alternate (1 oz. meat or cheese, 1 egg, 2 Tbs. peanut butter, *or* ¼ cup cooked dry beans or peas)

    ¼ cup (total) vegetables and/or fruits (more than one choice)

    ½ slice bread

Snack (Select two)

    ½ cup milk

    ½ oz. meat or meat alternate *or*

        2 oz. plain yogurt or ¼ cup flavored yogurt (*do not serve yogurt and milk at same snack*)

(continued)

TABLE 7–1 CACFP Nutritional Guidelines *(continued)*

Three to Five Years

Breakfast

    ¾ cup milk

    ½ cup fruit juice, fruit, or vegetable

    ½ slice bread *or*

    ⅓ cup cold cereal *or*

    ¼ cup hot cereal

Lunch

    ¾ cup milk

    Meat or meat alternate (1½ oz. meat, poultry, cheese, *or* 1 egg, *or* ⅜ cup cooked dry beans or peas *or* 3 Tbs. peanut butter *or* ¾ oz. nuts or seeds)

    ½ cup (total) vegetables and/or fruits (more than one choice)

    ½ slice bread

Snack (Select two)

    ½ cup milk

    ½ oz. meat or meat alternate *or* 2 oz. plain yogurt or ¼ cup flavored yogurt

    ½ cup fruit juice or fruit or vegetable

    Bread and/or cereal (½ slice bread, ⅓ cup cold cereal, ¼ cup hot cereal)

Other Programs

The other program that may be of help to child care environments in supplying food is the USDA Food Distribution Program. It is organized to distribute surplus foods such as cheese, grains, and canned goods. A child care site that participates in the CACFP program will automatically receive an application to participate in this program as well. Other licensed child care programs are also

These teachers are receiving nutrition education to help them teach children about nutrition.

eligible to apply. If the child care is selected to participate it can receive commodity foods or cash supplements for the surplus food.

The Summer Food Service Program for Children supplies children from low-income families nutritious foods when their regular schools are on summer vacation. Child care programs and family child care that provide care to school-aged children while on summer break may be eligible for these funds.

The Nutrition Education and Training Program provides education to teachers to help them teach children about nutrition. Funds can be used for instructional materials and instruction. The Expanded Food and Nutrition Education Program is run by cooperative extension. Extension professionals train others to teach food and nutrition to children and their families as well as food purchasing, safety, sanitation, and menu planning for child care. The National Food Service Management Institute at the University of Mississippi has a resource center for child care nutrition. The Web site for this is found at: http://www.olemiss.edu/depts/nfsmil.

KEY CONCEPT 7.2

Guidelines for Food Programs

There are a number of nutritional programs that offer assistance to child care centers or sites by providing funding or educational information. Other programs help children and their families access nutritional foods at no or low cost. The program that helps many child care sites is the Child and Adult Care Food Program. It provides specific guidelines for the food to be served, and it offers menu planning and nutritional information to caregivers. In return, caregivers agree to follow the guidelines and provide nutritious meals to children in care. Other programs that offer education support, training, and instructional materials are the Nutrition Education and Training Program, the Expanded Food and Nutrition Education Program, and the National Food Service Management Institute.

7.3 Menu Planning for Child Care

The American Dietetic Association has set recommended standards for child care programs; that is the child care should provide 67 percent of the nutritional needs for all children present for a full day (Briley & Roberts-Gray, 1999). The Food and Nutrition Service suggests that child nutrition programs should offer meals low in fats and cholesterol; plenty of fruits, vegetables, grains, and milk products; sugar and salt only in moderation; and a variety of foods (FNS, 2001). These guidelines follow the Dietary Guidelines for Americans.

Building a Menu

There are a number of considerations in menu planning and food preparation (see Figure 7–1). The best base for good menu planning is knowledge of nutrition and children's nutritional needs and developmental stages (see Table 7–1).

Figure 7–1

Factors Involved in Menu
Planning in Child Care

Factors Involved in Menu Planning in Child Care

Level One

Knowledge of Nutrition

Children's Nutritional Needs

A Child's Developmental Stages

Dietary Guidelines for Americans

Food Guide Pyramid

Level Two

Accessibility

for Health Choices

Cost   Convenience   Storage

Culinary Skills   Economy

Seasonal Food Considerations

Level Three

Environment

Goal of Child Care

Personal History

Cultural Diversity

Perceptions of

Child Food Choices

A caregiver with nutritional knowledge is more likely to create a better atmosphere for good nutrition practices, including the planning of menus (Spark et al., 1998). The menu should be the focal point for nutrition education and should reinforce healthy eating habits.

This first level of menu planning also includes understanding the Food Guide Pyramid, the Dietary Guidelines for Americans, and any regulations that may accompany a food program in which the child care may participate. It should be prepared to meet state licensing procedures. This level should also consider appetizing presentations. Offer a variety of flavors, textures, and temperatures in the foods that are served. Young children prefer foods that they can identify. The child caregiver will need to be able to apply this information to help create menus that are healthy and meet the children's nutritional needs as well as fit their developmental level.

The second level involved in menu planning is based on accessibility to healthy food choices. A number of factors influence this level. The cost of food and the economics of providing adequate nutrition heavily influence the food that is purchased or the subsidized food programs that the child care may access. Spark et al., (1998) found that financial incentives in the form of a salary bonus were given to cooks for coming in under their budget for food.

Another consideration at this level is the culinary skills of the caregiver or the food preparer who will cook the meals planned in the menu. Someone with limited skills will have fewer choices and may rely on more convenience type foods that may be less nutritional and more expensive. The literacy level of the person preparing food and the inability to follow a recipe may also provide a barrier and guide that person to the use of convenience foods (Aumann et al., 1999).

This lunch menu in a child care center reflects the recommended standards for child care programs.

Convenience itself may be a factor. Time is often limited, especially if there is only one caregiver present in the child care environment. This convenience factor may limit accessibility to the healthiest choices.

Access to healthy food is also affected by seasons. Foods that are in season are much more moderate in price and are more readily available. Fruits, vegetables, and occasionally meats are affected by seasonal availability.

The last factor at this level is the amount of storage available for foods. This includes both room in a refrigerator and room in a pantry or kitchen cabinet. Maintenance of proper food temperature has been found to be a problem at many child care sites (Kuratko, 2000). Child care environments with good storage facilities are able to buy in bulk and save money. These child care environments can also purchase more fresh foods at one time and plan for more frequent use of these foods.

The third level of influence on menu planning is the environment, including the goal of child care. The goal will affect food selection. The menu in a setting where the goal is the well-being of children will be different from the menu in a setting where the goal is to provide an income for the staff.

The cultural diversity of the child care environment often has an influence on menu planning. The diversity may be reflected in the caregiver's cultural background and may limit choices in the menu items for planning. Cultural and regional food preparations that are deep-seated habits may be difficult to ignore. Attempts to change these habits by outside forces, e.g., a director, may be looked upon as a threat to the person preparing the food (Spark et al., 1998). A positive process occurs when the menu selection is influenced by the diversity of the children in care.

Another influence at this level is the personal history of the caregiver, menu planner, or food purchaser, who in many cases will be the same person. The person who creates the menu and/or prepares the food is going to be influenced by her own food memories, prejudices, and preferences. If she hated lima beans as a child, they will probably never appear on the menu. It is important to discuss and understand why certain types of food or food prepa-

Convenience foods do not have to be unhealthy, as this caregiver shows with bananas.

rations might be excluded or used in lesser quantities. It is vital that the caregiver should receive some type of nutritional training. With basic nutritional knowledge it will be easier for the caregiver to provide a menu that reflects good nutrition and not food prejudices. If food preparation staff is unfamiliar with recommended foods included in the guidelines they may be resistant to including these foods or may prepare them in a less than acceptable manner. It is also important for the caregiver to recognize the fact that the minority population is growing, so cultural preferences of the children in care should also be considered (Briley & Roberts-Gray, 1999; Basch, Zybert, & Shea, 1994). To help the caregiver meet these needs, parents should be involved in the planning of menus in some way.

Some caregivers have a perception of what foods children will or will not eat. Many menus are planned and are limited by the choices that a caregiver "knows" are the only things a child will eat. Food preparation staff should not stereotype the foods they think children would not eat, or be prejudiced against foods because of their own backgrounds (Skinner et al., 1998). Children will accept 80 percent of the food offered to them at first and with repeated exposure, they will eat most foods.

Considering the influences at every level, the child caregiver can begin planning a menu. Care should be taken to remove all prejudices, preferences, and perceptions or any other factor that may be a barrier to good menu planning. The caregiver should also remove any barriers to the accessibility of the healthiest food selections. This may involve applying for subsidized food programs, taking cooking lessons, and looking for easier ways to cook nutritious fresh foods.

The caregiver should be equipped with the necessary nutritional knowledge and influences of the developmental stages by reading and referencing this text. If the caregiver feels more information would be helpful, further training and education in nutrition may be the next step.

Menu planning should be done on a regular basis, such as every two weeks or once per month. The menu should be reviewed and revised on a

Figure 7–2

Rate Your Plate *(1993 Pyramid Packet, Penn State Nutrition Center, 417 East Calder Way, University Park, PA 16801–5663; 814–865–6323)*

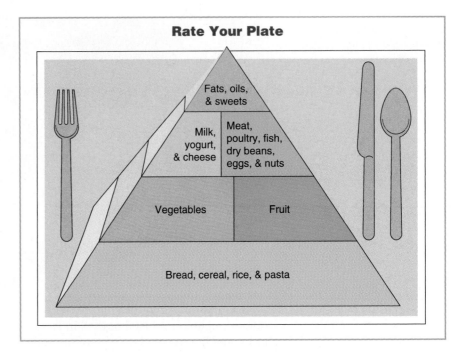

regular basis. Some child care centers have had the same menu for 15 years (Briley, Roberts-Gray, & Rowe, 1993). It is important to keep the menu updated and to change it so a variety of foods can be offered and seasonal availability can be accessed.

By applying the meal guidelines found in Table 7–1, or following specific meal guidelines supplied by a child care licensing agency, the caregiver can create menus that meet the needs of the children. Using the "Rate Your Plate" pyramid found in Figure 7–2 is a good beginning point. Several other considerations should be kept in mind.

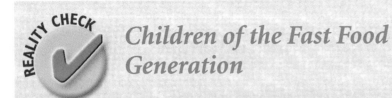

Children of the Fast Food Generation

Children are consuming fast food with increasing frequency. Children's most liked foods include french fries, pizza, hamburgers, fried chicken, and ketchup (Skinner et al., 1998). Americans spent more than $110 billion on fast food in 2000, as compared to $6 billion in 1970 (Schlosser, 2001). The amount spent in 2000 was more than we spent on higher education, personal computers, or new cars. The fast food industry has grown, in part, because so many mothers are in the workforce. Half of the money we spend on food today is spent at restaurants, and most of these are fast food restaurants. Fast food is available in malls, on main streets, in bowling alleys, on airplanes, and on cruise ships. Fast food is even available at schools where fast food chains and soft drink manufacturers "sponsor" the school in return for marketing their products on campus (Hung, 2001).

The rise in obesity in children, in part, is attributed to less play and more consumption of fast

(continued)

foods (Hall, 2000). Fast foods' most clever marketing has been directed toward children (Borzekowski & Robinson, 2001). Every month 90 percent of America's children between the ages of three and nine visit a McDonald's restaurant (Spake, 2001). A typical fast food meal for children can provide as much as 36 percent of their caloric needs for a day, but fall short of basic nutrients. The most typical meal a child eats at a fast food restaurant is the kid's meal that includes a main item, fries, and a soft drink. Occasionally these meals include a dessert and they almost always include a toy, which draws many children to this type of meal. Following are some typical kid's meals with nutritional breakdown.

Fast Food Kids Meals Nutritional Breakdown

	Calories	Fats (g)	Protein (g)	Sodium (mg)	Carbohydrates (g)
Daily Total	**2000**	**65**	**24**	**2400**	**300**
Burger King (Source: Burger King Corporation)					
Hamburger	275	11	15	510	28
French Fries	227	13	3	161	24
Cola	190	0	0	20	16
Total	**692**	**24**	**18**	**691**	**68**
McDonald's (Source: McDonald's Corporation)					
Cheeseburger	305	13	15	725	30
French Fries	220	12	3	110	30
Orange Drink	230	0	0	30	59
Total	**755**	**18**	**18**	**865**	**119**
Taco Bell (Source: Taco Bell Corporation)					
Taco	183	11	10	276	11
Cinn. Twists	231	11	3	316	32
Lemon-lime	190	0	0	90	48
Total	**604**	**22**	**13**	**682**	**91**
Kentucky Fried Chicken (Source: Kentucky Fried Chicken Corporation)					
Nuggets	276	17	17	840	13
Kentucky Fries	377	18	5	215	18
Root Beer	244	0	0	45	16
Total	**897**	**35**	**22**	**1100**	**46**

As this table reflects, children are getting an overabundance of fat and sodium and a large number of calories for the nutrients present in these meals. To further view nutritional breakdowns, check the fast food chain Web sites: http://www.mcdonalds.com; http://www.burgerking.com; http://www.kfc.com; and http://www.tacobell.com.

Because children are eating out so often, it is even more important for the caregiver to provide nutritious meals during child care. It is important to refrain from getting caught in the fast food challenge. Children prefer highly flavored, high fat meals, so this may be a challenge. However, caregivers can discuss this with children and help them select better choices when they do go out. For example, helping a child choose milk instead of a soft drink will bring the nutrients in the meal more in balance (Ludwig, Peterson, & Gortmaker, 2001).

Many child care menus fail to meet the energy needs of the young child. They also fail to provide enough fresh fruits and vegetables and often do not meet the daily requirements for iron and niacin. Child care menus have often been found to provide too much fat, sugar, and salt.

Another method of making sure the menu is planned properly is to use a checklist (Table 7–2).

A sample menu is found in Table 7–3. Further sample menu plans may be found in Appendix D.

TABLE 7–2 Menu Planning Checklist

☑ *Check for:*

☐ Menu fits budget.

☐ Food is seasonally available.

☐ Culinary skills are available to prepare foods selected.

☐ There is adequate time and labor to prepare food.

☐ Personal history barriers are removed.

☐ Different methods of preparation are used.

☐ There is adequate storage for the food.

☐ Cultural and ethnic diversity are considered.

☐ Meal pattern meets CAFCP guidelines or the Food Guide Pyramid guidelines.

☐ A few new foods are tried every menu planning period.

☐ Few foods are offered that have high fat, high sodium, or high sugar content.

☐ A source of vitamin C is served daily.

☐ A source of vitamin A is served 3 to 4 times per week.

☐ Whole grain breads and grains are offered.

☐ Raw vegetables and fruits are served often.

Breakfast

Breakfast may well be the most critical meal of the day. USDA recommends that 25 percent of RDI should be offered at breakfast (Fox et al., 1997). It has been reported that eating breakfast affects cognition, strength, attitude, and endurance (Evers, 1999; Brown & Marcotte, 1999). Children who skip breakfast do not make up for the nutritional loss over the rest of the day. People who eat breakfast are less likely to be obese because their nutritional needs are spread throughout the day. Poor nutrition among children in the United States is in part a result of skipping breakfast.

As reflected in Table 7–1 (page 240), breakfast should consist of milk, bread/cereal, and fruit. Breakfasts can be built around traditional breakfast foods such as cereal, toast, fruit, milk, and so forth. Breads, cereals, and grains in adequate quantities are consistently missing from child care (Briley et al., 1999). Cold cereal that has been fortified with iron has been suggested as an easy way to increase this food group (Briley, McBride, & Roberts-Gray, 1997). These food choices can be enhanced by making them more attractive. Fruits or nuts can be put on hot or cold cereals. A bagel can have cream cheese or cottage cheese and fruit on it. The child caregiver will have to understand the food habits of the children in care. Some children do not like mixing foods. Other children may be affected by cultural tradition or practices regarding breakfast choices.

Other nontraditional food choices for breakfast are available, such as dried fruits, peanut butter, burritos, pizza, fruit salad, and fruit smoothies, which all offer good nutrition and might encourage children to eat better at breakfast. Foods from other cultures such as stir fried rice may be served as an alternative to the traditional choices.

TABLE 7–3	Sample Menu for Child Care			
	Breakfast	**Snack**	**Lunch**	**Snack**
Monday	Cheerios Banana Milk	Rye crisp Cheese Apple juice	Spaghetti with meat sauce Salad & fruit Milk	Quesadillas Orange juice
Tuesday	French toast Applesauce Milk	Carrot sticks Saltine crackers Fruit juice	Chicken and vegetable soup Grilled cheese sandwich Melon slice Milk	Corn muffins Milk
Wednesday	Cinnamon whole wheat tortillas Peaches Milk	Popcorn Apple juice	Fettucini with cheese sauce Carrot rounds Fruit cup Milk	Banana bread with cream cheese Grape juice
Thursday	Yogurt Strawberries Wheat toast	Rice cakes with peanut butter Fruit juice	Chicken chow mein over crisp noodles Orange wedge Milk	Cranberry muffins Apple juice
Friday	Granola Pears Milk Water	Yogurt dip with vegetable sticks & tomato Milk	Beef tostado with beans, rice, lettuce Milk	Bread sticks Orange Water

A nutritious breakfast consisting of milk, bread/cereal, and fruit is just one way to provide a healthy start for children.

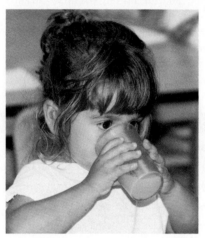
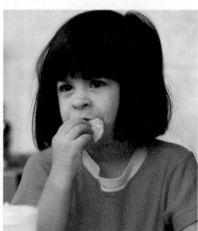

Snacks

Snacks are an essential part of a child's nutritional day. Snacks should provide adequate nutrition, and should be served at a sufficient time between meals for the children to be hungry but not too hungry. Snacks are a good time to begin to reflect the cultural diversity of the children in care. It is also the best time to introduce new foods. If children do not like the food, their nutritional needs for the day will be less at risk. If fruit juice is used in the menu, it should always be 100 percent juice (AAP, 2001). Children under the age of six years should have no more than 6 ounces and children under the age of twelve years should have no more than 12 ounces of fruit juice in a day (Skinner & Carruth, 2001).

As shown in Table 7–1, snacks should consist of a milk or meat/meat alternate choice, such as yogurt and a bread/grain or fruit choice. Some licensing standards dictate that there be pure fruit juice served at one snack and milk at the other snack. Ideally, there should always be a protein source either from milk, a meat, or a meat alternate. An example of this is peanut butter on celery or crackers. Protein should be spread throughout the day for optimum benefit. The fat in the meat or milk will offer satiety and help to fill up the child. Using a bread, grain, or fruit will provide bulk, flavor, and help the children meet the food pyramid guidelines.

Typical snacks might include bagels, tortillas, crackers, milk, yogurt, string cheese, and fresh fruit such as apples, bananas or oranges, or applesauce. Snacks may occasionally be more unusual such as a vegetable soup, a yogurt sundae, a cheese crisp, a bread pudding, a fruit smoothie, or a frozen banana pop with peanut butter and coconut. The type of snack may be impacted by food preparation time and cost.

Lunches

Lunches in child care help provide the greatest amount of nutrition in the child's day. The child's lunch should consist of milk, a meat, or meat alternate, fruits and/or vegetables (minimum of two), and a bread or grain. School lunches contain more than the average amount of fats and saturated fats (Bushweller, 1993). It is important to address this issue when planning menus.

Some child caregivers limit the lunches they prepare to those things children are familiar with or those things that may resemble fast food that children will eat. Menu items such as peanut butter sandwiches, burritos, pizza, hamburgers, spaghetti, fish sticks, tacos, macaroni and cheese, and hot dogs may appear often and in some cases may be the rotating menu. Infrequent exposure to many foods as young children may limit children's range of acceptable food choices later in life. Several of these items may contribute more fat at one meal than may be desired. This is a practice that should be examined and changed to better meet the nutritional needs of the children.

Caregivers who provide lunches for children should keep a menu in mind that offers less fat and a greater variety of food over time. Children who are involved in helping prepare lunches may be more likely to eat a wider variety of foods. Foods such as stir fries, baked chicken or fish, hearty soups, pita pockets, quesadillas, and different pastas can add variety and flavor to the menu. Most children will eat these foods.

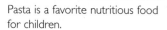

Pasta is a favorite nutritious food for children.

Lunches from Home.   Lunches may present a unique problem if they are not prepared at the child care site. When children bring their own lunches to school they are more likely to consume sugar, sweets, and sweetened beverages. They are also less likely to eat vegetables, drink milk, or have adequate amounts of meat or meat alternatives (Gordon & McKinney, 1995). Many licensed programs prohibit the presence of these less desirable foods. Caregivers should have a policy about foods brought from home, including a parent handout of unacceptable food choices such as high-density fat, sugar, and calorie-laden foods that offer little food value. That policy should also include the fact that foods from home should: (1) be properly labeled with name, date, and type of food; (2) be refrigerated, if necessary; and (3) not be shared with anyone.

Children on Vegetarian Diets

Some children in care may be from families that are vegetarians. There are four types of vegetarians: vegans, whose diets consist only of plant foods—grain, legumes, fruits, vegetables, nuts, seeds, and fats from vegetable sources; lacto-vegetarians, whose diets consist of those same foods but with the addition of milk and milk products; ovo-vegetarians, who eat eggs in addition to the plant foods; lacto-ovo-vegetarians, who eat both milk products and eggs in addition to the plant foods. It is not difficult to meet the nutritional needs of lacto, ovo, or lacto-ovo-vegetarian children because good sources of nutrients such as protein, iron, and calcium include milk, milk products, and eggs. Planning the menu for a vegan child can be more challenging. Well-planned vegan diets can meet the nutrient needs of children (AAP, 1998). You may want to consult a dietician to help with menu plans for a vegan child (Messina & Mangels, 2001). Another solution may be to ask the parent of the vegan child to help in the planning of the menu, or have them supply the snacks and lunches for that child.

Vegan children should consume a wide variety of fruits and vegetables, including green leafy vegetables, which can be a good source of calcium and iron. Dried beans, peas, lentils, and soy products are good sources of protein and iron. Soy milk that has been fortified with calcium and vitamin D is a good source to help meet the child's daily intake of calcium. Nuts and seeds help give the child the protein and essential fats that they need for energy and to help metabolize the fat soluble vitamins. In addition, cooking with vegetable oil and using vegetable margarine spread can help children meet their dietary need for fat.

KEY CONCEPT 7.3

Menu Planning

Menu planning begins with building a foundation of knowledge and eliminating barriers to accessing healthy food choices and background influences. Guidelines for meeting nutritional needs should be followed and a variety of foods, including fresh vegetables and fruits, should be provided. Child caregivers can look at each area of menu planning and relate it to the entire day's menu choices. They should use a checklist to examine if all criteria for food menu planning are met. A caregiver who understands the importance of breakfast, snacks, and lunch will plan more carefully to meet the needs of the children in care.

7.4 Food Safety in Child Care

Preventing foodborne illness should be a primary task of the caregiver who is planning and preparing meals for children in care (Kuratko, 2000). Food safety involves proper food purchasing, food storage, handling, and cooking. These practices and strategies for providing protection from risk and prevention of foodborne illnesses should be carefully monitored. It is recommended that the child caregiver responsible for food purchasing, storage, handling, and cooking use the Food Safety Checklists (Tables 7–4 to 7–7) to periodically monitor the child care environment for food safety.

Food Purchasing

Food purchasing is the starting point of making sure the food in the environment is safe. Food should be of good quality, fresh, and undamaged. To ensure quality, the purchases should be made from reputable wholesalers, markets, butchers, and others who provide food to the child care environment. These businesses should meet proper local and state health and sanitation codes as well as keep up with any federal regulations that may apply to them.

Buy fresh products before the "sell by" or "use by" dates. Any products that should be refrigerated, should be stored in that section of the store. Do not purchase foods that require refrigeration but are not. Avoid fresh products such as fish and poultry that have the label "frozen, defrosted." It is difficult to tell how long these items have been frozen or how long they have been sitting defrosted, or the manner in which they were defrosted.

When buying poultry and other meats, keep them away from fresh fruits, vegetables, and other foods that will not be cooked. This will avoid cross contamination. Always purchase perishable and fresh foods last. When having food packed, store fresh and frozen foods together to keep them cold.

Do not buy canned goods that are dented or otherwise compromised. The few cents that may be saved could be very costly later. Only buy prepackaged foods if the package is intact. A tear or a rip can allow the food to be contaminated. Table 7–4 lists some guidelines to ensure food safety when purchasing food.

Food Storage

Proper food storage is a key to keeping food safe. This involves proper wrapping, proper labeling, temperature, and arrangement of the food that has been purchased.

Foods need to be protected from contamination by insects, rodents, dust, coughing, sneezing, dirty utensils, and improper temperature while being stored. Proper temperature maintenance is primary. Improper temperature is responsible for 85 percent of cases of food-borne illness. Germs multiply rapidly in lukewarm foods.

Refrigerated Foods. Meats, poultry, and fish should be well wrapped so they do not contaminate other foods in the refrigerator. Placing the store package in a waterproof plastic bag works well. If these foods are being frozen, freezer bags or aluminum foil will help protect them from freezer burn and quality loss. It is essential that all food in child care be labeled by date of purchase to prevent waste and avoid risk.

TABLE 7–4 Food Safety Purchasing Checklist

☑ *Check for:*

- ☐ Buy from sources that are inspected for health and sanitation.
- ☐ Buy only good quality, fresh, and undamaged foods.
- ☐ Buy perishable food before "sell by" date.
- ☐ Perishable foods are refrigerated.
- ☐ Do not purchase "frozen, defrosted" foods.
- ☐ Purchase fresh foods last.
- ☐ Keep poultry and meats away from other foods.
- ☐ Do not buy damaged canned or packaged goods.

All refrigerated products should be refrigerated immediately. Quickly freeze all frozen foods. If they have thawed, they must be used within 24 hours. This avoids any contamination. Eggs should be stored in the refrigerator, preferably in their cartons.

Clean utensils must always be used if storing the food. Food must be refrigerated or stored in covered, shallow containers within two hours after cooking. Containers should be less than 2 inches high. If the food is planned for later use, they should be put immediately in the refrigerator. *Never store food in its cooking container!* There is a short period of time to cool the food to avoid contamination.

Cooked food should always be dated, so it will be used while still good and not be wasted or present risk. The caregiver should always reheat cooked foods to a minimum of 160°F and make sure runny foods like soups have come to a full rolling boil before serving.

The refrigerator should be maintained at a temperature of less than 40°F and the freezer should be maintained at less than 0°F. This inhibits growth of bacteria that can cause foodborne illnesses. There is a danger zone for contamination of foods above 40°F. Bacteria multiplies rapidly between 40° and 125°F.

The refrigerator should be arranged so that there is adequate circulation of cold air. A refrigerator that is too full may not keep the proper temperature and foods may be at risk for contamination.

Unrefrigerated Foods. All unrefrigerated products should be stored in clean, rodent-free areas, preferably with doors to cover the storage area. These areas should also be a minimum of 8 inches above the floor. Foods should be stored so that those items that were purchased first, will be used first. First in storage, first out of storage is the recommendation. This avoids waste and risk. Nonperishable items such as flour, sugar, and so forth, should be stored in airtight containers once the package is opened. A food safety storage checklist can be found in Table 7–5.

Proper food handling is essential to avoiding risks for foodborne illnesses. Using sanitary practices and developing healthy habits for handling food can prevent food contamination and growth of bacteria.

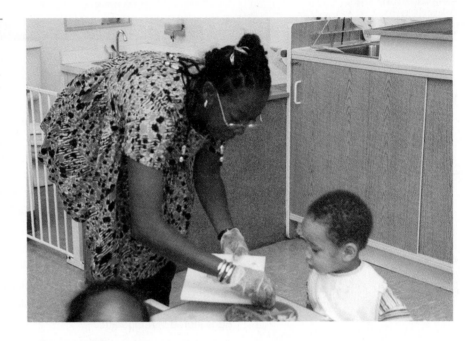

Food Handling

Anyone who has any signs of illness or infectious skin sores that cannot be covered should not be handling food. It is also preferable that the food handler not change diapers. This is more practical in a center situation where there are a number of caregivers. In a family child care home or in the child's own home the single caregiver must perform many roles. In these cases, extra care should be taken, including the use of disposable non-latex gloves. Regardless, it is important to remember a key to proper sanitation is good hand washing techniques.

Caregivers can avoid many risks for foodborne illnesses by handling food properly. Using sanitary practices and healthy habits for handling food (see Table 7–6) can avoid food contamination and growth of bacteria. Food may be handled in its raw form, or it may be frozen or cooked. *Never* thaw any food at room temperature. Thawing should take place in the refrigerator, the microwave oven, or by placing the item in a waterproof plastic bag and submerging it in cold water. Change the water every 30 minutes. When handling cooked foods, always wash hands.

The food handler's clothing should be clean and using a clean apron will help maintain a higher cleanliness standard. Other food handling safety measures are included in Table 7–6.

An excellent way to ensure that food is handled properly is to have the person who is preparing and serving food take a food handler's course that is offered in most communities.

Cooking Foods

Safe, sanitary, and healthy practices should always be used when preparing foods for cooking. As the foods are being cooked, other measures help to provide further protection. Poultry and meats should always be cooked to an

TABLE 7–5 Food Safety Storage Checklist

✓ *Check for:*

☐ Cold foods should be kept at 40°F or less and hot foods at more than 140°F. Foods not stored in proper temperature for more than 4 hours may cause food-borne illness.

☐ Meat, fish, and poultry wrapped in waterproof bags for refrigeration and in foil or freezer bags for freezer.

☐ Refrigerator set for 40°F or less. Freezer set at 0°F or less. Use special thermometers to measure the maintenance of these temperatures.

☐ Refrigerator has adequate circulation.

☐ All refrigerated foods placed in refrigerator immediately upon arrival at child care, including lunches brought from home until lunch time.

☐ All frozen foods immediately in freezer. Use thawed foods within one day.

☐ Label and date all foods. Use leftovers within two days after first use.

☐ Eggs stored in refrigerator.

☐ All food stored in clean, airtight containers.

☐ Hot foods placed in shallow containers (less than 2 inches) to promote rapid boiling.

☐ Nonperishable food stored in clean, rodent- and insect-proof containers, 8 inches from the ground, away from cleaning supplies or poisonous materials.

☐ First food in storage, first food out of storage.

☐ Nonperishable items stored in airtight containers.

internal temperature of 160° to 180°F. The minimum temperature of 160°F protects the food from causing foodborne illnesses. This is especially important for children. Recent outbreaks of E. coli bacteria have caused concern about the internal temperature of meats meeting the minimum degree criteria.

If a crockpot or slow cooker is used for cooking foods in child care several precautions should be taken to provide protection. The cooker should never be more than two-thirds full with plenty of liquid. If using meat, the pieces should be small and uniform and the internal temperature must be checked before serving to make sure it meets the 160°F requirement.

TABLE 7–6 Healthy Food Handling Tips

- Always wash hands.
- Use non-latex gloves to improve sanitation.
- Always prepare food handling environment using sanitary practices. This includes countertops, bread boards, and can openers.
- Keep nails well-trimmed and clean.
- Keep hair tied back, in a hat, or in a net.
- Wash all fruits, vegetables, and tops of cans prior to use. *(continued)*

TABLE 7–6 Healthy Food Handling Tips *(continued)*

- Do not thaw frozen foods at room temperature.
- After cutting poultry, meat, or fish follow sanitary cleaning procedures for cutting boards and hands.
- Never let meat, poultry, or fish juices get on other foods.
- Check internal temperatures of meats using a meat thermometer before serving. This is extremely important to prevent E. coli or salmonella bacteria from contaminating food. Follow temperature gauge for proper meat temperatures.
- Always reheat food to a minimum of 160°F, or if runny food like soup, bring to a full rolling boil.
- Refrigerate all cooked foods within two hours or foods for freezing immediately.
- Never reuse a spoon that has been used for tasting.
- Never reuse leftover food from serving bowls used on the table, except when the food is packaged and will not spoil.
- Never prepare food when you are ill.
- Do not help children with toileting, diapering, or blowing noses while preparing food.
- Keep cloth for wiping up food for that purpose only, or use disposable cloths.
- Wash dishes and preparation tools in hot, soapy water. Rinse. Dip for one minute in bleach solution that is at least 75°F. Let air dry. Do not use a dish towel to dry.
- If using a dishwasher, thoroughly rinse dishes first, then utilize hottest, sanitizing cycle. Allow to dry before removing.

If cooking foods in the microwave, the caregiver should make sure the foods are cooked through and allowed to sit for a short period so the cooking process may finish. Using a microwave probe or a meat thermometer ensures all meats are at an internal temperature of 160°F. Table 7–7 contains a checklist for food safety.

REALITY CHECK

E. coli and Children

In 1982 the first outbreak of E. coli occurred when 47 people in two states got sick from eating contaminated hamburger meat at a fast food restaurant (Mayoclinic.com, 2001). In 1993, a serious outbreak occurred for the same reason, and three children died and many more suffered lifelong disabilities (Evans, 1995). It is estimated that as many as 20,000 cases of E. coli infection appear each year, and as many as 500 people die from it (Cooper, 1995). In the past few years E. coli has been found in unpasturized fruit juices, alfalfa sprouts, dry-cured salami, lettuce, raw milk, and game meat (USDA, 2001; Mohle-Boetani et al., 2001).

(continued)

E. Coli stands for *Escherichia coli* and is one of the most abundant species of bacteria in our environment. It lives in the intestines of humans and animals. E. coli is common and works with other bacteria within our intestines to enable us to function properly and remain healthy. The problem occurs when the E. coli bacteria that are present in animal intestines produce different strains that can be harmful to humans. The rare strain that has occurred recently is referred to as E coli 0157:H7, and causes hemorrhaging, blood loss, and dehydration (Familydoctor.org, 2000).

The E. coli 0157:H7 bacteria has been infected with a strain of virus-producing toxins. The toxin appears as a protein that causes severe damage to the lining of the intestines. Salt and water are lost in the intestines and blood vessels are damaged. It can also result in hemolytic uremic syndrome that can cause acute kidney failure (Held & Griffin, 2000). Young children and elderly persons are the most susceptible to these toxins because dehydration, blood loss, and kidney failure can easily progress to lethal conditions (Reuter's Health, 2001).

Harmful E. coli bacteria can be found in a number of places, the most common of which is ground beef. E. coli is commonly found in cattle feces and can be spread by animals and people. This harmful strain is also found in roast beef, unpasteurized milk, apple cider, and municipal water.

The meat inspection system has undergone some radical changes recently, because the most common source of this bacteria is related to hamburger. On July 6, 1996, the U.S. Department of Agriculture announced its new four-step program to revamp the inspection system and to try to reduce the E. coli bacteria found in meat products (White House Press Briefing, 1996).

Other measures have been taken to protect the public from E. coli bacteria. The restaurant industry has adopted the HACCP system and directs restaurants to cook hamburgers to a thermometer tested 160 degrees Fahrenheit. The federal government has passed measures to regulate fruit juices and sprouted seeds. Healthy People 2010 has an objective to decrease the number of E. coli 0157: H7 cases by one-half (Healthy People 2010, 2000). An organization called S.T.O.P. (Safe Tables Our Priority) provides information on the E. coli bacteria and how safeguards can be practiced to prevent foodborne illnesses (STOP, 2001). Their Web site is located at http://www.stop-usa.org/.

Symptoms for the disease related to the E. coli bacteria may appear from several hours to several days. In young children, the time period is more likely to be short. In a healthy adult, symptoms may appear and be gone in about a week. In young children this disease is far more serious and should be reported to the physician immediately if blood is noticed in the diarrhea or if the stools appear watery.

It has been noted that the E. coli infection can easily be spread from one person to another in child care centers and nursing homes (Familydoctor.org, 2001). There are specific safeguards the caregiver can use to prevent the spread of the E. coli bacteria. These include:

■ If a child has been infected with the E. coli bacteria, he should not be allowed back in care until he has two negative stool cultures (Familydoctor.org, 2001).

■ All meat should be cooked to a temperature of 155°F. The juices should run clear and should not be pink.

■ Always clean any surface that has had raw meat on it, including utensils, before another item touches that surface.

■ Do not use the plate or tray that the raw meat was on to place the cooked meat on.

■ Always wash hands thoroughly before and after handling meat.

■ Do not serve unfiltered apple cider or unpasteurized milk.

■ Always handle diarrhea under strict universal hygiene conditions.

TABLE 7–7   Food Safety When Cooking

 Check for:

- ☐ Always cook meats to an internal temperature of 160 to 180°F.
- ☐ If using a crockpot, never fill more than two-thirds and always use plenty of liquids.
- ☐ For a crockpot, cut meat pieces small and uniform.
- ☐ Before serving foods from a crockpot, always make sure internal temperature is a minimum of 160°F.
- ☐ Let microwave foods sit for a short time to finish the cooking cycle.
- ☐ Check microwave foods for thorough cooking.
- ☐ Always check internal temperature of meats cooked in microwave to meet the 160°F criterion.

KEY CONCEPT 7.4

Food Safety

Food safety in child care is essential to prevent the spread of food-borne illnesses. Protecting the child care environment by using safe food practices and strategies will prevent risk. The caregiver can use safe, sanitary food handling practices to better manage food preparation activities to evade bacteria and food spoilage. Using good food-purchasing behaviors helps elliminate foods that may pose risk. The child caregiver can avoid contamination of foods by understanding how to store foods. The caregiver can offer protection from bacteria growth by cooking foods to a minimum of 160°F and checking all cooking methods to meet this temperature criterion.

7.5 Implications for Caregivers

As more children in this country enter child care, caregivers should understand that they are the people who will be meeting the majority of the nutritional needs for many of these children. The child caregiver will need to prepare to meet those needs (Fletcher & Branen, 1999).

Education

Familiarity with food programs such as Child and Adult Care Food Program will help the caregiver to access available funds to provide better nutrition for children from low- and limited-income families (Bruening et al., 1999). The caregiver can plan nutritious meals by using CACFP guidelines. Other

With all the appropriate information the caregiver can plan menus considering the child's nutritional needs as well as developmental level/stage.

programs provide nutritional training and instructional materials for the children and their parents.

Training for food safety and sanitation is essential for child caregivers (Kuratko, 2000; Briley & Roberts-Gray, 1999). Knowledge is the basis of menu planning. The child caregiver should know the basics of nutrition, what children's nutritional needs are, and how to use the Food Guide Pyramid and the Dietary Guidelines for Americans to apply that knowledge to create menus that meet those needs. The caregiver also should understand the child's developmental stages and how it affects the eating abilities and habits of children.

The person in charge of menu planning should have an understanding of accessibility for healthy choices. This understanding allows access to be maximized. Any barriers should be removed. The caregiver who plans menus should also do a personal checkup of practices, prejudices, and perceptions that may limit food selection.

The child caregiver should have knowledge of food safety practices and strategies that protect the food environment in child care. The caregiver can prevent waste and risk to health and safety by using good food purchasing, storage, handling, and cooking measures.

With Children. The caregiver can teach the children better nutritional practices by getting them to try new foods, eat a variety of foods, and consume more fruits and vegetables. Meeting a child's nutritional needs may take more than providing the food and the information. Information about foods is more meaningful, when the actual foods are involved (Fuhr & Barclay, 1998; Brown and Marcotte, 1999). One of the easiest ways a caregiver can help to educate children to eat the foods found on the menu is to cook it with them. Having a cooking experience for new foods, culturally diverse foods, and fruits and vegetables is a good way to get children to participate in eating them (Cason, 2001). Children are likely to eat foods that they helped to prepare. Having at least one cooking experience per week will encourage participation and variety.

Snacks are a fast meal for the children to help prepare. Some children may be able to make their own snacks. Simple items such as rice cakes and peanut butter are a way to begin. Children are capable of this from toddlerhood. More complicated dishes and meals can be made in stages. To prepare soups, for example, vegetables can be cut one day, and the rest of the ingredients prepared and cooked the next.

Children enjoy cooking experiences and feel they have contributed in a small way.

Another way to educate children is to take them on field trips to the market, vegetable stands, and even farms to see how and where food is grown. There are also excellent videos that provide this information if funding, time, and access prove to be constraints.

There are a number of books that feature foods, many of which involve fruits and vegetables. Having those fruits and vegetables for a snack or meal the same day may encourage children to try new things.

For Parents.   Education for the parent is also essential. Good menu planning is not as effective if the parents are not partners. Parents may be relying on the child care center or family child care home to be the gatekeeper of their children's nutrition. Parents and caregivers need to work together, instead of at cross-purposes (Briley et al., 1999). Posting menus is an easy way for parents to see what foods the child is eating at care. If parents are aware of the menu at school, they can plan to augment the nutritional needs that the child care has provided. Cooking and tasting demonstrations and videos are other choices for education of parents. When the parents are more educated they are more willing to participate in planning and encouraging their children to try more variety and new foods.

Another form of education that the caregiver may provide to the parents is how to access supplemental foods. Many families have limited or low incomes and food selections may be limited because of cost. Helping these families access food programs in order to provide them with better food at home may have a positive effect on the child care environment. Children who have well-balanced meals all the time are healthier and more ready to learn.

Information on food safety should also be provided to parents. This information may help the parent avoid foodborne illnesses and prevent the spread of infectious disease in the child care environment. Modeling these food safety behaviors is a good way to educate the parents. Handouts and workshops are another way.

Cultural Competence

Cultural competence needs to be practiced in menu planning. The caregiver should understand the daily and special event eating patterns of the diverse children in their care. Often the foods themselves are not different from the ones used in child care. However, the names, recipes, method of preparation, and condiments used may make the food appear very different (Block, Norris, Mandel, & Disogra, 1995).

The caregiver can ask families to share their recipes, and talk to them about food. This may be a way to discover the daily and special event choices. It is also a way to determine how food is served at home and how this environment is different from care (Kaiser et al., 1999; Shankar et al., 2001). Adjustments may be made to accommodate these differences. Parents may also be involved in the planning of the menu. Another way to break any barriers to food selection is to have a potluck several times a year, so families can bring a favorite dish that represents their culture. Using their recipes for menu selections is another way to have the children try new foods and have parents feel respected. Foods from other cultures can be included and introduced at snack time, as a beginning. They can later be incorporated into breakfast or lunch.

Hispanic children and other ethnic groups have a difficult time meeting their Food Pyramid Guidelines for fruits and vegetables. Only 7 percent of a study group ate the adequate amount of fruits and vegetables (Basch, Zybert, & Shea, 1994). Using a variety of fruits and vegetables may help. One reason for lacking fruits and vegetables may be the access to food purchasing due to a lack of funds. The caregiver may want to make sure these families get the food program information so that they may have more selections to choose from to meet their children's needs.

Supervision

If the child care is involved in a food program, it is up to the designated caregiver to make sure that all rules, regulations, and guidelines are met. If training or instructional materials are supplied by food programs, it is up to this person

KEY CONCEPT 7.5

Implications for Caregivers

The child caregiver needs to meet the nutritional and developmental needs of the child. Using guidelines and information from supplemental food programs may help. The caregiver needs to be educated in how to apply this knowledge to menu planning and breaking down any barriers that may prevent healthy food choices. Education also helps the caregiver to plan for safe food practices. Educating children through cooking and other methods can help them eat a greater variety of foods and try new foods. Parents can learn more about nutrition and better food selection at home. Cultural sensitivity provides information as well as help to remove barriers to both food selection and trying new foods. Supervision provides the method to ensure that proper menu planning and food safety are carried out.

to make sure this information is used properly and dispensed to the caregiver, the children, and the parents.

Supervision plays a key role in menu planning and food safety. Being able to make sure that these items are handled correctly and are properly supported is important. If the caregiver is also the menu planner, this offers checking and balance to the processes. Using the checklists for menu planning and food safety can ensure these processes are carried out properly.

It is up to the caregiver to supervise the children's reaction to the menu and observe whether or not they are eating what was prepared. This supervision may lead to more frequent review and revision. It is important that the guidelines and nutritional needs of the children are being met.

CHAPTER SUMMARY

More than 5 million children are eating meals in child care on a daily basis. The nutrition and food safety have been found to be inadequate in many child care environments. It is up to the caregiver who plans, and/or prepares meals for children to be adequately trained. There are a number of nutritional programs that offer assistance to child care environments by providing funding or educational information.

The caregiver should know how to select healthy foods, plan adequate menus, and prepare food that is safe. Understanding the importance of breakfast, snacks, and lunch helps the caregiver to plan more carefully to meet the needs of the children in care. Protecting the child care environment by using safe food practices and strategies will prevent risk.

The caregiver can use education, cultural sensitivity, observation, and supervision to ensure the child care environment is providing for the nutritional needs of the children in care.

TO GO BEYOND

In this section you will find a number of activities that you can use to apply and improve your knowledge of this chapter. There are also thorough Online Resources that accompany this text that can be found at http://www.early childed.delmar.com/resources/robertson/index.html. Included on this site are chapter practice quizzes, PowerPoint outlines, Web links, a discussion forum, and various other activities to help you better understand the material in this chapter. This site is updated regularly so check back often to receive the latest information about the subjects in this chapter.

Chapter Review Critical Thinking Applications

1. Discuss the importance of menu planning in child care. What are the components that a caregiver must consider when planning a menu? How might these impact menu planning?

2. Examine the ways a caregiver could connect to resources for help with nutrition and menu planning.

3. Discuss the CACFP program. How can it help a child care provide better food and nutrition to children?

As an Individual

1. Observe children eating at a fast food restaurant. How much food do they appear to be eating? What types of food do they appear to favor? Record your observations and bring to class to share with other students.

2. What food safety and storage practices have you observed in a fast food or other type of restaurant? What types of these practices have you observed in the home? If you have observed these practices in a child care facility, list them also. Compare the three. How might these practices be improved?

3. Watch parents and children in a checkout line of a supermarket for at least one-half hour. What types of food are they buying? Record your findings and be able to discuss what you found in class.

As a Group

1. In small groups plan one week's menu for a child care center. Be sure it is balanced nutritionally and culturally representative of your local area. Compare it to the menus of other groups. Have the menus duplicated and distributed to the class. Evaluate the menus.

2. Divide up into groups and have each group go to two or three fast food restaurants to obtain nutritional information. Create a scale that includes (1) how easy was the information to obtain; (2) were lighter foods offered?; and (3) what "hook" was used to influence children? Rate the restaurants using this scale.

3. How would you help a child select better menu items for nutrition at (1) a fast food restaurant; (2) child care; (3) a school lunch program; and (4) home?

4. Survey the community for information about food programs that offer help to child care programs. Compile the information and distribute to the class.

CHAPTER REFERENCES

American Academy of Pediatrics (AAP). (1998*). Pediatric Nutrition Handbook.* Elk Grove Village, IL: American Academy of Pediatrics Committee on Nutrition.

American Academy of Pediatrics Policy Statement (AAP). (2001). The use and misuse of fruit juice in pediatrics. *Pediatrics, 107*(5), 1210–1213.

Aronson, S. (2000, July). Juice abuse, monkey bars and lice. Child Care Information Exchange, 91–92.

Aumann, M., Briggs, M., Collett, M., Corrigan, K., & Hart, P. (1999). Cuisine for kids: A nutrition and culinary course for child nutrition program staff. *Journal of Nutrition Education, 31*(1), 119B.

Basch, C., Zybert, P., & Shea, S. (1994). Dietary behavior and the fruit and vegetable intake of Latino children. *Journal of Public Health, 94*(5), 914–918.

Block, G., Norris, J., Mandel, R., & Disogra, C. (1995). Sources of energy and six nutrients in diets of low-income Hispanic-American women and their children: Quantitative data from HHANES, 1982–1984. *Journal of the American Dietetic Association, 95*(2),195–208

Bomba, A., Oakley, C., & Knight, K. (1996). Planning the menu in the child care center. *Young Children, 51*(6), 62–67.

Borzekowski, D., & Robinson, T. (2001). The 30-second effect: An experiment revealing the impact of television commercials on the food preferences of preschoolers. *Journal of the American Dietetic Association, 101*(1), 42–46.

Briley, M., Jastrow, S., Vickers, J., & Roberts-Gray, C. (1998). Dietary intake at child-care centers and away: Are parents and care providers working as partners or at cross-purposes? *Journal of the American Dietetic Association, 99*(8), 950–954.

Briley, M., Jastrow, S., Vickers, J., & Roberts-Gray, C. (1999). Can ready to eat cereal solve common nutritional problems in child care menus? *Journal of the American Dietetic Association, 99*(2), 341–342.

Briley, M., McBride, A., & Roberts-Gray, C. (1997). Banking on nutrition. *Texas Child Care, 21*(3), 2–5.

Briley, M., & Roberts-Gray, C. (1999). Nutrition standards for child care programs—Position of ADA. *Journal of American Dietetic Association, 99*(6), 981–988.

Briley, M., Roberts-Gray, C., & Rowe, S. (1993). What can children learn from the menu at the child care center? *Journal of Community Health, 18*(6), 363–377.

Briley, M. Roberts-Gray, C., & Simpson, D. (1994). Identification of factors that influence the menu at child care centers: A grounded theory approach. *Journal of the American Dietetic Association 94*(3), 276–281.

Brown, J., & Marcotte, L. (1999, January/February). Nutrition and cognitive development in children. *Early Childhood News,* 13–17.

Bruening, K., Gilbride, J., Passannante, M., & McClowry, S., (1999). Dietary intake and health outcomes among young children attending 2 urban day-care centers. *Journal of the American Dietetic Association, 99*(12), 1529–1535.

Bushweller, K. (1993). Is school nutrition out to lunch? *Education Digest, 59*(3), 54–57.

Cason, K. (2001). Evaluation of a preschool nutrition education program based on the theory of multiple intelligences. *Journal of Nutrition Education, 33*(2), 161–164.

Cooper, J. (1995). Like your burgers on the raw side? E. coli may give you a raw deal: Death. *The Medical Reporter, 1*(1). Retrieved May 15, 2002, from http://medical reporter.health.org/tmr0495/tmr0495.html.

Evans, E. (1995, January 17). U.S. moves to update meat inspect tests two years after fatal E. coli outbreak. *San Diego Union-Tribune,* C-3.

Evers, C. (1999, February/March). Food moods. *Healthy Kids,* 75–82.

Familydoctor.org (2000, April). E. coli infection. American Academy of Family Physicians. Retrieved May 15, 2002, from http://familydoctor.org/handouts/242.html.

Fletcher, J., & Branen, L. (1999). Feeding young children in group settings: Using scenarios for staff development. *Journal of Nutrition Education, 31*(6), 360B.

Food and Nutrition Service (FNS). (2001). *Child nutrition.* U.S. Department of Agriculture. Retrieved May 15, 2002, from http://www.fns.usda.gov/cnd/.

Fox, M., Glanz, F., Endahl, J., & Wilde, J. (1997). *Early childhood and care study.* Alexandria, VA: U.S. Department of Agriculture.

Fuhr, J., & Barclay, K. (1998). The importance of appropriate nutrition and nutrition education. *Young Children, 53*(1), 74–80.

Gordon, A., & McKinney, R. (1995). Sources of nutrients of students. *Journal of Clinical Nutrition, 61*(1), 232–240.

Greenstein, R. (1992). *Improving the health of the poor: Strategies for prevention.* Menlo Park, CA: Henry J. Kaiser Foundation.

Hall, C. (2000, February 9). Fast food and no play make more children fat. *The Daily Telegraph.* Retrieved May 15, 2002, from http://millennium-debat.org/tel9febru2.htm.

Healthy People 2010. (2000). Healthy People 2010 summary of objectives: Food safety. Retrieved May 15, 2002, from http://web.health.gov/healthypeople/Document/HTML/Volume1/10Food.htm#_Toc490555746.

Held, T., & Griffin, K. (2000, July 26). E. coli sickens children, one critically. *Milwaukee Journal Sentinel.* Retrieved May 15, 2002, from http://www.jsonline.com/alive/family/jul00/coli26s1072500.asp.

Hung, M. (2001, April 17). Book review: Fast food nation: The dark side of the all-American meal. *Medscape General Medicine.* Retrieved May 15, 2002, from http://www.medscape.com/Medscape/GeneralMedicine.

Johnson, R., & Kennedy, E. (2000). The 2000 Dietary Guidelines for Americans: What are the changes and why were they made? *Journal of the American Dietetic Association, 100*(7), 769–774.

Kaiser, L., Martinez, N., Harwood, J., & Garcia, L. (1999). Child feeding strategies in low-income Latino households: Focus group observations. *Journal of the American Dietetic Association, 99*(5), 601–603.

Kuratko, C., Martin, R., Lan, W., Chappell, J., & Ahmad, M. (2000). Menu planning, food consumption and sanitation practices in day care facilities. *Family and Consumer Sciences Research Journal, 29*(1), 81–91.

Ludwig, D., Peterson, K., & Gortmaker, S. (2001). Relationship between consumption of sugar-sweetened drinks and childhood obesity: A perspective observational analysis. *Lancet, 357* (9255), 505–508.

MayoClinic.com. (2001, January 16). E. coli: Preventing a common type of food poisoning. Retrieved May 15, 2002, from http://www.mayoclinic.com/hom?id=DG00005.

Messina, V., & Mangels, A. (2001). Considerations in planning vegan diets: Children. *Journal of the American Dietetic Association, 101*(6), 661–669.

Mohle-Boetani, J., Farrar, J., Werner, S., Minassian, S., Bryant, R., Abbott, S., Slutsker, L., & Vugia, D. (2001). Escherichia coli 0157 and Salmonella infections associated with sprouts in California, 1996–1998. *Annals of Internal Medicine, 135*(4), 239–247.

Mydlenski, P. (2000). New eating right food pyramid. *Healthy Child Care, 3*(4). Retrieved May 15, 2002, from http://healthychild.net/Articles.

Nicklas, T. (2001). Consider nutrition when choosing day care. *Nutrition and Your Child, 2,* 1, 3.

Nicklas, T., Elkasabany, A., Srinivasen, S., & Berenson, G. (2001). Trends in nutrient intake of children in the past two decades. *American Journal of Epidemiology, 153*(5), 969–977.

Reuter's Health. (2001, August 20). Sprouts infected thousands in late 1990's: Report. Retrieved May 15, 2002, from http://www.nlm.h\nih/gov/medlineplus/news/fullstory_3348.html.

Safe Tables Our Priority (STOP). (2001). Foodborne illness in the United States. Retrieved May 15, 2002, from http://www.stop-usa.org/illness/diseases.html.

Schlosser, E. (2001). *Fast food nation: The dark side of the all-American meal.* New York, NY: Houghton Mifflin.

Shankar, A., Gittelsohn, J., Stallings, R., West, K., Gynwali, T., Dhungel, C., & Dahal, B. (2001). Comparison of visual estimates of children's portion sizes under both shared-plan and individual-plate conditions. *Journal of the American Dietetic Association, 101*(1), 47–52.

Skinner, J., & Carruth, B. (2001). A longitudinal study of children's juice intake and growth: The juice controversy revisited. *Journal of the American Dietetic Association, 101*(4), 432–437.

Skinner, J., Carruth, B., Moran, J. III, Houck, K., Schmidhammer, J., Reed, A., Coletta, F., Cotter, R., & Ott, D. (1998). Toddlers' food preferences: Concordance with family members' preferences. *Journal of Nutrition Education, 30*(1), 17–22.

Spake, A. (2001, January 22). How Mcnuggets changed the world: The story of fast food: Yes, you are what you eat. *USNews.Com.* Retrieved May 15, 2002, from http://www.usnew.com/usnew/issue/01122/fast.htm.

Spark, A., Pfau, J., Nicklas, T., & Williams, C. (1998). Reducing fat in preschool meals: Description of the foodservice intervention component of Health Start. *Journal of Nutrition Education, 30*(2), 170–177.

Story, M., Holt, K., & Sofka, D. (Eds.). (2000). *Bright futures in practice: Nutrition.* Arlington, VA: National Center for Education in Maternal and Child Health.

Tate, M., & Patrick, S. (2000). Healthy People 2010 targets healthy diet and healthy weight as critical goals. *Journal of the American Dietetic Association, 100*(3), 300.

U.S. Department of Agriculture (USDA). *Escherichia coli 0157:H7.* Retrieved May 1, 2002, from http://www.cdc.gov/ncidod/dbmd/diseaseinfo/escherichiacoli_g.htm.

SUGGESTIONS FOR READING

Bomba, A., Oakley, C., & Knight, K (1996). Planning the menu in the child care center. *Young Children, 51*(6), 62–67.

Johnson, R., & Nicklas, T. (1999). Dietary guidance for healthy children aged 2 to 11 years: Position of ADA. *Journal of the American Dietetic Association, 99*(1), 93–101.

Luckhardt, W., & Diana, S. (1991). Factors affecting child care program menu planning. *Food Service Research Review, 15,* 105–110.

Nicklas, T., Farris, R., Meyers, L., & Berenson, G. (1995). Dietary fiber intake of children and young adults: The Bogalusa Heart Study. *Journal of the American Dietetic Association, 95*(2), 209–214.

Pestano-Binghay, E., Reis, J., & Walters, M. (1993). Nutrition education issues for minority parents: A needs assessment. *Journal of Nutrition Education, 25*(3), 144.

Position of the American Dietetic Association: Nutrition standards for child care programs. (1994). *Journal of the American Dietetic Association, 94,* 323: Author.

Rolls, B., Engell, B., & Birch, L. (2000). Serving portion size influences 5-year-old, but not 3-year-old children's food intakes. *Journal of the American Dietetic Association, 100*(2), 232–236.

Skinner, J., Carruth, B., Houck, D., Bounds, W., Morris, M., Cox, D., Moran, J. III, & Coletta, F. (1999). Longitudinal study of nutrient and food intakes of white preschool children aged 24 to 60 months. *Journal of the American Dietetic Association, 99*(12), 1514–1521.

U.S. Department of Agriculture, Food and Nutrition Services. (1994). *Quantity recipes for child care centers.* FNS-86. Washington, DC: Author.

U.S. Department of Health and Human Services. (1993). *Learning readiness: Promising strategies.* Washington, DC: Author.

Wolfe, W., & Campbell, C. (1994). Food pattern, diet quality, and related characteristics of school children in New York State. *Journal of the American Dietetic Association, 93*(11), 1280–1284.

Wotecki, C. (1992). Nutrition in childhood and adolescence, I and II. *Contemporary Nutrition, 17*(I,II). [Brochures]. Minneapolis, MN: General Mills Nutrition Department.

For additional information on safety, nutrition, and health in early education, visit our Web site at **http://www.earlychilded.delmar.com**

Health in Child Care

III

In this section we will discuss four areas that deal with health:

8. Promoting Good Health for Children

9. Tools for Promoting Good Health in Children

10. Infection Control in Child Care

11. Health Care in Child Care

In order to properly cover these expansive topics we will relate them to basic health policies that work well in child care settings. These policies will connect health promotion and risk management tools to each chapter's focus.

Promoting Good Health for Children

After reading this chapter, you should be able to:

8.1 Health Policies

Define and discuss health policies and their use as a tool for health prevention, protection, and promotion.

8.2 Children's Health Records

Discuss the contents and importance of health records, including up-to-date immunizations.

8.3 Staff Health

Discuss the importance of health policies for staff, including staff health records and promoting staff health.

8.4 Providing a Mentally Healthy Environment

Indicate the importance that stable, responsive, and consistent caregiving has on providing a child with an optimum environment for good mental health.

8.5 Implications for Caregivers

Discuss the importance of parent and child education, role modeling positive health actions, and supervision for providing optimum health.

Health policies

framework for ensuring health and well-being in child care settings

8.1 Health Policies

Health policies help the caregiver manage risks to good physical and mental health that might be found in child care. These policies provide the framework for providing protection and prevention. A child caregiver who has health policies can improve the care of children. The following information indicates the need for improving the care of children:

- The overall quality of child care is not good (CQOST, 1995).
- Children of poor or low-income families are more likely to experience substandard care (Children's Defense Fund, 2001; Guendelman & Pearl, 2001).
- At least one in every five children has not received one or more of the vaccinations to prevent childhood diseases and this can lead to epidemic levels (Jiles, Fuchs, & Klevins, 2000). The national goal is for 90 percent of children to be immunized (HHS, 2000).
- Rates of illness for children in child care were higher than rates of illness for a child at home for the first two years of life (NICH, 2001).
- One in 10 children are at risk for their mental health (*USA Today,* 2001).
- Caregivers often overlook their own health needs while taking care of children in child care (Kunitz, 2001).

Designing a Health Policy

Health policies should be developed and directed toward the children and staff. They should promote healthy practices for the child, the caregiver, and the family. Basic health policies lay the foundation for the child care atmosphere.

Children are extremely active. In both private homes and public child care centers, it is the responsibility of the child caregiver to ensure their safety.

Caregivers need to take responsibility for providing the healthiest environment possible in the child care setting. Caregivers also need to provide examples of healthy practices and illness prevention strategies and model them for children and their families.

The first part of the process for designing a health policy is to understand the health risks present in the child care environment. Common infectious diseases, healthy practices for sanitation, and records for health for both children and providers are good beginning points. As the environment is examined for the risks to health, needed policies should be listed.

When the policies listed are created, they should be clearly written and include guidelines, limitations, and suggested methods of communication for each topic. Health policies help the caregiver develop proper practices based on the knowledge of health promotion, protection, and disease prevention.

Health policies should incorporate the four major goals of high-quality child care (see Figure 8–1):

- maximizing health status
- minimizing risk
- using education as a tool
- recognizing the importance of guidelines

Basic health policies for promoting good health should cover:

1. *Health Records:* specific records for the child to be accepted and stay in care
2. *Staff Health:* using staff health and health records to promote health and protect the environment
3. *Protective and Preventive Practices for a Mentally Healthy Environment:* specific practices for creating a proactive and interventive environment for good mental health
4. *Implications for Caregivers:* strategies and practices for health education, cultural sensitivity, role modeling, and supervision in child care

Figure 8–1
Four Major Goals of High-Quality Child Care

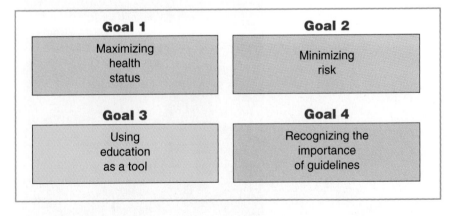

Goal 1	**Goal 2**
Maximizing health status	Minimizing risk

Goal 3	**Goal 4**
Using education as a tool	Recognizing the importance of guidelines

Health Policies

Basic health policies should be designed to provide protection, prevention, and promotion of good health in child care. These policies should include guidelines, records, and checklists. The health policy should define what is to be done and then outline the process for doing it. It should also define who is responsible and provide for follow-through. When time parameters are critical, the health policy should address them. Good health policies should address the basics of children's health records, staff health, providing a mentally healthy environment, and implications for caregivers that provide for education, role modeling, cultural sensitivity, and supervision.

8.2 Children's Health Records

Increased risk for poor health and mental health is often associated with group care (Belsky, 1988). To help reduce this risk, caregivers should create a health policy for children's health records that covers certain basic information regarding each child's health and should include guidelines for all children. The contents of each child's preadmission health history form are listed in Table 8–1. Table 8–2 lists the records that are kept for all children.

TABLE 8–I   Checklist for Child's Health History

Check for:

- ☐ Name, address, and phone number
- ☐ Physician's name, address, and phone number
- ☐ Emergency numbers (two minimum)
- ☐ State of child's health
- ☐ Record of immunizations
- ☐ Dietary restrictions
- ☐ Allergies and other conditions that may require medication
- ☐ Any condition that requires special consideration for care
- ☐ Any special problems or fears
- ☐ TB test for children over one year
- ☐ Any previous major illness or injury
- ☐ An emergency release form signed by the parent

TABLE 8–2 Records to Keep for Each Child
✓ *Check for:*
☐ Health history and preadmission exam form
☐ Immunization records
☐ Injury reports
☐ Assessment and screening results
☐ Medication log and permission slips, where applicable. Some states do not allow caregivers to administer medication.
☐ Health communication history between parents, staff, and health provider
☐ Reports of all illnesses that have occurred while in child care
☐ Growth chart
☐ Any update to the health history as it occurs

Orientation

meeting or discussion of a child new to care regarding health, special needs, and developmental history

Guidelines for this health policy should include an orientation for the caregiver for each child. Good quality caregivers are more likely to ask detailed questions about a child's health. This may determine whether the child care is a good match for the child and for the child care site (LACCCD, 2001). This orientation would cover the special developmental needs of the child, dietary restrictions, and any special health or nutritional needs. Caregivers should have a developmental health history in order to know the child and provide for a holistic approach to care. A checklist to review with parents is found in Appendix A.

Parents should provide the caregiver with a release to discuss medical information with the child's doctor. What information should be included on these forms?

Jon, a two-year-old boy, was new to the child care facility. The facility director read Jon's history, but Amanda, his primary child caregiver, never saw it. In his second week at school, Amanda gave Jon sliced bananas and a cup of raspberry yogurt for morning snack. In a short time, Jon broke out in hives and then went into anaphylactic shock. The child care center called an ambulance immediately. His records were provided to the emergency care technician, who noticed that Jon was allergic to bananas. The director had failed to pass on the information to Amanda. Jon recovered, but the incident frightened everyone involved with the child care facility, including all the children who witnessed it and the parents who heard about it. The center immediately changed its policy to require that all possible caregivers for each child must review the child's health history and any specific dietary information must be posted on the refrigerator, in the kitchen, and by each food serving station as a reminder. Information on other allergies was also posted in the corner of the room as a reminder to the caregivers.

Confidential
keeping information private

Although the information found in health records is very important to the caregiver, it must be a policy that this information remain **confidential** and not be discussed with anyone but the parents of the child, members of the staff, or the child's health care professional, if permitted. The parents should provide the caregiver with a release to discuss medical information with the child's doctor. Discussion among staff should remain at a professional level. Certain information in the developmental history could lead to labeling a child; the professionally competent child caregiver understands the need for discretion and confidentiality.

It is important to have a review procedure included in the health policy. Keeping records current allows for periodic review to look for specific warning signs, normal development rates, and immunization.

As parents drop off children, informal quick health assessments may be made by the child caregiver. Is the child lethargic and listless? Does the child look flushed or pale?

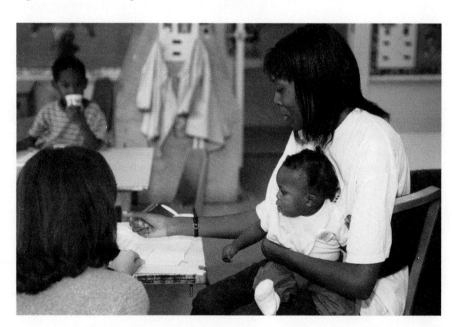

How can preventive and protective measures by the child caregiver help ensure a healthy environment?

Children's Health Records

Health policies created for the health records of children are vitally important for the prevention of diseases and the protection of everyone involved in child care. Health histories that include currency in immunizations, special considerations, and special needs of children can prevent the spread of infectious disease as well as alert staff to possible health-related problems that may occur in the child care setting. Procedures for orientation of new children in care, as well as the management of communications and confidentiality, give the caregiver guidelines for conduct.

8.3 Staff Health

The health policy that covers staff health records and health care is of primary importance. The child caregiver usually cares for a number of young children and the potential for spreading infectious diseases to other children, other employees, and her own family is great. Other occupational health hazards will be discussed later. Every child caregiver should be able to comfortably perform the duties of the job. The policy for health records and health care for staff should reflect preventive and protective measures. The health policy should apply to all staff members, including volunteers.

Infectious diseases
diseases capable of invading the body and causing an infection to occur; may or may not be contagious

Staff Records

Before any caregiver is hired or considers beginning a career working with children, he should have information available to complete a staff health record. The caregiver health history should include the information listed in Table 8–3 (see also Appendix A).

Potential caregivers should have a complete physical, including a general health evaluation and a review of immunizations before working with children.

Other items that might be included in an adult health history are limitations in common situations, such as allergies to art materials, medications, and the general health status of family members residing in the household. Some states have mandated forms that will be provided.

Before a potential caregiver cares for children, a complete physical should be given. This pre-employment health examination will evaluate general health and physical condition. It will also provide the opportunity to complete the schedule of immunizations if any of the required immunizations are missing. After employment, regular health checkups will evaluate maintenance of good health. An orientation for the new caregiver should include procedures to reduce risk for exposure to illness, including hand washing, universal precautions for blood-borne pathogens and proper sanitation practices (Calder, 2000).

TABLE 8–3   Checklist for Caregiver Health History
☑ *Check for:*
☐ Name, address, and phone number
☐ Physician's, name, address, and phone number
☐ Pre-employment examination that includes an evaluation of general health, the physical ability to perform job duties as outlined, and any condition that would create a hazard to children or other staff
☐ Immunization records including currency in all necessary immunizations and history of childhood diseases
☐ TB test results
☐ Hearing and vision screening

Maintaining Staff Health

A child caregiver should protect the health of children and should also be a role model for good health. Maintaining the health of a child caregiver can be challenging because of the following occupational hazards:

- exposure to infectious diseases
- stress
- risk for back injury
- potential exposure to environmental hazards

Exposure to Infectious Diseases. All caregivers should be immunized against or have a natural immunity to the following infectious diseases: diphtheria, tetanus, mumps, measles, rubella, hepatitis B, and polio. If the caregiver has had the disease, a natural immunity will have developed. Immunizations and occurrence of infectious disease should be thoroughly checked before employment. If the measles vaccine was given before the age of fifteen months, a booster should be given to an adult, especially if the adult is a female of childbearing age. Tuberculosis should also be checked before employment through a skin test. This test should be repeated approximately every two years.

Special safeguards should be in place for pregnant caregivers or women with childbearing potential. Unborn children may acquire certain infectious diseases in the child care setting that can cause birth defects and in some cases, miscarriage. Five of these infectious diseases that can be prevented by proper pre-pregnancy immunization are measles, mumps, rubella, chicken pox (varicella), and hepatitis B. Other occupational health hazards include herpes, cytomegalovirus (CMV), parvovirus, and AIDS.

Hand washing is the number one defense a caregiver uses to avoid the spread of infectious disease. Wearing non-latex gloves helps support the check of disease. Special care should be made to follow all sanitary procedures, especially those that deal with children's mucous secretions, blood, and urine and bowel movements. Caregivers should wear gloves each time a child's nose is

Staff meetings are an excellent forum for discussing the occupational health hazards that can affect caregivers.

Child care can be highly stressful and often results in job burnout. What measures can caregivers take to cope with stress and avoid burnout?

wiped, after dealing with a cut or injury, for assisting in toileting or diaper changing, and before food is handled. Use of latex gloves is not suggested because of possible allergic reactions to the caregivers or children. Hands should be washed immediately after removing gloves.

If a caregiver becomes ill, a sick day should be taken. A staff health policy should include a substitute list of caregivers for the protection of the children and the rest of the staff. There should also be substitutes or backup caregivers if a family child caregiver or nanny becomes ill. A family child caregiver may have to send the children to another family child caregivers' home. This backup care must be arranged in advance so that parents will not have to arrange for another form of care for a day or two.

Stress

nonspecific response of the body to any demand put on it

Stress.   Caring for children is a rewarding profession, but it has the potential for stress. There are a number of reasons why the potential for stress is present in caregiving. These reasons include:

- ▪ isolation from other adults. This is more likely to occur in family child care and nanny care.
- ▪ long hours and hard work. Working with children and needing to be constantly aware can be stressful. Breaks may be rare.
- ▪ trying to do too much in too little time. Packing the day with too many activities or expectations of yourself or the children in care
- ▪ balancing work and the rest of life. This may include family, roommates, or school.
- ▪ low wages and lack of recognition. Children and those who care for them are not adequately valued in our society.
- ▪ lack of training. Caregivers with more training have coping skills, organizational skills, and increased knowledge of appropriate activities for children that help them get through the day with less stress.
- ▪ dealing with parents and respecting their needs
- ▪ dealing with individual children with a variety of needs

Job burnout

inability to perform job due to excessive stress

Job burnout is one reaction to too much stress in life. Burnout is the combination of emotional and physical feelings of not being able to function. It is a result of the accumulation of stress, and is a hazard for caregivers. Studies show the job burnout rate for child caregivers in center-based care is 43 percent per year (University of Colorado at Denver et al., 1995). That means for every 100 people who begin the year as a child caregiver, only 57 are still on the job a year later. A major contributing factor to the significant turnover rate is too much stress.

It is important for the caregiver to learn the warning signals and signs of stress (Kunitz, 2000; Gruenberg, 1998). A caregiver needs to take care of her own stress level before she can really be of help to children. Awareness of stress is the first step in preventing it and protecting the caregiver. Stress is the body's response to a threat. A biochemical reaction occurs within the body whether the threat is real or imagined. Stressors are people, places, or events that an individual perceives as a threat. What may be a stressor to one person may not be a stressor to another person. Causes of stress and reactions to it are unique to the individual (see Table 8–4).

A person can learn how to cope with stress and may be able to reduce or eliminate it. Changing one's perception and reaction to the stressor is one way to deal with stress. Another way is to eliminate or reduce the cause or source of stress. Time management is also a helpful tool to eliminate stress.

There are several techniques for changing perception and reaction to stressors. Sharing stress with others helps one see the problem from another person's point of view. Just talking about it with a friend or family member may reduce the level of stress or even the perception that stress exists. A person

---

TABLE 8–4   Stress Warning Signal Checklist

✓ *Check for:*

☐ Persistent feelings of anxiety, nervousness, or depression	☐ Procrastination
☐ Fatigue	☐ Interpersonal conflicts with adults or children
☐ Frustration, moodiness, or irritability	☐ Frequent headaches
☐ Difficulty in concentrating or forgetfulness	☐ Neck and backaches
☐ Loneliness	☐ Asthma
☐ Perfectionism	☐ Muscle tension and/or spasms
☐ Restlessness	☐ Indigestion, diarrhea, or constipation
☐ Eating too much or too little	☐ Infections or skin rashes
☐ Sleeping too much or not being able to sleep	☐ Lowered immunity to illness
☐ Job dissatisfaction	☐ Sexual problems
☐ Absenteeism	☐ Increased smoking, use of alcohol or drugs

A child's schedule may not always agree with the caregiver's schedule, causing daily stress for both.

who learns to recognize limitations can help reduce stress and possibly understand why stress exists in certain situations. A person who realizes certain situations are not within her control should accept the fact that the situation cannot be changed. Instead, the person should take time to recognize what situations can be changed. At this time it is within the power of the individual to change the circumstance in order to reduce or eliminate stress.

Marcus had a difficult time with transitions, especially at lunch and snack time. First Marcus had to settle down and then he ate very slowly. His teacher, Lavonne, worked hard to follow a scheduled routine each day. She tried to get Marcus to eat faster, but he still dawdled at each meal. Lavonne's feelings of resentment toward Marcus and frustration that she was not meeting her own expectations were causing her stress. She went to Anita, her director, to discuss her feelings. They came to several conclusions. Marcus's behavior of transitioning might always be difficult at mealtimes. Lavonne would continue to try different strategies, but they agreed that in the meantime, she would try not to react to that behavior. In addition, Anita would try to give Lavonne some relief during this stressful time.

Lavonne realized that she could not fix everything, and that gave her the sense of freedom to accept the way Marcus acted at mealtime. Anita tried to provide someone to help Lavonne with the end of lunchtime as often as possible. This left the other caregiver with Marcus while Lavonne was free to continue with her plan of activities. Anita and Lavonne discussed what would happen if no one was available to help relieve Lavonne at lunchtime. They agreed that Lavonne's expectation that a schedule should be or could be followed rigidly was unrealistic. Lavonne learned to be more flexible and to not feel bad if everything did not go according to her plan. Lavonne was much happier in her work and the child care atmosphere was less stressful for everyone concerned.

Learning to manage time can also help reduce stress. Many people try to do too much. The pressure of having expectations of what can be accomplished in a certain time frame can lead to stress. To change perception about time, there are several positive techniques found in Table 8–5.

A number of other strategies are available to help reduce or eliminate stress as it occurs. These methods include both physical and mental coping skills. Some of the things one can do physically are to increase physical activity, eat a balanced diet, and get enough sleep. Exercise is particularly important. Exercising vigorously for 20 minutes, three times a week, can be a major reducer of stress. Hormones are released during excercise that help the body cope with stress. Eliminating sugar and caffeine in the diet can also help to relieve stress because both have physical side effects that may allow stress to occur more easily. Eating healthy foods, including lots of fresh fruits and vegetables, can help the body be more resilient to stress (Kunitz, 2001).

People who care for others often find it difficult to care for themselves. Making more time for leisure, daydreaming, crying when it is needed, and learning to relax are ways that help a person's mind adjust to stress. Some people find it difficult to relax. Learn to schedule a quiet time each day to relax

---

TABLE 8–5   Time Management Checklist

✔️ *Check for:*

- ☐ Do only one thing at a time. Some people try to manage three or four activities at a time. Child caregiving is an activity that almost demands that, but one can learn to try not to do too many things at one time.

- ☐ Slow down.

- ☐ When several children ask for help at the same time, find ways for them to help each other or explain your need to finish with another task first.

- ☐ Learn to say no to activities or events that are not productive or enjoyable.

- ☐ Make a "to do" list every morning or afternoon for the following day. Allow time for this activity. Prioritize the items that must be done, and eliminate those that can be done later.

- ☐ Try not to be a perfectionist. Use the worst case scenario for trying to reduce perfectionism. Ask "what's the worst that can happen" if something is not done up to the self-enforced standard.

- ☐ If you are stuck in a line or traffic, realize it is out of your control. Try relaxing or do deep breathing exercises.

- ☐ Do not try to do everything yourself. If someone offers to help, let them. If help is needed, ask for it.

Caregivers should bend at the knees, not the waist, when working with children to ensure proper caregiver–child interaction and reduce the risk of back strain.

and reflect. Personal reflection is an excellent tool to learn about yourself and can teach you what you should recognize about your own stress (Gruenberg, 1998). Reading, taking a bubble bath, or watching television may be relaxing. Other leisure activities such as hobbies may be more physically active, but they can be equally relaxing. Do not try the activity at a fast pace nor focus on its competitive nature. This may eliminate the stress reduction quality of the leisure activity. Instead, focus on the enjoyment and relaxation benefits of the activity.

When stress is present, try deep breathing exercises. Breathe in slowly, hold the breath for 1 or 2 seconds, and then let it out slowly. This helps the body to come to a more neutral point. Relaxation response techniques such as holding a group of muscles taut, then allowing them to relax may also help. This process usually involves the entire body, starting with the head and moving down to end with the feet.

Back Injury. Back problems are very common. Most people experience back pain at one time or another. Child caregivers may be called upon to lift and carry children many times in a day. They also bend over to play, change diapers, and feed children. Lifting, bending, twisting and sitting are frequent normal daily activities for the child caregiver. If these tasks are done correctly, problems with the back can be minimized. However, if they are done incorrectly, serious back problems can result. Many child caregivers are not as careful as they need to be; therefore, back injury is considered an occupational hazard (Calder, 2000).

It is important for the caregiver to learn how to correctly bend, lift, and sit. Lifting should be done by bending at the knees, not the waist. Bending at the knees can help relieve some stress from the back; bending at the waist adds stress to the back. When the knees are bent, the legs carry most of the load. If the waist is bent, the back carries the load. Whatever is being lifted should be kept close to the body, not held away from it. A firm footing is the first step to lifting. Feet should be kept apart with one near the child and the other a little behind it (HCC, 1999). During lifting, move the feet as needed but do not twist the body (see Figure 8–2). If possible, do not lift or pull heavy objects that need to be moved. Instead, push the object so that the stress on the back is lessened.

Bending over to talk to a child or to perform other common activities should also be done from the knees, not the waist. Getting at the child's level is important, but it can be done in less physically stressful ways. Position can be shifted from bending at the knees to kneeling, sitting in a chair, squatting, or even sitting cross-legged on the floor (see Figure 8–3).

Surprisingly, sitting down is more stressful on the back than standing or walking. If sitting is necessary, be sure to maintain good posture and try to sit in a way that supports the curve of the back (see Figure 8–4). When bending to sit or to stand from a sitting position, it is better to hang on to something stationary to help remove stress from the back. Child caregivers often sit in

Figure 8–2
How to Lift

Figure 8–3
Sitting on a chair or on the floor at a child's level is crucial for effective caregiver–child interactions, but can result in daily back strain. To relieve pressure on the back, bend from the knees when sitting or standing and hold onto something stationary.

Figure 8–4
Correct Body Alignment
When Sitting

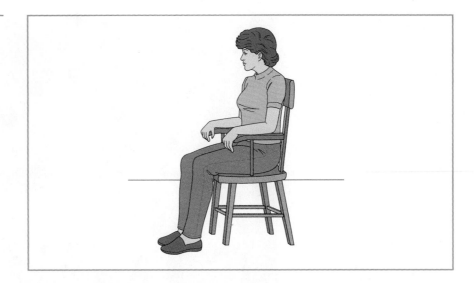

child-sized chairs. This is acceptable as long as it is comfortable, but it should be avoided if it causes back pain or discomfort. If the caregiver is holding or rocking a child, this should be done sitting down in an adult-sized chair with good back support.

Just as exercise can relieve stress, it can also build protection for the back. Regular exercise can strengthen the back muscles to support the spine (see Figure 8–5). This will help the back withstand the daily routine of the child caregiver.

Exposure to Environmental Hazards. There are numerous environmental hazards in child care (Aronson, 2000). The most common hazards are arts and crafts materials, cleaning supplies, and pesticides. All arts and crafts materials

Figure 8–5
Exercises for the Back

Arts and crafts materials are some of the most common environmental hazards in child care. Good ventilation is essential when working with these materials.

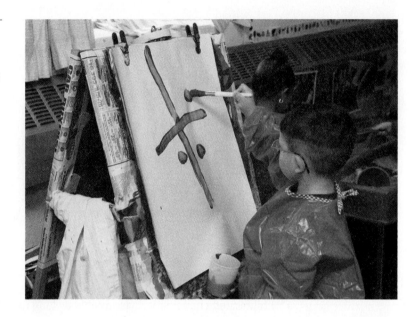

should be examined and labels should indicate that they are nontoxic. Throw away any materials that are not labeled nontoxic. If there are any questions, call the local Poison Control office. Some paints or other craft items may cause a harmful reaction. For example, several years ago, some child care centers stopped using shaving cream as an art supply because of the rashes it caused. Others continued using it, because it did not cause rashes. If any materials are found to be harmful to the children or caregiver, their use should be discontinued. It is also important to always maintain good ventilation when working with arts and crafts materials.

Cleaning supplies should also be nontoxic. Cleaning supplies may be strong enough to cause skin irritation so gloves should be worn when using them. The room should be ventilated and air kept circulating during cleaning. This will help lessen any irritation to the nose, lungs, and eyes. If there should be lingering odor, continue with ventilation and air circulation until the odor lessens.

When pesticides are necessary, they should be applied by a professional exterminator when children are not present. The area that the pesticide is applied to should be well ventilated after the application. A child caregiver should be present and watch the application to make sure that the pesticide

KEY CONCEPT 8.3

Staff Health Requirements

Staff health is an important factor in the prevention and protection of health in the child care environment. All personnel should have a pre-employment physical examination and should meet health record requirements. Staff health should be maintained by keeping up immunizations and by washing hands frequently. The caregiver should employ practices that help avoid stress, back pain, and exposure to hazardous environmental materials.

does not get on food, food preparation areas, or play areas. If minor use of pesticides, such as spraying for ants, is done by the caregiver, the same rules should apply. Gloves should be used and discarded. These cautions will help prevent skin, nose, or lung irritations.

8.4 Providing a Mentally Healthy Environment

Mental health is an area of health promotion that may be overlooked. One in every 10 children is at risk for mental health difficulties. (*USA Today*, 2001). Early childhood mental health is related to a child's well-being in relation to their social and emotional development (Smith, 2000). The importance of providing a consistent, loving, and protective environment cannot be stressed enough. Warm, responsive, one-on-one care is essential to providing a good mentally healthy environment (Honig, 1993; Raikes, 1996; Palmer, 2000). Consistent routines allow children the feeling of security and a sense of trust. Children need an atmosphere where they feel that they belong. Each child needs to feel unique and have a sense of power. The child also needs to feel the freedom to express himself through play, talk, and action. Feeling comfortable enough to express negative emotions may allow the child to work through these types of emotions. The ability of a child to deal with both positive and negative emotions may help the child deal better with life (Bowling & Rogers, 2001).

When a health policy is being developed for mental health, several considerations need to be included. Attention to a child's family situation and cultural background is essential for developing a rapport with the child. Some caution signs for stressful environmental factors that a child may have and that may negatively affect health are found in Table 8–6.

Self-esteem in a child is the general product of a mentally healthy environment. When a child has a sense of self-esteem, that child feels both lovable and capable. A child's self-esteem evolves primarily through the quality of relationships with people in her life. Responsiveness in caregiving enables the

Self-esteem

positive sense of self

A primary caregiver for an infant provides emotional security through an atmosphere of caring and trust. This security is an important foundation of self-esteem.

TABLE 8–6	Caution Signs for Environmental Factors Affecting Mental Health

⚠ WARNINGS

- ☐ Poverty
- ☐ Divorce/single parent family/stepfamily
- ☐ Drug abuse in the home
- ☐ Child abuse
- ☐ Other at-risk home environments
- ☐ Frequent relocation
- ☐ Immigration
- ☐ Cultural considerations, including English as a second language
- ☐ Lack of bonding or attachment
- ☐ Special needs
- ☐ Lack of resiliency
- ☐ Poor health or nutrition

child to feel good about herself. A caregiver offering emotional security and encouragement can provide the foundation for success in later life.

Caregiver behaviors that promote a mentally healthy environment can not only provide this in the moment, but they can alleviate past problems and may help the child in the future. Table 8–7 outlines caregiver behaviors that are useful in providing a mentally healthy environment.

The health policy for mental health should include a provision for a primary caregiver for each child. Each child should have one special person to bond with and form a healthy attachment. The primary caregiver can create an atmosphere of caring and trust for the child. This offers the child a sense of stability and consistency. A child who is at risk for mental health difficulties may recognize positive qualities in the caregiver and may be able to seek those same qualities in other adults in the future (Raikes, 1996). Stability, understanding, and consistency in the caregiving situation may help the child to become more **resilient** in the home environment (Wallach, 1993).

Resilient
the ability to recover after being exposed to risk

Lauren, a withdrawn three-year-old child whose parents had recently divorced, lived with her father, Jim. Jim hired Julie, a live-in nanny, to help care for Lauren. Jim often traveled, sometimes with little notice. Lauren was not allowed to visit her alcoholic mother due to a court order. Julie was there for Lauren whenever a change or an unexpected event happened. Although Lauren's world seemed to have turned upside down, Julie offered comfort and security. Whenever Jim traveled, Julie stayed with

Lauren, and she took Lauren home with her on her days off. Julie understood Lauren's need for stability and she was willing to make sacrifices to ensure that Lauren knew she could depend on Julie. Julie was Lauren's nanny for almost two years. Jim remarried when Lauren was ready to attend kindergarten. Today, Lauren is a happy, outgoing seven-year-old who still occasionally talks to Julie on the phone.

TABLE 8–7   Providing a Mentally Healthy Environment

 Check for:

☐ Establish a good relationship with parents, including respect and mutual communication.

☐ Respond with consistency, predictability, and regularity.

☐ Establish daily routines for a sense of security.

☐ Provide support and emotional assurance for the child, including attention, affection, respect, and mutual communication.

☐ Allow children to safely explore and master the environment.

☐ Help children to express and identify emotions.

☐ Redirect anger and aggression through play and discussion.

☐ Provide a quiet area so the child can remove himself from stimulation when needed.

☐ Value each child's uniqueness, including cultural considerations.

☐ Promote responsive caregiving for staff and parents.

☐ Be flexible and reasonable in expectations.

KEY CONCEPT 8.4

Mental Health Environment

Many children are at risk for poor mental health. Providing a stable, responsive, and consistent environment can help children acquire protective tools that will help them become more resilient to environmental factors that negatively affect mental health. Providing a primary caregiver for each child in care will help to ensure that the child can form a relationship that will provide those protective tools. A caregiver who regards a child as unique, understands the child's temperament, and is aware of the family helps to individualize the caregiving and provide the optimum environment for good mental health for each child.

The Resilient Child

Vulnerability
inability to protect from risk

Some children manage to thrive despite much stress and turmoil in their lives. Other children who have very little stress and turmoil in their lives may not manage as well. According to researchers, the terminology for these two circumstances is referred to as a child's resiliency or **vulnerability** (Osofsky, 1999).

A child who is vulnerable may be so due to a variety of factors. These factors may be inborn and include genetic abnormalities, malnutrition, preterm birth, prenatal stress, or drug exposure. Temperament may also be a factor. Difficult children have a harder time adapting and getting into a rhythm in life. Parents may have a more difficult time coping with and attaching to a difficult child.

Outside circumstances that may make a child more vulnerable are usually related to significant relationships. The bonding process is extremely important. Children who are insecurely attached may be more vulnerable to outside environmental stresses such as poverty, abandonment, or chaotic living. A child whose physical circumstances may make him vulnerable can have that vulnerability lessened by having a secure attachment to a significant person in his life (Osofsky, 1999). First-born children who begin life with no physical difficulties and who are easy in temperament are thought to be most resilient (Werner, 1986).

Another protective factor found in resilient children is high intelligence (Osofsky, 1999). Children who possess these qualities are more likely to form close relationships and have a greater ability to solve problems as they grow older. Children who are resilient have been found to have positive qualities from both sexes. They are outgoing and autonomous, and nurturing and emotionally sen-

sitive (Sullivan, 2001). These qualities allow resilient children to adapt to many situations and circumstances.

Resilient children find it much easier to develop key trusting relationships with an adult. This adult can be a parent, grandparent, other relative, or a teacher. This relationship allows the resilient child the freedom to know that she is significant. As long as the resilient child has someone who cares for her, she can handle almost any situation that comes along.

Both vulnerability and resiliency are significant to the child caregiver. The caregiver may watch a vulnerable child who is insecurely attached have great difficulty coping with life. She may observe a resilient child cope with problems that seem insurmountable. The more supportive the environment is for either of these children, the less the stress and the risk for poor mental health.

The vulnerable child may need extra support from the caregiver through responsive and stimulating care (Levin, 1999). He may need the caregiver to adapt to his needs. The vulnerable child will definitely benefit from a secure attachment with the caregiver. This factor can help the child deal with other factors in his life.

The resilient child will need the care and support of the caregiver, much as a cheerleader helps a team play a game. Although this child is already equipped for success, he will need the secure attachment of an adult to remain successful. If a secure attachment with an adult is unavailable elsewhere but is found during child care, the child may retain his resiliency to the problems and stresses that life may bring (ACT, 2001; Smith, 2000).

8.5 Implications for Caregivers

Children's attitudes and behavior in relation to health are affected by the adults they observe. The well-being of children is influenced by caregiver

role modeling
setting a behavioral example

cultural competence
perceptive, responsive behavior
to cultural differences

training and good practices (Aronson & Aiken, 1980). Caregivers can use role modeling, cultural competence, education, and supervision to influence health.

Role Modeling

A health policy for role modeling should reflect practices that will affect the actions of children through their observation of their caregivers. Good role modeling includes exhibiting the knowledge and practice of healthy behaviors. Caregivers should display good personal grooming and hygiene and face each day with a positive mental attitude.

Good modeling uses reinforcement through observation and discussion with children. A caregiver who teaches children to use healthy practices and models those behaviors can also help the parent learn. Seeing the child and caregiver modeling healthy behavior may encourage the parent to adapt a healthy practice.

A caregiver's actions set the stage for children to learn from those actions (Bredekamp & Copple, 1997). If a caregiver encourages children to wash their hands a certain way but does not do it in the same manner, the children will not readily adopt those hand washing techniques. If the caregiver comes to work ill, the children will wonder why they should stay home when not feeling well. Children often act as a video camera by repeating what they see and hear.

Haim Ginott described the effect that a teacher's actions can have on a child:

> I have come to a frightening conclusion. It is my personal approach that creates the climate. It is my daily mood that makes the weather. As a teacher, I possess tremendous power to make a child's life miserable or joyous. I can be a tool of torture or an instrument of inspiration. I can humiliate or humor, hurt or heal. In all situations it is my response that decides whether a crisis will be escalated or de-escalated, a child humanized or de-humanized. (p. 15)

Because children view the caregiver as a role model, under no circumstances should smoking be permitted at anytime during child care. Smoking is a definite health hazard and caregivers should be good role models for health. Many states do not allow smoking on the premises of child care centers. Secondhand smoke has a detrimental effect on children, so they should be isolated from it as much as possible (see ✓ Reality Check: Secondhand Smoke). A family child caregiver might consider not smoking or giving up the profession to prevent these effects from harming the children in care (Figure 8–6).

Cultural Competence

Our country's increased cultural diversity is reflected in child care. It is important for the caregiver to be sensitive to the needs of children and families concerning health, safety, and nutrition. The caregiver needs to learn more about the cultures of children in care. People from diverse cultural backgrounds may have different views and responses to situations concerning health (Zamani, 2000b). These beliefs are an integral part of cultural expression (Anderson, 2000). When health behaviors are viewed in the context of culture, they may be

Caregivers should practice healthy behaviors

Figure 8–6
Cigarette companies often appear to target children.

Philip Morris Can't Be Trusted With America's Children

When Philip Morris looks at its future, it sees our children. Only kids can replace the 3,000 adult smokers who quit or die every day.

Now Philip Morris executives have launched a slick ad campaign claiming they don't want kids to smoke. Yet they also claim tobacco doesn't cause disease, advertising doesn't influence children and nicotine isn't addictive.

If tobacco companies *really* didn't want kids as customers, they would:

- Tell children that tobacco causes addiction and death.
- Stop fighting effective laws to protect children from tobacco.
- Stop spending billions on youth-oriented advertising, event sponsorship and merchandise that kids love.

Don't trust tobacco companies with our children. Tell your elected officials and candidates we need action to protect kids from tobacco marketing.

To contact your Members of Congress or to learn more, call **1-800-284-KIDS.**

CAMPAIGN for TOBACCO-FREE Kids

more easily explained. When cultures are not understood, there may be barriers to communication.

Health issues may be critical and there should always be a clear path for communications. Conflicting cultures can make immigrant and refugee children prone to psychological problems, and they may have a difficult time forming a self-identity or feeling a sense of self-esteem (Carbello & Nerukar, 2001; Duarte & Rafanello, 2001). These children may also be at much greater risk for illness due to their living conditions. By using a bias-sensitive curriculum and understanding cultural values and traditional backgrounds, the caregiver can help provide children with the tools to maintain their health and feel good about themselves (Zamani, 2000a).

REALITY CHECK

Secondhand Smoke

Smoking has long been an acceptable behavior in our culture. For the last 30 or so years, medical research on the effects of smoking has found that smoking can lead to certain cancers, lung diseases, and heart disease. In the United States, 350,000 deaths occur every year because of tobacco use. Cigarettes, cigars, and tobacco carry warning labels about these facts. It has only recently been concluded that secondhand smoke may cause health problems for those exposed to a smoker's environment.

Children of smokers have a greater risk for health problems. Low birth weight in newborns may be caused because the mother smoked during pregnancy. If smoking were eliminated, it is estimated that there would be 25 percent fewer low birth-weight infants. The U.S. Surgeon General also estimates that there would be a 10 percent reduction in infant deaths if smoking ceased. Recent studies have shown that the secondhand smoke of the pregnant mother's coworkers or families may pass bloodborne chemicals to her unborn child. These chemicals have been found to prelude childhood leukemia and other cancers (Husted, 1996).

Approximately 38 percent of children between the ages of two months and five years are exposed to secondhand smoke, also known as environmental tobacco smoke, while in their own homes (Emmons et al., 2001). One quarter of these children are also exposed to smoke while in their mother's wombs. Children from low-income, less educated families are more likely to be exposed to secondhand smoke. Children can also be exposed to secondhand smoke away from home. More than one-third of children who were not exposed at home were exposed to secondhand smoke by other people. Most exposure to secondhand smoke came from grandparents (Hopper & Craig, 2000). Some exposure to secondhand smoke may come from caregivers.

It has been estimated that exposure to secondhand smoke can account for $4.6 billion in medical expenses to treat children (Aligne & Stoddard, 1997). Secondhand smoke is responsible each year for up to 40 percent of the cases of SIDS, 20 percent of lower-respiratory tract infections of children under five, up to 13 percent of otitis media cases, and asthma in children under fourteen years of age (Greider, 1998). Chances for otitis media increase greatly if the mother smoked during pregnancy (Stathis et al., 1999). Where asthma occurs as a result of secondhand smoke, there is an increased risk for a greater number of episodes, as well as school absences and emergency room visits (Emmons et al., 2001). More than 350,000 respiratory diseases are found in children each year that are directly related to secondhand smoke (Males, 1995).

Other common childhood health issues of secondhand smoke are:

■ pneumonia
■ bronchitis
■ asthma
■ middle-ear effusion (hearing loss)
■ more difficulty getting over colds
■ reduced lung function
■ sudden infant death syndrome (SIDS)
■ allergic complications
■ behavioral problems

The American Academy of Pediatrics Committee on Substance Abuse has called for a tobacco-free environment for all children. The policy statement concludes that tobacco smoke has harmful effects to the health and psychosocial well-being of children and adolescents. The policy also calls for a ban on all advertising for tobacco products. It calls on parents and health professionals to be good role models who do not use tobacco products. Since a major health function of a child caregiver is role modeling, smoking is a behavior that should be avoided.

(continued)

Secondhand smoke has also been linked to vitamin C deficiency. Lower levels of vitamin C increase the risk for cancer, respiratory illness, and heart disease. The connection to heart disease may also come from smoking households that tend to watch more television, eat less healthy diets, and are less physically active (Burke et al., 1998). Inhaling tobacco smoke may also contribute to harmful effects on cognitive development (Park, 1999). Secondhand smoke exposure has also been related to negative behaviors in toddlers (Brook, Brook, & Whiteman, 2000).

Secondhand smoke may be considered an environmental issue that goes beyond the home. Elevated levels of cotinine, a biomarker for nicotine, were found in 85 percent of children in a recent study (Mannino et al., 2001). Children between the ages of four to six years were the hardest hit by the exposure. They were five times more likely to have asthma than children who were not exposed. Many of these children came from nonsmoking homes.

Children have also been known to eat cigarettes or cigarette butts. This can cause low blood pressure and seizure disorders. It is important for caregivers to provide a smoke-free environment. Caregivers can also help to educate parents about the hazards of exposing their children to secondhand smoke.

Education

Education is a tool that can be used to promote health. Education for current needs and new developments in health and child care will help caregivers maintain a healthy environment. Caregivers should have the ability to understand the importance of health records for children and staff. Sound training will offer preventive measures to avoid risk to staff health. Caregivers who understand the importance of a mentally healthy environment can develop policies that provide it.

Teaching children how to recognize their own feelings can help them to be better able to cope when problems occur. Offering information to parents about creating good, mentally healthy environments may help them provide this at home.

Culturally diverse early childhood classrooms provide additional challenges for caregivers. It is crucial to understand critical values and traditional background to develop a bias sensitive curriculum and effectively communicate with the children and their families.

Supervision

Supervision is an important tool for caregivers to maintain healthy environments. Supervision includes the maintenance of health records for both children and staff. In situations where the caregiver is in charge of staff, supervision should be used to prevent stress, eliminate environmental hazards, and prevent backaches. Gentle reminders may help the staff to alter behaviors.

Supervision is also necessary to ensure the maintenance of a mentally healthy environment. Behaviors of children and caregivers should be monitored. Children may be at risk due to certain environmental factors and a caregiver who notices this early can help provide intervention. The caregiver should be providing consistent, responsive care.

CHAPTER SUMMARY

Health policies help the caregiver manage the environment for good physical and mental health. These policies should reflect high-quality child care. Accurate child and staff health histories should be maintained, including immunization records. Staff should model and maintain good health by avoiding exposure to infectious diseases, stress, back injury, and environmental hazards. Caregivers need to be warm and responsive and give consistent care in order to provide a mentally healthy environment for children. Caregivers can affect the health environment of child care by role modeling, using cultural sensitivity, and providing education and supervision.

TO GO BEYOND

In this section you will find a number of activities that you can use to apply and improve your knowledge of this chapter. There are also thorough Online Resources that accompany this text that can be found at http://www.early childed.delmar.com/resources/robertson/index.html. Included on this site are chapter practice quizzes, PowerPoint outlines, Web links, a discussion forum, and various other activities to help you better understand the material in this chapter. This site is updated regularly so check back often to receive the latest information about the subjects in this chapter.

Chapter Review Critical Thinking Applications

1. Discuss how health policies impact child care.
2. What general health policies should be considered in child care? List and evaluate them.
3. Request health policies from local child care programs and family child care sites. Examine and discuss the elements found in these policies. Interview caregivers from these programs to determine the impact of these policies.

4. What is the interrelationship between the caregiver's actions and a mentally healthy child care environment?

As an Individual

1. How do you as a person respond to stress? Identify your responses to stress. Identify your particular stressors.

2. List and discuss the coping mechanisms that you have to deal with stress and your stressors. How could they be improved?

3. How would you deal with a child that is distressed or suffering from outside stresses? What practices would improve the help offered to children who are feeling this way in a child care environment?

4. Compare your family of origin practices at mealtime to the rules found in a child care environment. Compare and contrast their similarities and differences.

As a Group

1. Observe multicultural approaches in a preschool setting that support bias sensitive curriculum. Discuss how that might differ from other curriculums found in the same setting.

2. In small groups of four or five students, compare cultural health practices that may be present in your community. List those practices and cultural origins. As a class, compare the lists and create a master list. How might these practices impact a child care environment?

3. How might stress be reduced in a child care environment? Discuss coping skills that might be used to reduce stress in this environment.

4. What policies might a child care have about caregiver injury prevention, stress, and burnout? In small groups, design a policy for each item that the class considers important.

CHAPTER REFERENCES

Adults and Children Together (ACT). (2001). Violence prevention for teachers of young children. Retrieved May 15, 2002, from http://www.actagainstviolence.org/class.html.

Aligne, C., & Stoddard, J. (1997). Tobacco and children: An economic evaluation of the medical effect of parental smoking. *Archives of Pediatrics and Adolescent Medicine, 151*(6), 648–653.

Anderson, B. (2000). School health education in a multicultural society. [ERIC Digest] Champaign, IL: Eric Clearinghouse.

Aronson, S. (2000, January). Environmental health in child care settings. *Child Care Information Exchange, 35.*

Aronson, S., & Aiken, L. (1980). Compliance of child care programs with health and safety standards: impact of program evaluation and advocate training. *Pediatrics, 65.*

Belsky, J. (1988). The effects of infant day care reconsidered. *Early Childhood Research Quarterly, 3*(3).

Bowling, H., & Rogers, S. (2001). The value of healing in education. *Young Children, 56*(2), 79–81.

Bredekamp, S., & Copple, C. (Eds.). (1997). *Developmentally appropriate practice.* Washington, DC: National Association for the Education of Young Children.

Brook, J., Brook, D., & Whiteman, M. (2000). The influence of maternal smoking during pregnancy on toddlers negativity. *Archives of Pediatric Medicine, 154*(4), 381–385.

Burke, V., Gracey, M., Milligan, R., Thompson, C., Taggart, A., & Beilan, L. (1998). Parental smoking and risk factors for cardiovascular diseases in 10 to 12 year old children. *Journal of Pediatrics, 133*(2), 206–213.

Calder, J. (2000). Oh my aching back . . . and other caregiver health challenges. *Child Care Health Connections, 13*(3), 10–11.

Carballo, M., & Nerukar, A. (2001). Migration, refugees and health risks. *Emerging Infectious Diseases, 7*(3), 556–560.

Children's Defense Fund (CDF). (2001a). Every child deserves to start life with a healthy body and mind. . . . Retrieved May 15, 2002, from http://www.childrensdefense.org.

Clements, D., Zaref, J., Bland, C., Walter, E., & Coplan, P. (2001). Partial uptake of varicellas vaccine and the epidemiological effect on varicella disease in 11 day-care centers in North Carolina. *Archives of Pediatrics and Adolescent Medicine, 155*(4), 455–461.

Cost, Quality and Outcomes Study Team. (CQOST). (1995, January). *Cost, quality and child care outcomes in child care centers.* [Executive Summary] Denver, CO: Economics Department, University of Colorado at Denver.

Duarte, G., & Rafanello, D. (2001). The migrant child: a special place in the field. *Young Children, 56*(2), 26–34.

Emmons, K., Wong, M., Hammond, S., Velicer, W., Fava, J., Monroe, A., & Evans, J. (2001). Intervention and policy issues related to children's exposure to environmental tobacco smoke. *Preventive Medicine, 32*(2), 321–331.

Frede, E. (1995). The role of program quality in producing early childhood program benefits. *The Future of Children, 5*(3), 115–132.

Ginott, H. (1972). *Teacher and child.* New York: Macmillan.

Greider, K. (1998, November). Secondhand smoke: risks to kids range from ear infections to SIDS. *Parent's Magazine,* 42–45.

Gruenberg, A. (1998). Creative stress management: "Put your own oxygen mask on first." *Young Children, 53*(1), 38–42.

Guendelman, S., & Pearl, M. (2001). Access to care for children of the working poor. *Archives of Pediatrics and Adolescent Medicine, 155*(6), 651–658.

Healthy Child Care (HCC). (1999). Back injuries are preventable. *Healthy Child Care, 1*(2). Retrieved May 15, 2002, from http://www.healthychild.net/Articles.

Honig, A. (1993). Mental health for babies: What do theory and research tell us? *Young Children, 48*(3), 69–76.

Hopper, J., & Craig, K. (2000). Environmental tobacco smoke exposure among urban children. *Pediatrics, 106*(4), e47.

Husted, A. (1996, April 23). Secondhand smoke can hurt unborn babies. Retrieved May 15, 2002, from http://www.fensende.com/Users/swnymph/refs/smoke.html.

Jiles, R., Fuchs, C., & Klevins, R. (2000, September 22). Vacation coverage among children enrolled in Head Start programs or day care facilities or entering school. *MMWR Surveillance Summaries 49* (SS09), 27–38.

Kunitz, J. (2000). Avoiding provider burnout. *Child Care Health Connections, 13*(6), 9.

Kunitz, J. (2001). Provider health: Caring for ourselves. *Child Care Health Connections, 14*(1), 10.

Levin, D. (1999). Changing needs, changing responses: Rethinking how we teach children. *Child Care Information Exchange, 99*(7), 46–49.

Los Angeles County Child Care Directory. (LACCD). (2001). *What to look for in quality child care.* Los Angeles, CA: Author. Retrieved May 15, 2002, from http://www.childca. co.la.us.qualitycc1.htm.

Males, M. (1995, September, 9). It's the adults, stupid: A flawed war on drugs and smoking. *New York Times,* 50179.

Mannino, D., Moorman, J., Kingsley, B., Rose, D., & Repace, J. (2001). Health effects related to environmental tobacco smoke exposure in children in the United States. *Archives of Pediatrics and Adolescent Medicine, 155*(1), 36–41.

National Institute of Child Health and Human Development Early Child Care Research Network (NICH). (2001). Child care and common communicable illnesses. *Archives of Pediatrics and Adolescent Medicine, 155*(4), 481–488.

Osofsky, J. (1999). The impact of violence on children. *The Future of Children, 9*(3), 33–49.

Palmer, D. (2000). Violence prevention: What childcare providers can—must!—do about it. *Healthy Child Care, 3*(6). Retrieved May 15, 2002, from http://www.healthchild.net/Articles.

Park, A. (1999, August 9). Your health: Bad news. *Time Magazine.* Retrieved from http://www.time.com/time/magazine/archive/.

Raikes, H. (1996). A secure base for babies. *Young Children, 51*(4), 59–67.

Smith, J. (2000). Naptime for young children. *Child Care Health Connections, 13*(1), 8.

Stathis, S., O'Callaghan, M., Williams, G., Najman, J., Anderson, M., & Bor, W. (1999). Maternal cigarette smoking during pregnancy is an independent predictor for symptoms of middle ear disease at five years postdelivery. *Pediatrics, 104*(2), e16.

Sullivan, R. (2001, March 11). What makes a child resilient? *Time Magazine.* Retrieved from http://www.time.com/time/magazine/archive/.

University of Colorado at Denver, University of California at Los Angeles, University of North Carolina, & Yale University. (1995, January). *Cost, quality, and child outcomes in child care centers* [Executive Summary].

USA Today. (2001, January 3). Many children untreated for mental illness. Retrieved May 15, 2002, from http://www.usatoday.com/life/health/child/lhchi007.htm.

U.S. Department of Health and Human Services (HHS). (2000). Healthy People 2010. Office of Disease Prevention and Health Promotion. Retrieved May 15, 2002, from http://www.health.gov/healthypeople/.

Wallach, L. (1993). Four ways to help children cope with violence. *Education Digest, 59*(2), 29–32.

Werner, E. (1986). A longitudinal study of perinatal risk. In D. C. Gerran & J. D. McKinney (Eds.). *Risk in intellectual and psychosocial development* (3–28). Orlando, FL: Academic Press.

Zamani, R. (2000a). Diversity: Facing the diverse needs of all children. *Child Care Health Connections, 13*(6), 8.

Zamani, R. (2000b). Traditional practices can affect the health of children. *Child Care Health Connections, 13*(5), 9.

SUGGESTIONS FOR READING

Cadiz, S. (1994). Striving for mental health in the early childhood center setting. *Young Children, 49*(2), 84–87.

Child Care Action Campaign (CCAC). (2001). Key facts on child care and early education. New York: Author. Retrieved May 15, 2002, from http://www.childcareaction.org/rfacts.html.

Children's Defense Fund (CDF). (2001b). *The state of America's children: Yearbook 2001.* Washington, DC: Author.

Miller, L., Ford, D., & Liberante, D. (1990). *Providing a healthy environment for children in early childhood program.* Coolidge, AZ: Central Arizona College.

Public sector vaccination efforts in response to the resurgence of measles among school aged children. (1992). *Morbidity and Mortality Weekly Report* (29), 522–525.

Raikes, H. (1996). A secure base for babies: Applying attachment concepts to the infant care setting. *Young Children, 51*(4), 59–67.

Readdick, C., & Walters-Chapman, C. (1994, Fall). *Texas Child Care,* 3–6.

U.S. Department of Health and Human Services. (1990). *Healthy people year 2000.* Washington, DC: U.S. Government Printing Office.

U.S. Department of Health and Human Services (HHS). (1999). *Mental Health: A Report of the Surgeon General—Executive Summary.* Rockville, MD: U.S. Department of Health and Human Services, Substance Abuse and Mental Health Services Administration, Center for Mental Health Services, National Institutes of Health, National Institute of Mental Health.

When parents puff. (1996, April 22). *U.S. News and World Report,* 22.

Ziegler, T. (1996, July). Children at risk: The director's role in identification and early intervention. *Child Care Information Exchange,* 32–34.

For additional information on safety, nutrition, and health in early education, visit our Web site at **http://www.earlychilded.delmar.com**

Tools for Promoting Good Health in Children

After reading this chapter, you should be able to:

9.1 Health Policies

Define and discuss health policies for appraising, screening, and assessment.

9.2 Recording Health Status of Children

Describe and detail the process of recording appraisals, screening, and assessment.

9.3 Assessing a Child's Health Status

Summarize the different components of a child's health and how they are assessed.

9.4 Implications for Caregivers

Relate the importance of education, observation, and the use of appraisals, screening, and assessment.

9.1 Health Policies

Children grow and develop at different rates. They also have different levels of health and well-being. Each child must be looked at individually for accurate health assessment. Forming a health policy for appraising, screening, and assessing a child's health is a major task of the child caregiver. A child's health is a very significant factor in her overall well-being. The following indicators show the need for creating and implementing policies for observation, record keeping, and assessment:

■ All child caregivers should have good tools to assess a child's development (Schweinhart, 1993).

■ Child caregivers should be able to recognize developmental delay, signs of abuse, disabilities, and other possible health problems (NAEYC, 1999).

■ Failure to evaluate and assess a child's progress may deprive the child of needed intervention and corrective measures (Katz, 1997).

■ Observation helps meet the needs of children from all types of backgrounds (Lakin, 1994).

■ Recorded observations about the child's health, habits, and behaviors help in the early identification of possible problems (Bassett, 1995).

Using health policies for observing, recording, and evaluating a child's health will allow for uniformity in how **appraisals** and **screenings** are carried out. These policies will provide information for **early intervention**, if necessary, and will help protect other children from contagious situations. **Assessment** provides a multitude of tools and procedures that are used to support the child's healthy development and to signify difficulties as they occur.

The caregiver is the **primary health assessor**. In a child care center, the director and aides may also contribute to the assessment of the child's health. Creating open lines of communication with the parent is essential to the evaluation of a child's health status. Successful communication begins before issues of concern may appear (Dailey, 1999). If there is observation or other information that indicates a child needs screening and **referral**, a discussion with the parent can clarify information and a decision about the next step can be made. Some families may come into care with more services needed than just a caregiver can provide (Shaw & Zehaye, 2000). If the decision is for referral, then other professionals such as a speech therapist or audiologist will contribute to the overall assessment and any resulting intervention.

It is important to understand that as primary health assessor, the caregiver is a participant observer (Cartwright, 1994). Rarely in child care does a caregiver have the opportunity to stand back for long periods of time and either casually or formally observe children without interruption. In addition, the caregiver brings her own perspective as an assessor. The caregiver's temperament, ethnicity, culture, gender, and experience will affect how she assesses a child's health and development (Lakin, 1994).

Appraisals
regular process of evaluation of a child's health or developmental norms

Screenings
to select or evaluate through a process

Early intervention
decision to modify a child's at-risk behavior or condition in its early stage(s) in order to lessen the impact of the behavior or condition on the life of the child

Assessment
in-depth appraisal to determine if a particular health or developmental condition is occurring

Primary health assessor
caregiver who knows the children very well and can observe for health and well-being

Referral
sending a child for further testing or screening and making available resources that will intervene and aid risk that is posed to the child

Eric, an active four-year-old, seemed to have difficulty following directions and appeared not to pay attention during group time at the child care center. Carol, his teacher, noticed this and asked the aide, Miriam, to observe Eric during those times to see if Carol was correct in her observation. Miriam observed Eric for several weeks and documented what she observed. She agreed with Carol that Eric had attention problems. Carol discussed the situation with Eric's father, Joe, and asked Joe to watch Eric at home. Joe agreed to do this, but he seemed to think that Eric's problem might be related to a recent divorce and living in a single parent family situation. Joe reported to Carol after a weekend of observation that Eric did seem to have attention problems in certain circumstances. Carol, Joe, and Raoul, the director, met to discuss the situation.

Raoul suggested that they begin with a hearing assessment. Eric went to his physician, who felt further tests were needed and sent Eric to a hearing specialist. The specialist concluded that Eric had a hearing deficit that went unnoticed during language development, but was serious enough to cause problems at his present age.

Eric was fitted for a hearing aid and the difference in his attention was remarkable. No one had realized how much Eric had done to compensate for his problem. Now that he could hear, he was like a sponge, trying to soak up information. He asked many questions and was involved in the learning process. Eric's father was grateful that Carol had noticed Eric's problem and had pursued it.

All of the preceding factors contribute to the need for definite policies to evaluate a child's health status. These health policies include:

- ■ *Record Keeping:* specific objectives and methods of recording health information
- ■ *Assessing a Child's Health Status:* procedures for translating and evaluating information to form assessment; includes using indicators of health difficulties
- ■ *Implications for Caregivers:* specific practices for observation, education, cultural sensitivity, and supervision

The caregiver, as the primary health assessor, is responsible for ongoing observations of the health status of each child in his care. Recorded observations are an additional benefit of presenting a complete picture of a child's health status to parents and can aid doctors in diagnosing health problems.

KEY CONCEPT 9.1

Health Policies

Specific health policies for appraising, screening, and assessment are necessary to enable the caregiver, as the primary assessor, to accurately evaluate the health status of children. These policies include record keeping and assessing health status. Implications for caregivers include practices for observation, education, cultural competence, and supervision.

9.2 Recording Health Status of Children

Observation helps present a specific picture of an individual child's health status as well as his temperament, personality, behavioral characteristics, and abilities. What a caregiver considers significant and what needs further deliberation depends on the individual's insight and intuition. These insights from observation are included in the child's permanent health record.

Observation
primary means of data gathering in order to understand children's development and behavior

Record Keeping Management Tools

Health policies for record keeping should consider what may be implied as a result of what has been observed. Care should be taken to be as accurate as possible when taking notes and recording information (Beaty, 2001). Caregivers should remember that they are making observations, not diagnoses. A number of different types of record keeping management tools can be used to decrease bias and to present a more accurate picture of the health status of the child.

Precise Words. The first of these tools is the use of precise words to describe the condition or event that is observed. For example, "Joey has a snotty nose" might be better recorded as "Joey's nose is constantly oozing yellow-green mucus." Children can get runny noses from colds, allergies, changes in temperature, communicable diseases, and so forth. The fact that the mucus is yellow-green and constantly oozing might infer something more serious than sniffles. If Joey's nose runs often, a comparison between more precise descriptions might show a pattern for an allergy or a more serious problem. Using adjectives that clearly describe what was observed can be a way to increase perceptions about the children in care (Cartwright, 1994).

Type of Record. The next health management tool for record keeping is the type of record that will be kept. There are a number of different types of records that are helpful and there are advantages and disadvantages for each type. Table 9–1 indicates the major types of records for observing health status and the conditions where each type would be most accurate.

Child Care Situation. Another matter affecting the type of record keeping used is the child care situation. A child care center might use checklists as a major source of record keeping due to the number of children assigned to each

Time sampling

occurs when an observer records a particular behavior over a specific period of time

Event sampling

when an observer records a specific preselected behavior as it occurs, every time it occurs

Anecdotal

a brief narrative account that describes a child's behavior that is significant to the observer

Running records

a detailed narrative account that describes a child's behavior in sequence, as it occurs

caregiver. There also may be more need for **time sampling** and **event sampling** due to the number of children involved. **Anecdotal** and **running records** would be used occasionally as time permits or as a situation demands. A caregiver in a child care center might use a tape recorder for anecdotal and running records (Benjamin, 1994). A child care center caregiver would be the most likely to use all types of record keeping.

A family child caregiver would more likely use a combination of anecdotal records and checklists as the major source of record keeping. A family child care home usually has children of mixed ages; thus, the provider has a wider age range to observe. A running record would be used only as necessary and there probably would be little need for time sampling or event sampling unless a condition or behavior were serious enough to merit their use.

A nanny or in-home caregiver would rely mostly on anecdotal records. A nanny should keep a daily log that records the child's health and developmental milestones or difficulties. A running record may be used if the nanny or parents have a specific concern about the child. Since the nanny usually has fewer children to care for and generally spends more time with each child than other types of caregivers, there would be little need for time sampling or event sampling because the behavior recurrence or conditions leading to behavior would probably already have been noted. A nanny might use a checklist for the daily quick health check, but she would be more likely to do it mentally than to record any significant factors in the daily log.

How to Keep Records. The type of record keeping used usually determines how the record will be kept. Anecdotal notes can be kept in the child's health record, on file cards, or in a notebook and later placed in the child's health file.

TABLE 9–1	Types of Health Assessment Records		
Type of Record	**Definition**	**Best Used For**	**Limitations**
Anecdotal	Brief narrative accounts that describe health conditions and behavior	Daily open-ended observation	Relies on memory of observer, can be out of context
Running Record	Detailed narrative account in sequence of health status conditions and behaviors	More comprehensive and keeps better track over time	Time consuming; caregiver must have time apart from children to record
Checklist	Lists of specific health status, communicable diseases, absence of sign, symptom; monthly, quarterly, and yearly growth and development observations	Daily scan	Specific traits and behaviors; does not describe
Time Sampling	Records frequency of health status condition or behavior occurrences	Good for over time, takes less time; objective and controlled	Does not describe condition or behavior
Event Sampling	Waits for health condition or behavior to occur, then records specific behaviors	Reoccurring problem; objective and defined ahead of time	Misses details of condition or behavior

Adapted from: Observing the Development of Young Children, *by Janice J. Beaty, 1994, New York: Macmillan.*

The type of record keeping tool used for health observation differs depending on the type of care. For example, a family child caregiver would be likely to use a combination of anecdotal notes and checklists, whereas a nanny might keep a daily log.

Running records are usually recorded on separate sheets of paper and then filed. Checklists and time and event samples are usually printed forms that can be added to the child's file.

The child's health record file should include all observations made. The file will give a view of the child's health status, conditions, and development over time and may be invaluable to a health professional if a child has warning signals for specific problems. The health file is also a tool for creating good two-way communication with the parent about the child and his development. The health file can be used as part of the regular parent/caregiver conferences to discuss the child's overall development.

KEY CONCEPT 9.2

Health Records

Record keeping is a good tool for health management. The wording used to record what is observed should be accurate and descriptive. The type of record that is kept will depend on the care situation as well as the conditions or behaviors that are being recorded. The records that are kept are a valuable tool for communicating with parents and for providing information to health professionals.

9.3 Assessing a Child's Health Status

Appraising a child's health and well-being, screening for developmental norms, and evaluating the information allow the caregiver to assess a child's health status. This is done at several levels that include:

Developmental norms
statistically average age that children will demonstrate certain developmental abilities and behaviors

■ a daily quick health check

■ a general health appraisal

■ screening for growth and developmental norms

Recorded health observations should be accurate and informative. It is important that caregivers realize they are presenting observed behaviors, not diagnosing a problem.

■ a mental health appraisal

■ a nutritional assessment

Daily Quick Health Check

The caregiver needs to determine on a daily basis if a child who is ill or has a health condition that may put other children at risk should be excluded from care. The health policy for daily appraisal will be an important tool for preventing the spread of illness and disease.

It is done rapidly and is often referred to as a quick health check. The child's health condition is appraised daily when the child enters care. Table 9–2 shows the signs to watch for while performing the daily quick health check observation.

If a child exhibits any of the signs listed in Table 9–2, the caregiver should inform the parents and discuss the observations with them immediately. However, if the symptoms are included in the child care exclusion policy, the parent should take the child home. If the observation is of something vague, the caregiver and parent will need to discuss how the child should be managed that day and at what point the caregiver will contact the parent. The discussion could reveal a simple explanation of the problem and may alleviate the caregiver's concerns.

Figure 9–1 shows the signs that the caregiver should be on alert for throughout the day as well as over time if there is a more serious problem.

TABLE 9–2   Daily Health Checklist
✓ *Check for:*
☐ Activity level
☐ Severe sneezing or coughing
☐ Discharge from nose, eyes, or ears
☐ Breathing difficulties
☐ Sores
☐ Swelling or bruises
☐ Rashes or unusual spots
☐ General mood and behavior
☐ Skin color (pale or flushed)

Raphael, a fifteen-month-old active toddler, was being dropped off at the family child care home by his mother, Anna. Frances, the caregiver, noticed that Raphael was not his normally happy self and that he appeared to be feverish. Anna explained that she had taken Raphael to the doctor for a checkup the day before and he had received his current series of immunizations. Anna told Frances that the doctor had said that Raphael might be cranky and have a slight fever for 24 hours. Armed with that information, Frances said good-bye to Anna and kept a close watch on Raphael. He played quietly and did not eat as much as normal, but he did not have any other symptoms.

Frances was glad to have the information because when she had first started her child care business, a mother had dropped off a child whose fever had become elevated later in the day. Frances had not been able to reach the mother and had been worried for several hours until the child's doctor returned her call. The doctor told Frances that the girl had had an immunization the day before and that the girl's reaction was normal.

Figure 9–1
Daily Health Check

STOP DISEASE

Morning Health Check:
Signs to observe:
• Activity level
• Severe coughing, sneezing
• Discharge from nose, eyes, ears
• Breathing difficulties
• Sores
• Swelling or bruises
• Unusual spots or rashes
• General mood/unusual behavior
• Skin color

Use All Your Senses...
Look
Listen
Feel
and
Smell

General Health Appraisal

A general health appraisal is used when warning signs of questionable health or illness are observed. It can also be used to track the recurrence of illness or health conditions. This appraisal goes into more depth as to the signs of health and illness the caregiver might observe in the children in care.

If the caregiver notices frequent recurring conditions or that a child is not acting normally, the caregiver may want to take a closer look at the child's health. Recurring physical problems such as frequent colds or ear infections may indicate a child has an allergy or other health problem that needs to be evaluated by a physician. The frequency of a condition will be noted in the child's health record. The parent should be consulted about the frequency before gathering further information.

If the caregiver feels more information is needed, she should seek the help of a health consultant with the parent's permission. That person can help the caregiver decide if the child needs to be seen by a physician or community health clinic. Discussions with the health consultant can assist the caregiver in being better prepared to seek further cooperation with the parent about the child's specific health concern.

Screening for Growth and Developmental Norms

Screening for growth and development is an essential component of the health status assessment process (NAEYC, 1999). Screening identifies whether growth and development fall into the normal pattern and can indicate a potential problem or impairment. An observer should have some knowledge of the normal range of age expectations for developmental milestones (Katz, 1997). Summaries of milestones for development are listed in this section as are assessment tools, where applicable.

An alert caregiver can help detect whether a child falls within the normal range for growth and development. This could be vital in the child's future health status. A child who is small and light for her age may have a growth abnormality and should see a physician, and perhaps a dietician. A child whose speech is garbled at two-and-a-half may need a therapist or audiologist. Many different conditions that can be corrected can be uncovered through careful observation and recording. A policy of quarterly screening for developmental norms can aid in this process.

A change in a child's behavior or a child with behavioral difficulties may indicate mental health risk, a nutritional deficiency, child abuse, or a physical health impairment. Appraising a child's physical and mental health and nutritional intake will enable discussions with parents to help determine whether a referral should be made. If child abuse is suspected, reporting the observation and showing the records that have been kept to proper authorities will be necessary. A health policy for appraisals and consequent discussion or referral is necessary to allow the process to run smoothly.

The American Public Health Association (APHA) and the American Academy of Pediatrics (AAP) suggest that child caregivers have some form of a health consultant on whom to call when they need a resource for assessing health and well-being. The consultant can be a physician, a pediatric or family nurse practitioner, or a registered nurse (APHA & AAP, 2002). The consultant should have some knowledge about nonparental child care, the community, and available resources. Many communities in this country have health consultants available through the resource and referral network or the medical community.

Screening is routinely done in child care centers and can easily be done in family child care homes or in the child's own home. It is neither expensive nor sophisticated. Screening takes a closer look at specific areas and can add important information to the overall assessment process. The health consultant can assist with any questions the caregiver may have about specific screening methods. Screening is used to:

- measure height and weight
- appraise motor development
- check vision
- appraise hearing
- evaluate speech and language
- assess nutritional intake and deficiencies

Measuring Height and Weight.   Children of all ages fall into a range of normal heights and weights that are calculated on a growth chart (see Appendix B). Growth charts are easy to follow and are used to direct attention to body size for age that is not the norm. These growth charts are also available on the Web site of the National Centers for Health Statistics branch of the Centers for Disease Control. The address is: http://www.cdc.gov/growthcharts/. Physicians routinely use these charts to detect problems or abnormalities in a child's growth.

Recording a child's height and weight is part of the normal screening process that a caregiver performs on a quarterly basis. It helps familiarize children with their bodies and helps them to better understand the screening process in the doctor's office. Children enjoy knowing how tall they are and how much they weigh. Even though they do not understand what the numbers mean, children seem to gain a sense of self-identification from them.

Periodic height and weight checks are exciting for the children and foster a knowledge of and pride in their own bodies. The height and weight assessment can be incorporated into the classroom curriculum by visually representing each child's height and weight (on a wall or piece of posterboard) at regular intervals.

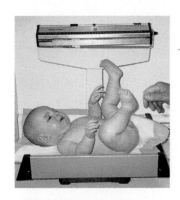

Infancy is a period of dramatic weight and height gains. Infants should be weighed regularly to ensure that they are growing at a normal rate. A weight and height that is below the normal range for their age could indicate a condition called *failure to thrive*.

Failure to thrive
failure of a child to grow physically and develop mentally according to the norms. This condition may occur because of organic defects, or may be due to lack of emotional bonding

Gross motor skills
physical skills related to large body movements such as running, jumping, and climbing

Fine motor skills
physical skills related to small body movements, particularly of the hands and fingers. These skills include using scissors, holding a crayon, or working a puzzle.

Karla, a healthy three-and-a-half-year-old, was very self-confident. She enjoyed having her family child caregiver measure her and liked to get on the scale and see how much she weighed. Martine, the caregiver, had a special place on her family room wall that was used to measure the height of children in her care. Every two months Martine would bring out the scale and let the children stand against their spot on the wall to measure them so they could see how they were growing. One day when the children went through this process, Karla could not wait to tell her mother, "I'm three-and-a-half, and three (feet tall), and I weigh 34." She looked forward to these screening opportunities and they helped her be more comfortable when she had to go to the doctor.

If a child seems unusually small, thin, obese, or tall for his age, there may be a good reason to compare his height and weight to the growth chart. These conditions may indicate poor nutrition, a hormonal imbalance, or a disease that causes retarded or accelerated growth. Sometimes children exhibit a condition called **failure to thrive** that indicates they are below the normal height and/or weight range for their age. Other children may be overweight for their height. Screening and early intervention may help prevent obesity. The results of the chart comparison should be discussed with a parent. If there is an indicator for further examination, a referral course should be planned. A discussion with the health consultant would be helpful at this point. The most common starting point for a referral of this sort would be the child's own physician. If the child does not have a primary physician, a community health clinic would be the next most likely source that the caregiver could recommend to the family.

If changes in diet are indicated, the caregiver can support those changes. The caregiver will need to be informed by the parent or health professional what should be done to help the child. The caregiver could turn to the health consultant for further assistance.

Appraising Motor Development. As a child develops, her ability to perform physical activities and use acquired motor skills is one of the most evident areas in growth and development. It is easily observable and is fairly easy to screen. A child should be able to perform the **gross motor skills** and **fine motor skills** that are normal for her age range. A certain degree of coordination should also be present. Table 9–3 indicates the developmental motor skill norms for the first two years of life.

For children over age two, there are other motor skills and degrees of coordination that should be present. Between ages 2.5 and 3.5 years, a child should be able to perform the gross motor and fine motor skills listed in Table 9–4.

When a child does not appear to be following the development norms for his age, there are usually caution signs present. The warning signals for motor development difficulties are included in Table 9–5.

Some assessment tools that can be used to further evaluate a child's motor skills are The Denver Developmental Screening Tool, The Mullin Scale, The Hawaii Early Learning Profile, the Bayley Assessment Tool, and the Gessell

Throwing a ball in the air is an example of a gross motor skill that children normally master between 2.5 and 3.5 years of age.

TABLE 9–3 Developmental Norms for Gross Motor Skills in Infants

Motor Skill	Month at which 90% of infants master skill
Lifts head up while lying on stomach	3.2
Sits with head steady	4.2
Rolls over	4.7
Sits alone	7.8
Stands holding on	10
Walks holding on	12.7
Stands alone steadily	13.9
Walks well	14.3
Walks up stairs with help	22.0
Kicks ball forward	24.0

Reprinted with permission of DDM. © 1969, 1989, 1990 W. K. Frankenburg and J. B. Dodds © 1978 W. K. Frankenburg.

TABLE 9–4 Developmental Norms for Motor Skills of Children 2.5 Years to 3.5 Years

Gross Motor Skills	Fine Motor Skills
• Walk well with a normal gait	• Use eating utensils well
• Run in a straight line	• Copy a circle
• Jump in the air with both feet	• Scribble
• Throw a ball	• Stack blocks
• Reach for objects with one hand	• Manipulate large puzzle pieces
• Climb	• Smear paint
• Hang by both hands	

TABLE 9–5 Caution Signs for Motor Development

⚠ *Warnings*

☐ Has difficulty judging distances in relation to himself

☐ Lacks large muscle control and appears clumsy and uncoordinated

☐ Has difficulty pointing out or locating parts of the body

☐ Lacks small muscle control in things like cutting and coloring

☐ Lacks steady hand or arm when reaching or stacking; arm or hand appears to tremble

Assessment Tool. A health consultant could help the caregiver decide which developmental tool would be most appropriate and might also assist in the administration of the assessment tool or refer the caregiver to a source for help. These tools are not commonly administered by the caregiver because they require specialized training.

If it is determined that a child appears to have a motor skill problem, the caregiver and a parent should discuss the referral procedure. The child's physician, a community health agency, or a local **regional center** are good starting points. Physical activities may be prescribed to help the child learn to cope with the motor skill difficulties. The caregiver will be a source of support for both the child and parent during this period.

Checking Vision. Children use vision to take in the information about the world around them, sort it, and then make sense out of it. Visual difficulties should be caught as early as possible for correction and treatment. Children are normally screened for vision during their regular checkups with a physician. If there appears to be a problem, the physician will refer the child to an eye specialist to determine if there is a visual deficiency. Some children may not have regular physical checkups, so vision problems may not be caught. Vision difficulties can appear over time or rapidly. The signs that indicate a child may have hidden eye problems or that may be indicators of visual perception difficulties are listed in Table 9–6.

If the caregiver observes any of the conditions listed in Table 9–6, the concerns should be discussed with a parent. The parents may have noticed the same conditions or may already have the child in care for that condition. If that is the case, it is important for the parent to share the information. If the child is not

Regional center

a center in a particular geographic area dedicated to helping families that have children with special needs. The center acts as a resource, a referral agency, and a source of support for families.

TABLE 9–6   Caution Signs for Vision Problems

⚠️ *Warnings*

Eye Problems:	Visual Perception Difficulties:
☐ Persistent redness, swelling, crusting, or discharge in eyes or eyelids	☐ Short attention span
☐ Excessive tearing	☐ Visually distractible
☐ Frequent squinting	☐ Unable to visually sequence
☐ Eyes that look crooked or crossed or that do not move together	☐ Difficulty with color vision
☐ Head held in a tilted position	
☐ Drooping eyelids	
☐ Continuous rubbing	
☐ Eyes that wander	
☐ Inability to see objects unless holding them close	

Effects of Lead Poisoning on Children

It is estimated that one out of every six children under the age of six has lead poisoning (Jaroff, 2001). Four to five million children live in homes where lead levels are above safety thresholds, and another 1.5 million children have elevated blood levels (Brooks-Gunn & Duncan, 1997). Lead poisoning affects all families, but African American and inner-city children are most likely to be affected. As many as one in two inner-city children may have some effects of lead poisoning. Lead poisoning has been called the number one environmental threat to children for many years (Waldman, 1991; Jaroff, 2001).

Lead poisoning can cause mild to severe lasting effects on children. It can affect all systems in the body and does not always show definite symptoms (CDC, 2001). Even low levels of lead are harmful and are correlated with decreased intelligence, affect the development of the nervous system and brain, and can retard growth. The effects of damage to the nervous system and brain may manifest themselves as cognitive deficits, lack of ability to concentrate, and even to learn (Ryan et al., 1999). Reading, writing, math, visual, and motor skills can be affected. Signs that children may have elevated levels of lead include irritability, insomnia, colic, hearing difficulties, lack of eye-hand coordination, and anemia.

Lead poisoning has been found to cause learning difficulties and behavior problems. Children with high levels of lead have been found to be six times more likely to have reading disabilities. Some experts believe that lead poisoning can contribute to aggression, antisocial and delinquent behaviors (AAP, 1998). One study found that there is a relationship between lead exposure and violent behavior in the commission of homicide (Stretesky & Lynch, 2001).

Lead poisoning knows no boundaries. Children under seven years of age live in almost four million homes that have peeling lead paint or lead dust

in the environment. Families from these houses are almost equally divided between lower and middle/upper incomes. Renters and homeowners are equally likely to have this problem. Children affected by lead poisoning come from all cultural and racial groups (Jaroff, 2001).

Seventy-four percent of houses built before 1980 have lead-based paint (AAP, 1998). Lead-based paint was banned in 1978. Lead was removed from gasoline in the 1980s. This has helped to reduce lead levels, but it has not removed it as an environmental hazard to children (Kidshealth.org, 1999).

Lead poisoning is most likely to occur if leaded dust or lead paint chips are swallowed. Lead dust is the primary pathway to lead exposure. Children are especially susceptible to lead poisoning because they put many objects in their mouths. They may play in dirt that contains toxic levels of lead, then put contaminated fingers and toys in their mouths. Children encounter lead chips or dust on window sills, door jams, railings, radiators, and near baseboards. Lead is also found in paint on old toys and furniture and in some jewelry.

Lead is absorbed into the bloodstream, then, like calcium, is absorbed by the bone. Lead can accumulate through life. It can be stored in the bone and then return to the bloodstream at any time (Jaroff, 2001). Children's bodies are inclined to absorb more lead, especially if there is an iron deficiency.

The National Association for the Education of Young Children recommends a number of protective practices to keep children safe from lead poisoning (Kendrick, Kaufmann, & Messenger, 1995), including screening children, paint, water, and soil for lead levels. If lead is found, deleading should be done very carefully, and professional assistance may be required. The Department of Health will provide the caregiver with this information.

(continued)

The NAEYC also suggests that providing an iron- and calcium-rich diet and washing fruits and vegetables may be preventive measures. Frequent washing of hands, toys, and floors can cut down on lead levels, if present. Thorough housecleaning was found to correlate with reducing blood levels of lead. When houses were cleaned thoroughly 20 or more times per year, children experienced a 34 percent decrease in lead blood levels (Rhoads et al., 1999). For further information the National Lead Information Web site can be accessed at: http://www.epa.gov/lead/nlic.htm; this organization may be called at 1–800–424–LEAD.

under care, it is important for the parent to understand the potential seriousness of an eye condition and refer the child to her physician or local health clinic.

There are three common eye conditions found in children: nearsightedness, strabismus, and amblyopia. Nearsightedness, the inability to see distant objects clearly, is the most common visual problem in young children. It may not be readily detected before the age of two, but corrective lenses will enable the child to see normally. Strabismus is the misalignment of the eyes, which occurs because of an imbalance in the eye muscles. It becomes difficult for the eyes to focus on the same point at the same time. Corrective lenses, eye exercises, eyedrops, and sometimes eye surgeries help to correct this problem. Amblyopia, also called "lazy eye," occurs when one eye does not see well or is injured, and the other eye takes over almost exclusively. Treatment of this condition is most successful when it is caught before age three years. The child wears a patch to prevent vision in the good eye, thereby forcing him to use the inactive eye.

Caring for a child with any of these eye conditions will take patience and assistance on the part of the caregiver. A child may become easily frustrated or embarrassed over the visual difficulties he is having. It is important that other children understand and not make fun of the child.

Nearsightedness
lack of ability to see well, other than close up

Strabismus
a condition that occurs in children that causes one or both eyes to appear crossed

Amblyopia
an unequal balance of a child's eye muscles often referred to as "lazy eye." Condition is improved through the use of eye patches to enable the weaker eye to strengthen with greater use

Vision screening is normally done during a child's regularly scheduled physician visit. However, centers and schools that have a nurse on staff may conduct this screening on site.

Aaron, two-and-a-half years old, was found to have amblyopia in his right eye. The doctor prescribed glasses with a patch on the right lens. The first day at the day care center Aaron felt awkward and embarrassed. The other children were curious; some appeared to be fearful and did not understand why Aaron had the patch. At circle time, Regina, the teacher, talked about it with the children. They talked about eyes and how it felt to see things with two eyes and how different it would be to have to use just one eye to help make the other eye see better.

After hearing the comments and questions of the children and sensing Aaron's discomfort, Regina had the children make their own patches and decorate them. Regina, and the children who wanted to, wore the patches tied with yarn during afternoon snack. They were all excited and felt rather glamorous, like a group of pirates. By the end of snack the children with patches could grasp that it was not as easy to see and coordinate with one eye. They all talked about this and asked Aaron questions. These children became helpers to Aaron and their concern restored Aaron's confidence. Regina helped defuse a difficult situation for Aaron.

Appraising Hearing.   Hearing loss is caused by a number of factors. For example, a mother may have had an illness while pregnant or there may have been a genetic factor that caused an abnormal development. Or a child may have been born prematurely or may suffer from recurrent ear infections, allergies, or colds. It is not always easy to detect a hearing loss, but the caregiver may notice some caution signals. Table 9–7 contains the ages and questions recommended by the National Association for Speech and Hearing to help the caregiver detect whether the child may have a hearing problem.

If a child's responses are not developmentally appropriate, the caregiver should discuss with a parent what has been noticed and decide with the parent what action to take for a referral. A conference with the health consultant would help the caregiver and the family know how to proceed. Early detection

---

TABLE 9–7   Developmental Hearing Norms

✓ *Check for:*

Birth to 3 months	☐	Does the child listen to speech?
	☐	Does the child cry or startle at noises?
3 to 6 months	☐	Does the child smile when spoken to?
	☐	Does the child try to turn toward speaker?
	☐	Does the child seem to recognize mother's voice?
6 to 9 months	☐	Does the child respond to his name?
	☐	Does the child turn head toward where the sound is coming from?
	☐	Does the child notice and look around for source of new sounds?

(continued)

TABLE 9–7	Developmental Hearing Norms *(continued)*

✓ *Check for:*

9 months to 1 year	☐ Does the child listen to people talking?
	☐ Does the child look up when you call?
	☐ Does the child look around when hearing new sounds?
1 to 2 years	☐ Can the child follow two requests such as "go to the kitchen and get your cup?"
2 to 4 years	☐ Can the child point to pictures in a book upon hearing the object named?
	☐ Does the child understand conversation easily?
	☐ Does the child hear the television or music at the same loudness level as everyone else in the room?
	☐ Does the child notice normal sounds like the phone, the doorbell, or a dog's bark?
	☐ Does the child hear you when you call from another room?

Adapted from How Does Your Child Hear and Talk?, *by Psi Iota Xi Sorority and American Speech-Language-Hearing Foundation, 1986. Copyright 1986 by The National Association for Hearing and Speech Action.*

of a hearing problem can help a child learn to cope and adapt to hearing loss or possibly have the hearing repaired.

If a hearing referral is necessary, there are several places to send the child. A visit to the family physician is a good start. Other sources would include an **audiologist**, a speech language hearing clinic, or a community health agency. Often, school districts have a speech-language and hearing program that will help children in that district before they enter school.

If a hearing loss is detected, the caregiver can help the child adapt by speaking slowly and directly at the child, using hand gestures when applicable, and demonstrating more complex instructions where appropriate. Other children in care should be taught these same methods of communicating with the child who has a hearing loss. The child caregiver can also help to educate and support the parent in the use of these communication methods.

Evaluating Speech and Language. Speech and language acquisition come at varying ages in children. Girls tend to verbalize earlier than boys. Children in bilingual households may acquire speech more slowly (Brazelton, 1992). Some children do not acquire speech and language as rapidly as might be expected. These are normal speech and language patterns for children. Table 9–8 can help the caregiver notice how children use expressive language and if they have the ability to understand at the developmental level given. If a child does not follow this pattern, then the caregiver should check the list of warning signals found in Table 9–9.

Audiologist
person trained to identify types of hearing losses, to interpret audiometric tests, and to recommend equipment and procedures to assist the hearing impaired

Caregivers are a good source for observations regarding a child's hearing. It is essential that the caregiver be aware of the developmental norms for speech development, which can be an identifier of hearing problems. Caregivers may also have access to resources to help parents identify the proper type of specialist to test the child's hearing.

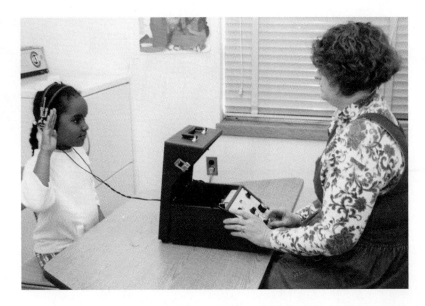

If a child exhibits any of the caution signs listed in Table 9–9 or is not at the appropriate developmental level, the child caregiver should discuss this with the parent to determine if the parent agrees that a problem may exist. A discussion with the health consultant may help the caregiver and the parent determine the best course of action. The child may have to be referred to a physician or other specialist such as a speech therapist.

TABLE 9–8	Normal Speech and Language Developmental Patterns	
Age	**Expressive Language**	**Ability to Understand**
3 to 6 months	Babbling, vocalizing pleasure	Smiles in response to speech; seeks sound source; recognizes familiar people and objects
7 to 9 months	Consonants—b,d,m,t,p,z; babbling; imitates speech sounds	Responds to gestures and "no"; can play peek-a-boo, pat-a-cake, and bye-bye
10 to 12 months	First true word may appear; intonations begin; uses all sounds in vocal play	Relates object and name; can follow simple body action commands; always responds to own name
1 to 1½ years	Uses 3 to 20 single words; uses gestures	Follows simple commands; recognizes some body parts and names for objects
1½ to 2 years	Uses 20 to 60 words; combines two words in sentences; 65% speech intelligible	Understands 200 to 300 words; can answer simple yes or no questions
2 to 3 years	Uses 200 to 500 words; three- and four-word sentences; grammar emerges; 70 to 80% speech intelligible	Understands 800 to 900 words; what, why, where questions; can listen to short stories
3 to 4 years	Uses 800 to 1,500 words; four- and five-word sentences; asks questions	Understands 1,200 to 1,500 words; can compare (up and down); responds to two-part commands
4 to 5 years	Uses 1,500 to 2,000 words; very intelligible speech; eight-word sentences; can tell long stories	Understands 2,500 words; answers complex questions; has some color and number concepts

Peer interaction during playtime is an ideal time to observe children's speech patterns.

A child who has a speech or language problem will need much patience and understanding. The caregiver can help the child by allowing him time to speak clearly. The caregiver can offer encouragement and reward the child's effort. The child needs caring and warmth. By modeling these supportive

TABLE 9–9   Caution Signs for Screening and Referral
Warnings
☐ No intelligible speech by two years of age
☐ Voice is monotone, too loud or soft, or of poor quality
☐ Difficult to understand after age three
☐ Nasal quality to voice
☐ Speech too fast or too slow
☐ Difficulty in expressing self, organizing thoughts
☐ Makes very few or no attempts to speak
☐ Inability to produce all speech sounds, thus interferes with communication
☐ Difficulty following directions at appropriate developmental language level
☐ Difficulty in engaging in verbal activities with other children
☐ Stuttering

actions, other children will begin to imitate these actions. This support will make it easier for the child with the problem to practice for success. A child with a good sense of self will be less hesitant or self-conscious, enabling the child to attempt to use speech and language at every opportunity.

Mental Health Appraisal.   During observation, the caregiver should be aware of at-risk indicators and other behavioral characteristics that may indicate poor social, emotional, or mental health. Table 9–10 shows a number of characteristics that may indicate the child is at risk.

There are many behaviors that may be annoying to adults but are perfectly normal and a part of a child's development between the ages of one-and-one-half years and four years of age. Children often do not pay attention and do not do what they are asked. They can be hard to reason with sometimes and may sulk or cry easily. They may not be able to sit still. Some may boss other children around and try to show off.

Younger children may not want to share and will say "no" often when requested to cooperate. They may grab toys, hit, shove, or attack others who have what they want.

It is not uncommon for some children to whine and complain. Other children may have a special blanket or suck their thumbs. Some children are shy and afraid of unfamiliar people and situations. It is not unusual for children to make up stories and tell them as truths.

These typical behaviors are not necessarily indicators of risk for mental difficulties. Behaviors that may indicate children are at risk for problems in mental health are found in Table 9–10.

When a child shows a number of disturbing behaviors, especially with increasing frequency, it is a good idea to discuss the child's behavior with a parent. If there is no explanation or if the parent expresses concern, the caregiver, with the parent's permission, may want to contact the health consultant.

Richard, a bright, cheerful three-year-old, attended a campus child care center three mornings a week. Two full days a week he attended a special school for children with developmental difficulties. Richard was born with a problem with his tongue that was not detected until he was almost two years old. Surgery and the school helped Richard begin to learn how to verbalize. He attended the campus child care center to help him acquire language from his interaction with other children who had good language skills. In the beginning, Richard was hesitant to speak and was somewhat withdrawn. Cathy, his teacher, read several books to the children that dealt with characters who were different. These books helped bring about a dialogue that concluded that there were more similarities than differences among these characters. After this, Richard seemed less hesitant to speak and began to relate to the other children. The children observed how Cathy listened to and spoke with Richard. They began to follow her lead. The inclusion was a success for both Richard and the other children. Richard's language became more intelligible and the other children learned that differences were not threatening.

Many conditions that cause a great deal of stress for a child may be at the root of the problem. Collaboration on the part of the caregiver, the family, and a health professional may detect the problem and enable early intervention to alleviate the difficulty. A referral to a physician or mental health counselor or psychologist may be necessary if the difficulties are not easily solved.

TABLE 9–10   At-Risk Indicators for Children's Vulnerability to Poor Mental Health

⚠️ *Warnings*

- ☐ Aggression or acting out behaviors, without provocation
- ☐ Passivity, lack of response, or totally withdrawn
- ☐ Disorganized behavior socially or in play
- ☐ Poor or inappropriate attachment patterns
- ☐ Low self-esteem
- ☐ Easily overstimulated
- ☐ Unresponsive to verbal cues or affectionate overtures
- ☐ Clingy, dependent
- ☐ Hypersensitive
- ☐ Unable to make decisions or solve problems
- ☐ Temper tantrums or very irritable
- ☐ Mood swings with no explanation
- ☐ Lack of attention or ability to focus
- ☐ Easily frustrated
- ☐ Overreaction or inappropriate response to everyday events
- ☐ Inability to transition easily
- ☐ Indifference to parent
- ☐ Avoids eye contact
- ☐ Anxiously follows caregiver everywhere
- ☐ Little or no interest in others

Identifying at-risk indicators and behavioral characteristics that may indicate a child's poor mental health is an important part of early intervention. It is important for caregivers to recognize that normal behaviors, such as crying or shyness, do not necessarily indicate a problem and may instead be just a normal aspect of the child's personality.

REALITY CHECK

Poverty and Childhood

Over 12 million children live in poverty and 4.2 million of those are under the age of six. Although the figures are down from the early 1990s, they are still higher than they should be. The poverty rate in the United States is often two to three times higher than other Western industrialized countries (NCCP, 2001). Poverty is more likely to affect children of color. Thirty-seven percent of African American children under age six live in poverty. Thirty-one percent of Hispanic children live in poverty, while the figure for white children is at about 10 percent (NCCP, 2001). A correlation with the rise of poverty from the 1970s to the 1990s is the significant rise in single parent families, which have doubled during that period. In total, approximately 28 percent of children live in single parent homes. Almost 60 percent of children from single parent families live in poverty, compared to less than 15 percent of children from two parent families.

There are many contributing factors to poverty, including family composition, parent education, and family income (Nelson, 2000). Although there is a higher total number of Caucasian children living in poverty, the total percentage of African American and Hispanic and other children living in poverty is at a higher level. Fifty-eight percent of minority children live at the poverty rate, compared to 42 percent of Caucasian children (Atkins, 1993). Children living in urban areas represent one-third of the children living in poverty. Children who live in rural areas represent 26 percent of children living in poverty. Children living in suburban areas represent 17 percent of children living in poverty (NCCP, 2001).

Children from families in poverty make up the largest growing segment of the homeless. More than one-fourth of the homeless are families with children (Jones, 1999). Families with children are

(continued)

the largest growing segment of the homeless population. The risk to children due to poverty is even greater for homeless children because of their lack of housing.

Impoverished living conditions can result in poor health, lack of safety, and poor nutrition. Poor families are six times more likely to report that their children are in poor or fair health than families that have adequate income (Newacheck, Jameson, & Halfon, 1994). Health problems are reflected in lower blood iron levels and higher levels of vision, hearing, and dental problems. Blood levels of lead are also higher for children living in poverty. Children in poverty have more frequent, more severe, and longer lasting infectious diseases (Brooks-Gunn & Duncan, 1997). Families in poverty may seek primary medical attention in the emergency room (Nelson, 2000). Homeless children are at an even higher risk. Because of living conditions, these children are more likely to have higher levels of respiratory infections and food-borne infections.

Children in poverty are also more likely to have developmental difficulties, which may be related to poor or nonexistent prenatal care for the mother. The difficulties may also relate to being born to teenage mothers. Health conditions are more likely to go untreated for these children.

Poverty appears to contribute to emotional and behavioral problems for children (Brooks-Gunn & Duncan, 1997). Children living in poverty are more likely to be affected by drug and alcohol abuse and child abuse, which lead to increased risk for mental health problems that result in emotional and behavioral problems. Homeless children are even more likely to suffer from emotional and behavioral problems. These children are more likely to have frequent changes of residence, be at risk for safety, and suffer from domestic conflict (Burg, 1994).

Children living in poverty are more likely to be at risk for safety in their living conditions

(Shonkoff & Meisels, 1998). Poor housing conditions can lead to higher levels of lead and unsafe neighborhoods. The economic stress of living at the poverty level causes higher levels of domestic abuse, including neglect and physical, sexual, and emotional abuse.

Income level affects food consumption practices. Financial resources help families meet basic food needs. The less income, the less likely the basic needs for nutrition will be met (OSUE, 1998). Children living in poverty are far less likely to have their needs for fruits and vegetables met. Inadequate nutrition can affect cognitive development and behavior (Kleinman et al., 1998). Pollitt (1994) reported that worldwide research shows three conditions correlated with poverty and poor nutrition:

1. effects of poor nutrition and illness on school performance

2. relationship between poor motor and mental development and anemia

3. positive effects of supplemental food programs

Recent evidence has shown that children need enough protein, calories, vitamins, and minerals to prevent malnutrition. Homeless children may be at greater risk for nutritional deficits because their basic food needs may depend on food programs that are not geared to children.

Caregivers can have a profound effect on the lives of poor children. They are in the position to provide an environment for a significant portion of the day that will offer children greater physical safety and good nutrition. Child caregivers can help improve the health of children through good screening and sanitation practices. They can also help families access health care and nutritional supplement programs. Caregivers can offer children emotional stability that may help to counteract the problems that poverty brings to their lives.

Nutritional Assessment. Assessment of a child's nutritional status may be warranted for a child whose growth is different from the norm, such as children who appear obese, who may have a food intolerance, or who may show an increased susceptibility to infections or illness. Assessing a child's food intake pattern may be very helpful in determining if there is a physical or organic difficulty that is affecting a child's growth, health, or well-being. The types of foods a child eats, how much food is eaten, and when and where the child eats may be pertinent information. If necessary, the caregiver and the parent can work together to provide this information for a health professional who may further assess the child's condition.

The nutritional assessment will help reveal:

- what types of foods the child eats
- how much food the child eats
- when the child eats
- under what circumstances the child eats
- adequacy of nutrition provided to the child
- parental knowledge of nutrients offered to child
- adequacy of the child's diet
- why the child eats what she eats
- why the child refuses to eat certain foods

Nutritional screening is usually accomplished in several ways. The first is the 24-hour dietary recall method. This information is relatively easy to obtain and can be done in several ways. With this method, the parent and caregiver create a list of foods eaten, including an estimate of how much food is eaten. This can be done for either a one-day or three-day period. Since any one day may not reflect the child's normal diet, a three-day record may be more beneficial. Some difficulties with this method are that the estimates may not be accurate and gaining the cooperation of the parent to record more than one day may be difficult. The recall method may reveal potential patterns of consumption that put the child at risk for nutritional deficiency. See the sample in Table 9–11.

As far as diets for children are concerned, the sample given in Table 9–11 might be a typical diet for a three-year-old. If one were to compare this sample to the food pyramid and the recommended daily allowances, there are definite indicators that the diet is lacking in grains, vegetables, and fruits and that there is overconsumption in the milk and milk product category.

Another method of nutritional assessment is the food frequency questionnaire (see Table 9–12). This tool will show how often foods are consumed in the four food groups plus the "other" group in the period of one week. This questionnaire relies on the parent for recall, but it might be an easier tool to use to find out if the child is lacking in or excessively consuming certain food groups. This tool may also establish a cultural or ethnic eating pattern that may put the child at risk for nutritional problems.

Both of the nutritional assessment tools require understanding and cooperation between the parent and the caregiver. Working together to establish what the child's eating patterns are and making changes to help the child follow the recommended diet pattern can be an effective method for establishing respect and forming an alliance between the caregiver and the parent. Discussing the dietary pattern with the health consultant or a dietician might be helpful, if a problem is indicated. A referral to the child's physician or local health clinic may be recommended.

TABLE 9–11 24-Hour Dietary Recall

Name: Dane Leonard   **Age: 3 years, 2 months**

G = Grains, bread, and cereals   MM = Milk and milk products
V = Vegetables   M = Meat   F = Fruits

Breakfast
½ cup sugared cereal (1 G)
1 cup milk (1 MM)
1 banana (1 F)

Lunch
1 corn dog (1 M)
chips
punch
½ cup pudding (1 MM)

Dinner
1 chicken leg (1 M)
peas (1 V)
mashed potatoes (1 V)
1 cup milk (1 MM)

Snacks
1 apple (1 F)
2 chocolate chip cookies
1 cup grape juice (1 F)
1 cup milk (1 MM)

How many servings of each in one day?
Grains, Breads, and Cereals
(G)—1
Fruits (F)—3
Vegetables (V)—2
Milk and Milk Products (MM)—4
Meats (M)—2

Assessment: Low on grains, breads, and cereals; high on milk and milk products

TABLE 9–12 Food Frequency Questionnaire for Children

Name _____ **Age** _____

Indicate how many times on average your child eats the following foods in a week by marking down the number of times in the category that most describes your child's eating pattern.

D = Daily   O = Often   S = Sometimes   R = Rarely

	Frequency			
Food	**D**	**O**	**S**	**R**
Milk and milk products: cheese, milk, yogurt, ice cream, and pudding	☐	☐	☐	☐
Meat, meat products, and meat substitutes: beef, chicken, pork, lamb, fish, egg, lunch meat, bacon, dried beans, peas, and peanut butter	☐	☐	☐	☐
Grains, breads, and cereals: rice, pasta, tortillas, grits, breads, cereals	☐	☐	☐	☐
Fruits and vegetables	☐	☐	☐	☐
Other: fats, oils, sweet bakery goods, fast foods, and candy	☐	☐	☐	☐

What type of milk does your child drink?

skim	1% lowfat	2% lowfat	whole	formula	breast
☐	☐	☐	☐	☐	☐

(continued)

TABLE 9–12   Food Frequency Questionnaire for Children *(continued)*
How many meals, including snacks, does the child eat in one day? _____
Also, explain the child's eating habits: _____   _____   _____
Are there any dietary restrictions or limitations practiced by your family? If yes, please explain. Yes ☐   No ☐   _____   _____

KEY CONCEPT 9.3

Health Status Assessment

Assessing a child's health status is a major task for the child caregiver. Using daily health checks, general health appraisal, screening for developmental norms, screening for good mental health, and assessing nutrition are the tools that the caregiver would use to detect any problems or deficits that a child may have. Early detection may lead to early intervention to correct the problem.

9.4 Implications for Caregivers

Child caregivers are a key link in establishing the promotion of good health for children. Caregivers have the opportunity to contribute to the health and well-being of children in care. These areas include observation, education, cultural sensitivity, and supervision.

Observation

Observation of children is a significant portion of a caregiver's job because it allows a caregiver to get to know and understand a child's temperament, personality, abilities, and limitations. When the caregiver is specifically observing a child's health and well-being, there are several goals to keep in mind.

What Is Going to Be Observed?   The first goal is to decide what is going to be observed. Is the child being observed for physical well-being, how she performs physically, or acts emotionally? Is the caregiver specifically looking for a particular health condition or communicable disease? Has the parent indicated a problem he may have observed? What is the age of the child being observed? A three-year-old has different physical and emotional capacities than a two-year-old. Some other considerations that may affect the observations follow:

■ Are there cultural differences?

■ Is the child at risk?

■ Does the child have special needs?

■ Has there been a recent event in the child's life that may affect her well-being or behavior (e.g., birth of a baby, loss of a pet, a move)?

These factors will influence what is observed.

How Will the Observation Take Place? A second goal is to understand how the observation will take place. The caregiver needs to be aware that his own childhood, feelings, and experiences will affect the interpretation of what is observed and how it is translated. Lakin (1994) suggests that the observer go through stages of observation.

■ to act like a scientist and observe physical data
■ to be the inspector and sort out feelings from the physical data
■ to behave as an advocate and look at the situation from the child's point of view and consider why the child acted in a certain manner
■ to act as an artist and use what is observed to take action to support the development and interests of the child (this method enforces a holistic approach to observation)

The "how" of observation also includes what was physically done to carry out the observation. In order to be accurate in the first stage of observation of a child's health and well-being one needs to use all of the physical senses. The child caregiver will need to:

■ look   ■ feel
■ listen   ■ smell

Looking at the child includes all physical aspects of the child as well as how the child is acting. Listening to the child involves hearing what the child sounds like, as well as what the child says and how it is said. Feeling the child involves touching the child to see if she is feverish, clammy, or has swollen glands or other physical symptoms that a touch could help determine if a problem exists. Smelling a child would make the caregiver aware concerning personal hygiene as well as toileting accidents.

When to Observe? The caregiver should also know when the appropriate time to observe is. It is very important that a health check be made daily when the child first enters child care. This quick check should be done before the parent leaves the child. If the child is ill and must be excluded from care, it should be done before other children are exposed.

It is at the drop-off time that the parent may share any particular concerns he may have about the child's health or well-being. This helps the caregiver to be on the alert for observation of that concern.

In addition to the daily quick check, a child should be observed for physical and mental health on an ongoing basis. If there has been an outbreak of an infectious disease, special care should be taken to observe for that particular disease.

A plan and health policy for monthly, quarterly, and yearly observations for health in regard to assessment and screening for growth and developmental norms should be created and carried out.

Education

Assessment is a helpful communication device between the caregiver and the parent and can lead to collaborative practices that involve all factors of the child's environment: the child, the caregiver, the parents, the school, and the community. Information about the child's growth and development is collected and recorded at certain intervals. It is important that the caregiver be trained and have a base of knowledge to perform basic assessments. Another good practice is to discuss concerns with a health consultant before talking to the parent so that you are better informed as to the implications of those concerns. The health consultant can also be a source for referrals for the child if there is a difficulty.

The daily appraisal need not be discussed unless there is a problem or concern. All other forms of assessment should be discussed thoroughly with the parent. The parent may need to be educated as to the importance of any assessment. Any difficulty with the child's health and well-being should be addressed early in the process.

When a referral is made, the caregiver should follow up. If there is a problem, the caregiver should be aware of it and should be given instructions on how best to help the child cope with any difficulty. A discussion with the parent and the person to whom the child was referred would be most helpful to give the child the continuity of care that she might need.

Cultural Competence

A child whose first language is not English may appear not to follow developmental norms. A child who is exposed to two languages may have difficulty switching from the home language to the language while in child care. Patience and understanding are important. It is helpful to have a caregiver or someone that a caregiver can call upon who speaks the same language as the child to make the shift between the two languages easier.

If the caregiver notices real difficulties in hearing, speech, or language, she might want to discuss it with the parent to see if the child seems to have these same difficulties in the native language. If the child seems to have a problem, discussions with the parent and then referral should be approached with cultural sensitivity. Many cultures view any problem with a child as an imperfection that is a source of guilt and shame for the parent. An understanding of the child's native culture helps the caregiver relate better with the parent.

Dietary patterns are greatly influenced by cultural and ethnic considerations. Certain cultures such as southeast Asians and Indochinese rarely consume milk products. Other cultures may not have a varying menu that allows for the meats or fresh fruits and vegetables that a child needs in his diet. When assessing the child's diet, it is extremely important to have some knowledge of the family's customs. This will allow the caregiver to be culturally sensitive when talking to the parent. A health consultant, dietician, or family member who speaks both the child's and the caregiver's languages can help alleviate any problems that a language barrier might cause. It may be a challenge to help a family from a different cultural background adjust to dietary allowances recommended for the child. A health professional could prove to be an invaluable source of support to the caregiver.

Supervision

The caregiver needs to supervise child care to make sure that record keeping and assessments are carried out on a regular basis. A director in a child care center usually supervises the assessments and makes sure that the records are kept up to date. In family child care or in-home care, there may only be one caregiver present. It is up to this caregiver to make sure that children's health is supported through regular use of record keeping and assessment.

A communication system also needs to be established within the child care environment. Child caregivers need to work together and collaborate on promoting the good health of the child. A family child caregiver may have an aide or a substitute who could assist in appraisals and assessment. In a child care center, the child may see several caregivers and aides in one day, as well as the director and perhaps a kitchen helper. All of the staff should be trained to cooperate and help in appraising and assessing a child's health status.

KEY CONCEPT 9.4

Implications for Caregivers

The child caregiver needs to promote the good health and well-being of a child. The caregiver does this by using observation, education, cultural sensitivity, and supervision as tools to promote health and prevent risk.

CHAPTER SUMMARY

Children must be observed as individuals to assess their health and well-being. Caregivers can appraise and assess children for physical health, mental health, and nutrition. They can screen children for growth and developmental norms. Caregivers can document their observations through several forms of records. If there appears to be a difficulty in any area, they can discuss it with the parents and offer a referral, if necessary. Caregivers need to employ observation, education, cultural competence, and supervision to provide adequate assessment measures for children in care.

TO GO BEYOND

In this section you will find a number of activities that you can use to apply and improve your knowledge of this chapter. There are also thorough Online Resources that accompany this text that can be found at http://www.early childed.delmar.com/resources/robertson/index.html. Included on this site are chapter practice quizzes, PowerPoint outlines, Web links, a discussion forum, and various other activities to help you better understand the material in this chapter. This site is updated regularly so check back often to receive the latest information about the subjects in this chapter.

Chapter Review Critical Thinking Applications

1. Explain the interrelationship of assessment and early intervention.
2. Compare the differences between observing children and diagnosing them. Discuss how to observe without making judgments or diagnoses.

3. Discuss how homelessness would impact a preschool-age child. What benefits would that child receive if he or she attended a preschool? What local resources in your community might help this happen?

As an Individual

1. Assess your own physical health by self-observation. Record how you feel physically for a period of three days. Be sure to use precise words. When you are done, evaluate whether you have been observing or diagnosing your health.

2. Observe two children in a child care situation, if possible. If that is not available to you go to a local playground or park. Use the anecdotal type of record to document your observations. Write two paragraphs explaining how you felt documenting and what you learned from it.

3. Find two articles on lead poisoning and compare and contrast them. Be able to report on these articles in class.

As a Group

1. Bring several two-year-olds to class. Provide a number of toys and books for them. Watch them and observe their actions and interactions. Compare these observations for developmental norms for speech, language, and gross motor skills. Discuss how each child develops at their own rate.

2. Examine mental health indicators that put children at risk. Select the indicators that are most likely to prelude mental health risk. How would a child caregiver help to ameliorate these risks?

3. In small groups of four or five, go out into the community and collect resource information that offers help to those people in poverty. Share the resource information in a class discussion. Why does poverty greatly impact the development of children?

CHAPTER REFERENCES

American Academy of Pediatrics (AAP). (1998). Screening for elevated blood lead levels. *Pediatrics, 101*(6), 1072–1078.

American Public Health Association & American Academy of Pediatrics (APHA & APA). (2002). *Caring for our children: National health and safety performance standards: Guidelines for out-of-home care.* Washington, DC: American Public Health Association.

Atkins, B. (Ed.). (1993). *Dilemma of the working poor. 1992 update.* New York: National Center for Children in Poverty.

Bassett, M. M. (1995). *Infant and child care skills.* Clifton Park, NY: Delmar Learning.

Beaty, J. (2001). *Observing the development of young children.* New York: Prentice-Hall.

Benjamin, A. (1994). Observations in early childhood classrooms: Advice from the field. *Young Children, 49*(9), 14–20.

Brazelton, T. (1992). *Touchpoints: Your child's emotional and behavioral development.* Reading, MA: Addison-Wesley.

Brooks-Gunn, J., & Duncan, G. (1997). The effects of poverty on children. *The Future of Children 7*(2), 55–71.

Burg, M. (1994, May). Health problems of sheltered homeless women and their dependent children. *Health and Social Work, 19*(2), 125–131.

Cartwright, S. (1994, June). When we really see the child. *Child Care Information Exchange,* 5–9.

Centers for Disease Control (CDC). (2001). *CDC's lead poisoning prevention program.* National Center for Environmental Health. Retrieved May 15, 2002, from http://www.cdc.gov.nceh/lead/factsheets/leadfcts.htm.

Dailey, L. (1999). Communicating health, safety and developmental concerns to parents. *Child Care Health Connections, 12*(5), 4.

Jaroff, L. (2001, June 24). Lead poisoning poses the biggest environmental threat to children. *Time Magazine.*

Jones, M. (1999, May). Without a home. *Parenting Magazine,* 86–92.

Katz, L. (1997). A developmental approach to assessment of young children. [ERIC Digest] Champaign, IL: Eric Clearinghouse.

Katz, L., & Chard, S. (1996). The contribution of documentation to the quality of early childhood education. [ERIC Digest] Champaign, IL: Eric Clearinghouse.

Kendrick, A., Kaufmann, R, & Messenger, K. (1995). *Healthy young children: A manual for programs.* Washington, DC: NAEYC.

Kidshealth.org. (1999). Environmental health issues. Retrieved May 15, 2002, from http://kidshealth.org/parent/safety/environ.html.

Kleinman, R., Murphy, J., Little, M., Pagano, M., Wehler, C., Regal, K., & Jellinek, M. (1998). Hunger in children in the United States: Potential behavioral and emotional correlates. *Pediatrics, 101*(1), e3.

Lakin, M. (1994, January). Observing from a different point of view. *Child Care Information Exchange,* 65–69.

NAEYC. (1999). Early years are learning years: Working together to keep children healthy. Retrieved May 15, 2002, from http://www.naeyc.org/resources/eyle/1999/14.htm.

National Center for Children in Poverty, (NCCP). (2001). Children poverty fact sheet: June 2001. Retrieved May 15, 2002, from http://cpmcnet.columbia.edu/dept/nccp/ycpt/html.

Nelson, D. (2000). Connections count: Alternative framework for understanding and strengthening America's vulnerable families. *Young Children 55*(6), 39–42.

Newacheck, P., Jameson, W., & Halfon, N. (1994). Health status and income: The impact of poverty on child health. *Journal of School Health, 64*(6), 229–234.

Ohio State University Extension (OSUE). (1998). Poverty facts about children. Retrieved May 15, 2002, from www.ag.ohio-state.edu/~online/hyg-fact/5000/5704.html.

Pollitt, E. (1994). Poverty and child development: Relevance of research in developing countries to the United States. *Child Development, 65*(2), 283–295.

Rhoads, G., Ettinger, A., Weisel, C., Buckley, T., Goldman, K., Adgate, J., & Lioy, P. (1999). The effect of dust lead control on blood lead in toddlers: A randomized trial. *Pediatrics, 103*(3), 551–555.

Ryan, D., Levy, B., Pollack, S., & Walker, B. (1999). Protecting children from lead poisoning and building healthy communities. *American Journal of Public Health, 89*(6), 822–824.

Schweinhart, L. (1993). Observing young children in action: The key to early childhood assessment. *Young Children, 48*(7), 29–33.

Shaw, P., & Zehaye, S. (2000). Do I have the tools? *Child Care Health Connections, 13*(5), 10.

Shonkoff, J., & Phillips, J. (Eds.), & The Committee on Integrating the Science of Early Childhood Development. (2000). *Neurons to neighborhoods.* Committee on Integrating the Science of Early Childhood Development, Board of Children, Youth and Families. Washington, DC: National Academy Press. Retrieved May 15, 2002, from http://www.nap.edu.

Shonkoff, J. P., & Meisels, S. J. (1998). Early childhood intervention: A continuing evolution. In J. P. Shonkoff & S. J. Meisels (Eds.), *Handbook of early childhood intervention,* 2nd ed. (pp. 3–34). Cambridge, England: Cambridge University Press.

Stretesky, P., & Lynch, M. (2001). The relationship between lead exposure and homicide. *Archives of Pediatrics and Adolescent Medicine, 155*(5), 579–582.

Waldman, S. (1991, July 15). Lead and your kids. *Newsweek Magazine,* 42–48.

SUGGESTION FOR READING

Barness, L. E. (Ed.). (1993). *Pediatric nutrition handbook.* Elk Grove Village, IL: American Academy of Pediatrics.

Eddowes, E. A. (1994). School providing safer environments for homeless children. *Childhood Education, 70*(5), 271–273.

National Institute of Child Health and Human Development Early Child Care Research Network (NICH). (2001). Child care and common communicable illnesses. *Archives of Pediatrics and Adolescent Medicine, 155*(4), 481–488.

Oesterreich, L. (1995). Ages and stages—individual differences. National Network for Child Care. Retrieved May 15, 2002, from http://www/nncc.org/Child.Dev/ages.stages.indiv.dif.html.

For additional information on safety, nutrition, and health in early education, visit our Web site at **http://www.earlychilded.delmar.com**

10

Infection Control in Child Care

After reading this chapter, you should be able to:

10.1 Health Policies for Infection Control

Define and discuss health for the prevention of childhood infectious diseases.

10.2 Mechanisms of Infectious Disease Spread

Explain the mechanisms of communicable disease spread.

10.3 Immunizations for Disease Prevention

Relate the importance of immunizations in the prevention and reduction of communicable diseases.

10.4 Universal Sanitary Practices for the Child Care Environment

Summarize sanitation methods used in the prevention of spread of disease in child care.

10.5 Environmental Quality Control for Disease Prevention

Discuss factors in the environment that quality control can help to curb the spread of disease.

10.6 Implications for Caregivers

Describe the importance of education, supervision, and role modeling in the prevention of communicable diseases.

Infection control

control of infectious agents by sanitary practices

Immunization

vaccines given in order to protect individuals through the development of antibodies against specific infectious diseases

Hygiene

protective measures and sanitary practices to limit the spread of infection and help to promote health

10.1 Health Policies for Infection Control

Policies for infection control are essential to maintain the health and to prevent serious illness of children. Children in child care are more likely to become ill than children who stay at home. Immunization and hygiene can provide barriers to the spread of infectious diseases and illness of children who are in child care. The need for these policies is reinforced by the following:

- The United States ranks behind sixty-nine other countries in its immunization rate (Graham, 1994).
- Good practices in sanitation and hygiene can greatly reduce disease in child care (Aronson, 2001).
- Children under three years of age are more vulnerable to disease than are older children (Nich, 2001).
- Twelve million children including 30 percent Latinos, 20 percent African Americans, 17 percent Asians, and 11 percent Caucasian whites lack health insurance. These children are less likely to get preventive care such as immunizations and treatment for asthma (Sokol-Gutierrez, 2000).
- In order to protect all children in care and prevent illness, the child care day should start with a health check (CCHP, 2001).

The key tools of risk management for health are prevention, protection, and promotion. In order to utilize these tools properly, there must be an understanding of how disease is spread and how it is controlled. It is also important to know that educating caregivers, parents, and children can help prevent the spread of disease.

There are many people involved in the child care setting, both directly and indirectly. The potential for the spread of infectious diseases is increased as these numbers increase. There are the caregivers, the children, and the families whose interactions with each other make them more vulnerable than the general population. An added risk is present for a caregiver who is pregnant.

Developing health policies is essential for the control of infection and the spread of diseases. Even more important is communicating these policies to caregivers and parents. The distribution of written policies, meetings to articulate and reinforce the written policies, and new staff and parent training sessions are ways to communicate health policies.

A fetus is particularly vulnerable to certain infectious diseases. Health policies for the control of infectious diseases are critical for all people involved in the child care environment. These health policies should include:

1. *Mechanisms of Communicable Disease Spread:* understanding the mechanisms that spread disease and practices that will prevent it

2. *Immunizations for Disease Prevention:* understanding the importance of immunizations for protection and prevention and implementing strategies to be sure that children and adults are properly immunized

3. *Sanitation for Disease Prevention:* practices for sanitation, hygiene, and cleanliness that offer protective and preventive measures

4. *Environmental Quality Control for Disease Prevention:* strategies that help prevent the spread of disease in the rest of the child care environment

5. *Implications for Caregivers:* methods and practices that provide minimum risk and maximum health protection for child care

KEY CONCEPT 10.1

Health Policies for Infection Control

Health policies for the control of infection and the spread of disease are essential in child care. These policies should cover the mechanisms of disease control, the immunizations, and sanitation needed for disease prevention. Health policies should also address environmental quality control and education for disease prevention. The caregiver needs to understand the methods and practices that provide protection and prevention.

10.2 Mechanisms of Infectious Disease Spread

To many people, child care is thought of as a barrier to health. Infectious diseases are common in child care. Some child caregivers often complain about frequent illnesses. What most people do not understand is that the frequency of infectious diseases and the potential for disease spread can be greatly reduced through use of sanitary practices.

In order to place barriers against infectious diseases and to try to control them in child care, one must fully understand how disease is spread. It does not matter whether in child care, in an office, or in a home, **germs** are always present. The fact that they cannot be seen does not mean they are not there.

There are several major reasons why the spread of infectious diseases is more likely in child care. The young children present have not yet learned good hygiene practices and germs multiply in warm, moist places. Child care and the children present offer germs many warm, moist places in which to grow. Diseases are spread through the air and person-to-person contact.

Certain practices or lack of practices in child care greatly contribute to the spread of infectious diseases. Table 10–1 lists those practices.

Germs
microscopic organisms that can cause disease

Child care centers present a challenge for germ control. The frequent exchange of toys among children who have not yet mastered personal hygiene is one example. Important prevention measures are regularly disinfecting mouthed toys and frequent hand washing.

TABLE 10–1   Child Care Practices that Contribute to the Spread of Infectious Disease

 Warnings

- ☐ Failure to wash hands as needed
- ☐ Presence of children in diapers who put toys in the mouth
- ☐ Mixed ages where older children play with children in diapers
- ☐ Large numbers of children present, especially if within a contained area
- ☐ Improper diaper changing procedures, including disposal and cleanup
- ☐ Staff who have dual duties, such as preparing food and working with children
- ☐ Lack of facilities, such as not enough bathrooms, small rooms, or diaper area not separated from rest of care
- ☐ Water tables or wading pools that are not sanitized or do not have the water changed frequently
- ☐ Pets in the environment that are handled by children or caregivers
- ☐ Not requiring or checking immunization records for completion or update for all children in child care
- ☐ Not requiring or checking immunization records for all staff
- ☐ Failure to perform daily health check
- ☐ Not excluding ill staff
- ☐ Not having a good backup substitute list for replacing ill caregivers
- ☐ Not having a policy for exclusion of ill children
- ☐ Not properly informing families when the children are exposed to a communicable disease
- ☐ Lack of proper sanitation and cleaning, especially of toys and food preparation, bathroom, and sleeping areas
- ☐ Improper storage of food
- ☐ Lack of hygiene in food handling
- ☐ Inadequate circulation of air
- ☐ Children sharing sleeping space or equipment

For greater understanding of why the practices in Table 10–1 are so careless, it is helpful to know exactly how germs are spread to cause infectious diseases. There are four basic ways diseases are spread:

1. respiratory tract transmission
2. fecal-oral transmission
3. direct contact transmission
4. blood contact transmission

Respiratory Tract Transmission

Respiratory tract transmission germs that are passed through the air from the respiratory tract of one person to another person

Respiratory tract transmission is perhaps the most common method of disease spread in child care. Tiny droplets from the eyes, mouth, or nose get into the air when a child sneezes, coughs, drools, or even talks, and these droplets are transmitted to another person through the air they breathe. These droplets can also land on toys, food, and other things in the environment. Germs can live for many hours and activate once they come into contact with the mouth, nose, throat, lungs, or eyes of an uninfected person. When germs come into contact with an uninfected person, they can multiply and cause illness. Colds occur more often in the winter when children spend more time in a confined environment, and are spread by sharing tissues, food, and cups. They can also be spread when coughing or sneezing without covering the mouth.

The best ways to prevent germs from spreading are to disinfect toys that are put in the mouth often, wash hands at appropriate times (see Table 10–4), and teach children to protect others when they cough, sneeze, or blow their noses. Children under the age of three are more likely to have respiratory tract infections and they are also more likely to mouth toys and other objects.

Fecal-Oral Transmission

Fecal-oral transmission passing of germs from an infected person's bowel movement via the hand into another person's system via the mouth

Fecal-oral transmission occurs when the germs from one person's feces get into another person's mouth and then are swallowed and introduced into the digestive tract of that person. The most common way for germs to spread is when hands are not washed after toileting, before eating, or before preparing food. Fecal-oral transmitted diseases can affect a number of children. Rotavirus is a type of fecal-oral disease that is commonly found in child care settings (Ford-Jones et al., 2000).

Sanitized removal of bacteria, filth, and dirt that makes transmission of disease unlikely

In child care another common way that germs are spread is in the water. Water tables that are not **sanitized** and do not have the water changed frequently are hosts to germs that are transmitted from unwashed hands. The APA and AAHA do not recommend water tables in the child care environment for this reason. However, many child caregivers feel the benefits of having a water table outweigh the risks. Therefore, special care must be taken to maintain these water tables so they are not good hosts to germs and do not encourage the spread of disease.

Hand washing at proper times, proper care of a water table, and proper food safety can help obstruct the spread of disease through the fecal-oral route.

TABLE 10–2 Infectious Disease Spread in Child Care		
Method	**How Spread**	**Diseases**
Respiratory tract	Infectious droplets from the mouth, nose, and eyes get in air via talking, sneezing, coughing, and blowing nose.	Colds Strep throat Meningitis Chicken pox Measles Flu, Hib flu Tuberculosis Whooping cough Ear infections Fifth disease Sixth disease
Fecal-Oral	Germs from stool of one person get in mouth of another person and are swallowed. Not washing hands after toileting, before preparing food, before eating, and not disinfecting toys that have been put in the mouth. Also handling pets such as birds, snakes, and lizards can spread bacteria from salmonella.	Hepatitis A Giardia Shigella Salmonella Diarrhea
Direct Contact	Infected articles or secretions from infected area. Spread through touching toys, faucets, food, tables touched by infected person. By parasites through bedding, clothing, shared hats, combs, brushes, or dress-up clothing.	Impetigo Lice Scabies Cold sores Pink eye CMV
Blood	Infected blood from one person entering bloodstream of another person. Infected blood can come in contact through cuts, chapped hands, a hangnail, and other broken skin, or lining of mouth eyes, nose, and rectum. In child care common transmitters are child biting, bloody noses, and skinned knees.	Hepatitis B HIV-AIDS

REALITY CHECK

The Issue of Head Lice in Child Care

Lice are small parasitic insects that are spread through direct contact. Historically, the appearance of head lice on a person has been associated with lack of cleanliness and low socioeconomic class. This is one of the reasons that parents get offended and defensive when their child appears with a lice infestation. Because of these historical connotations, parents whose children have lice often feel guilty. Since children are more frequently

(continued)

affected than adults, it can have a significant effect on the child care environment. Communication is the key to keeping this situation and the emotional reactions to it in a manageable form, where directors, teachers, and parents work together to solve the problem.

Head lice survive by feeding on a person's blood via the scalp and cannot survive for more than 24 hours without access to it. It takes eight days for a single louse to hatch from the egg and that louse begins to feed somewhere around 10 days after hatching. Each fertile female egg can lay as many as 100 eggs over a period of more than a month. Left unchecked this can cause a major infestation, which can spread to others via *direct contact*.

More than anything, a head lice infestation is annoying. It is not life threatening, nor does it carry disease. But it can cause a lot of itching and if that itching is out of hand, an infection from it may occur. The biggest threat to a person with head lice is the overexposure to the toxic substances used to eliminate them (Pollack, 2000).

Most child care centers and elementary schools in this country have a "no-nits" policy that states if children are found to have an active sign of head lice infestation they will be sent home and must not return until all signs of infestation are gone. The Harvard School of Public Health has found that although these policies are helpful in principle, they present problems (Pollack, Kiszewski, & Spielman, 2000). Most schools lack expertise and tools to distinguish an active from an inactive infestation. Many inactive or nonexistent infestations have been erroneously found to be "active." The conclusion of Harvard's Public Health study was that since head lice is often misdiagnosed, an exclusion policy for head lice might well be unwarranted (Pollack, 2000). Others have found that information about head lice was based on anecdotal evidence, not scientific principle (Figueroa, 2000). In fact, many researchers have found the surrounding hysteria much more disturbing than head lice itself. Many researchers have concluded that a "no-nits" policy for lice is excessive (Williams et al., 2001; Pollack, Kiszewski, & Spielman, 2000).

Recently, the "no-nits" policy has hit another road block, which is that many products that are supposed to get rid of lice seem to be ineffective. It

has been suggested that head lice may have developed an immunity to those products. Overuse of such products can have toxic effects, so other ways to rid a child of head lice have been studied. The general guidelines to eradicate head lice are:

- use a shampoo that contains active ingredients that will kill the lice
- use a special lice comb that can be used to remove lice after shampooing
- machine wash all possibly infested items using hot water
- all nonwashable items go into dryer for 20 minutes
- vacuum surroundings, throw away bag
- soak combs and brushes in a bleach solution for one hour and then clean
- items such as stuffed animals should be placed in sealed plastic bags for a period of 3 to 4 weeks

If a parent has followed the above guidelines and head lice are still found on the child, frustration begins. Many directors and teachers have become very discouraged because they have complied with all guildelines, and lice remain. A number of home remedies have been presented, but none are "scientifically" effective and some may actually be very toxic. The only home remedy that may be effective, according to the Harvard School of Public Health, is the use of olive oil, which they do not endorse because of lack of scientific evidence. Some child care center directors and teachers have found that this treatment seemed to be effective in those cases that appeared to be resistant to the "normal" head lice shampoos. Another solution is the use of a really good lice comb to examine for nits thoroughly, instead of a visual examination, which may not be as accurate (Mumcuoglu et al., 2001).

Directors and teachers have often been at odds over the "no-nits" policy. In many cases, teachers trying to follow the exclusion policy for lice have tried to send the child home, or not allow the child to return if head lice or nits (even dead ones) were found. Directors, understanding the parent's frustration, have tended to be more lenient and allowed the child to stay in school. There are a number of

(continued)

factors against a "no nits" policy. These include (1) a child without a live infestation being unnecessarily excluded; (2) families that cannot comply may be penalized; and (3) exclusion can cause stigma or hysteria (Dailey, 2000).

In favor of a "no nits" policy are several other factors. The focus could be on manual removal of nits, not chemical treatment. When relying on manual removal with a lice comb, there is no worry about toxicity from the chemicals or treating something that might not have been lice in the first place. A "no nits" policy also would prevent reinfestations if lice were actually present. Having such a policy puts the responsibility for the removal of nits on the parents. Another guideline for exclusion could be the degree of risk, using a scale to determine if risk was high or low (Richardson et al., 2001). The best policy for lice for each child care situation should be discussed at length and a consensus among the caregivers should be reached so that everyone is comfortable. Communication and consensus about this issue is critical.

Direct Contact Transmission

Direct contact transmission
passing of germs from one person's body or clothing to another person through direct contact

Direct contact transmission occurs when one person has direct contact with **secretions** from an infected person. Secretions can be left on toys, doorknobs, or other objects that come in direct contact with the uninfected person. Direct contact transmission also occurs when a person picks up parasites from infested objects such as bedding, toys, clothing, or combs. Diseases can spread easily through direct contact among children and caregivers in a child care environment if precautions are not taken to curb it. Good hygiene, including hand washing, sanitizing, and proper food handling, can help block the spread of disease through direct contact.

Secretions
saliva, mucus, urine, and blood produced by the body for specific purposes

Blood Contact Transmission

Blood contact
passing of germs through the blood from one person's circulatory system to another person's circulatory system

Transmitting disease through **blood contact** occurs when the infected blood of one person enters the bloodstream of another person. The infected blood can

Sherry, a director in a college lab school setting felt that since head lice was not life threatening, and Amanda's mother desperately needed the support of child care to stay in school and work, she was willing to bend. Without communication, this situation could have created real animosity among staff. If the teachers were trying to enforce the "no-nits" policy and Sherry was allowing the child to stay in care, they would not present a united front. What Sherry and the teachers at this center did was to sit down and review the policy and make some changes.

Amanda's mother had had a very difficult time getting rid of the head lice. Through cooperation, either Sherry or a teacher, Damaris, would spend 10 minutes at the beginning of each day with a lice comb and comb through Amanda's hair as she played a computer game in the director's office. After three weeks, the lice were eradicated and Amanda's family and the child care center had developed a trust that still exists to this day. Amanda has graduated from child care, but her parents still come by to volunteer and to help in any way to support this center.

be transmitted and absorbed easily. For example, spread can occur when an infected person has a cut, scraped skin (such as from a skinned knee), or a bloody nose and is treated by a person with a hangnail, chapped hands, or a small cut. Spread also can occur when mucous membranes such as the inside lining of the mouth, eyes, and nose come in contact with another person's blood through a broken surface. The major risk for this would be child-biting. Caregivers should wear non-latex disposable gloves when caring for a child with an open wound and any secretions. Any child-biting should be handled immediately (see Table 2–9, page 82).

Following guidelines set up in the remainder of this chapter, the caregiver should be able to forestall or deter the spread of disease in the child care environment as shown in Table 10–2. Figure 10–1 shows the five most effective ways to prevent the spread of disease in child care.

Figure 10–1

Five Fabulous Forestallers of Disease Spread in Child Care

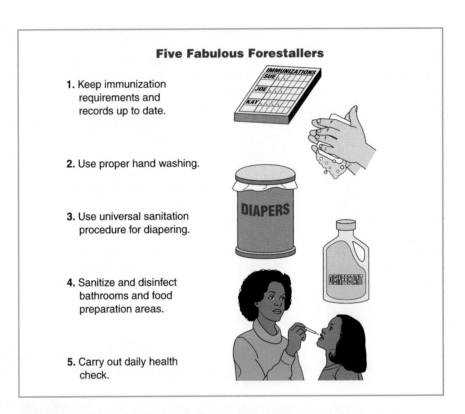

Five Fabulous Forestallers

1. Keep immunization requirements and records up to date.

2. Use proper hand washing.

3. Use universal sanitation procedure for diapering.

4. Sanitize and disinfect bathrooms and food preparation areas.

5. Carry out daily health check.

KEY CONCEPT 10.2

Mechanisms of Disease Spread

Infectious diseases are common in child care. In order to protect children's health, barriers must be in place. The caregiver must understand how diseases spread. The four methods of transmission are respiratory tract, fecal-oral, direct contact, and blood. This knowledge will provide a foundation for the caregiver to construct barriers to disease spread.

Communicable diseases

a disease spread from one person to another through means of respiratory spray or infected body fluids

Vaccinations

inactivated, dead, or weakened live organism of infectious diseases to which the body builds resistance

10.3 Immunizations for Disease Prevention

One of the major deterrents of communicable disease spread is immunization against those diseases. Immunizations can protect children from diseases that caused epidemics. These outbreaks could make children violently ill, disable them, and even kill them. Through medical science, a number of these diseases have been controlled by a regular schedule of immunizations for children at particular ages (see Table 10–3 for an immunization schedule).

There are immunizations or vaccinations available for a number of diseases that are associated with children and child care. Diseases that can be prevented include measles, mumps, rubella, whooping cough (pertussis), diphtheria, Hib (Haemophilus Influenza Type B—Meningitis), chicken pox, and hepatitis B. Immunizations for these diseases are recommended by the American Academy of Pediatrics and are required for entrance into elementary schools. There is also a vaccination available for hepatitis A, and it is suggested for inclusion to a child's immunization schedule in certain area (AAP, 2001). Ask your local health department if your area is one of the recommended places that should include it. The AAP is now also recommending a pneumococcal conjugate vaccine that can prevent meningitis, pneumonia, and serious infections transferred by the blood (AAP, 2001a).

Immunizations against disease are effective as a preventive measure only if they are administered according to schedule. Parents do not always realize that many serious childhood diseases can still pose threats and they need to prevent those threats through immunization. In recent years, whooping cough and measles have greatly increased because enough children have failed to be vaccinated against them. Adult caregivers need to make sure that boosters are administered as scheduled.

Children in child care not only need protection from the classic childhood diseases, but also from those diseases that seem to flourish in child care environments if proper precautions are not practiced. Recent outbreaks of childhood diseases seem to be traced to child care situations. These outbreaks include

Completion of the immunization schedule for both children and child care providers is essential. Children who come to the center after receiving their immunization shots may exhibit a low-grade fever or sleepiness.

TABLE 10–3 Recommended Childhood Immunization Schedule United States, 2002

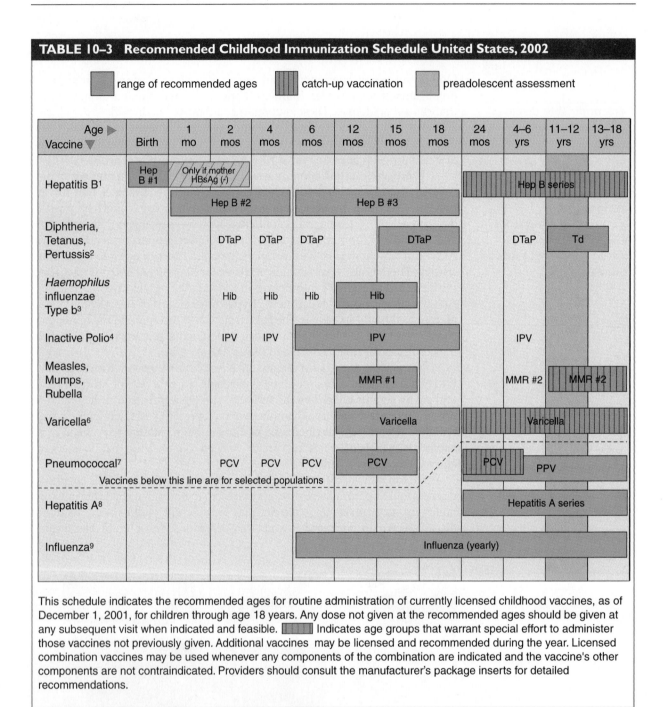

▨ range of recommended ages	▥ catch-up vaccination	▨ preadolescent assessment

Age ▶ / Vaccine ▼	Birth	1 mo	2 mos	4 mos	6 mos	12 mos	15 mos	18 mos	24 mos	4–6 yrs	11–12 yrs	13–18 yrs
Hepatitis B[1]	Hep B #1	Only if mother HBsAg (-)									Hep B series	
			Hep B #2			Hep B #3						
Diphtheria, Tetanus, Pertussis[2]			DTaP	DTaP	DTaP		DTaP			DTaP	Td	
Haemophilus influenzae Type b[3]			Hib	Hib	Hib	Hib						
Inactive Polio[4]			IPV	IPV	IPV					IPV		
Measles, Mumps, Rubella						MMR #1				MMR #2	MMR #2	
Varicella[6]						Varicella				Varicella		
Pneumococcal[7]			PCV	PCV	PCV	PCV			PCV	PPV		
Vaccines below this line are for selected populations												
Hepatitis A[8]										Hepatitis A series		
Influenza[9]					Influenza (yearly)							

This schedule indicates the recommended ages for routine administration of currently licensed childhood vaccines, as of December 1, 2001, for children through age 18 years. Any dose not given at the recommended ages should be given at any subsequent visit when indicated and feasible. ▥ Indicates age groups that warrant special effort to administer those vaccines not previously given. Additional vaccines may be licensed and recommended during the year. Licensed combination vaccines may be used whenever any components of the combination are indicated and the vaccine's other components are not contraindicated. Providers should consult the manufacturer's package inserts for detailed recommendations.

Approved by the Advisory Committe on Immunization Practices (ACIP), the American Academy of Pediatrics (AAP), and the American Academy of Family Physicians (AAFP). From the Centers for Disease Control and Prevention. Courtesy of the Centers for Disease Control http//www.cdc.gov/nip/recs/childschedule.htm.

hepatitis B, hepatitis A, and Hib, which is a flulike form of meningitis. Vaccines available for each of these diseases will help protect children in child care.

As a child caregiver, it is imperative to protect the children and the caregivers in the child care environment by requiring the completion of the immunization schedule (Spence, 1999). Parents of children in care must provide an immunization record filled out by a physician or local health clinic on the form provided by the state in which the child resides. A copy of this record should be on file with each child's health record and should be periodically updated if the child is in the process of receiving a series of vaccinations.

Children who have not followed the immunization schedule, and have missed a particular vaccination will not be protected from that particular disease. If a child has not met all of the requirements of an immunization schedule he must do so immediately. A quarterly check of children's records can help keep them up to date. To simplify record keeping, the caregiver can place a "red flag" or special sticker on each child's file who must still complete the immunization schedule.

If a child in child care has not completed the schedule and the parents do not have any plans to complete this schedule, the child should be excluded from care until the process of immunization is resumed. An exception to this would be a child who, for medical or religious reasons, is exempt from the immunizations. An exemption or release form must be signed by the parent before the child is admitted or readmitted into care. The difficulty with this situation is that it puts other children at greater risk. A child who is exempt from following the schedule for measles, mumps, and rubella is 35 times more likely to have measles and spread them than is a vaccinated child (Salmon, Haber, & Cangarosa, 1999).

The issue of the relationship between increase in autism and vaccinations given for measles, mumps, and rubella and diphtheria, tetanus, and pertussis has caused concern among parents in both the United States and Great Britain. This relationship has proven to have no validity (Manning, 2001). Vaccines rarely cause life-threatening or life-changing reactions (Sachs, 1999). Quite the opposite is true. A child is far more at risk if they are not immunized properly. It has been found that when more children have been vaccinated with the varicella vaccine, fewer children in child care without the vaccination actually got chicken pox (Clements et al., 2001).

There has been a 40 percent increase in immunizations since 1992 and now 80 percent of all children are immunized for diphtheria, pertussis, tetanus, measles, mumps, rubella, and polio. One goal of Healthy People 2010 is that at least 90 percent of children will be immunized.

The more children in child care who are properly immunized, the less the risk for the spread of those childhood diseases. Caregivers also need to verify their own immunity to childhood diseases and should follow the vaccination schedule for Hib, hepatitis A, and hepatitis B.

KEY CONCEPT 10.3

Immunizations for Disease Prevention

Immunizations are a major deterrent to disease. In order to be effective, they must be administered according to schedule. Both the children and caregivers in the child care environment should meet the immunization requirements.

Sanitary practices
practices that remove bacteria, filth, and dirt that cut down on disease transmission

Virus
a small microorganism that is produced in living cells and that can cause disease

Otitis media
infection of the middle ear

Disinfecting
procedures to eliminate all germs through use of chemicals or heat

10.4 Universal Sanitary Practices for the Child Care Environment

One of the most effective tools you have to create a healthy environment for the child is to incorporate universal **sanitary practices** to keep the environment as clean and germ-free as possible. These protective and preventive actions can greatly reduce risk for infection or disease. Proper sanitary practices can help in the prevention of the spread of **virus**, bacteria, parasites, respiratory diseases, and **otitis media**.

Cleaning, sanitation, and disinfection procedures should be the main points of a health policy for a sanitary environment. These procedures should include:

- hand washing
- diapering
- toileting
- cleaning and **disinfecting**

It is very important that a written explanation of the sanitary practice policy be sent home with children so that parents understand that an effort is being made to keep the environment healthy and germ-free. Cooperation may also be elicited to encourage children to use these sanitary practices in the home by providing parents with a flyer on correct hand washing procedures.

Hand Washing

Washing the hands is perhaps the single most important thing the caregiver can do to prevent illness personally and to keep it from spreading to the children in care (NAEYC, 1999) (see Table 10–4). It is essential that the caregiver develop the habit of frequent hand washing. Often when the pace of life is hectic, it is easy to forget that hand washing should be done. If it is developed into a routine and becomes a habit, hand washing will be second nature and will be done regardless of the pace.

The times for routine hand washing shown in Table 10–4 reflect when the caregiver should wash hands and help the children wash their hands. By modeling hand washing behavior, the children can easily follow the caregiver's direction. Caregiver hand washing should be part of training, as well as monitoring the environment. The combination of training and monitoring leads to a very significant decrease in diarrhea in children in child care (Aronson, 2001). Another issue that could be looked at from a hand washing viewpoint is the presence of long or artificial nails in child care. Nurses with long or artificial nails were found to cause illness in young babies that they worked with and when they got rid of the nails, the rate of infection and illness decreased (Moolenaar et al., 2000). It has also been suggested that elaborate wrist and hand jewelry not be used in child care because it too could harbor germs that good hand washing will not catch (Aronson, 2001).

TABLE 10–4 Universal Sanitary Hand Washing Practices

When:

Both the Child and the Caregiver

- Upon arrival at child care
- Before eating or drinking
- After touching a child who may be sick
- After using the toilet or changing diapers

Caregiver

- After handling body secretions (vomit, mucus, and so forth)
- Before and after handling or preparing food
- After cleaning
- Before and after giving medication, if applicable

How:

- Use running water that drains. Do not use a stoppered sink or container.
- You must use soap. Liquid soap is preferable, because germs can grow on soap bars.
- Use friction. Rub hands together for germ removal. Rub between fingers and around nails.
- Rinse thoroughly in running water.
- Turn off faucet with paper towel. Touching the faucet can recontaminate your hands.

Adapted from Control of Communicable and Infectious Diseases: A Manual for Child Care Providers, *California Child Care Health Project.*

Friction

rubbing together

Diapering

Fecal contamination

contamination occurring through exposure to feces

Fecal contamination in the child care environment leads to the spread of infection from the carrier to others. Containment of fecal matter, use of disposable changing table pads, proper hand washing, and use of disposable gloves are protective measures that control this spread. These measures manage the risk of contamination and spread of disease. Bacteria can also be spread through urine and the same protective measures help to manage this risk.

The area where diapering occurs should be isolated and equipped for cleanliness and safety (see Table 10–5). A correct procedure for changing diapers should be developed and placed above the diaper changing area. Maintaining the procedure as well as a clean and sanitary area to change diapers greatly reduces risk (see Table 10–6).

If a child uses cloth diapers, the diapers should be placed in a second plastic bag and sent home with the child. There is too much risk of spreading disease by rinsing or laundering diapers at a child care facility.

Routine hand washing should be a part of training in the day for any child. It is important to have sinks at a child's level, or safe footstools, so the child can comfortably wash.

TABLE 10–5 Creating a Sanitary Diapering Environment

- Use area for diapering only.
- Provide running water to wash hands before and after.
- Put it as far away from food preparation area as possible.
- Surface should be flat, safe, and preferably three feet off the floor.
- Make sure surface is clean, waterproof, and free of cracks. Use disposable covers such as squares, rolls of paper, paper bags, or used computer paper. Throw away immediately after use.
- For safety, keep all lotions out of the reach of children. Restrain child. Never leave child unattended.

Adapted from Control of Communicable and Infectious Diseases: A Manual for Child Care Providers, *California Child Care Health Project.*

Proper diapering procedures should be followed to avoid the spread of infection. A sanitary diapering area as well as using disposable rubber gloves are examples of proper diapering procedures.

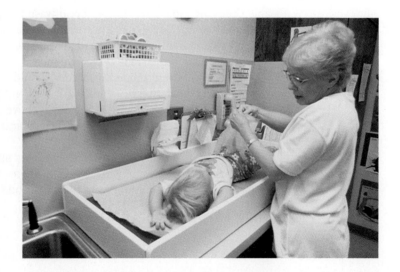

TABLE 10–6 Universal Sanitary Diapering Procedures

- Have area and supplies ready.
- Put on disposable gloves.
- Pick up child. If diaper is soiled, hold child away from you.
- Lay child down on diapering surface.
- Remove soiled or wet diaper. If clothes are contaminated, remove them.
- Place disposable diapers in a plastic bag and then throw away in a lined, covered trash can.
- Clean child's bottom with moist disposable wipes. Wipe from front to back, using towelette. Use another towelette if needed.
- Pat dry with paper towel.
- Dispose of towelette and towel in lined, covered trash can with lid.
- Wipe your hands with moist towelette and dispose of in lined, covered trash can with lid.
- Diaper child and dress.
- Wash the child's hands.
- Remove disposable covering from diaper surface.
- Wash area and disinfect with bleach solution.
- Remove disposable gloves.
- Wash your own hands thoroughly.

Adapted from Control of Communicable and Infectious Diseases: A Manual for Child Care Providers, *California Child Care Health Project.*

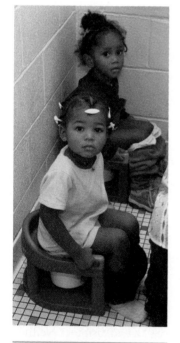

Toileting is a good opportunity to teach children about the importance of hand washing. Some states require that caregivers use disposable gloves when helping children with toileting.

Toileting

Toileting in a center is easier to control than toileting in a family child care or the child's own home. In most cases, centers have child-sized toilets that need to be cleaned and sanitized daily. If the toilet is contaminated with diarrhea, it should be cleaned and sanitized immediately. When training children to use the toilet they should be taught about the importance of washing hands. Instruction in hand washing should be given before and after toileting. Observing the children when they wash their hands will help to know which children need assistance in thorough hand washing.

Toileting in a home environment often involves a potty chair. Ideally, each child learning to toilet should bring his own potty chair to the caregiver, because it decreases the risk of spreading germs. The potty chairs should be kept out of the reach of children and away from other surfaces that may have germs. Table 10–7 reviews sanitary procedures for potty chair use.

The use of disposable gloves is also helpful in reducing the risk of spreading disease. Caregivers should check the requirements of their state licensing agencies, as some require the use of disposable gloves for helping with toileting.

Recording information about a child's progress during toileting can be useful for the parents who must further the progress at home.

TABLE 10–7 Sanitary Procedures for Potty Chairs

- Wash child's hands.

- Empty into toilet.

- Rinse with water. This should be in a sink used for no other purpose. If it is used for hand washing of the child, clean and sanitize sink after toileting.

- Wash chair with soap and water. Empty into toilet.

- Rinse again and place contents in toilet.

- Spray with bleach solution.

- Air dry.

- Wash hands.

Adapted from Control of Communicable and Infectious Diseases: A Manual for Child Care Providers, *California Child Care Health Project.*

Cleaning and Disinfecting

The best way to stop the spread of germs is to both clean and disinfect. Neither is adequate alone. Cleaning gets rid of dirt and some surface germs while disinfecting rids the surface of the remaining germs by using a sanitizing solution. In child care, the most common effective and least expensive sanitizing solution is bleach.

Several strengths of the solution are necessary for disinfecting different surfaces or contaminants. Figure 10–2 shows a general purpose sanitation mix.

Figure 10–2
General Purpose Cleaning Solution. Use in the bathroom, kitchen, diapering area, and on toys.

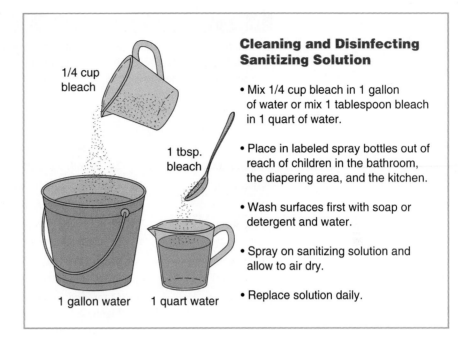

1/4 cup bleach

1 tbsp. bleach

1 gallon water

1 quart water

Cleaning and Disinfecting Sanitizing Solution

• Mix 1/4 cup bleach in 1 gallon of water or mix 1 tablespoon bleach in 1 quart of water.

• Place in labeled spray bottles out of reach of children in the bathroom, the diapering area, and the kitchen.

• Wash surfaces first with soap or detergent and water.

• Spray on sanitizing solution and allow to air dry.

• Replace solution daily.

The solution is placed in spray bottles and used in the bathroom, kitchen, diapering area, and on other surfaces and toys. This solution is also used on floors and to clean sleeping mats. See Table 10–8 for frequency of cleaning and disinfecting needed in the child care environment.

For cleaning more infectious items such as blood, blood spills, and body fluids, including vomit, a stronger solution is needed. This stronger solution is found in Figure 10–3. The contamination cleaning solution is also used for regular cleaning when outbreaks of infectious disease occur.

A standard solution of bleach to water should be used to clean and sanitize the classroom, toy surfaces, and floors. What other surfaces should be sanitized?

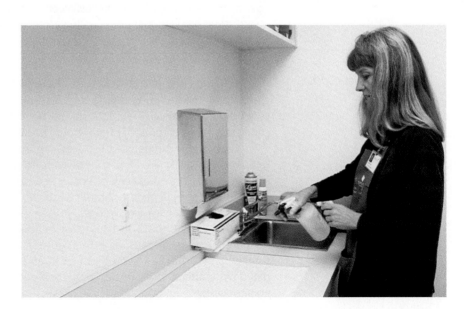

TABLE 10–8 Cleaning and Disinfecting Guidelines

- Clean objects and surfaces with detergent and water first.
- Next apply bleach solution by spraying from bottle or dipping object in bleach solution and allow to air dry.

Cleaning and Disinfecting Schedule:

Object or area	Frequency
Diaper changing area, toilets, and potty chairs	Clean after every use. Spray with sanitizing solution after cleaning.
Bathroom	Clean thoroughly one or more times daily.
Kitchen	Clean thoroughly one or more times daily.
Play Areas	Mop or vacuum daily. Remove litter or food immediately.
Cribs and Cots	Change linen when wet or soiled; otherwise, weekly Disinfect weekly.
Toys	Clean and sanitize all mouthed toys daily. Machine wash stuffed toys frequently. Sanitize water tables and wading pools after each use. Throw away mouthed play dough or clay immediately. Change frequently.

Cleaning: All-purpose liquid detergents and water are used to remove dirt, urine, or vomit by washing and scrubbing.

Sanitizing: Soap, detergents, and abrasive cleaners are used to remove filth, soil, and a small amount of bacteria. To be considered sanitary, surfaces must be clean and germs must be reduced to a level at which disease transmission is unlikely.

Disinfecting: A solution of bleach and water is used to eliminate practically all germs from surfaces. For normal disinfecting, a general-purpose solution is used. When working with blood or stools from bowel movement, a contamination solution is used.

When a child has soiled her clothing with fecal or bodily fluid, the item should be removed immediately and placed in a plastic bag for the parent to take home and launder. Parents should be informed of this policy when the child enters care. A reminder note should be attached to the soiled clothing bag.

Clothing and hats used for dress-up in play areas should be laundered frequently with bleach. Hats should be sprayed frequently with a disinfectant such as Lysol. If an outbreak of lice or skin infections such as scabies occurs, these clothes should be temporarily removed, laundered, and placed in airtight plastic bags for at least two weeks.

Each child should use his own bedding only. These items should be stored separately in bins or boxes labeled with the child's name. Regular weekly laundering can keep them fresh and clean. If they become contaminated with mucus, feces, urine, vomit, or blood, send them home with the parents to wash.

Figure 10–3
Contamination Cleaning Solution.
Use to clean blood, body fluids,
and vomit.

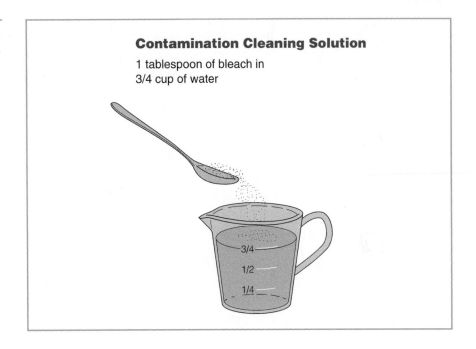

Contamination Cleaning Solution

1 tablespoon of bleach in
3/4 cup of water

When soiled or contaminated items are sent home with the child, a reminder note accompanying the items is an effective communication tool. It will explain to the parents why the item was not rinsed and alert them that they should closely observe their child for illness. The prevention, protection, and control of infectious disease are not always easily understood, but are very necessary in maintaining a sanitary environment.

Water play is an engrossing and
enjoyable activity for young
children, but opens up the playing
field for germs when the table or
container is not properly cleaned.

10.5 Environmental Quality Control for Disease Prevention

There are certain other areas of the child care environment that may contribute to the spread of disease. These special areas of consideration include water play, play dough, air quality, and contamination.

Water Play

Water play occurs in a container that, if not properly cleaned, can be an environment where germs multiply. If the water becomes warm, it offers the warm, moist place where germs thrive and rapidly multiply. For optimal use of a water table in the child care environment, follow the water table health tips found in Table 10–9.

Play Dough and Clay

Play dough and clay are also good hosts for germs because they are moist and get warm through frequent contact with children's hands. Safety tips for having play dough and clay in the child care environment are included in Table 10–10.

TABLE 10–9 Water Table Health Guidelines
• Clean and sanitize the water table with the general purpose sanitation mix daily.
• Change water at least daily; more frequently, if it gets warm (over 72°F). Use fresh, cool water.
• Children should wash hands before playing in water table.
• Wash water play toys daily either with general purpose solution or in the dishwasher.
• Use plastic throwaway items when possible.

Play dough is a classroom staple, but health precautions should be taken to make this fun manipulative germ-free and safe for children.

TABLE 10–10 Play Dough and Clay Health Guidelines

- Children must wash hands before and after playing with the play dough.
- Do not use scents in play dough because it encourages mouthing.
- Replace play dough frequently and always after being mouthed or when dirty.
- Store play dough in the refrigerator.
- Keep clay in a cool, dry place and make sure it is well covered.
- Clean and sanitize tables before and after play dough or clay is used.
- Allow only a small amount of clay at a time so it can be replaced more often and the expense will not be as great.
- Do not use play dough or clay for a day or two if a fecal-oral disease has been identified in the environment.

During naptime at least 3 feet of space should be maintained between cribs and cots.

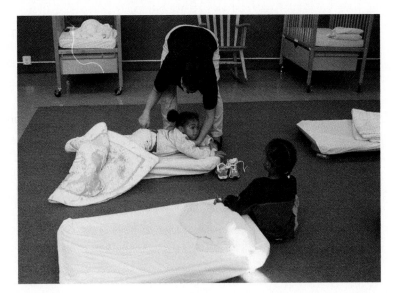

Air Quality

Air flow in the child care environment is especially important to help control the spread of germs. Crowding of children contributes to poor air quality (Aronson, 2000). If the air is not moving or if there are too many children in one area, the air will not flow as well as it should, resulting in a better environment for germs. Air fresheners do not help air quality, but merely mask odors. They may also pose a threat to some children with allergies and asthma and may trigger a reaction. To avoid poor air quality, follow the air quality health guidelines in Table 10–11.

TABLE 10–11 Air Quality Health Guidelines
• Keep air temperature cool; under 72°F helps prevent disease spread.
• Circulate fresh air as much as possible—open windows as daily weather permits.
• Make sure children get outside to breathe fresh air daily, weather permitting.
• Heating and cooling equipment should be checked several times a year and should be cleaned every three months. Any filters should be replaced when serviced to prevent buildup of molds and dust.
• Arrange your environment so that there is plenty of open space. This discourages the spread of germs.
• Keep at least 3 feet of space between cribs and cots in the sleeping area.
• Follow guidelines of indoor space per child so that there is no crowding.

Contamination in Child Care

Special precautions should be taken to minimize the effects of contaminants such as blood, vomit, urine, and loose stools or diarrhea in the child environment. For proper health precautions see Table 10–12.

TABLE 10–12 Health Guidelines for Disease Prevention
• Minimize the number of people who handle contaminated materials.
• Use disposable gloves and paper towels to clean up spills from diarrhea, blood, urine, or vomit.
• Clean and disinfect surfaces involved with contamination sanitation mix.
• Dispose of cleanup materials, disposable gloves, and so forth in a plastic bag, covered and tied, and placed in an outside trash can immediately.
• If any contaminated materials soil the child's or caregiver's clothes, they should be changed immediately.
• Wash hands immediately.
• Place contaminated clothing in a plastic bag with tie. Double bag it in another plastic bag and send home with child or caregiver to launder the clothing at home.

KEY CONCEPT 10.5

Environmental Quality Control for Disease Prevention

There are special areas of need for environmental quality control for infectious disease spread found in the child care environment. These areas include water tables, play dough and clay, air quality, and contamination. Using preventive strategies and techniques for these items can help the child caregiver control the spread of infectious disease.

10.6 Implications for Caregivers

Child caregivers must use a number of tools to prevent the risk of infectious disease spread. These tools include education and role modeling, cultural sensitivity, and supervision to make sure protective measures are carried out.

Education and Role Modeling

Education is one of the best preventive tools a caregiver has to help control the spread of infectious disease in child care. The effort to prevent the spread of germs and disease needs to be a cooperative venture. Caregivers need to model proper health behaviors. Children need to be taught to perform proper health practices. Parents need to understand the need for these practices and help children remember to carry these out at home so they get into the habit of good hygiene.

Children need to focus on several things to play their role in prevention. Good hand washing techniques at the right times is the most important tool for children to prevent the spread of disease. This can be done in a number of ways. Modeling the hand washing techniques is important.

Modeling hand washing should include:

- showing
- helping
- telling
- feedback

When the caregiver is washing her hands or helping a child to wash his, the caregiver should talk about what is happening and why. Reinforcing the conversation and hand washing method with feedback is important for the caregiver to see that the child is grasping: (1) why hands are being washed; (2) when hands should be washed; and (3) how hands should be washed.

Reminders should be given throughout the day at times when hand washing is a must. A poster or line drawing showing proper hand washing procedures placed by the hand washing sink offers a visual reminder when the caregiver is not present.

To ensure a healthy environment, one of the caregiver's most important tasks is to help children form the good hygiene habit of hand washing. If hand

Hand washing at scheduled intervals throughout the day can be a fun activity and teaches the children good hygiene.

washing is made a fun task, the children will more likely participate and remember when and how to use the hand washing techniques. Caregivers who develop or use songs that focus on hands while in circle groups or at the sink at hand washing times may make it easier for some children to grasp good hand washing behaviors. Using books that focus on hands or good hygiene will also help.

Cultural Competence

Cultural competence may be needed, especially when dealing with the issue of immunization. A parent may be unaware of the need for immunizations or may lack access to immunizations. Recent immigrant families may not be aware of the need for immunization or may even feel it is unnecessary. Some children from culturally diverse or immigrant, low-income working families may not have ready access to health care (Guendelman & Pearl, 2001). These families have higher rates of infectious diseases as well as chronic illnesses (Duarte & Rafanello, 2001). Resistance to participation in immunization and screening may also result from culturally defined acceptable behavior or language difficulties (Carballo & Nerukar, 2001). It is important for the caregiver to help the parents understand how vital it is to follow the immunization schedule and get regular health care for their children. Child caregivers can provide resources to help these families connect with public funds for low cost health insurance for low-income families. It is important for the caregiver to help the parents understand how vital it is to follow the immunization schedule. Following this schedule is vital to the child's own health as well as the child care environment.

Supervision

Parents have a significant degree of responsibility in preventing the spread of disease in the child care environment where their children attend. Parent education is critical in the prevention of outbreaks such as chicken pox, Hib, and meningitis. Parents can make sure their children are immunized according to schedule. They can reinforce the hygiene practices that children learn at school and they can make sure not to send their children to school when they are ill. Some of the supportive behaviors that are essential on the part of the parents may need some special effort on the part of the caregiver. It is up to the caregiver to supervise the environment so that the children come into care as risk-free as possible.

There are five basic commandments for infectious disease control that must be monitored by the child caregiver. These include:

- prevent the spread of disease
- require and monitor immunizations
- report some illnesses
- exclude some children
- be prepared

KEY CONCEPT 10.6

Implications for Caregivers

The effort to prevent the spread of infectious disease is a cooperative venture. The child caregiver can educate and model behaviors to the children. Modeling will also help the parent reinforce these behaviors at home. The caregiver must be especially culturally sensitive about the need for immunizations and help the parents understand the necessity of a current immunization schedule for children. The caregiver must supervise the child care environment to make sure sanitary practices are carried out.

CHAPTER SUMMARY

Health policies for infection control maintain health and prevent some illnesses in children and adults present in child care. Two practices that contribute to this are good hygiene and sanitary practices. Checking the immunization schedule is another preventive practice. Food safety and storage are other practices that help manage the spread of disease. The four methods of infectious disease spread should be understood and proactive measures taken to reduce the spread.

TO GO BEYOND

In this section you will find a number of activities that you can use to apply and improve your knowledge of this chapter. There are also thorough Online Resources that accompany this text that can be found at http://www.early childed.delmar.com/resources/robertson/index.html. Included on this site are chapter practice quizzes, PowerPoint outlines, Web links, a discussion forum, and various other activities to help you better understand the material in this chapter. This site is updated regularly so check back often to receive the latest information about the subjects in this chapter.

Chapter Review Critical Thinking Applications

1. Discuss the four methods of transmission of infectious diseases. Relate these methods of transmission to sanitary practices that could be performed to prevent spread.

2. Examine the importance of immunization schedules. How much have these schedules changed in recent years, compared to when the students were young children?

3. Debate the question of whether or not children with lice should be allowed to stay in care or should be excluded from care.

As an Individual

1. Observe hand washing practices in a child care environment. Next, observe hand washing practices in a public restroom. Compare and contrast these two environments. Were universal hand washing procedures used at appropriate times? Record your observations.

2. Research and report on the programs in your state and local area that help low-income children and their families gain access to health care.

As a Group

1. Discuss environmental quality control in child care. What further measures might be taken to improve the health of that environment? Discuss the impact of children's cots or sleeping pads being placed so close together.

2. In small groups of four to five students design health policies for (1) lice, (2) long nails on caregivers, and (3) hand washing.

3. Research the topic of the present controversy over immunizations. Divide the class in half and debate the issue. What are your conclusions? Should a child be allowed in care without immunizations?

4. Discuss how diversity in child care might affect health policies or health practices. List measures that may help culturally diverse families understand these child care policies and practices.

CHAPTER REFERENCES

American Academy of Pediatrics (AAP). (2001a). *Immunizations and your child.* AAP Parent Pages (a brochure). Elk Grove Village, IL: American Academy of Pediatrics.

American Academy of Pediatrics (AAP). (2001b, June). *Recommended childhood immunization schedule United States, January–December 2001.* Retrieved May 15, 2002, from http://pediatrics.about.com/library/nimmunizationschedule.htm.

Aronson, S. (1999, March). Gloves, immunizations, and standards. *Child Care Information Exchange,* 26–27.

Aronson, S. (2000, January). Environmental health in child care settings. *Child Care Information Exchange,* 35.

Aronson, S. (2001, January). Maintaining a sanitary child care environment. *Child Care Information Exchange*, 94–97.

California Child Care Health Program (CCHP). (2001). Excluding children due to illness: Four steps to a healthier program. *Child Care Health Connections, 14*(4), 6–7.

Carballo, M., & Nerukar, A. (2001). Migration, refugees and health risks. *Emerging Infectious Diseases, 7*(3), 556–560.

Clements, D., Zaref, J., Bland, C., Walter, E., & Coplan, P. (2001). Partial uptake of varicella vaccine and the epidemiological effect on varicella disease in 11 day-care centers in North Carolina. *Archives of Pediatrics and Adolescent Medicine, 155*(4), 455–461.

Dailey, L. (2000). Is that nit dead or alive—or does it matter? *Child Care Health Connections, 13*(6), 4.

Duarte, G., & Rafanello, D. (2001). The migrant child: a special place in the field. *Young Children, 56*(2), 26–34.

Figueroa, J. (2000). Head lice: Is there a solution? *Current Opinion in Infectious Diseases, 13*(2), 135–139.

Ford-Jones, L., Wang, E., Petric, M., Corey, P., Moineddin, R., & Fearon, M. (2000). Rotavirus-associated diarrhea in outpatient setting and child care centers. *Archives of Pediatrics and Adolescent Medicine, 154*(6), 586–593.

Graham, J. (994, April/May). Immunization update. *Healthy Kids,* 58–61.

Guendelman, S., & Pearl, M. (2001). Access to care for children of the working poor. *Archives of Pediatrics and Adolescent Medicine, 155*(6), 651–658.

Manning, A. (2001, August 13). Vaccine is off the hook as the cause of autism. *USA Today.* Retrieved May 15, 2002, from http://www.usatoday.com/news/health/2001–04–23-vaccine-autism.htm.

Moolenaar, R., Crutcher, J., San Joaquin, V., Sewell, L., Hutwagner, L., Carson, L., Robison, D., Smithee, L., & Jarvis, W. (2000). A prolonged outbreak of *pseduomonas aeruginosa* in a neonatal intensive care unit: Did staff fingernails play a role in disease transmission. *Journal of Infection Control and Hospital Epidemiology, 21*(2), 80–85.

Mumcuoglu, K., Friger, M, Ioffe-Upensky, I., Ben-Ishai, F., & Miller, J. (2001). Louse comb versus direct visual examination for the diagnosis of head louse infestations. *Pediatric Dermatology, 18*(1), 9–12.

National Association for the Education of Young Children (NAEYC). (1999). *Keeping Healthy* (a brochure). Washington, DC: NAEYC.

National Institute of Child Health and Human Development Early Child Care Research Network (NICH). (2001). Child care and common communicable illnesses. *Archives of Pediatrics and Adolescent Medicine, 155*(4), 481–488.

Pollack, R., Kiszewski, A., & Spielman, A. (2000). Overdiagnosis and consequent mismanagement of head louse infestations in North America. *The Pediatric Infectious Disease Journal, 19*(4), 689–694.

Pollack, R. (2000). Head lice information. Harvard School of Public Health. Retrieved May 15, 2002, from http://www.hsph.harvard.edu/headlice.html.

Richardson, M., Elliman, D., Macguire, H., Simpson, J., & Nicoll, A. (2001). Evidence base of incubation periods, periods of infectiousness and exclusion policies for the control of communicable diseases in schools and preschools. *The Pediatric Infectious Disease Journal, 20*(2), 380–391.

Sachs, J. (1999, March). Vaccines: The real risks and benefits. *Parenting Magazine,* 113–118.

Salmon, D., Haber, M., & Cangarosa, E. (1999). Consequences of religious and philosophical exemptions from immunization laws. *Journal of the American Medical Association, 292*(1), 47–53.

Sokol-Gutierrez, K. (2000, January). Partners in health: Helping families advocate for their children's health. *Child Care Information Exchange,* 51–53.

Spence, A. (1999, February/March). Hot shots. *Healthy Kids Magazine,* 42–50.

Williams, L., Reichert, A., Mackenzie, W., Hightower, A., & Blake, P. (2001). Lice, nits and school policy. *Pediatrics, 107*(5), 1011–1015.

SUGGESTIONS FOR READING

Adler, S. (1989). Cytomegalovirus and child day care: Evidence for an increased infection rate among day care workers. *New England Journal of Medicine, 321*(19), 1290–1296.

American Academy of Pediatrics & American Public Health Association (AAP & APHA). (2001). *Caring for our children: National health and safety performance standards: Guidelines for out-of-home care.* Washington, DC: American Public Health Association.

Arnold, C., Makintube, S., & Istre, G. (1993). Day care attendance and other risk factors for invasive Haemophilus influenzae type b disease. *American Journal of Epidemiology, 138*(5), 333–340.

Jaroff, L. (1999, September 5). Vaccine jitters. *Time Magazine.*

Wood, S. (1996, February). Should your child get the chicken pox vaccine? *Child Magazine,* 72–73.

Young, K. (1994, May 1). From zero to three: Millions of American children are at risk because of improper parenting, neglect. *San Diego Union-Tribune,* G-4.

For additional information on safety, nutrition, and health in early education, visit our Web site at **http://www.earlychilded.delmar.com**

Health Care in Child Care

After reading this chapter, you should be able to:

11.1 Health Policies

Describe and discuss health policies for the identification and management of childhood communicable diseases.

11.2 Identification of Infectious Diseases

Describe the methods and means of identifying childhood infectious diseases for early interventions and prevention of disease spread.

11.3 Managing Infectious Diseases in Child Care

Describe the methods and practices for managing childhood infectious diseases for early identification and disease spread.

11.4 Managing Care for Mildly Ill Children

Summarize and indicate the importance of policies and protocols for care of mildly ill children in child care situations.

11.5 Implications for Caregivers

Indicate the need and importance of education, observation, and supervision for early intervention to manage childhood communicable diseases in the child care setting.

11.1 Health Policies

Health policies for health care in child care are essential to keep children as healthy as possible, to prevent disease spread, and to care for mildly ill children. The following are indicators of the need for good health care policies for child care:

■ Children under the age of three years are more vulnerable to infectious diseases because their immune systems are not fully developed (NICH, 2001).

■ The chances of diseases being transmitted depend on three things: (1) the characteristics of the children in the group; (2) the nature of the disease; and (3) the health policies and practices of the child care facility (Kendrick, Kaufmann, & Messenger, 1995).

■ With most illnesses, children are contagious for at least three to five days before they develop any symptoms (Child Care Action Campaign, 1993).

■ When children with common infectious diseases are sent to child care, they contribute to the spread of these diseases (Heymann & Earle, 1999). Policies should be in place for exclusion (CCCHP, 2001).

■ Many children are being excluded from child care who are not really ill or contagious (Pappas et al., 2000). This is especially true if there is a family history of allergies or asthma (Celedon et al., 2001).

Health care in child care is a complex issue. A child caregiver must be able to identify the signs and symptoms of illness and parasite infestations. The identification process helps put an exclusion policy into operation. The exclusion policy enables the caregiver to separate those children who are very ill or who are contagious and have to leave from those children who are not contagious or very ill and may remain in child care. If children are not excluded from

A center's health policy should specify that when a child exhibits signs and symptoms of a contagious disease or infection, the parents must be notified and an authorized person contacted to come pick up the child.

child care, the caregiver needs to manage the care for mildly ill children without putting others at risk in the child care setting.

Parents and caregivers need to work together to help identify and manage risks to the health of the children in the child care environment. Caregivers need to supervise child care to intervene and minimize risk, and to help maintain the health of all of the children in their care.

To provide the child care environment with the optimum health care there should be policies for:

■ *Identification of Childhood Infectious Diseases:* practices for recognizing signs and symptoms of infectious disease for early intervention

■ *Management of Childhood Infectious Diseases:* practices for managing childhood infectious diseases, including exclusion

■ *Managing Care for Mildly Ill Children:* strategies and practices for managing the care of mildly ill children

■ *Implications for Caregivers:* methods and practices to provide minimum risk and maximum protection for health in child care through education, observation, and supervision

KEY CONCEPT 11.1

Health Policy

Managing health care in child care may be a challenge to the caregiver, because it includes a number of aspects. The caregiver must learn how to identify infectious diseases and know when to exclude children from care. The caregiver must understand how to prevent the spread of infectious disease and protect the health of the children in care.

11.2 Identification of Infectious Diseases

The first line of defense for illnesses in child care is the control of infectious diseases through good hygiene and sanitary practices.

Identifying Infectious Diseases and Illness in Children

The second line of defense is the caregiver's ability to identify illness as quickly as possible. Many illnesses may be present several days before signs or symptoms appear. Guidelines for helping a caregiver recognize signs and symptoms provide a barrier to the spread of an infectious disease.

Signs and Symptoms of Illness. Children may show few signs of illness, then may suddenly appear to be ill. The caregiver needs to observe for certain signs and symptoms that will help identify an ill child (Figure 11–1). Observation can help determine if the illness is the type that may spread rapidly and necessitate excluding a child from care. Some signs and symptoms are serious, while others need special consideration because they may signify an oncoming illness.

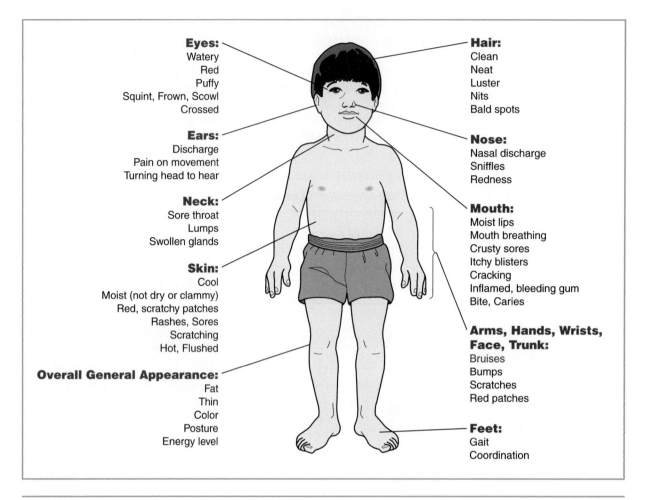

Eyes:
Watery
Red
Puffy
Squint, Frown, Scowl
Crossed

Ears:
Discharge
Pain on movement
Turning head to hear

Neck:
Sore throat
Lumps
Swollen glands

Skin:
Cool
Moist (not dry or clammy)
Red, scratchy patches
Rashes, Sores
Scratching
Hot, Flushed

Overall General Appearance:
Fat
Thin
Color
Posture
Energy level

Hair:
Clean
Neat
Luster
Nits
Bald spots

Nose:
Nasal discharge
Sniffles
Redness

Mouth:
Moist lips
Mouth breathing
Crusty sores
Itchy blisters
Cracking
Inflamed, bleeding gum
Bite, Caries

Arms, Hands, Wrists, Face, Trunk:
Bruises
Bumps
Scratches
Red patches

Feet:
Gait
Coordination

Figure 11–1
Head to Toe Signs and Symptoms of Disease or Infection

Conducting a daily health check as the child arrives is the first point of the day to watch for caution signs for health or illness. The health policy for child care should state that any child who exhibits infectious disease signs and symptoms be excluded from child care. This should be strictly enforced. (Table 11–5, on page 377, presents the conditions for exclusion.)

The child who appears to be below the normal level of mood or activity should be monitored for further symptoms. Signs or symptoms may not be exhibited in the first stages, yet the child may indeed be ill.

The following are some common primary indicators of whether a child is ill:

■ unusual crankiness or listlessness

■ complaint of sore throat or difficulty swallowing

■ runny nose (clear discharge indicates allergies; green or yellow indicates infection)

- complaint of stomachache or cramping
- diarrhea
- complaint of headache or earache
- red, watery, or draining eyes
- unusual rashes or spots
- infected skin lesions

More serious indicators of illness that need *immediate attention* include:

- fever
- vomiting
- severe coughing
- breathing problems
- urine with a strong odor
- unusual drowsiness
- excessive crying

The caregiver must determine whether the child is just under the weather or is ill and may have an infectious disease. The caregiver can identify illness with the signs and symptoms listed in Tables 11–1 through 11–4.

Infectious diseases are spread through four methods of transmission: respiratory tract, fecal-oral, direct contact, and blood contact. The signs and symptoms that diseases exhibit may directly relate to the method of transmission.

Respiratory Tract Transmitted Diseases

Respiratory tract infectious diseases range from a mild cold to bacterial meningitis, which can be life threatening. Many of these diseases affect all age groups. Other diseases are more common in children like Haemophilus Influenza Type B (Hib). Table 11–1 describes the identification of and management methods for respiratory tract transmitted diseases.

TABLE 11–1 Identification and Management of Respiratory Tract Transmitted Diseases

Disease	Signs/Symptoms	Caregiver's Role
Colds	Sneezing, runny nose, stuffy nose, watery eyes, sore throat, fever Most contagious 2 to 3 days before and 3 to 5 days after symptoms appear	Wipe runny noses; use gloves. Wash hands often. Do not share food, drink. Disinfect mouthed toys. Teach children to cover mouth when coughing.
Influenza	Fever, chills, headache, drowsiness, muscle aches, nausea, vomiting	Wipe runny noses; use gloves. Wash hands often. Do not share food, drink. Disinfect mouthed toys. Call parent if fever or vomiting is present.

(continued)

TABLE 11–1 **Identification and Management of Respiratory Tract Transmitted Diseases** *(continued)*

Disease	Signs/Symptoms	Caregiver's Role
Strep Throat	Painful, scratchy throat, tender/swollen glands, fever, spots on throat	Wash hands often. Do not share food, drink. Disinfect mouthed toys. Call parent if fever is present or child is unable to swallow. Notify all parents if strep throat is present. Be alert to outbreak. Exclude child from care until antibiotic treatment has begun.
Scarlet Fever	Same as above Red, sandpapery rash on trunk, neck, groin Red tongue, flushed cheeks	Wash hands often. Do not share food, drink. Disinfect mouthed toys. Call parent if fever is present. Be alert to outbreak. Exclude child from care. Notify all parents.
Chicken Pox	Fever, runny nose, blistery rash, cough	Exclude if chicken pox is suspected until doctor confirms. Readmit after rash is crusted and dry. Follow same procedures as listed under Colds. Children in care should be immunized.
Fifth Disease (Parvovirus)	Headache, body ache, sore throat, fever, chills, lacy rash	Follow same procedures listed under Colds. If pregnant, report to doctor.
Sixth Disease (Roseola)	High fever, lacy rash	Follow same procedure listed under Colds.
Meningitis	Fever, lethargy, poor feeding, fine red rash, stiff neck, headache, irritability	Exclude if suspected. Report to local health department. Notify all in contact with child immediately. Those in contact begin rifampin antibiotic treatment in 24 hours. See doctor immediately if symptoms appear. Same as colds.
Hib (Haemophilus Influenza type B)	Same as meningitis, earache, rapid onset of difficult breathing, red/swollen joints, red/purple area of skin	Follow procedures listed under Meningitis. All should be immunized. See doctor immediately if symptoms appear.
Measles	Brownish/red rash beginning on face, fever, white spots in mouth, runny nose, cough	Exclude if suspected. Allow to return 6 days after rash appears. Report to public health. Notify parents. Wash hands often; use gloves. Do not share food, drink. Disinfect mouthed toys. All in child care should be immunized.

(continued)

TABLE 11–1 **Identification and Management of Respiratory Tract Transmitted Diseases** *(continued)*

Disease	Signs/Symptoms	Caregiver's Role
Rubella (German Measles)	Joint pain, red rash, enlarged lymph glands	Follow procedures listed under Measles. If child caregiver is pregnant, notify doctor. All in child care should be immunized.
Mumps	Fever, at least one swollen salivary gland near jaw, earache, headache	Exclude if suspected. Allow to return after 9 days. All in child care should be immunized.
Whooping Cough	Coughing spells with whoop sounds, vomiting, runny nose	Exclude if suspected. Notify local health department. Notify parents. Allow to return 5 days after antibiotic regime or 3 weeks after onset of cough. Do not share food, drink. Disinfect mouthed toys. Wash hands often; use gloves. All in care should be immunized.
Otitis Media (Ear Infection)	Fever, difficulty hearing, pain, drainage from ear	Wash hands often; use gloves. Do not share food, drink. Children with frequent ear infections should be followed for speech or language difficulties.
Tuberculosis	Cough, fever, weight loss, or no symptoms present	Exclude anyone with active TB. Allow to return when no longer contagious. Notify the health department. Notify parents. All in care should be tested before entrance to care, then every two years.

REALITY CHECK

Otitis Media and Child Care

Ear infection, or otitis media, is the second most frequently diagnosed childhood disease (Teele, Klein, & Rossner, 1984). These infections are probably the most common bacterial infection found in children. It is estimated that as many as 50 percent of cases are missed because they have no symptoms (Feagans, Kipp, & Blood, 1994). Children in child care are more likely to have these ear infections than children who are cared for at home. Boys are more often affected with otitis media than are girls (Zamani & Shaw, 2001). Children under three years are the most susceptible to otitis media (CDC, 1997).

More than 85 percent of children have experienced at least one episode of otitis media (Poole, 2001). By the age of three 35 percent of children will have had repeated episodes, which can be termed chronic otitis media (ASHA, 2000). One association with repeated episodes of otitis media is the use of a pacifier (Niemela et al., 2000).

(continued)

Otitis media is an infection in the middle ear that is directly behind the ear drum. The ear infection commonly begins as a cold. It is suspected that children in child care are more likely to get otitis media because of the number of colds found in that environment. Several environmental reasons associated with day care include close contact with other children who may have respiratory infections, pets present, or a carpet present near the sleeping area (Celedon et al., 1999).

The bacteria and virus germs move up the Eustachian tube, which is a passageway between the throat and middle ear. If the bacteria settles in the middle ear, pus forms and pressure develops. This causes the pain that is experienced. If left unchecked, the infection can spread to the bone behind the ear and cause a condition called mastoiditis. Fluid from otitis media may remain in the ear for months after the infection is gone. This condition can cause hearing loss for the child.

Otitis media is diagnosed by a doctor and treated with antibiotics. The medication should work within several days. For children with chronic otitis media, antibiotics may not be as effective. In these cases, children may require surgery for placement of small tubes to allow the fluid to drain. Children who have received the recommended vaccine that prevents pneumonia and meningitis can decrease the incidence of otitis media by decreasing respiratory infections due to the flu or other illnesses.

It is important for the caregiver to recognize symptoms of otitis media so that treatment is begun early. Signs of otitis media include fever, irritability, ear pain, hearing loss, loss of appetite, and ear discharge. Nonverbal children often pull their ears or cry (ASHA, 2000). Lack of attention during story or group time may also be a sign that the child has an ear infection. It has been found that high-quality child care with a low teacher–child ratio may cushion the effects of these ear infections (Feagans, Kipp, & Blood, 1994). It is important for the caregiver to alert the parent to these conditions. Children who develop early life otitis media may be especially vulnerable for impairments in receptive language and verbal cognition (Paradise et al., 2000). The caregiver may need to recommend a referral for hearing or speech problems.

The caregiver can help reduce otitis media in the child care environment by washing hands, keeping toys clean, not propping bottles for babies, and teaching children to cover their mouths with a disposable tissue when they cough or blow their nose (CDC, 1997). Also, the caregiver should never use cotton swabs on children's ears and should watch for any sign of hearing or speech problems (Zamani & Shaw, 2000).

Ear infections are not contagious and children can stay in care if they are comfortable. If allowed, the caregiver may administer medication. The caregiver may try to reduce the distractions and sound level for a child with an ear infection (Watt, Roberts, & Zeisel, 1993).

Infectious Diseases Transmitted Through the Fecal-Oral Route

Diseases spread by the fecal-oral route are caused by bacteria, parasites, and viruses that grow and spread in the intestines. The stool is the main vehicle of disease spread to others. Child care environments that have infants and toddlers in diapers are especially at risk for these types of diseases. The best course for preventing the spread of disease is to always use special precautions. Table 11–2 relates how to identify and manage diseases transmitted through the fecal-oral route.

Infectious Diseases Transmitted by Direct Contact

Diseases transmitted by direct contact are spread from the secretions of one person that penetrate through the skin or mucous membranes of another person. These germs may be in the form of bacterial infections, parasites, or viral

TABLE 11–2 **Identification and Management of Diseases Transmitted Through the Fecal-Oral Route**

Disease	Signs/Symptoms	Caregiver's Role
Giardia	Diarrhea, gas, poor appetite, weight loss, cramping, bloating	Frequent hand washing according to schedule. Use sanitary procedures and gloves during diapering, toileting, and before handling food. Exclude if diarrhea is uncontrolled. Allow return once diarrhea is gone.
Shigella	Diarrhea, fever, pain, mucus or blood in stool, vomiting, headache, convulsions	Wash hands following schedule. Use sanitary procedures and gloves during diapering, toileting, and before food handling. Exclude if fever is present. Call parent immediately if convulsion occurs.
Salmonella	Stomach cramps, diarrhea, fever, fatigue, poor appetite	Wash hands following schedule. Use sanitary procedures and gloves during diapering, toileting, and before food handling. Notify local health department. Notify parents. See doctor if diarrhea occurs.
Hepatitis A	Fever, jaundice, nausea, poor appetite, dark-brown urine	Wash hands following schedule. Use sanitary procedures and gloves during diapering, toileting, and before food handling. Exclude; allow to return one week after onset and when fever is gone. Notify local health department. Notify parents. All exposed should have immune globulin treatment.
Campylobacter	Fever, vomiting, stomach cramps, diarrhea or severe bloody diarrhea	Wash hands following schedule. Use sanitary procedures and gloves during diapering, toileting, and before handling food. Notify local health department. Notify all parents. See doctor if diarrhea occurs.
E. Coli	Diarrhea or blood diarrhea	Wash hands following schedule. Use sanitary procedures during diapering, toileting, and before handling food. Cook all hamburger meat to 155°F. Notify local health department. Notify parents. Exclude until diarrhea is gone and stool specimen is negative.
Cocksackie virus (Hand, foot, and mouth disease)	Fever, stomach pain, sore throat, rash with tiny blisters on hands, feet, and mouth, diarrhea	Wash hands following schedule. Use sanitary procedures and gloves during diapering, toileting, and before handling food. Notify parents. Notify staff.
Pinworms	Anal itching, worms that crawl out during sleep or no symptoms present	Follow procedures in Cocksackie virus. Each child should have own crib, mat, or cot. Exclude only until treatment has begun.

A clean and sanitary diapering area, as well as disposable gloves, are essential in preventing fecal-oral transmission of disease.

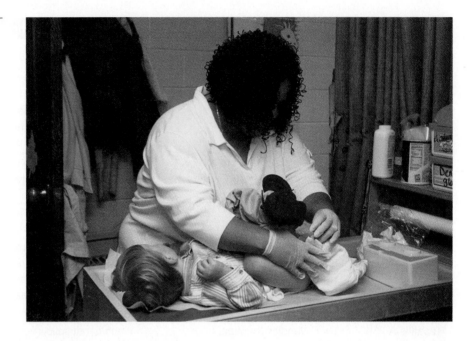

infections. Contact may be made directly through the infected or infested skin areas or by touching an infested article of clothing, a brush, or bed linens. The child caregiver should provide protective measures to prevent the spread of these diseases. Two methods of protection are offered through identification and management as shown in Table 11–3.

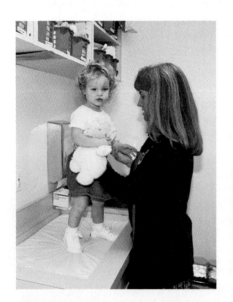

After diapering, both the caregiver and the child should wash their hands to prevent the spread of infectious disease. It is good to start the hand washing routine with young toddlers, who are at a higher risk for infectious disease due to mouthing and diapering/toileting activities.

TABLE 11–3 Identification and Management of Infectious Diseases Transmitted by Direct Contact

Disease	Signs/Symptoms	Caregiver's Role
Conjunctivitis (Pinkeye)	Mucus in eye, watery eyes, red/pink eyes, painful eyes, red eyelids, itchy eyes	Keep eye wiped free of discharge. Always wash hands after wiping. Teach children to wipe eyes and wash hands. If child's eyes come in contact with any toys, clean them well. Have child see doctor. Exclude only if white or yellow discharge is present. Allow to return 24 hours after start of antibiotics. Notify parents and staff.
Impetigo	Red/cracking/oozing pimples, scaly rash, often on face or a sore that will not heal	If suspected, wash and cover rash with a bandage or gauze. If child scrapes or cuts another area, clean thoroughly. Follow good hand washing procedures. Have child see doctor. Follow sanitary cleaning schedule. Notify parents and staff.
Ringworm (Tinea)	Flat, growing ring-shaped rash, often scaly, may be in between toes, on scalp, or body	Keep environment clean, cool, and dry. Wash hands thoroughly. Follow sanitary cleaning schedule. Have child see doctor. If more than one case in care, notify parents and staff.
Head Lice (see Reality Check on page 337)	Lice (sesame seed sized insects) on scalp or hair, nits (eggs) behind ears or nape of neck	Learn to identify nits and regularly check near scalp of children for them (see Figure 11–2). Notify parents with handout concerning procedures. Machine wash all possibly infested items using hot water. All nonwashable items go in dryer for 20 minutes. All other items placed in sealed plastic bags for 30 days. Soak all combs and brushes for one hour in bleach solution. Vacuum rugs, furniture, and mattresses; then throw away vacuum bag.
Scabies	Very itchy red bumps or blisters, often between toes or fingers, head, neck, feet	Wash and dry all items contacted by the child 72 hours before outbreak. Use hot cycle wash and dry. Vacuum as for ringworm. Have child see doctor. If a serious problem exists, all children and caregivers need treatment. Notify parents.
Cytomegalovirus (CMV)	Often no symptoms, fever, swollen glands, fatigue, jaundice	Always wash hands after contact with urine, saliva, or blood. Do not share food or drinks. Do not share utensils or glasses. Do not kiss children on mouth. Have child see doctor. Can cause problems for pregnant caregivers; notify doctor if pregnant.
Herpes Simplex (Cold Sores)	Fever, painful, small blisters on lips, mouth, or gums; may ooze	If blisters are oozing and child bites or is drooling, exclude until sores are crusted over. Do not share food, utensils, or glasses. Do not kiss children on mouth. Wash hands often. Follow sanitary cleaning schedule.

Bloodborne Infectious Diseases

Infectious diseases are spread through the blood when blood containing the virus in one person enters the bloodstream of another person. This usually occurs if the infected blood comes in contact with broken skin or mucous membranes such as the inside of the nose, mouth, eyes, anal area, or sex organs. The two diseases that are transmitted in this manner are hepatitis B and HIV/AIDS. These viruses may be present without any symptoms. It is important that all blood and body fluids contacted in child care be treated as if they were contaminated. Prevention of these diseases is critical. All blood spills should be cleaned up immediately and the area disinfected.

All surfaces should be thoroughly disinfected with the bleach solution for contaminated items. If the caregiver is aware that another adult or child in care has hepatitis B or HIV/AIDS, then the stronger solution should be used in all cleaning and disinfecting tasks. Table 11–4 lists bloodborne infectious diseases.

Disease Note: Another childhood disease, Kawasaki disease, should also be recognized. No cause has yet been related to this disease (Burns, 2001). Signs and symptoms include: a fever that lasts five or more days, redness of the eye, mouth, throat, tongue, and lips, swollen glands, and extreme irritability (CCHP 2000). This disease is the number one cause of acquired heart disease in children. One in four children who have it may develop permanent damage to the coronary artery (Burns, 2001). It is important to pass this information on to parents whose child may be showing symptoms, so that the child is seen by a physician before the disease progresses.

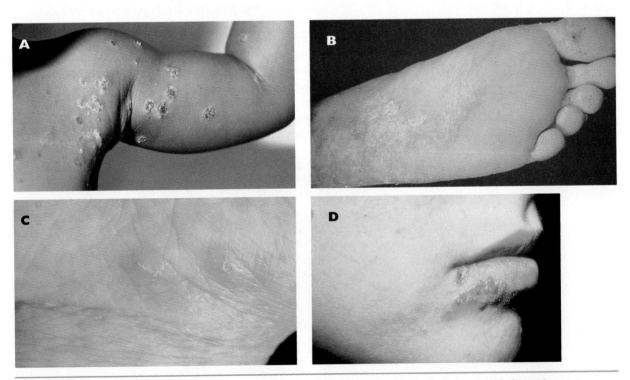

A. Impetigo. **B.** Ringworm. **C.**Scabies. **D.** Herpes Simplex I (Cold Sore). *Courtesy of Robert A. Silverman, MD, Clinical Association Professor, Department of Pediatrics, Georgetown University)*

Figure 11–2
Cycle of Head Lice Treatment
(See Reality Check on Head Lice,
page 337.)

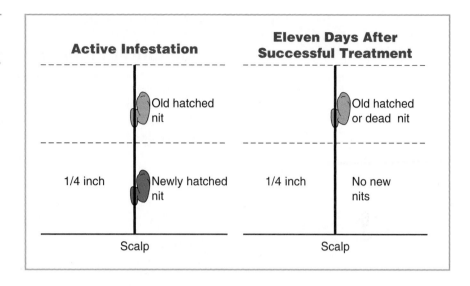

TABLE 11–4	**Identification and Management of Bloodborne Infectious Diseases**	
Disease	**Signs/Symptoms**	**Caregiver's Role**
Hepatitis B	Fever, loss of appetite, nausea, jaundice, pain in joints, skin rash	All present in care should be immunized. All blood and bodily fluids should be cleaned up immediately and treated as if contaminated. All disposable items with blood should be thrown out in plastic bags, then placed in covered trash cans. Everyone washes hands often. Do not share personal items that could be contaminated. Send home contaminated personal clothing with instruction for parents to wash them with bleach and hot water. Discourage aggressive behaviors. Children infected with hepatitis A who demonstrate behaviors such as biting, have no control over bodily secretions, and other risky behaviors will need to be supervised closely. Where this is not possible, the child may have to be excluded from child care. Consult with health department and health consultant. If someone is bitten by an infected person, contact doctor.
HIV/AIDS	Failure to grow and develop, enlarged lymph and gland, frequent infections, illness	Follow procedures as in hepatitis B except for immunization. Protect those with HIV or AIDS from infectious disease outbreaks by exclusion. Allow to return when outbreak is over. Maintain confidentiality of child with HIV or AIDS. Provide staff with information.

KEY CONCEPT 11.2

Identification of Infectious Disease

It is an important task of the caregiver to be able to identify infectious diseases. Child caregivers must have a base of knowledge to recognize signs and symptoms of infectious diseases. They must be able to identify symptoms that are serious for the child and that indicate the presence of a contagious disease.

11.3 Managing Infectious Diseases in Child Care

Caregivers who use universal sanitary practices and can recognize and identify signs and symptoms of illness protect the environment and prevent disease from spreading. An additional way to provide management of infectious diseases is to require that everyone involved in child care be immunized for those infectious diseases that have vaccines and immunization schedules. (Refer to Table 10–3 on page 342 for the immunization schedule for children.) Children's records should be kept current and checked for compliance on a regular basis. The same process should be performed for staff. No one should be hired or should care for children if they do not comply with all of the required immunizations. (Refer to Tables 11–1 and 11–4 for those diseases that should be complied with for immunizations.)

Certain symptoms in children, such as fever, may not necessarily indicate an illness. A fever may be a result of too much activity, warm weather, teething, or the body overheating due to other circumstances. If the child does not appear to be ill, a fever may not be a problem. The child caregiver needs to learn how to take a temperature, how to read it, and how to evaluate whether or not it is a serious indicator of illness (see Figure 11–3).

The caregiver who recognizes serious symptoms knows when to call a parent and when to exclude the child from care. The ability to identify serious symptoms will help the child caregiver know when to notify parents that children in care have been exposed to an infectious disease. Parents can monitor children for further signs and symptoms. Children who need medical attention should go to the doctor immediately. Certain infectious diseases must be reported to the local public health department. This information is available at the local health department that has jurisdiction over the area in which the child care is performed.

When a child shows some signs of illness, the caregiver should observe the child and write down the symptoms. Do not draw conclusions. Report measurable facts, such as "Joanna has a temperature of 101°F and looks flushed." If the symptoms are mild and do not affect the child's ability to participate, continue observing the child, and go on with regular activities.

Exclusion

An exclusion policy should be carefully created for the child care environment. This policy should be given to both caregivers and parents and should also be

Sick children who are isolated from the group need a comfortable place to rest and, if possible, the company and reassurance of a caregiver until the child's parents or emergency contacts arrive.

posted. It is much easier to enforce a policy that is widely known beforehand. One of the reasons for exclusion would be that child care cannot provide the care and comfort an ill child would need. A child also might not feel well enough to engage in normal activities. And any child that shows symptoms that may be on the list of reasons for exclusion should be sent home (AAP & APHA, 2001).

Of special note is the fact that many children have been unnecessarily excluded (Pappas et al., 2000; Skull et al., 2000). This is primarily due to the part of a policy that would exclude children who have fevers but do not show any other symptoms. Fever by itself is rarely a condition for exclusion (AAP & APHA, 2001). The exception to this would be infants from seven weeks to four months of age with a rectal temperature of 101°F or a temperature taken in the armpit of 100°F (Aronson, 2000). Use of newer types of thermometers such as a tympanic thermometer that measures temperatures in the ear can be a more accurate tool for taking a temperature. If a child has a fever with no other signs, the parent should still be notified. The decision as to what to do should be made with the parent (Aronson, 2000).

If a child shows symptoms that are serious or that might be highly contagious, the child should be isolated from the rest of the children in care. The child caregiver needs to have an area set aside that will allow for isolation. Once serious symptoms are recognized, the parents should be notified immediately. If the parents cannot be reached, there should be backup or emergency contacts in the permanent health file for who to call next. The caregiver should ask the parent on a regular basis whether the emergency information is still current. While the child waits for the parent or other emergency contact person, it is important to reassure the child.

In addition to any serious signs or symptoms of illness, conditions such as uncontrolled diarrhea, a yellowish tint to the skin, and discharge of the eyes also indicate the need to immediately isolate the child and call the parent.

Table 11–5 indicates the guidelines for exclusion of ill or infected children. It relates the type of illness or disease, gives the signs and symptoms, and the conditions for return to child care. These guidelines are a major tool for the child caregiver to help manage the spread of infectious disease in child care and are the basis for the health policy for exclusion.

Another important consideration for exclusion is the adults in the child care environment. If a caregiver has any of the signs or symptoms in Table 11–5, he should also be excluded from participating in care and not return until the conditions for return are met.

When the child is excluded from care, there are several things the caregiver will need to do. The parents should be provided with information on the infectious disease that caused the child to be excluded. This is usually in the form of a letter or handout. The information includes the exclusion policy for that disease, the period of time the disease lasts, and the conditions for return to child care. The caregiver should remove and sanitize any toys the ill child has been playing with or mouthing. Make sure hands are carefully washed and that the hand washing policy is strictly enforced. The illness and caregiver actions should be documented and added to the child's health record (Dailey, 2001).

Information on how to care for the disease or condition should also be included. For example, if the child has lice, the information given to the parent would include consulting the physician for the type of shampoo to use, how

Mercury	Digital	Tympanic

Mercury	Digital	Tympanic
✓ **Positives**	✓ **Positives**	✓ **Positives**
• Lowest cost • Accuracy	• Easy to read • Beeps when ready • Temperature reading is recorded digitally	• Quick reading • Easy to use with fussy children
⚠ **Cautions**	⚠ **Cautions**	⚠ **Cautions**
• Hard to read • Delicate • Child must be still	• Child must be still • Battery powered	• Must be placed correctly in ear canal for accurate reading • Battery powered • Highest cost
Methods	**Methods**	**Methods**
A. Shake until mercury line falls below 96° F (30.6°C). B. Clean with soap and water or alcohol. Rinse with cool water.	A. Clean with soap and water or alcohol. Rinse with cool water. B. Switch on (it beeps at child's highest temperature).	A. Place new plastic covering over end. B. Set for rectal or oral temperature equivalent. C. When small window reads "ready," position the end gently into the ear canal and press the start button.
Rectal: (children under 3 yrs) 1. Coat bulb with petroleum jelly. 2. Place child stomach down. 3. Insert bulb end first 1½ inches into anal canal.	**Rectal:** Use with nonpetroleum lubricant (K-Y jelly).	After one second, a digital readout of the child's temperature will appear on the small window.
Oral: (children 5 and older) 1. Slowly insert thermometer under tongue. 2. Child closes lips for 2–3 minutes.	**Oral:** Place far under tongue for one minute.	
Underarm: (any age, any type—oral or rectal) 1. Snugly bury bulb under armpit for 3–4 minutes.	**Underarm:** Keep tight under arm.	

Figure 11–3
Guide to Thermometers

often to use it, and what else needs to be done to rid the child's home of lice so the process does not repeat itself.

The caregiver should discuss the return to care policy for that particular disease or condition at the same time. Parents like to know the time parameters of a child's illness, if possible, so that necessary work or backup care arrangements can be made.

TABLE 11–5 Guidelines for Exclusion of Ill or Infected Children

Illness or Infection	Sign or Symptom	Return
Temperature	Oral temperature of 101°F or more; rectal temperature of 102°F; should be accompanied by behavior changes or other symptoms	Until doctor releases child to return to care
Symptoms of severe illness	Unusual lethargy; irritability; uncontrolled coughing; wheezing	Until doctor releases child to return to care
Uncontrolled diarrhea	Increase in number of stools, water, and/or decreased form that cannot be contained in a diaper or underwear	Until diarrhea stops
Vomiting illness	Two or more episodes in 24 hours	Until vomiting stops and child is not dehydrated or doctor determines illness not infectious
Mouth sores with drooling		Until condition is determined to be noninfectious
Rash	Rash accompanied by fever or behavior change	Doctor determines it is noninfectious
Conjunctivitis	White or yellow discharge in eye(s) accompanied by eye pain and/or redness around eyes	Until 24 hours after treatment has begun
Head lice, scabies, or other infestations	Infestation present	Until 24 hours after treatment has begun; no remaining lice on hair or scalp
Tuberculosis	Cough; fever; chest pain; coughing up blood	Until doctor or health official allows child to return to care
Impetigo	Rash-blister to honey-colored crusts; lesions occur around mouth, nose, and on chin	Until 24 hours after treatment has begun
Strep throat	Fever; sore throat; throat drainage and tender nodes in lymph	After cessation of fever or 24 hours after antibiotic treatment
Chicken pox	Sudden onset of slight fever, fatigue, and loss of appetite followed by skin eruption	Until 6 days after eruption of rash or until blister eruption has dried and crusted over
Whooping cough	Severe, persistent cough	Until 5 days after antibiotic treatment to prevent infection

(continued)

TABLE 11–5 Guidelines for Exclusion of Ill or Infected Children *(continued)*

Illness or Infection	Sign or Symptom	Return
Mumps	Tender/swollen glands and/or fever	Until 9 days after onset of gland swelling
Hepatitis A virus	Fever, fatigue, loss of appetite, abdominal pain, nausea, vomiting, and/or jaundice	Until 1 week after onset of illness or as directed by local health department; immune serum globulin should be administered to staff and children who have been exposed
Measles	Rash, high fever, runny nose, and red/watery eyes	Until 6 days from onset of rash
Rubella	Mild fever, rash, swollen lymph nodes	Until 6 days after onset of rash
Unspecified respiratory illness	Severe illness with cold, croup, bronchitis, otitis media, pneumonia	Until child feels well enough to participate
Shingles	Lesions	Until doctor allows child to return to care or if child can wear clothing that covers lesions
Herpes simplex (1)	Clear, painful blisters	Until lesions that ooze, involving face and lips, have no secretions

Notification of Public Health

A number of infectious diseases should be reported to the local health department so that they may track the disease for patterns of outbreak. This helps to prevent the spread of infectious illnesses in the community. The types of disease typically requiring reporting are those that can spread rapidly and may cause serious illness. Table 11–6 gives a list of infectious diseases that most health departments want reported. It is also a good idea to notify the health department if a large number of cases of infectious diseases not requiring reporting should occur at the child care site.

The child caregiver should be familiar with the reporting procedures of the local public health department. The health advocate caregiver at the child care site should be the person to contact the health department.

Notification of Parents

It is important to notify all families in care of infectious disease occurrences that will cause exclusion or will need a follow-up by the parents. This notification provides them with information such as signs, symptoms, and incubation period (Figure 11–4).

If the infectious disease is serious and is one that has preventive measures such as hepatitis A, the caregiver should notify the parents. This will allow the parents to take the child in care to the family physician, who may administer a course of treatment. It is critically important for the parent of a child exposed to a serious infectious disease to understand the need for taking the child to a physician. The caregiver needs to make sure that parents understand the role they play in the prevention of disease and preserving the child's health.

TABLE 11–6	**Checklist of Commonly Reported Childhood Infectious Diseases**

 Check for:

- [ ] AIDS
- [ ] E. Coli
- [ ] Giardia
- [ ] Hepatitis
- [ ] Hib (haemophilus influenza type B)
- [ ] Measles (rubeola)
- [ ] Meningitis
- [ ] Mumps
- [ ] Polio
- [ ] Rubella (German measles)
- [ ] Salmonella
- [ ] Shigella
- [ ] Tuberculosis
- [ ] Whooping Cough (pertussis)

KEY CONCEPT 11.3

Management of Infectious Diseases

The role that the caregiver plays in managing the infectious diseases must be clearly perceived. The first line of defense is the use of sanitary procedures for hand washing and the use of gloves. The next step is to make sure immunizations are current for everyone in the child care environment. The child caregiver must understand the procedures and policies for exclusion from and return to child care. The caregiver must recognize when to notify the public health department and when to notify the parents of children in child care.

Figure 11–4
Sample Notice to Parents

*A Child's Place
Day Care Center*

NOTIFICATION

A case of strep throat was identified in the center today. If your child develops any of the symptoms, you will be called by a staff member to take him/her home. Please make arrangements to pick up your child immediately for the safety of other children/staff and the comfort of your child.

Please do not return the child to the center until your doctor advises you in writing that it is safe to do so.

Thank you for your cooperation.

Sincerely,

Maria Anderson

1553 Winding Way Drive
(555)444-8888

11.4 Managing Care for Mildly Ill Children

The child caregiver has a number of tools that will help make the decision as to whether or not to care for mildly ill children. The most effective tool for managing care for mildly ill children is a series of three questions that the caregiver should ask (see Figure 11–5).

Figure 11–5

The three questions a caregiver should ask are: (1) is it a highly infectious or communicable disease? (2) Does the child feel well enough to participate in child care? (3) Can the caregiver provide the mildly ill child adequate child care?

Three Questions

The first question a caregiver should ask is: *"Is the child's infectious disease highly communicable or communicable at this time?"*

There are certain childhood infectious diseases that do not pose a health threat. Some of these infectious diseases may be viruses that are no longer contagious once the symptoms appear or the infectious disease might be one that is not highly contagious. For example, colds are very common in young children. Most children average six to ten colds in the period of a year. Ear infections are not easily spread and therefore should not cause a child to be excluded from care. The child caregiver needs to be familiar with those diseases that are not at risk for spread and that will allow the child to participate in care.

The decision-making process proceeds to the next step once it has been established that the infectious disease is not highly communicable or does not pose risk to others in care. The question *"Does the child feel well enough to participate in child care?"* addresses the issue of whether or not the child feels well enough to be in care.

Families are busy and parents may have deadlines or have difficulty missing work. It may be tempting to take a child who is ill but not contagious to school. The daily quick health check is an effective tool for the caregiver to help prevent this from happening. Parents need to understand their responsibility to keep a child who does not feel well at home.

The final question in the decision-making process is *"Can the caregiver provide the mildly ill child adequate care?"* This question addresses several issues:

- Is there a place for the child to rest or play quietly?
- Is there a caregiver who can be responsible for caring for the mildly ill child?
- If not, are the parents willing to pay extra for care so the caregiver can hire a helper?

There may be a number of additional tasks that have to be performed and the child caregiver should only agree to provide care for the mildly ill child if the quality of care is consistent with regular child care.

If the answers to any of the three questions indicate that the caregiver would have difficulty caring for the child, the parent must take responsibility for caring for the ill child. There may be an alternative care site that specializes in caring for mildly ill children. Contact the local resource and referral agencies for information.

Special Considerations for Care of Mildly Ill Children

If the decision to care for the mildly ill child is made, the child caregiver should be prepared to provide the degree of care needed. Table 11–7 provides a checklist of strategies that will help the caregiver meet the needs of the mildly ill child.

If the illness requires the administration of medications, there are special procedures that should be followed. In some states administering medication is prohibited. Caregivers should check with the local licensing agency. The procedures are found in Table 11–8.

TABLE 11–7 Care Checklist for the Mildly Ill Child

Check for:

☐ Observe the child for signs and symptoms of the illness. Share this information with the parents at a midday phone call and when the child is picked up.

☐ Record the signs and symptoms.

☐ Frequently check with the child to provide the extra attention and care she may need while ill.

☐ Provide quiet activities that will hold the interest of the child, such as tapes, videos, books, stories, and artwork.

☐ Set aside a quiet corner or separate space for the child to be quiet, rest, or nap.

☐ Administer prescribed medication as directed, if allowed.

☐ Supply foods and beverages that provide good nutrition and follow guidelines as indicated by illness or recommended by a physician.

TABLE 11–8   Procedures for Administering Medication in Child Care

- No medication will be administered without the written order of a doctor, which would be on a prescription bottle, but over-the-counter medications should have a doctor's note attached. The child's name should appear on the original container. Over-the-counter medications should have the manufacturer's label and contain clear instructions for use.

- Parents must provide written permission authorizing the administration of medication. This should include the frequency, dose, and method of administering the medication. The note should be dated and should be done each time a child is ill, unless it is for a chronic condition such as allergies or asthma. Monitor those medications that are kept in case of emergency and should not be used beyond the expiration date. If a child has had over-the-counter medicine prescribed, it should be administered according to the directions on the bottle.

- Always wash hands before and after administering medication.

- Administer medication according to method, dose, time, and frequency prescribed. Explain to the child what you are giving and why. Never refer to medicine as candy (see Figure 11–6). Always give medication away from diapering, toileting, or food handling areas.

- Maintain a medication log. Record the administration of the medication in the log, the instructions for giving medication, and attach parents' consent form. This log will be kept in the child's permanent health history.

- Have a list of possible side effects of medication to watch for.

- Keep medications at proper temperature as directed. Some liquid antibiotics need to be refrigerated.

- Store all medications out of the reach of children, preferably in a locked cabinet, on a high shelf, or in the back of the top shelf of a refrigerator.

REALITY CHECK

Special Care for Mildly Ill Children

Many companies experience high absenteeism rates from their employees because their children are ill. A child's illness causes missed deadlines, parents who feel guilty, and coworkers who must do extra work because of the absent worker (Child Care Action Campaign, 1993). This situation can cause many problems for the parents and discomfort for the child. Children are most comfortable in a familiar setting with familiar people when they are ill. This familiarity offers emotional support for the ill child. It is not always possible to provide this familiar comfort so parents may have to settle for physical care alone.

(continued)

Care for mildly ill children may take place in several ways.

■ care in the child's own center, family child care, or in-home care

■ family child care homes or centers that specialize in caring for mildly ill children

■ corporate on-site care for ill children of employees

■ in the child's home by specialized caregivers

Many centers and family child care homes are providing this care within their regular programs. Most states permit child care centers to offer get-well care for mildly ill children. Some centers provide a designated caregiver for these mildly ill children. Some caregivers specialize in the care of mildly ill children.

To address this situation, many corporations are cooperating by providing care for mildly ill children. New York City Emergency Child Care Services and Tucson Association for Child Care Inc. are two examples of in-home care services that have contracted with companies to provide mildly ill care (Cassidy, 1991). Johnson and Johnson provides on-site care for mildly ill children at their head-

quarters in New Brunswick, New Jersey. This is offered at their child care center in an infirmary.

There are centers specifically designed for the care of mildly ill children. These centers must meet licensing standards that are more stringent than the regular standards. They must also be very careful of preventing the spread of infectious diseases. The AAHP and APA suggest that these special centers have the following for each child:

■ information concerning the diagnosis and the attending physician's name

■ prognosis for illness, including activity level, diet, and so forth

■ health care plan

■ open communication line with parents

Mildly ill children can still be relatively active. Mildly ill child care should include provision of toys, games, and other activities that provide children stimulation as needed.

The licensing regulations should be determined for the local area and state where the care will take place, if the caregiver intends to provide this type of care for mildly ill children.

KEY CONCEPT 11.4

Special Considerations for Care of Mildly Ill Children

Taking care of mildly ill children is not something all caregivers or child care situations are prepared to do. Determining the ability to handle this type of care will be based on three questions:

1. Is the infectious disease contagious or will it put others at risk?

2. Is the child able to participate in care?

3. Can the caregiver accommodate the needs of the mildly ill child?

When the determination is made, the caregiver will need to understand the issues of the special care he will be providing for the child. One of the special considerations is the administration of medication. The caregiver should follow exact procedure for this.

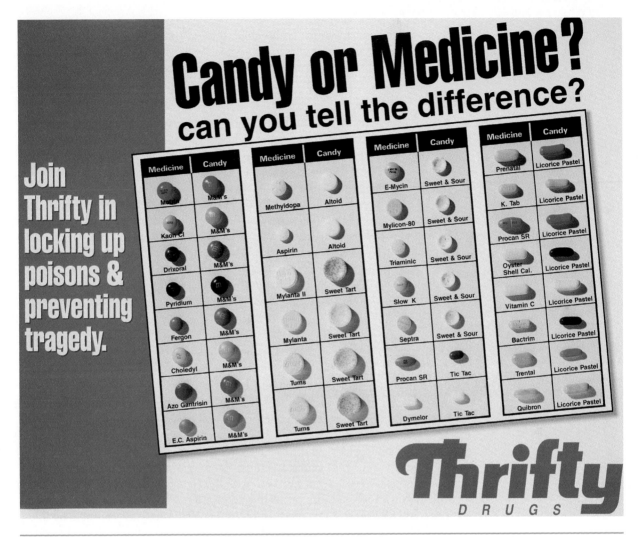

Figure 11–6
Children can very easily mistake medication for candy. Medications should be stored in a locked cabinet at all times. *(Courtesy of Payless Drug Stores)*

11.5 Implications for Caregivers

Caregivers need the tools of observation and supervision in order to provide and maintain a healthy environment. Education and cultural sensitivity also help them to manage the spread of disease as well as to manage mildly ill child care.

Observation

Observation provides the caregiver the ability to recognize any symptoms of infectious disease early. The daily quick health check allows the child caregiver to monitor the health of a child on a regular basis. Recording any signs, symptoms, or irregular behaviors can give the caregivers indicators of illness. When a child is observed, the question "Is the child able to participate?" can be answered more readily. A caregiver who knows a child well will recognize whether or not the child is acting in a normal enough manner to be in the child care setting.

Supervision

Supervision is a powerful tool that helps the caregiver to manage health care in child care. Supervising the setting for proper immunizations and sanitary hand washing and cleaning procedures can reduce the amount of infectious diseases seen in child care. Supervising for exclusion and return policies help keep contagious diseases from child care.

Notifying the public health department allows the caregiver to help manage the spread of infectious diseases both in and out of child care. When the health department tracks infectious diseases, another child care setting may benefit from the notification. This may prevent further outbreaks.

Caregivers need to notify all parents when a child in care has an infectious disease that is highly contagious and/or can cause serious diseases. The parents can observe for the signs and symptoms and can prepare for follow-up care after exposure to the infectious disease.

Education

Education provides a wonderful tool for the promotion of healthy habits and the prevention of disease. All participants in the child care environment should be educated to avoid exposure to and reduce the spread of infectious diseases.

Education offers caregivers the base of knowledge and training needed to carry out their daily task of creating a healthy environment. Caregivers who have the ability to identify the signs and symptoms of infectious diseases protect the environment against any further spread of the infectious disease.

Education helps parents work with the caregiver as a team. It also allows the family to offer a more protective environment in the home. Teaching parents about hand washing and the importance of immunizations will help them understand their own responsibility to protect their children and to prevent disease. Parents who understand proper procedures for the care of a child with an infectious disease may be able to reduce the seriousness of the disease.

Education for children in child care incorporates several things. The first educational tool the caregiver will use is to share the importance of hand washing along with the "how-tos" and "when tos." Teaching children to recognize when they feel ill may help the caregiver identify an infectious disease before outward symptoms appear. This may provide another level of protection for all of the children in care. Teaching children at their own level about an infectious disease that is present in child care may reinforce the information sent home concerning that disease.

It is suggested that every child should have a "medical home." This is a primary health care provider that takes care of both well care and screening measures as well as treating illnesses (Sokol-Gutierrez, 2000; Lombardi, 1999). A medical home allows for regular visits and should help prevent serious health problems. Today, most children are eligible for some type of health care insurance. A Web site to check is http://www.insurekidsnow.gov. A caregiver should help educate parents who lack access to health care to use resources available to provide a medical home for their children.

Parents may not have children immunized because of fears, cultural beliefs, or lack of understanding of the importance of immunizations. Although caregivers need to respect the beliefs of different cultures, the "No immunization, no care" rule must be enforced to protect all children in care.

Cultural Competence

The caregiver needs to understand that early access to health care for ill children is perhaps the major issue for cultural competence. This may be especially true of recent immigrants. Certain cultures may have had little access to health care. Parents of these children may not understand the importance of early health care for children. For example, there appears to be a pattern of delayed care for Latin American children (Zambrana, Ell, Dorrington, Wachsmur, & Hodge, 1994). Emergency medical services appear to be the primary care for many of these children (Carballo & Nerukar, 2001).

When a child becomes ill, the caregiver may have to help the parent access health care. Many cultures use the emergency room as their first contact of care. This is dangerous for the child and it is not protective for the child care environment. It may take extra effort on the part of the child caregiver to help parents from other cultures provide the health care needed for these children (Sokol-Gutierrez, 2000).

Immunization may be another culturally sensitive issue. Many families do not understand the need for immunization. If the child is from a country where immunizations are not readily available, the thought of having a child stuck with needles may be fearful (Gonzalez-Mena, 1997). The need for immunization should be dealt with when the child enters care. The rule, "No immunization, no care," must be understood by both the caregiver and the parents. No exceptions should be made. The caregiver may need to educate potential child care parents of the need to adhere to the immunization schedule. When a child is in care, it is up to the caregiver to follow up and make sure that immunizations occur.

The child caregiver should understand the sanitary habits of the different cultures that are represented in care. The caregiver may have to provide extra education or acquire interpreters to inform parents of their responsibility in keeping their children well.

KEY CONCEPT II.5

Implications for Caregivers
The implications for the child caregiver are the tools of observation, supervision, education, and cultural competence that help the caregiver create the holistic approach needed to deal with the many issues raised. Observation can identify infectious diseases early and thus provide some protection for others in care. Supervision will give the caregiver the tools needed for exclusion and notification. The caregiver must be educated, and must educate parents and children in methods that will forestall the spread of infectious diseases. Cultural competence should be practiced to help the caregiver include all children and parents in providing the best preventive environment possible.

CHAPTER SUMMARY

Caregivers need to prevent disease spread and to care for mildly ill children. They need to form exclusion policies and understand reporting procedures. Caregivers need to determine if they have the ability to care for children who become ill and are not contagious. Observation and supervision will help the caregiver identify and manage infectious diseases. Education will help the caregiver teach healthy habits to children and their parents.

TO GO BEYOND

In this section you will find a number of activities that you can use to apply and improve your knowledge of this chapter. There are also thorough Online Resources that accompany this text that can be found at http://www.early childed.delmar.com/resources/robertson/index.html. Included on this site are chapter practice quizzes, PowerPoint outlines, Web links, a discussion forum, and various other activities to help you better understand the material in this chapter. This site is updated regularly so check back often to receive the latest information about the subjects in this chapter.

Chapter Review Critical Thinking Applications

1. Discuss the identification and management of infectious diseases. How should these be applied in child care situations?

2. Describe the particular skills needed to manage infectious diseases. How well prepared are you for these skills? What could you do to improve these skills?

3. How might child care in your area be improved if there were a child care facility that specifically dealt with mildly ill children?

As an Individual

1. Obtain the local licensing guidelines for exclusion. Compare and contrast those to the ones in this text. Should they be more thorough?

2. Describe the type of child care you intend to participate in, then ask the three questions about caring for ill children. How do they relate to the particular care situation you have in mind?

As a Group

1. Discuss exclusion policies. In small groups, design an exclusion policy for center-based care and family child care. How are they different? Why?

2. Examine the idea of "medical home." Does this make sense, or are there other solutions that might better help keep children well? How does this work in your own community?

3. In small groups, design a center for mildly ill children. Describe what this type of center would look like and what type of training might be necessary to run it. Is this a possibility for your own community?

CHAPTER REFERENCES

American Academy of Pediatrics & American Public Health Association (AAP & APHA). (2002). *Caring for our children: National health and safety performance standards: Guidelines for out-of-home care.* Washington, DC: American Public Health Association.

American Speech and Hearing Association (ASHA). (2000). Questions and answers about otitis media, hearing and language development. Retrieved May 15, 2002, from http://www.kidsource.com/asha/otitis.htm.

Aronson, S. (2000, November). Exclusion of children with fevers from child care. *Child Care Information Exchange,* 88–89.

Burns, J. (2001). Kawasaki disease. *Advances in Pediatrics, 48*(2), 157–177.

California Childcare Health Program (CCHP). (2000). Could a child in your care have Kawasaki disease? *Child Care Health Connections, 13*(5), 1.

Carballo, M., & Nerukar, A. (2001). Migration, refugees and health risks. *Emerging Infectious Diseases,* 7(3), 556–560.

Cassidy, A. (1991, January). When your child is ill. *Working Mother,* 74–76.

Celedon, J., Litonjua, A., Weiss, S., & Gold, D. (1999). Day care attendance in the first year of life and illnesses of upper and lower respiratory tract in children with a familial history of atopy. *Pediatrics, 104*(3), 495–500.

Centers for Disease Control (CDC). (1997). Earache (otitis media) in the child care setting. Retrieved May 15, 2002, from http://www.cdc.gov/ncidod/hip/abc/facts12.htm.

Child Care Action Campaign. (1993). Temporary care for the mildly sick child (CCAC Information Guide 21). New York: Author.

Dailey, L. (2001). Excluding children due to illness: Four steps to a healthier program. *Child Care Health Connections, 14*(4), 6–7.

Feagans, L., Kipp, E., & Blood, I. (1994). The effects of otitis media on the attention skills of day-care-attending toddlers. *Developmental Psychology, 30*(5), 701–708.

Gonzalez-Mena, J. (1997). *Multicultural issues in child care.* Menlo Park, CA: Mayfield.

Heyman, S., & Earle, A. (1999). The impact of welfare reform on parents' ability to care for their children's health. *American Journal of Public Health, 89*(4), 502–505.

Kendrick, A., Kaufmann, R., & Messenger, K. (1995). *Healthy young children: A manual for programs.* Washington, DC: NAEYC.

Lombardi, J. (1999). Viewpoint: child care is education . . . and more. *Young Children 54*(1), 48.

National Institute of Child Health and Human Development Early Child Care Research Network (NICH). (2001). Child care and common communicable illnesses. *Archives of Pediatrics and Adolescent Medicine, 155*(4), 481–488.

Niemela, M., Pihakari, O., Pokka, T., Uhari, M., & Uhari, M. (2000). Pacifier as a risk factor for acute otitis media: A randomized controlled trial of parental counseling. *Pediatrics, 106*(3), 483–488.

Pappas, D., Schwartz, R., Sheridan, M., & Hayden, G. (2000). Medical exclusion of sick children from child care centers: A plea for reconciliation. *Southern Medical Journal, 93*(6), 575–578.

Paradise, J., Dollaghan, C., Campbell, T., Feldman, H., Bernard, B., Colborn, D., Rockette, H., Janoksy, J., Pitcairn, D., Sabo, D., Kurs-Lasky, M., & Smith, C. (2000). Language, speech sound production and cognition in three-year-old children in relation to otitis media in their first three years of life. *Pediatrics, 105*(5), 1119–1130.

Poole, J. (2001). Ear infections. *Healthy Child Care,* 4(2). Retrieved May 15, 2002, from http://healthychild.net/Articles.

Skull, S., Ford-Jones, E., Kulin, N., Einarson, T., & Wang, E. (2000). Child care center staff contribute to physicians visits and pressure for antibiotic prescription. *Archives of Pediatrics and Adolescent Medicine, 154*(2), 180–183.

Sokol-Gutierrez, K. (2000, January). Partners in health: Helping families advocate for their children's health. *Child Care Information Exchange, 51–53.*

Teele, D., Klein, J., & Rossner, B. (1984). Otitis media with effusion during the first years of life and development of speech and language. *Pediatrics, 74,* 282–287.

Watt, M., Roberts, J., & Zeisel, S. (1993). Ear infections in young children: The role of the early childhood educator. *Young Children, 48*(11), 64–72.

Zamani, R., & Shaw, P. (2000). Ear infections (otitis media) and hearing loss in young children. Retrieved May 15, 2002, from http://ericps.ed.uiuc.edu/cchp/factsheet/earinfection.html.

Zambrana, R., Ell, K., Dorrington, C., Wachsmur, L., & Hodge, D. (1994). The relationship between psychosocial status of immigrant Latina mothers and use of emergency pediatric services. *Health and Social Work, 19*(2), 98–102.

SUGGESTIONS FOR READING

American Academy of Pediatrics (AAP). *Health in day care: A manual for health professionals.* Elk Grove, IL: American Academy of Pediatrics.

Aronson, S., Smith, H., & Martin, J. (1993). *Model child care health policies.* Bryn Mawr, PA: Pennsylvania Chapter of the American Academy of Pediatrics.

California Child Health Care Project. (1990). *Control of communicable and infectious diseases: A manual for providers.* San Diego, CA: Author.

Frieman, B., & Settle, J. (1994). What the classroom teacher needs to know about children with chronic medical problems. *Childhood Education, 70*(4), 196–201.

Seattle-King County Department of Public Health. (1991). *Child care health handbook.* Seattle: Washington State Department of Social and Health Services.

For additional information on safety, nutrition, and health in early education, visit our Web site at **http://www.earlychilded.delmar.com**

Current Issues in Child Care Safety, Nutrition, and Health

IV

In this section we will discuss four areas that deal with current issues:

12. Child Abuse

13. Special Topics in Safety, Nutrition, and Health

14. Creating Linkages

15. Building Curriculum for Safety, Nutrition, and Health

These topics will prepare the caregiver to deal with sensitive issues, create linkages with children, families, and the community, and develop curriculum for safety, nutrition, and health in child care.

Child Abuse

After reading this chapter, you should be able to:

12–1 Policies for Child Abuse

Define and discuss policies for child abuse that may affect the child care setting.

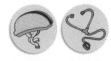

12–2 Preventive Measures for Child Abuse

Describe and discuss measures for preventing child abuse.

12–3 Protective Measures for Child Abuse

Describe and discuss how to recognize, document, and report child abuse, and methods for caring for an abused child.

12–4 Implications for Caregivers

Describe and discuss the importance of education, observation, role modeling, and supervision in dealing with special topics issues.

12.1 Policies for Child Abuse

A child caregiver may encounter child abuse that involves a child in care. Child abuse is becoming a serious threat to the health, safety, and well-being of the children in this country. It is up to the caregiver to offer preventive and protective measures to all children in care. The following issues show the need to create policies that deal with child abuse (see Figure 12–1).

- Child abuse and neglect have become a major threat to children four and younger. Every year 2,000 die, 18,000 are permanently disabled, and 142,000 are seriously injured (Dixon, 1995).

- Child abuse affected 3.24 million children in 1999. This figure is 133 percent higher than in 1989 (Peddle & Wang, 2001).

- Children under the age of six are the most at risk for being abused and neglected. Infants are the largest proportion of victims (CDF, 2000a).

- Abuse fatalities have increased 34 percent since 1985 (Wang & Daro, 1998). Eighty percent of fatalities are children under five, and 40 percent are infants (Peddle & Wang, 2001).

- Helping parents recognize behaviors that may develop into abusive behaviors can produce positive parent–child relationships instead of the cycle of abuse (Massey, 1998; NAEYC, 1997).

- A supportive adult can make a difference in the life of a child who is in an abusive family (Groves et al., 2000).

- Children over the age of three years can learn abuse prevention concepts (Crosson-Tower, 2002).

The child caregiver should provide a child care environment that supports the children's well-being. The environment and the actions of the caregivers must be beyond reproach. Methods of practices for preventing accusations must be used.

The child caregiver should learn to recognize any indicators that a family may be at risk for abusing the children. Intervention methods and strategies should be used when necessary. The child caregiver is mandated to report any

Figure 12–1

Abuse Statistics. *(From Peddle & Wang, 2001)*

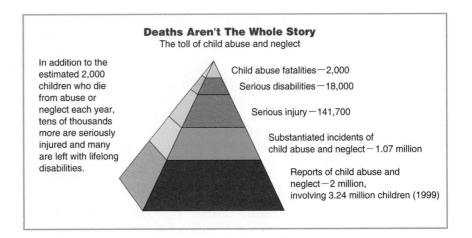

abuse that may be observed. She should learn to recognize the signs and symptoms of abuse. The caregiver needs to know how to document and report any indicators of abuse that have been observed (Nunnelley & Fields, 1999). Caregivers should know the methods and strategies used to provide for the well-being of a child in care who has been abused.

The following are areas in which policies should be created for child abuse prevention and protection:

1. *Preventive Measures:* understanding how to prevent accusations and how to intervene to protect children in care from abuse

2. *Protective Measures:* practices to recognize, document, and report all forms of child abuse and methods for working with abused children

3. *Implications for Caregivers:* practices that use the tools of education, cultural sensitivity, observation, and supervision to provide children with protection and prevention from harm and to offer an environment that fosters well-being

KEY CONCEPT 12.1

Policies for Child Abuse

Child abuse affects over 3 million children annually. Caregivers should learn preventive, protective, and promotional measures that will help provide for the well-being of children. Policies should be created to help the caregiver provide intervention and prevent accusation. These policies should offer the caregiver methods and practices needed for recognition, documentation, and reporting of child abuse. The caregiver should understand protective strategies to provide the child who has been abused with an atmosphere of support and a sense of trust in the caregiver.

12.2 Preventive Measures for Child Abuse

Child abuse is a very sensitive issue that needs to be carefully handled. Child abuse can be complex when it surfaces as an issue in child care. The caregiver has a number of responsibilities for handling this issue. Prevention, protection, and promotion of child safety are essential. "Above all, we should not harm children" (NAEYC, 1997). Prevention of child maltreatment can be effective and is less costly in terms of human suffering as well as financial cost needed to remedy it (Donnelly, 1992).

Caregivers can offer preventive measures by cooperating with their state licensing agency. Many states will screen caregivers for a history of abuse. The caregiver who employs others can make sure all prospective employees are screened for child abuse and neglect and conform to the licensing regulations. This screening would include caregivers, janitors, secretaries, cooks, substitutes, and volunteers. If it is difficult to get local licensing or screening information, NAEYC recommends using the screening decision model developed by the American Bar Association (Wells et al., 1995). This instrument is very

A good policy for hiring new child care providers is to carefully screen them, including an in-depth interview and checking all references.

thorough (NAEYC, 1997). Other screening methods might include the state department of motor vehicles for driving records and educational transcripts. It is important that at least three professional and personal references be checked.

In addition to the licensing process, each prospective employee should be carefully interviewed and all referrals from previous employment should be checked. Table 12–1 lists a sample of questions the caregiver may ask prospective employees. If there are any doubts about the person after the interview, the caregiver should listen to his intuition. There is no room for doubt when it comes to the safety of children in care. New employees should go through a probationary period so that the employing caregiver may carefully observe them as they relate to the children. If the caregiver does not meet the standards of behavior on or off the job, a policy should be in place to terminate her.

Proper teacher–child ratios also act as a preventive measure. If the ratio is followed, teachers are able to best meet each child's individual needs. Check your state for regulations on ratios. If your state does not have them, NAEYC accreditation suggests:

- ■ 1:6–8 for infants
- ■ 1:8–12 for toddlers
- ■ 1:14–20 for preschoolers
- ■ 1:16–20 for kindergartners
- ■ 1:20 for primary grades

Preservice orientation and in-service training should be given to keep caregivers up to date about child abuse in a group setting. This should include the definition of child abuse, identification of signs of abuse, and how to document and report child abuse. Many cases of abuse are either erroneously reported or go unreported because the caregiver does not understand what constitutes abuse and how it should be reported (Nunnelley & Fields, 1999).

TABLE 12–1 Sample Interview Questions to Screen for Abuse Potential
• Why do you want to work with children?
• How would you describe your own childhood?
• What is your viewpoint on discipline?
• Do you believe in corporal punishment (hitting a child)?
• Does child behavior ever make you angry?
• How do you express your anger?
• A series of "What would you do if?" questions that relate to anger, discipline, etc.
• What are some coping skills you have to alleviate stress?

Another preventive measure is to set up the child care environment so that children and caregivers are never isolated from view of others. Restrooms should have an open door policy that require the door to remain open so that there is no opportunity for privacy. Supervision should be provided to support this.

Preventing Accusations

Mandate
an order by law

Caregivers should inform parents who sign their children up for care that there is a policy that covers child abuse. The caregiver needs the parent to understand that any suspected abuse must be reported. Most states **mandate** that caregivers report any suspected child abuse. The parents should also be informed of the steps the caregiver uses to prevent abuse from occurring in the care situation. The caregiver should make sure the parents understand the philosophy of discipline, guidance, and child care.

Use injury incident reports for any time an accident or injury occurs in your care. Discuss these daily with the parents as they pick up the children.

Caregivers are in a good position to identify possible abuse. In most states, they are mandated to report suspected abuse.

Save a copy of the report in the child's file to document each accident or injury. If the child comes to care with an unexplained bruise or physical injury, the caregiver should ask the parent about it. The report of the bruise and the explanation should be recorded and added to the child's file. Any injury incident report should include the date, time, nature of the injury, and any comments by the parent. Documentation is the caregiver's best defense (see Figure 12–2). Visitors to the child care should be required to sign in and out. A clear directive should be given by parents concerning who is allowed to pick up their child or children in care. If a substitute or new volunteer is present or will be coming later in the day, the parents should always be informed before they leave children in care (NAEYC, 1997).

Intervention

Intervention strategies such as observation, discussion, and action may prevent abuse. The caregiver should learn to identify when parents or their children are under stress. The caregiver should work closely with parents to establish a good, communicative relationship (NAEYC, 1997). Developing trust and respect keeps the line of communication open between caregiver and parent. The caregiver may observe a parent or child under stress over a period of time. Talking with the parent may help to relieve the stress or open up other avenues to relieve stress. The caregiver can inform the parent that there may be coping skills or outside help for this stress. Information regarding stages of child development and effective ways to handle guidelines and discipline should be made available to families. Children from the age of three can be taught preventive strategies and concepts. They can easily learn about what abuse is, what the body parts are, and the types of touching (Crosson-Tower, 2002). This may provide the action needed to impede the progress of abuse.

Table 12–2 relates some factors that may exhibit potential for abuse. These behaviors may be exhibited to greater extent when a parent is under stress.

Stress is a major factor in abusive situations involving parents and children. Training is available for caregivers that teaches sensitivity to these areas and provides resources for parents.

Injury Incident Report

Child's name: _____

Date: _____ Time: _____

Where did the incident take place? _____

Description of incident: _____

_____

_____

_____

Caregiver initials: _____

Action taken by caregiver: _____

_____

_____

_____

Observations of behavior changes, if any: _____

_____

_____

_____

Parent notified: _____

Caregiver initials: _____

Caregiver signature _____ Parent signature _____

Figure 12–2
Injury Incident Report

TABLE 12-2 Factors That May Lead to Abusive Behaviors
• Significant changes in lifestyle: death of family member, divorce, unemployment, marital difficulties, or a recent move.
• Poor knowledge of child development and unrealistic expectations of the child's capabilities; e.g., the child is a little adult.
• Isolation from support; little or no contact with extended family, neighbors, and friends.
• Low self-esteem.
• Few coping abilities.
• Poor impulse control. Gets angry for even minor things.
• Questionable communication behaviors. May appear to feel threatened or defensive when ordinary questions are asked concerning the child or children.
• Lack of bonding or attachment to a child or children.
• Appears to be under the influence of alcohol or drugs.

A child's behavior may not always be consistent, due to temperament and developmental changes. The caregiver will, however, probably be able to find a pattern of behavior for most children. When a child begins to exhibit increases in poor behavior or appears sad or withdrawn, he may be experiencing stress in his life. The caregiver can talk with the child about his feelings, and alert a parent to these changes. Children can also use coping skills to relieve stress.

KEY CONCEPT 12.2

Preventive Measures

Preventive measures such as screening caregivers and having an open door policy can help prevent undue accusations against responsible caregivers. Caregivers should always document an accident, injury, or illness that a child may have while in care. The caregiver should be aware of the indicators of social circumstances and behaviors of children and parents that could escalate into child abuse. Intervention may help prevent abuse from occurring.

12.3 Protective Measures for Child Abuse

It is imperative that every caregiver be aware of the physical and behavioral indicators of abuse. Child abuse can be defined as "harm or neglect of a child by a parent, relative, babysitter, caregiver, or any other adult" (Seattle-King County Department of Public Health, 1991).

Recognition

A child caregiver needs to know how to recognize the indicators of child abuse. Child abuse is divided into four categories: physical, emotional, sexual, and neglect. Each type of abuse has signs and symptoms that may indicate that child abuse has taken place. A child may suffer from abuse in one or more areas.

Each type of abuse has signs and symptoms that a caregiver should be on the lookout for.

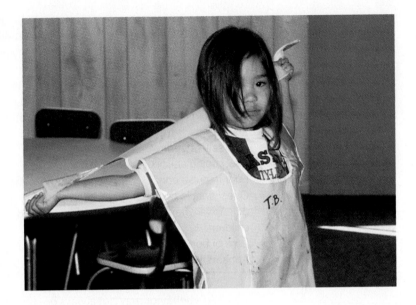

It is essential that the caregiver have an awareness of the indicators of abuse. All states mandate that people who care for children are to report suspected abuse. In most states, failure to report abuse brings penalties, including a monetary fine. Some caregivers may feel reluctant to report because they feel that the parents may retaliate or that their relationship with the parents may be compromised. Regardless of reluctance or feelings of guilt, a caregiver who suspects child abuse must report it. The report may make a lasting difference in a child's life. It may prevent death or injury and may help the family to access resources and assistance. In some states, the only follow-up to the abuse report may have to come from the child care center unless the children were removed from parental custody. This places the child caregiver in an awkward situation. All states protect the caregiver from criminal or civil liability due to reporting of abuse.

Physical Abuse. Physical abuse is any act that results in a nonaccidental physical injury. This type of abuse may be a result of severe corporal punishment or intentional injury by deliberate assault. Table 12–3 includes many physical and behavioral indicators of physical abuse.

TABLE 12–3 Indicators of Physical Abuse

Physical

- Bruises—in linear markings, clusters, on several different areas at a time, and at various stages of healing. May appear after absence, weekend, or vacation.
- Burns—cigarette or cigar, immersion burns (on buttocks and genitalia), patterns (iron, grid), rope or infected burns for which treatment may have been delayed.
- Unexplained bite marks.
- Lacerations or abrasions—typically around mouth, eyes, and external genitalia and may be in various stages of healing. *(continued)*

TABLE 12–3 Indicators of Physical Abuse *(continued)*

- Internal injuries.
- Head injury or whiplash—from shaking the child, known as shaken infant syndrome.

Behavioral

- Tells you parents or other adult hurt him.
- Overcompliant.
- Poor self-concept.
- Wary of adult contact, may be frightened of parent or parents or other adults.
- Does not want to leave child care.
- Extremes in behavior.
- Feels deserving of punishment.
- Vacant, withdrawn, or detached.
- Indiscriminately seeks affection.
- Chronic ailments—stomachaches, headaches, vomiting.

REALITY CHECK

Shaken Baby Syndrome

Shaken baby syndrome is a form of child abuse involving forceful or violent shaking of a child from birth to five years of age. It most commonly occurs in children under two years of age, especially those between six and eight months of age (Palmer, 1998). This type of shaking makes infants and young children especially vulnerable to injury because their heads are larger, their neck muscles are not well developed, and their brain and surrounding tissue are very fragile. The violent shaking of the baby is usually done in anger and frustration. When this type of shaking occurs, it multiplies the force between five and ten times that of a child who trips or falls. Anyone who might witness this type of force could easily see how the child would be in a life-threatening situation (AAP, 2001). The sudden movements occurring with this type of force can cause some parts of the brain to pull away. The result is torn brain cells and blood vessels (AHA, 2001).

Shaken baby syndrome does not occur with short falls, seizures, or because a child has been vaccinated. It only occurs through violent shaking, which does not have to last more than 20 seconds or 40–50 shakes to do damage that can be fatal (NCSBS, 2000). One baby in four dies as a result of shaking. Very few babies escape permanent injury, and most survivors suffer brain damage (AHA, 2001b). Permanent injury for the majority of these babies can range from partial to complete blindness and hearing loss, as well as seizure disorder, cerebral palsy, developmental disabilities, autism, behavior problems, and sucking and swallowing disorders. It can also result in a permanent vegetative state.

Adult males in their twenties who are the father of the child or the boyfriend of the mother are the most common perpetrators of shaking a baby (Palmer, 1998). Estimates that adult males are the perpetrators range from 65 to 90 percent. Often they are involved in domestic violence and substance abuse (AAP, 2001). Females who shake babies are more likely to be baby-sitters or child caregivers than mothers. Several recent sensational cases across the nation have been focused

(continued)

on child caregivers who are accused of shaking a baby and causing death or permanent damage.

Immediate medical help can reduce the degree of impact of shaking. Many people who do shake an infant put them down, thinking they will sleep and later wake up and be fine (AAP, 2001). Any opportunity for recovery may be lost during this time. People who shake an infant often claim to have no knowledge of how the child got injured. This claim prevents vital care, because medical tests that take a great deal of time are used to determine the cause of the injury before proper care may be initiated.

Frustration with a crying child seems to be the biggest cause of the act of shaking. Most people are unaware that this type of shaking can cause permanent damage or death to a child. A normal baby will spend between two and three hours a day crying. Approximately one-fourth of infants will cry much longer than that. There may be no apparent reason for the crying. Infants in the one- to four-month-old range are more likely to display this excess crying (NCSBS, 2000). A caregiver who is easily frustrated or angered may respond by shaking in an attempt to get the baby to stop crying. Shaking may stop the crying, but it may also kill the baby or injure it to an extent that it will never fully recover. It is very important for the caregiver of young children to understand this and never, ever, shake a baby.

Some methods have worked to help stop a baby from crying. First, the caregiver must *calm down*. Running a vacuum cleaner near a baby, giving the baby a pacifier, and cuddling the child gently may help to alleviate the crying (AHA, 2001a). If none of those suggestions work, realize that a baby can be left in a safe place to cry. Walk away after putting the baby in a safe place. Listen to music or call someone for support or advice. If the crying continues, call the doctor. After you have calmed down, resume trying to help the baby (Palmer, 1998). If you become desperate, call the parents to come get the child and then call CHILDHELP (800–4–ACHILD) to talk to someone while you wait for the parent. If crying is difficult for you to hear, you may want to consider working with older children, who may be less frustrating for you, or not working with children at all.

Parents should also be educated about shaken baby syndrome. Obtain brochures to hand out and put up a poster warning about shaken baby syndrome. These can found by e-mailing the National Center on Shaken Baby Syndrome at *dontshake@mindspring.com* or faxing 801–627–3321. This will help the parent to better understand and prevent shaking at home. It will also help the parent to understand that it is best for the caregiver to call the parent when help is needed.

Emotional Abuse.   Emotional abuse includes placing unrealistic demands, excessive yelling, or unnecessary criticism that results in emotional harm or mental suffering. It is perhaps the most difficult to prove, but it may be observed when the interaction between a child and parent is seen. See Table 12–4 for a list of indicators of this type of abuse.

Sexual Abuse.   Child sexual abuse can be sexual exploitation as well as sexual assault upon the child by an adult or older child. Sexual exploitation includes fondling, mouth to genital contact, exhibition, and showing or using the child for obscene materials. The offender is known to the child in 80 percent of the cases. Sexual abuse is a reality in the United States. As many as one in five adult women were abused as children (ERIC Digest, 1990). Table 12–5 includes indicators of sexual abuse.

Neglect.   Neglect causes death more frequently than abuse does (California Child Care Resource and Referral Network [CCRRN], 1987). Neglect of a child

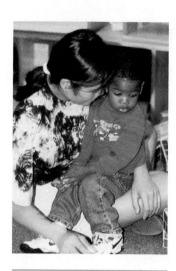

A consistently vacant, withdrawn, or detached child may be a victim of emotional abuse.

TABLE 12–4   Indicators of Emotional Abuse

Physical

- Failure to thrive.
- Withdrawn or depressed.
- Disruptive or hyperactive.
- Speech or language disorders.
- Repetitive rhythmic movements.
- Little facial effect—no signs of emotional response.
- Bedwetting or toileting accidents for older children.

Behavioral

- Rigid in conformity to authority.
- Parent is demanding and unrealistic about the capabilities of the child.
- Destructive or antisocial.
- Sleep disorders.
- Unusual fears.
- Behind in mental or emotional development.
- Aggressive or compliant behavioral extremes.

TABLE 12–5   Indicators of Sexual Abuse

Physical

- Torn, stained, or bloody underclothing.
- Pain, itching, or swelling in genital area.
- Bruises, lacerations, or bleeding in genital, vaginal, or anal area.
- Discharge in vaginal/genital area.
- Venereal disease.
- Difficulty in walking or sitting.
- Pain when urinating or defecating.

Behavioral

- Withdrawn, fantasy, or infantile.
- Poor self-esteem and self-image.
- Poor peer relationships.
- Depression.
- Abrupt changes in behavior such as eating, sleeping, or school performance.
- Excessively clingy or inappropriate attachment.
- Exceptional fear of a person or place.
- Draws scary pictures that include plenty of black and red coloring.
- Inappropriate sexual knowledge or behavior.

includes depriving the child of food, shelter, medical care, supervision, or education. Negligence occurs in both actions and failure to act on behalf of the child. Severe neglect includes intentional failure to provide and allowing danger to the child's person or health. Table 12–6 includes the indicators of neglect.

TABLE 12–6 Indicators of Neglect

Physical

- Always hungry, dirty, or inappropriately dressed.
- Unsupervised for long periods of time.
- Lacks medical or dental care.
- Lack of supervision, especially for long periods of time.
- Unsanitary home.
- Abandonment.
- Underweight, poor growth.
- Consistently absent from school.

Behavioral

- Stealing or begging for food or money for food.
- Parent brings child early and picks up late.
- Inappropriate attachment or affection.
- Shows or expresses no emotions.
- Parent abusing drugs or alcohol.
- Overly responsible; assumes adult role.

Documentation

If the caregiver suspects or has reason to believe that abuse is occurring, then it must be reported. The caregiver does not have to personally witness the abuse or have positive proof that it occurred. Caregivers need to understand how to document suspected abuse and how to report it (Nunnelley & Fields, 1999).

Observing children is one of the major jobs of a caregiver. The caregiver needs to be aware of the indicators of abuse to observe in order to notice a

Children who are unsupervised for long periods of time (a sign of neglect) are at a higher risk for death than children who are physically abused.

problem. The caregiver should observe the child at different times of day and in different settings and record the observation in note form.

The caregiver should record behavior, conversation, and physical signs. This type of anecdotal record may signify a pattern that indicates abuse may be present. It may also indicate that there is no pattern present and what the caregiver noticed about a bruise and limp might have been a result of a fall. The records should be kept in the child's health record in case there is need to refer to them again.

Reporting

If the caregiver needs to report child abuse, the reporting process should be clear. In most states there is a Child Welfare Office or Child Protective Services. If the caregiver is unsure then he should contact the local Department of Social Services or law enforcement agency. This should be done before any suspected abuse. There may be forms that the caregiver should keep on hand. The caregiver should also inquire if there is a 24-hour hotline so the number may be posted.

When a report is filed, the child's name, address, and age must be included. The parents' names and address or addresses (if they have separate homes) should also be given. The caregiver should provide her name and address. Anonymity for the caregiver will be provided. The caregiver must realize that the parents might be able to tell who reported the abuse, because it is likely she will have more information about the child than anyone else.

The caregiver may want to talk to the parent before reporting the abuse. Some parents may be relieved that help is available, although anger and hostility are another common reaction and may result in the parents removing the child from child care. If the caregiver decides to tell the parents before the report, once again, she should explain the requirement to report any suspected abuse. As difficult as it may be to tell the parents before reporting the suspected abuse, it may be better that they still have trust in the caregiver for her honesty. The best course is for the caregiver to plan to help the parents through the process. Supporting the family after reporting abuse is often a center-based responsibility and includes referrals to meet the needs of the family.

A roadblock that a caregiver may run into is reluctance to report abuse. Human emotions enter into matters that are this grave. Reluctance may be based on the caregiver's personal background, the lack of support from supervisorial personnel, or family rights issues. In some cultures, a family's rights over their children are deeply held beliefs (Zamani, 2000). Often, the caregiver may feel like they are betraying the child and the family by reporting suspected abuse (Nunnelley & Fields, 1999). "Knowing how, when and what to report about child abuse and neglect may make a life or death difference for a child" (AHA, 2001a).

Caring for the Abused Child

If abuse is blatant and puts the child in real danger, the child may be removed from the family. If this is the case, the courts, foster families, or other family members who gain custody of the child may wish to continue to keep the child in the care situation to maintain some consistency in the child's life.

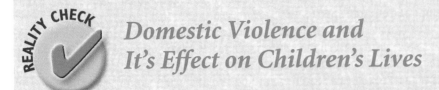

Domestic Violence and It's Effect on Children's Lives

The home can be a more dangerous place than the streets. Women are nine times more likely to get hurt in the home than on the streets. Three-quarters of domestic violence occurs in the home (CDF, 2000b). It is estimated that between 25 and 30 percent of women have been beaten at least one time in an intimate relationship. More than 3.3 million children witness either physical or verbal abuse of their mothers. This ranges from insults to beatings to homicide (Osofsky, 1999). Experts believe that domestic violence is the single major precursor that leads to child abuse and neglect. Studies have found that in homes where domestic violence is present, children are 15 times more likely to be physically abused or neglected. It has been estimated that in 60 to 75 percent of homes where the mother is battered, the children are also battered. (Osofsky, 1999).

Changes that have occurred in family systems in recent decades have led to greater stress in families. Some of these include poverty, social isolation, low educational levels, marital discord, and lack of coping abilities. All of these can lead to children suffering abuse and neglect. Families are no longer like those that were portrayed on television in the 1950s and 1960s. Divorce affects almost one in two families and more than one in four families are headed by a single parent. Parents may not be able to stay at home with children due to economic stresses, so younger children may be in nonparental care and older children may become latchkey children. More families with children live in poverty, and there is a greater degree of drug and alcohol abuse than we have previously seen in this country. All of these factors contribute to stress that can manifest into domestic violence.

Domestic violence occurs at every socioeconomic level and in every racial, cultural, religious, and ethnic group. Men are more likely than women to commit domestic violence. Women who commit domestic violence usually do so in self-defense or in retaliation for abuse.

Even if children themselves are not abused, witnessing abuse can have traumatic effects on them. Witnessing violence may lead to fear, discipline problems, depression, poor social interaction, and drug abuse among children (FNMPD, 2001). Long-term effects may include posttraumatic stress disorder and personality disorders (Groves et al., 2000). Physical problems can be present as well as cognitive developmental delays (Osofsky, 1999). Witnessing violence may lead to the child performing violent acts as they get older (Garbarino, 2001).

It has been reported that 79 percent of children in institutions for violent behavior have witnessed violence. Boys who witness violence are more likely than girls to act out. They are three times more likely to become abusive to their domestic partners later in life. Girls are much more likely to allow abuse to occur to them as women. Both behaviors perpetuate domestic violence.

Many professionals believe that witnessing domestic violence is the most harmful type of violence that a child could experience (Groves, 2001) (see Figure 3–1, page 109 for the Continuum of Violence scale). When children see violence in their own homes with their own families, they realize they have no safe place. If a child cannot feel safe at home, he is less likely to develop trust and later explore his environment. Without trust and exploration, achieving autonomy as a normal course of development is difficult. Children may also feel guilty that they could not prevent the act or that they did something to trigger the act (FNMPD, 2001). Children who witness domestic violence may become anxious and fearful under most conditions.

Children who have an adult they can trust are likely to cope better. Frequent positive interactions can help a child feel safe (ACT, 2001). The most protective factor for a child who does not feel safe at home is "the existence of a strong, positive relationship between the child and a competent and

(continued)

caring adult" (CFC, 1999). Child caregivers can provide this type of relationship and can develop trust between themselves and the children in their care. Caregivers can help to foster resiliency and teach children conflict resolution. A model program for this has been created in Texas (Texas Child Care, 1994).

Caregivers can model prosocial behaviors and help children have a greater sense of acceptance and self-esteem. Children can be praised and recognized for good behaviors and redirected away from aggressive behaviors. Caregivers can also provide a safe haven from a difficult home life for a few hours a day.

When dealing with an abused child, caregivers must first identify their own feelings about abuse and determine if they are ready emotionally to support the child.

Caregivers need to understand how to support a child and his family or custodian once the abuse has been established. The first step in this process is for the caregiver to examine her confidence level, her knowledge of human development, and how she feels about the abuse. How the caregiver feels about herself will affect whether or not she can offer support. If the caregiver has a low confidence level, it will be difficult to help the child raise his.

The caregiver needs to determine her level of understanding about what is normal behavior. She needs to understand what behaviors need to be redirected. These factors will determine the skill level the caregiver has to do the job. The child may need to address factors of his social and emotional development process. Can the caregiver help a child learn to trust and live within safe boundaries? Judging the abuse can impede the caregiver's ability to perform. Placing blame and being angry will not help the caregiver perform her job.

It is estimated that one out of three women was sexually abused as a child (Stith, 1998). If the caregiver has personally suffered from abuse in some form as a child there may be unresolved feelings. Will these feelings hinder the relationship with the child or parent?

If the caregiver determines that she is capable of helping and supporting an abused child, there are several critical things that she can provide the child:

- trust
- predictable routines
- consistent behavior
- safe boundaries
- confidence
- good communication skills

These will offer the child the sense of well-being needed to progress beyond the abuse.

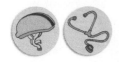

KEY CONCEPT 12.3

Protective Measures for Child Abuse

Protective measures such as recognition of abuse, documentation, and reporting give the caregivers the tools needed to protect children from abuse. The caregiver should be able to recognize the physical and behavioral indicators of physical abuse, emotional abuse, sexual abuse, and neglect. The caregiver should understand the procedures for documenting and reporting abuse, and know the practices and strategies that will offer care to an abused child.

12.4 Implications for Caregivers

Caregivers need to see that there is a policy created for child abuse. The policy should include the processes needed to help prevent child abuse and protect the children in child care. These methods and strategies should include education, cultural competence, observation, and supervision. Education for the caregivers, as well as the parents and children offers prevention and protection. Cultural competence is crucial because in some cultures child abuse may not be seen as a problem, but may be a parental right. Observation helps the caregiver to recognize and document. Supervision maintains a set of checks and balances to provide the protection of the children in child care and prevent some abuse from occurring.

Education

It is essential that the child caregiver understand what child abuse is and how to recognize it. Awareness and familiarity with the indicators of abuse of the four areas—physical, emotional, sexual, and neglect—can help a caregiver observe for them. Caregivers need to understand the process to report abuse because they are the mandated reporters of child abuse. The child caregiver must know how to report abuse, and in order to do so the caregiver must know how to document for accuracy and support.

For the Parents. Education can also help the caregiver help to prevent abuse. Having methods and strategies for working with children and parents can help the caregiver offer greater protection for the children. The child caregiver can educate the parents and children to help prevent abuse. Parents can be educated about normal child development and the behaviors that can be expected at that point of development. Parents who have an understanding of the capabilities of their children may have more realistic expectations. The caregiver should keep an open line of communication with the parent. They can share common concerns about the child or about stress in the family envi-

Cultural competence and good communication skills will assist a caregiver in dealing with children and their families to help prevent child abuse and protect the children in their care.

ronment. This can help to form a partnership. The caregiver can also support the parent during times of stress or other difficulties by providing referrals or resources. Caregivers may help reduce the likelihood of child abuse by family members. Working with families and giving them support may help to break the cycle of abuse (NAEYC, 1997).

With Children. The caregiver can help to educate the child about what is and what is not acceptable behavior between the child and an adult. The caregiver can promote safety from sexual abuse from an early stage. At eighteen months children can learn about body parts. From three to five years of age they can learn about the body parts and what parts are unacceptable for others to touch. A child who learns to use the word "no" will be empowered to help protect himself.

A child who learns to achieve mastery in her life by making choices may be more prepared to act if she is abused. A caregiver can provide opportunities that allow the child choices.

A caregiver can model self-control, verbalize feelings and fears, and provide a predictable, stable environment. These actions will offer the child a protective environment where he feels safe enough to talk. A child who experiences this environment may be more willing to share difficulties in his life.

Cultural Competence

Cultural competence is a preventive measure. The process of childrearing may be culturally defined. What is normal and acceptable in one culture may not be considered normal or acceptable in another. The United States has a large **immigrant** and **migrant** population that is ever increasing. A caregiver who cares for children from a culture other than her own should try to learn about the childrearing practices and behavior of that culture. Some of the diverse cultural practices that may be seen as child abuse include female circumcision, coining, cupping, scarring, and burning of the skin and use of poisonous herbal remedies (Zamani, 2000).

The family's view on discipline and punishment may be in conflict with the laws of this country. Some cultures believe in corporal punishment as a consequence for unquestioning obedience and unrealistic expectations. The caregiver can ask a family about their cultural customs. This is a good way to understand if this is the case. If it is the case, the caregiver may need to begin a dialogue with the family. The caregiver should show respect about differing cultural beliefs of the family, but should also clearly inform them about the law (Gonzalez-Mena, 1997).

Families who recently immigrated or migrated may have experienced a great deal of stress (Duarte and Rafanello, 2001). Stressful events related to the relocation of families may affect their psychological well-being. Strange customs, lack of support networks, and inability to speak English may all contribute to the stress of a child and family.

Observation

Observation is the most important tool that a child caregiver has to protect a child from abuse. The observation for signs and symptoms of child abuse can

Immigrant
one who leaves a country to settle in another

Migrant
a transient who travels from place to place to find work

make the caregiver aware of the possibility that the child's safety and well-being are in jeopardy. Observation is also the key tool for documentation of suspected abuse. A good observer will use the tools of the senses to report what was seen, heard, felt, and smelled.

Observation also plays a part in preventing abuse. It is important to observe the caregiving environment for practices that offer prevention from abuse. The caregiver may also observe for the stressors and behaviors of families, because the caregiver can intervene before abuse takes place.

Supervision

Everyone in the caregiver's employ must be trained to recognize, document, and report abuse. Employees should learn to recognize their own stress. The caregiver should supervise the child care environment to prevent any situation or practice that does not offer protection from, and prevention of child abuse. Discipline should be supervised to make sure it is correct and that all child caregivers offer good guidance and discipline and do not cross the line into punishment.

The caregiver should supervise to make sure all protective measures such as recognition, documentation, and reporting of child abuse are done when necessary, in the right way, and in a timely manner. It is important for the caregiver to supervise the care of an abused child and to make sure the child is being offered a supportive environment. The caregiver should make sure the child's health, safety, and well-being are promoted by healthy interactions.

KEY CONCEPT 12.4

Implications for Caregivers

The caregiver can promote a safe environment by using tools that prevent and protect children from child abuse. The tools of education, cultural competence, observation, and supervision can help the caregiver to offer a safe environment for the well-being of the children in care. Education helps the caregiver recognize the signs and symptoms of behaviors prior to abuse and the four types of abuse. It helps the caregiver understand how to document and report abuse. Education gives the caregiver strategies to help the abused child. Cultural competence may offer an intervening measure to prevent children from being abused. Observation is the major tool used to recognize, document, and report abuse. Supervision provides the necessary checks to make sure the environment is offering protection and prevention of abuse.

CHAPTER SUMMARY

Considering the large number of children abused or neglected each year, caregivers should learn preventive, protective, and promotional measures that will help provide for children's well-being. Policies should be created that will help the caregiver ensure preventive measures such as freedom from accusation and the ability to intervene. Protective measures such as recognizing abuse, documentation, and reporting give caregivers the tools needed to protect children from abuse. The caregiver should know the practices and strategies that will offer care to an abused child. The tools of education, cultural competence, observation, and supervision can help the caregiver to provide an environment that offers safety and well-being to the children in care.

TO GO BEYOND

In this section you will find a number of activities that you can use to apply and improve your knowledge of this chapter. There are also thorough Online Resources that accompany this text that can be found at http://www.early childed.delmar.com/resources/robertson/index.html. Included on this site are chapter practice quizzes, PowerPoint outlines, Web links, a discussion forum, and various other activities to help you better understand the material in this chapter. This site is updated regularly so check back often to receive the latest information about the subjects in this chapter.

Chapter Review Critical Thinking Applications

1. Define and discuss the different forms of child abuse.
2. Describe some of the factors that are involved in child abuse, including what might lead an adult to abuse a child.
3. Explain how child abuse is recognized.
4. Describe how a caregiver would report child abuse.

As an Individual

1. Collect information about child abuse services available in your community.
2. Research shaken baby syndrome, finding at least two articles on the topic. Write a one-page paper on the subject and be prepared to discuss it in class. Why is it important to understand this topic?
3. List ways that cultural differences might impact abuse. Be prepared to discuss in class.

As a Group

1. Watch a film or video that describes child abuse. Compare the film to the reality of child abuse. Was the film/video realistic?
2. Invite a speaker from the local child abuse hotline to talk about reporting child abuse.
3. Invite a local physician who deals with child abuse in the emergency room to speak and describe what he/she sees occurring in your own community.
4. Examine some factors in today's society that might lead to child abuse. Especially discuss domestic violence and its effect on the family.

5. Discuss the conflicting feelings that a caregiver who suspects abuse has in making the decision to report. What should be done to ensure the right decision is made?

6. Create a policy for child abuse reporting for child care.

CHAPTER REFERENCES

Adults and Children Together (ACT). 2001. Violence prevention for teachers of young children. Retrieved May 15, 2002, from http://www.actagainstviolence.org/class.html.

American Academy of Pediatrics (AAP). (2001). Shaken baby syndrome: Rotational cranial injuries—technical report. Committee on Child Abuse and Neglect. *Pediatrics, 108*(1), 206–210.

American Humane Association (AHA). (2001a). America's children: How are they doing? Retrieved May 15, 2002, from http://www.americanhumane.org/children/factsheets/amer_child.htm.

American Humane Association (AHA). (2001b). Shaken baby syndrome. Retrieved May 15, 2002, from http://www.americanhumane.org/children/factsheets/shake.htm.

California Child Care Resource and Referral Network (CCRRN). (1987). *Making a difference: Handbook for child care providers.* San Francisco, CA: Author.

Children's Defense Fund (CDF). (2000a). Child abuse and neglect fact sheet. Retrieved May 15, 2002, from http://www.childrensdefense.org/ss_child_abuse.htm.

Children's Defense Fund (CDF). (2000b). Domestic violence and its impact on children. Retrieved May 15, 2002, from http://www.childrensdefense.org/ss_domestic_violence.htm.

Crosson-Tower, C. (2002). *Understanding child abuse and neglect.* Boston, MA: Allyn and Bacon.

Dixon, J. (1995, April 27). Child abuse, parental neglect blamed in 200 deaths per year. *San Diego Union-Tribune,* A-7.

Donnelly, A. (1992). Healthy families in America. *Children Today, 21*(2), 25–26.

Duarte, G., & Rafanello, D. (2001). The migrant child: A special place in the field. *Young Children, 56*(2), 26–34.

ERIC Digest. (1990). *Child sexual abuse, what it is and how to prevent it.* Champaign, IL: Eric Clearinghouse for Elementary and Early Childhood Education.

Fantuzzo, J., & Mohr, W. (1999). Prevalence and effects of child exposure to domestic violence. Center for the Future of Children: The David and Lucille Packard Foundation. *The Future of Children, 9*(3), 21–32.

Farmington, New Mexico Police Department (FNMPD). (2001). How domestic violence affects children. Retrieved May 15, 2002, from http://www.farington.nm.us/dept/police/domesticviolence/affectchildren/html.

Garbarino, J. (2001). Violent children: Where do we point the finger of blame? *Archives of Pediatrics and Adolescent Medicine, 155*(1), 13–14.

Gonzalez-Mena, J. (1997). *Multicultural issues in child care.* Mountain View, CA: Mayfield Publishing.

Groves, B. (2001). Children who witness violence. Family Communcations. Retrieved May 15, 2002, from http://www/fci.org/early_care/violence_whitness_article.asp.

Groves, B., Lieberman, A., Osofsky, J., & Fenichel, E. (2000, April/May). Protecting young children in violent environments: A framework to build on. *Zero to Three, 5.*

Massey, M. (1998). *Early childhood violence prevention.* ERIC Digest. Champaign, IL: Eric Clearinghouse on Elementary and Early Childhood Education.

NAEYC. (1997). NAEYC position statement on the prevention of child abuse in early childhood programs and the responsibility of early childhood professionals to prevent child abuse. *Young Children, 52*(3), 42–46.

National Center on Shaken Baby Syndrome (NCSBS). (2000). Shaken baby syndrome questions. Retrieved May 15, 2002, from http://www.dontshake.com/sbsquestions.html.

Nunnelley, J., & Fields, T. (1999). Anger, dismay, guilt, anxiety—The realities and roles in reporting child abuse. *Young Children, 54*(5), 74–79.

Osofsky, J. (1999). The impact of violence on children. *The Future of Children, 9*(3), 33–49.

Palmer, D., & Smith, C. (2000). Violence prevention: What childcare providers can—must!—do about it. *Healthy Child Care, 3*(6). Retrieved May 15, 2002, from http://www.healthchild.net/Articles.

Palmer, S. (1998). Shaken baby syndrome. The Arc. Retrieved May 15, 2002, from http://www.thearc.org/faqs/Shaken.html.

Peddle, N., & Wang, C. (2001). *Current trends in child abuse prevention, reporting, and fatalities: The 1999 fifty state survey.* Chicago, IL: Prevent Child Abuse America. Retrieved May 15, 2002, from http://www.preventchildabuse.org.

Seattle-King County Department of Public Health. (1991). *Child care health handbook.* Seattle, WA: Washington State Department of Social and Health Services.

Stith, A. (1998, July). Recognizing child abuse: The first step toward preventing false reports. *San Diego Family Magazine,* 32–34.

Texas Child Care. (1994, Fall). Child violence. *Texas Child Care Magazine,* 29.

Wang, C., & Daro, D. (1998). *Current trends in child abuse reporting and fatalities: The results of the 1997 annual fifty state survey.* Chicago, IL: Prevent Child Abuse America.

Wells, S., Davis, N., Dennis, K., Chipman. R., Sandt, C., & Liss, M. (1995). *Effective screening of child care and youth service workers.* Washington, DC: American Bar Association Center for Children and the Law.

Zamani, R. (2000). Traditional practices can affect the health of children. *Child Care Health Connections, 13*(5), 9.

SUGGESTIONS FOR READING

Chernofsky, B. (1992). *Child abuse awareness and prevention program: A home study course for family day care providers.* La Mesa, CA: Advocates for Better Childcare.

Crittenden, P. (1992). Children's strategies for coping with adverse home environments: An interpretation using attachment theory. *Child Abuse and Neglect, 16,* 329–343.

Elrod, J., & Rubine, R. (1993). Parental involvement in sexual abuse prevention education. *Child Abuse and Neglect, 17,* 527–538.

Good, L. (1996). When a child has been sexually abused: Several resources for parents and early childhood professionals. *Young Children, 51*(5), 84–85.

Haberman, M. (1994). Gentle teaching in a violent society. *Educational Horizons, 73*(3), 131–135.

Jordan, N. (1993). Sexual abuse prevention programs in early childhood education: A caveat. *Young Children, 48*(6), 76–79.

Spaccarelli, S., Sandler, I., & Roosa, M. (1994). History of spouse violence against mother: Correlated risk and unique effects in child mental health. *Journal of Family Violence, 91*(1), 79–98.

Wright, R. (1994, April). Child abuse is a tragedy: It takes many forms. *San Diego Family Press,* 66–67.

For additional information on safety, nutrition, and health in early education, visit our Web site at **http://www.earlychilded.delmar.com**

Special Topics in Safety, Nutrition, and Health

After reading this chapter, you should be able to:

 **13.1 Policies for Special Topics**
Define and discuss policies for special topics that may affect the child care setting.

 **13.2 Inclusion of Children with Special Needs into Child Care**
Describe and discuss the process of including children with special needs into your child care setting.

 **13.3 Children with Chronic Illnesses**
Describe and discuss special considerations for caring for children with chronic illnesses.

 **13.4 Children with Stress**
Describe and discuss common stressors and their impact on children.

 **13.5 Working with Children from Drug-Abusing Families**
Describe and discuss the common problems and their solutions that may arise in child care when working with children from drug-abusing families.

 13.6 Implications for Caregivers
Describe and discuss the importance of education, observation, role modeling, and supervision in dealing with special topics issues.

13.1 Policies for Special Topics

Policies need to be developed for special topics that may appear in child care. The caregiver may deal with some of these issues often, while other issues may never emerge. These issues should be examined in order to provide protection and prevention in the child care environment. The following are reasons for the development of policies on special issues:

■ Children who have disabilities and are in care with nondisabled children show more advanced play than if they were in special care for disabled children alone (Diamond, Hestenes, & O'Connor, 1994).

■ The Americans with Disabilities Act requires that all public accommodations, including family child care homes and day care programs, must provide access to children with disabilities (Olson, Murphy, & Olson, 1999).

■ As many as one in three children may suffer from chronic stress. These children get frequent headaches, stomachaches, and may even have ulcers (McCarthy, 2001).

■ Three percent of children under five have activity limitations due to one or more chronic health conditions (CSG, 2002). Eighteen percent of children need more specialized care than children who follow developmental norms (Aronson, 2000).

■ Six percent of pregnant women use illicit drugs and 18 percent regularly use alcohol. This makes 24 percent of children prenatally substance or drug exposed (NIDA, 1998).

Some children may come to child care with no issues that affect their health, safety, and well-being. Preventive measures can help these children remain risk-free in care. Other children may have special needs, chronic illness, stress, or are in families with drug histories that will affect them and their care.

All children can benefit from play in an inclusive environment.

Children with special health care needs are now defined as "those who have or are at risk for a chronic physical, developmental, behavioral or emotional condition and who also require health and related services of a type or amount beyond that required by children generally" (HRSA, 2001). In order to provide the most protective and healthy environment, policies need to be created to deal with some of these special issues. The special issues that are most likely to emerge as the caregiver performs child care are:

1. *Inclusion of Children with Special Needs:* understanding the effects of accommodation on child care and strategies to offer the optimum environment for the child with special needs

2. *Children with Chronic Illnesses:* understanding coping skills and strategies needed to provide the most protective and preventive environment for these children in child care

3. *Children with Stress:* practices for recognizing and supporting children with stress to protect them and promote their well-being

4. *Children from Drug Abusing Families:* strategies and practices for working with children from drug abusing families

KEY CONCEPT 13.1

Policies for Special Needs

Many children in care have no special issues in their lives that will affect caregiving. Others may have one or more that the caregiver must help them deal with while they are in care. Three child care issues that are the most likely to affect the caregiver and the care site are: inclusion of children with special needs, children with chronic illnesses, and children who are suffering from stress in their lives.

13.2 Inclusion of Children with Special Needs into Child Care

The Americans with Disabilities Act (ADA) of 1990 is federal legislation enacted to protect people with physical or mental disabilities from discrimination. The ADA defines disability as "a physical or mental impairment that substantially limits a major life activity." Title III of this act states that public accommodations must make reasonable modification to accommodate people with disabilities. Under the law, privately operated child care is considered a public accommodation. Title II of the ADA applies to child care programs that are operated by state or local government agencies such as school districts or municipalities.

The ADA basically applies to all child care situations except for a nanny caring for children in their home and church-operated programs. A caregiver cannot discriminate against a child because of a disability. This nondiscrimination policy might be included on any promotional literature the caregiver offers and should be included in the caregiver's health care policies. A caregiver should be willing to make reasonable adjustments or adaptations in order to accept a child with special needs into care.

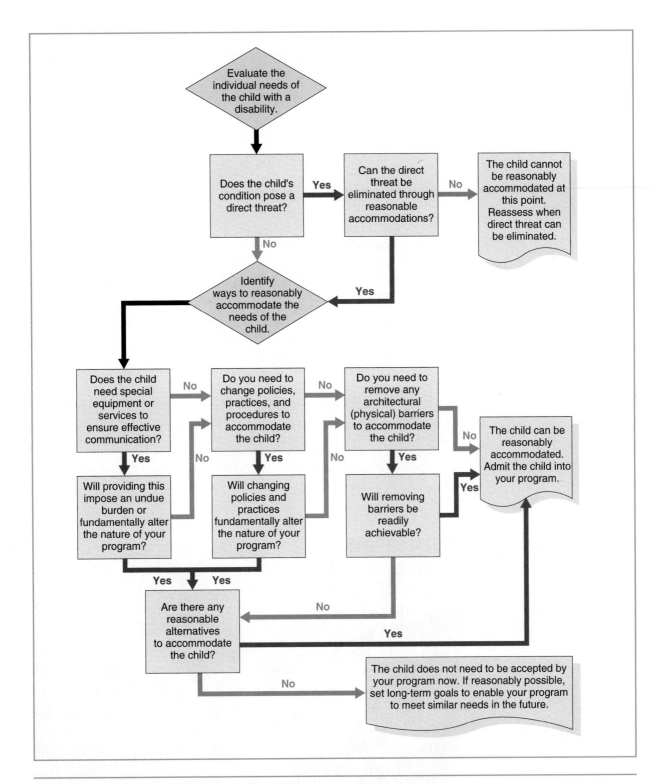

Figure 13–1

Use the flowchart to help determine whether the child care setting can accommodate a child with special needs. *(Courtesy of Child Care Law Center. © 1994 Child Care Law Center. Not to be reproduced without permission; 415–495–5498. Revised January 1994.)*

Reasonable accommodation in child care can include modifications in toys, equipment, policies, activities or some easily changeable architectural barriers. The ADA does not require any "undue burden" (significant difficulty or expense) on the part of the accommodator. See Figures 13–1 (p. 417) and 13–2 for directions in determining the effects of this law on the child care situation.

Benefits of Inclusion

The ADA legislation was created to encourage acceptance and lessen discrimination. Some children with disabilities can easily be accommodated into care, while others may require some adaptation. Some children with disabilities may be beyond the caregiver's abilities to accommodate. These decisions should never be made automatically. Rather, a decision of whether a child can be reasonably accommodated needs to be made on a case-by-case basis. Including children with special needs in regular care settings has many benefits.

For the child with special needs, child care offers opportunities to play and grow. These children make better developmental progress when mainstreamed with children with no disabilities. Their play is more advanced (Diamond, Hestenes, & O'Connor, 1994). Children with special needs learn better interaction skills and become more self-reliant.

Children with no disabilities benefit from being around children with disabilities. They can learn empathy and can see that diversity is not so scary. Those children who have disabilities are more like those who do not have disabilities than they are different (Olson, Murphy, & Olson, 1999). Opportunities for interaction between children with special needs and other children reinforces this concept. Children may actually help the adults in the environment reach a good comfort level with children with special needs. Children usually ask a few questions about a disability, then focus on the child and not the disability (Grechus, 2000). Caregivers can learn from them.

By offering a setting where children with special needs are included with children without impairments, children learn acceptance and self-esteem.

Figure 13–2

Accommodating the child with special needs

ADA Goal

To *reasonably accommodate* individuals with disabilities in order to *integrate* them into the program to the extent feasible, given *each individual's* limitations.

ADA Principles

INDIVIDUALITY
the limitations and needs of *each* individual;

REASONABLENESS
of the accommodation to the *program* and to the *individual;*

INTEGRATION
of the individual *with others* in the program.

Types of Accommodations

AUXILIARY AIDS AND SERVICES
special equipment and services to ensure effective communication;

CHANGES IN POLICIES, PRACTICES, AND PROCEDURES;

REMOVAL OF BARRIERS
architectural, arrangement of furniture and equipment, vehicular.

Reason to Deny Care

ACCOMMODATION IS UNREASONABLE, and there are no reasonable alternatives.

☐ For **auxiliary aids and services,** if accommodations pose an ***UNDUE BURDEN*** (will result in a significant difficulty or expense to the program);

☐ For **auxiliary aids and services,** or **changes in policies, practices, or procedures,** if accommodations ***FUNDAMENTALLY ALTER*** the nature of the program;

☐ For **removal of barriers,** if accommodations are ***NOT READILY ACHIEVABLE*** (cannot be done without much difficulty or expense to the program).

DIRECT THREAT
The individual's condition will pose or does pose a significant threat to the health or safety of other children or staff in the program, and there are no reasonable means of removing the threat.

Courtesy of Child Care Law Center. © 1994 Child Care Law Center. Not to be reproduced without permission; 415-495-5498. Revised January 1994.

Caregivers can also benefit by realizing that all children are more alike than different. By focusing on the child's strengths, not weaknesses, a caregiver can be more successful (NNCC, 1998). The caregiver working with a child with special needs will learn patience and self-confidence in his ability to care for the child. Children have the same basic needs, and every caregiver skill that is strengthened is shared with all the children in care.

The parents may learn that the child with special needs is more like other children than they expected, and this awareness may allow them a comfort they had not experienced before. The parents of children with special needs will receive support from the caregiver to carry on everyday life.

The Team Approach

Caring for a child with special needs should not be done without help and support. The parents who approach a caregiver about providing care for their special child should provide contact to a number of professionals who are dealing with the child. Some typical members of this group might be a physician, an audiologist, an occupational therapist, a nutritional consultant, a speech pathologist, and a counselor.

The Health Resources and Services Administration of the Maternal and Child Health Bureau are working in conjunction with Healthy People 2010 to support children with special health care needs. They suggest that care be coordinated through a medical home (see Chapter 11). They also suggest children be screened early and often so that where intervention is needed, it is immediate. A major goal is a community-based service system where families, caregivers, health practitioners, and other community resources work together for the benefit of the child. The timeline for this to be in place is by 2010 (HRSA, 2001). Olson, Murphy, and Olson (1999) suggest an inclusive community such as this empowers parents, gives caregivers the training and support they need, and provides necessary support services.

Each child has unique needs and the people who will help the child are selected to meet those needs. In the classroom additional assistance may be needed depending on the particular needs of the child. For example, a child with hearing impairment may need a sign language translator; or a child with cerebral palsy may need an occupational therapy technician to visit regularly to help the child reach his maximum potential for physical movement and coordination.

The Individuals with Disabilities Education Act was passed in 1990. This act provides special education and other services related to disabilities or developmental delay in children. It provides the means to create a team for each child with special needs. This team approach supports the child and offers everyone involved a common sense of purpose. Everyone on the team works together to help the child reach his maximum potential developmental growth level. It is essential that those involved participate in the team on an equal level.

Each professional may have ownership in part of the process, and may tend to see that part as the most significant. Each part of the team has a key ingredient to help the child. Each player on the team must contribute his unique ingredient and cooperate to make this holistic approach work.

Individualized family service plan

plan that coordinates services to meet the needs of the child with special needs and his or her family

The Individualized Family Service Plan.   The team should work together to prepare what is called an individualized family service plan (IFSP). The IFSP provides for an organized goal and delivery of services to the child and the family. The plan should be made up of measurable outcome objectives, which help guide the team to provide what the child needs. It is much easier to assess the success of the plan based on whether the objectives have been met or not.

Usually one person is designated the coordinator of the service plan. This is often the representative of the group that has financial responsibility. It can be a professional who represents the Department of Health or the Department of Education and varies from state to state.

There should be one contact person who would designate the coordinating of the care of the child with special needs in the child care situation (Allred, Briem, & Black, 1998). For a center, it might be the director or the child's primary teacher. In a family day care home it would most likely be the caregiver. In an in-home care situation, it would be the nanny who has agreed to care for the child with special needs.

If a child with special needs is accepted into child care, the caregiver should be prepared to accept the responsibilities that go along with caring for that child. The team effort continues at the child care site. All people involved in the care of the child should be privy to what is planned for the child. The IFSP should be shared and the objectives should be reviewed to identify the progress of the child. If any training is needed to provide care for the child, all members of the caregiving team should receive it. The child care that accepts a special needs team should provide the skills necessary to help the child reach maximum potential.

Supporting the Child with Special Needs

Each child with special needs has his or her own particular needs for support. Support can be offered to all children with special needs in some general ways.

The cooperative team should work together, each bringing to the system their unique expertise to benefit the child.

The caregiver and the special needs team should develop goals that match the needs and abilities of the child. The caregiver is the one who will carry out these goals on a daily basis and should be involved in the process.

The Environment. Adjusting the physical environment to adapt to whatever special needs are present is a good starting point. Removing obstacles assist children who are visually impaired or who have physical disabilities that may require a walker or a wheelchair. For children with emotional disabilities the caregiver may need to provide a quiet corner. The area needed for adaptive equipment should be a place that does not interfere with other activities.

The toys that are present in the environment should be safe and durable for the sake of all children. They should provide opportunities for learning, interaction, exploration, and engagement. Modifying toys as needed may help the child with special needs use the toy for its intended purpose. As an example, the ring in a ring toss game may need to be cut larger for the child with special needs to feel successful. After a child with special needs has been in care for a while, the caregiver may notice what types of toys that child is most likely to choose and use. Selecting new toys that have similarities will offer new challenges or things to explore. Table 13–1 includes strategies for the successful inclusion of children with differing abilities in the child care environment. Whatever goals are chosen for the IFSP should be incorporated with routine care. To help reinforce this, signs might be posted as reminders (Allred, Briem, & Black, 1998). Daily routines help reinforce the skills and competencies of a child with special needs.

Intervention. If the caregiver observes the child having difficulty playing with certain toys, games, and other materials, she may need to intervene. The caregiver may help the child learn how to play with a toy or adapt the toy to

A least restrictive environment should be provided for all children with special needs.

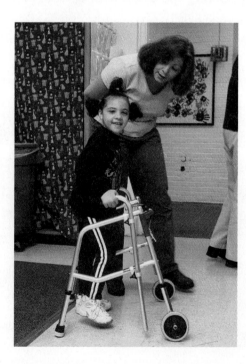

play. She may have to show the child how to use or adapt for use other play materials. Modeling appropriate play behavior may help the child learn how to be a player.

The caregiver may also encourage other children to assist the child. The children who are not disabled may need help in learning how to understand and accept the child with a disability. The caregiver may teach specific skills such as eye contact or appropriate language. The children in the group can learn to help the child with a disability to accomplish tasks on her own when capable and learn specific helping behaviors when appropriate. The caregiver can also model acceptance and show understanding. Her actions and words with the child with special needs are the most effective tools she has to teach the other children about interaction. The nondisabled child can role model and provide opportunities for positive interaction with the child with special needs.

TABLE 13–1 Strategies for Successfully Including Children with Differing Abilities	
Language delay	Expand on what child says; talk about what you are doing; model the correct usage and pronunciation instead of correcting. Provide frequent visual or concrete reinforcement. Keep directions simple; encourage child to repeat them for reinforcement. Explain new concepts or vocabulary.
Attention problems	Start with short group sessions and activities. Provide visual clues (e.g., define floor space with tape). Offer a limited number of choices. Provide positive reinforcement for sustained attention. Help child quiet down after vigorous play. Plan for transition times, including arrival and departure.
Developmental delays and learning disabilities	Allow for extra demonstrations and practice sessions. Keep all directions simple, sequenced, and organized. Offer extra help in developing fine and gross motor skills, if needed.
Emotional/social problems	Provide extra structure by limiting toys and defining physical space for activities. Allow shy child to observe group activities until ready to participate. Help aggressive child control behavior through consistent enforcement of rules. Observe dramatic play for important clues about feelings and concerns. Help child learn how to express feelings in appropriate ways.
Mental retardation	Establish realistic goals for each child. Provide frequent positive feedback. Sequence learning activities into small steps. Allow adequate time for performance and learning. Encourage cooperative play and help the child move from independent to parallel to group interaction.
Impaired hearing	Obtain child's attention when speaking; seat child close to voice or music. Repeat, rephrase as needed; alert other children to use same technique. Learn some sign language and teach signing to the entire class. Provide visual clues (e.g., pictures or . . — . . —to represent rhythm). Demonstrate new activities or tasks.

(continued)

TABLE 13–1 Strategies for Successfully Including Children with Differing Abilities *(continued)*	
Impaired vision	Ensure child's safety at all times without being overprotective.
	Provide verbal clues for activities.
	Introduce child to equipment and space verbally and through touch.
	Use a "buddy" system.
Physical disability or poor coordination	*Accessibility*
	Organize physical space to accommodate child in wheelchair.
	Use tables that accommodate wheelchairs or provide trays on wheelchairs.
	Use bolsters or other supports for floor activities.
	Provide adaptive equipment for standing.
	Learn about the availability of assistive technology and devices.
	Manual dexterity
	Use magnetic toys to facilitate small muscle activities.
	Attach bells to wrist or ankles for musical activities.
	Use adaptive scissors or spoons as needed.

Reprinted from The Creative Curriculum® for Early Childhood *(3rd Ed.) Washington, DC: © 1992, Teaching Strategies, Inc.*

Activity based

activities that promote adaptive behavior

Functional skills

skills that allow children to adapt to their environment

Generalizable skills

common skills that can be practiced and used in different settings

Caregiver intervention should be **activity based** and occur in a natural manner. Opportunities for this type of intervention occur in everyday activities. The objective of activity-based intervention is to help develop two different skills for the child with special needs (Bracer & Cripe, 1992). The first skill is referred to as **functional skill** and offers the child the opportunities to adapt to the physical and social environments in care. The child receives personal satisfaction and a sense of accomplishment that helps the child gain confidence.

The other type of skill is referred to as **generalizable skill** and transfers from one setting to another. An example of this would be a child with a speech or language disorder learning how to name a particular object. A ball is a ball whether it is at child care, at home, or in the park.

Tamara, an autistic child, was acquiring some sign language capabilities. She spent part of her morning in a special school and then went to Kate's family day care before lunch. Her favorite food was watermelon, and whenever Kate served Tamara watermelon she could sign the word *more*.

Kate felt that there was an opportunity for learning here, so she went to the special education teacher at Tamara's school and learned how to sign the word *watermelon*. She used it every opportunity she could when she gave Tamara watermelon for lunch or snack. Eventually, Tamara learned how to sign the word. Her mother was so excited when she informed Kate several days later that Tamara had asked through signing for watermelon for dinner. It was a real milestone in Tamara's limited language.

The caregiver should recognize the strengths in all children in care. The holistic approach to child care focuses on the whole child. Activities and opportunities that focus on strengths, support, and minimize difficulties should be provided. All children want to feel capable, successful, and confident. A caregiver who is aware of this can easily provide the environment a child needs.

Intervention may also include the caregiver being able to identify a child who is already in care. Some children may have special needs that have not been detected and need to be addressed. The caregiver should look for help to identify the behaviors or characteristics that appear to be a special need. Local regional centers, maternal and child health services, and other resources are helpful sources for this information.

Attention Deficit/Hyperactivity Disorder (AD/HD)

Attention Deficit/Hyperactivity Disorder is a condition that has two basic symptoms: inattention and a combination of hyperactivity and impulsive behaviors. It is estimated to affect between 2 and 9.5 percent of children worldwide (Barkley, 1998). The behavior patterns that typify AD/HD usually begin appearing between the ages of three and five years. Most children of this age are more active, more impulsive, and are less able to focus their attention than are adults. Children are also more likely to be unaware of time and future events in comparison to here and now wants and desires. If these behaviors seem to be out of hand or occurring more often in one child in comparison to others, that child may be exhibiting the beginning behaviors of AD/HD. Boys are at least three times more likely to exhibit these behaviors than girls. In fact, some studies show that boys may be as much as nine times more likely to exhibit these behaviors because they are more likely to be genetically linked to nervous system irregularities than are girls (Barkley, 1998).

Typical Attention Deficit/Hyperactivity Disorder behaviors listed by the American Psychological Association (Nadeau & Dixon, 1994) include:

- failure to give close attention to details of "work" at school or other activities
- difficulty in focusing attention in play activities or tasks

- difficulty in listening when spoken to
- apparent inability to follow through on instructions
- difficulty in transitioning from one activity to another
- avoidance of activities that call for concentrated mental activity
- apparent inability to organize himself/herself for activities or tasks
- easily distracted by stimulus in the environment
- talks when inappropriate, often interrupts conversation
- easily loses things and seems forgetful
- difficulty in awaiting his or her turn for activities
- difficulty sitting still, squirms with hands or feet
- leaves group when expected to remain
- runs around excessively at inappropriate times
- difficulty participating in quiet activities
- talks excessively
- appears to be active at all times

Not all children who have some or many of these symptoms have AD/HD. There are other conditions and problems that may cause these

(continued)

behaviors. It is very important to have the child diagnosed, so that corrective measures can take place to assist the child in coping and overcoming some of the obstacles of this condition. If a child in care is exhibiting a significant number of these behaviors, the parent should be asked to have the child screened for this condition. Careful consideration should be made in discussing this with the parents. Historically, it was believed that this condition was caused by dysfunction in the home. Another belief for the cause of AD/HD has been the child's diet being high in sugar and food additives. Recent studies have shown that neither of these items are related to AD/HD, so parents may feel relieved to know that their parenting is not the cause for the child's condition.

What has been found to be linked to AD/HD are connections and chemicals found in the brain. In new research, lower levels of attention activity and glucose have been found in the brains of people with AD/HD. Other studies have been investigating neural connections and causal factors for interruption. These factors have included genetics and prenatal exposure to chemicals, drugs, alcohol, and tobacco. Brain cells developed during pregnancy enable the transmission of neural signals from the eyes, ears, and skin and allow for the control of responses to the environment. Some research has focused in the direction of vision problems affecting information that is taken in and organized. The fact remains that it is not known what causes AD/HD.

For a child to be diagnosed, there are several areas that will be checked. First, the child has a physical exam that includes a thorough family medical history. The parents and perhaps the child's teacher are interviewed and complete a behavior rating scale. The child is observed in several situations and a variety of psychological tests may be given. If the parents cannot afford this type of diagnostic screening, the child care center should help the parent link to helpful community resources. Often, a child's school district may be of assistance, even before the child enters kindergarten. Many school districts feel that early diagnosis of conditions such as AD/HD will help them manage the situation for the school-age child.

Child care center teachers and directors can help these children even before a diagnosis is made by controlling and monitoring the environment so that the child can be more successful. Some of these helping strategies developed for the U.S. Office of Special Education, U.S. Department of Education include:

■ Anticipate events, help with transition from one event to another. This includes informing the child of the change before and during the transition.

■ Break tasks down into smaller, more manageable steps.

■ Use immediate rewards for completed tasks and positive behaviors, which should always include praise for a job well done. This might include a special chart for this child and the use of stickers to show the child how well they are doing. You might want to focus on a few tasks at a time, in order to allow the child greater success.

■ Keep this child near you when working on tasks so that you can maintain eye contact.

■ Use gestures to emphasize directions.

■ Eliminate unnecessary materials, so that the child can focus on the task at hand.

■ Provide a quiet area for the child to go to if he or she is feeling overloaded. Distractions can cause the overload and exacerbate the problem.

■ Have a special place for the child's belongings and tools and ask the parents to do the same for the child at home.

■ When speaking directly to the child, use the child's name, focus attention, including eye contact with the child, until the signal to communicate has been received by the child.

■ Communicate often with the parent as to how the child is doing in child care, and inquire about behavior at home so that a partnership in helping the child is created.

■ Establish clear rules with immediate consequences, so that the child understands that the behavior exhibited was not acceptable. This might include a time-out area for the child to go to when they cannot control their behavior.

A child-centered approach focuses on the child's individual needs.

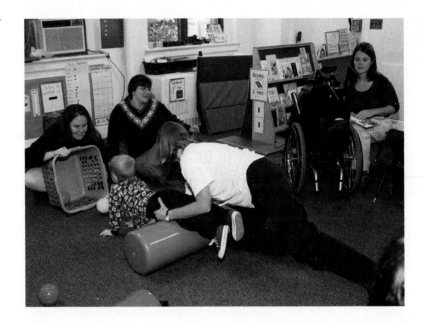

KEY CONCEPT 13.2

Children with Special Needs

Children with special needs may be included in child care. The Americans with Disabilities Act discusses public accommodations. This act may affect a child care site. If children with disabilities are included, the caregiver should work as part of a team and help to support the child with special needs. The caregiver should provide a safe, protective environment and should also do whatever possible to help challenge the child. When intervention is necessary, the caregiver should provide it or have another child help. Children with disabilities generally thrive in an environment that includes children from all backgrounds and capabilities.

Chronic illnesses

medical conditions requiring continuous treatment

13.3 Children with Chronic Illnesses

Chronic illnesses or conditions may affect more than 24 percent of the population under the age of eighteen years (CSG, 2002; Aronson, 2000). A chronic illness requires continued treatment. The range of the condition can be from mild to severe. Caregivers are most likely to be confronted with children who have a mild or moderate form of a chronic illness.

Each chronic illness has its own unique causes, indicators, and medical responses. Most chronic illnesses have organizations that can provide the caregiver with a wealth of resources. The following chronic illnesses are covered in this text: allergies, asthma, diabetes mellitus, HIV, seizure disorders, and sickle cell anemia. These are the most common chronic illnesses that may be found in child care. Whatever chronic condition presents itself, the caregiver should gather as much information and resources on the condition as possible

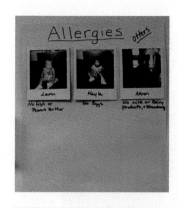

Caregivers need to be aware of allergies or potential allergies for all children in their care.

(Alexander, 1999). Know what constitutes an emergency for that condition and be prepared to act in an emergency. Practice for that emergency can reduce stress and help actions if that emergency occurs.

The following information should help a caregiver provide care for a child in care who has one of these chronic illnesses. Each chronic illness description provides the definition, significance, and how the disease occurs. This information gives the caregiver a background in order to understand the rest of the table. The remaining information gives the caregiver some triggers, identifiers, and strategies for care of the child who may have the chronic illness. It is important to note that some states do not allow child caregivers to administer medication. If this is the case, a health professional should be close by if help is needed, or the family of a child with chronic illness should make provisions for emergencies.

Allergies

Definition.　An allergy is a heightened response to a substance.

Significance.　Some children have known allergies; many others may have undiagnosed allergies.

How Does It Occur?　The person who is allergic to a substance is exposed to it by ingestion, touch, or breathing.

Triggers
substances or conditions that activate a response

When Does It Occur?　It occurs when the person is exposed to a substance that causes the response. Common allergy **triggers** are:

■ foods such as peanut butter, nuts, wheat, chocolate, milk, fish, and citrus

■ pollen from flowers, grasses, hay, weeds, or trees

■ mold spores

■ dust

■ animal fur, feathers, or dander; this may be on a live animal, feathers in a comforter, or an animal skin on a wall

■ insects including stings or parts from dead insects like cockroaches

Identifiers of Reaction.　Allergic reaction may take the form of sneezing, hay fever, asthma, swelling/hives, eczema, or cold-like symptoms.

Child Care Support.　Be alert to the signs of allergic reactions of children in care. Discuss any allergies with parents and avoid those triggers that are observed to cause a response. For more serious allergic reactions, the child may have medication that will need to be administered.

Asthma

Definition.　Asthma occurs when there is a narrowing of the small airways in the lungs called bronchi and bronchioles. Muscles around the airways tighten and when mucus clogs these airways, breathing difficulty results.

Significance.   Approximately 12 million people have asthma, more than half of whom are children (Frieman & Settle, 1994).

How Does It Occur?   Most asthmatics have persistent bronchial irritation. Environmental irritants trigger reactions that lead to an attack or episode.

When Does It Occur?   The asthma episode or attack may occur if the child is exposed to one or more of the following triggers:

- the same items found on the allergy list
- household products—vapors, deodorants, sprays, cleaning solvents, paints
- dust from clothes, broom, furniture, or filters on furnaces and air conditioners
- weather—humidity, cold, wind
- exercise—overexertion
- infections such as colds, bronchitis, or other viruses
- smoke—cigarette, pipe, or cigar
- strong emotions—fear, laughing, crying, anger
- aspirin
- at the end of the day when tired, lying down and mucus accumulates

Identifiers of Reaction.   Tightening of airways and muscles cause difficulty breathing. Wheezing, coughing, and spitting up mucus may also occur.

Child Care Support.   Be aware of asthmatic reactions especially after exercise, emotional display, or exposure to allergens. The caregiver should keep the child free from infection by providing a healthy, safe environment. If an episode does occur, the caregiver should make sure the child is sitting up and is calm, and encourage the child to focus on slow, deep breathing. Follow procedures if medication should be given.

Diabetes Mellitus

Definition.   Diabetes mellitus occurs when insulin is not produced in the pancreas at the rate the body needs it. Insulin is involved in the process that stores and uses glucose for energy. There are two types of diabetes: type I, which is insulin dependent, and type II, which is noninsulin dependent.

Significance.   Type I diabetes is often referred to as juvenile onset diabetes and is the most common type for children. Approximately 127,000 American children have type I diabetes (Zamani, 2001a). This type of diabetes requires insulin injections at least twice daily. Food and exercise levels must be controlled, and blood sugar needs to be tested several times throughout the day.

How Does It Occur?   Since adequate insulin is missing, the amount of glucose produced by the body cannot absorb the excess glucose. Glucose levels: (1) build in the blood and spill into the urine; (2) sugar not used for energy is stored in fats and when broken down the resulting chemicals, ketones, can poison the blood if they are allowed to accumulate.

When Does It Occur?   Diabetes reaction is triggered when there is:

- too much exercise
- not enough food
- too much sugar
- too much insulin

Identifiers of Reaction.   Lack of insulin can cause numerous reactions. Among them are:

- disorientation, confusion, blurred vision
- excessive sweating
- dizziness, poor coordination
- irritability, behavior change
- excessive thirst or sudden hunger
- coma

Child Care Support.   The caregiver will need to be educated in what to watch for when caring for a diabetic child. Glucose levels are affected by food and exercise so those activities should be monitored. If several of the preceding indicators are present, the caregiver may need to provide glucose in the form of sugar, such as ½ cup orange juice or soda, 1 graham cracker, or several sugar cubes. Follow the procedures the caregiver has worked out with the parent. If there is no improvement in the condition the caregiver should call the parent or physician.

HIV/AIDS

Definition.   Human immunodeficiency virus is a viral infection that threatens the immune system's ability to fight off infection. It can lead to acquired immunodeficiency syndrome (AIDS), which is a combination of illnesses that may become life threatening.

Significance.   AIDS is listed as the seventh leading cause of death for children (NPFHRC, 1997).

How Does It Occur?   The methods of transmission that affects children are: in utero, blood from their mothers who have HIV; breast milk from HIV positive mother; sexual abuse by a person with AIDS; and exposure to blood or blood products from an infected person through a cut or sore.

When Does It Occur?   Exposure to infection or normal childhood diseases can trigger an immunosuppressed response. Chicken pox is especially dangerous.

Identifiers of Reaction.   Some symptoms found in children with HIV/AIDS are:

- multiple bacterial infections
- enlarged spleen and liver
- abnormal growth patterns
- frequent illnesses

Child Care Support.   There are two areas of support that a caregiver needs to give. The first area is protecting the child with HIV/AIDS from exposure to childhood diseases, especially chicken pox. To protect all other children and caregivers from HIV/AIDS, universal precautions should be followed. These include hand washing and sanitary procedures, and wearing gloves when in contact with blood or other bodily fluids. Everyone with sores, scratches, or lesions should keep them covered. The caregiver should also attempt to prevent and handle immediately any biting by any child in care.

Children with HIV/AIDS in Child Care

Approximately 1,800 children are born with HIV each year in the United States (Gorman, 1994). Worldwide, there are 1,000 children born with HIV each day. AIDS is listed as the seventh leading cause of death of children in the United States. Minority children represent a disproportionate number of the children who have HIV/AIDS (NPFHRC, 1997).

It is estimated that at a point in every teacher's career he or she will have a child with AIDS in the classroom (Jessee, Nagy, & Poteet-Johnson, 1993). Caregivers must realize that children with HIV/AIDS may be present in a number of child care situations. A caregiver may be taking care of a child infected with HIV and not know it (Black, 1999). These children need special care, as well as special consideration. There is a great deal of controversy, fear, and lack of understanding about children who may be infected with HIV/AIDS (Black, 1999). A number of people are not educated about how the virus spreads (see HIV/AIDS in this chapter). Some people feel casual contact is a way for children with this disease to spread the disease. Others may be rightfully concerned about child biting in a child care environment. Regardless of the confusion and concern, a number of these children will filter into child care. Children with HIV infection or the AIDS virus may exhibit some developmental factors that may need special considerations from child caregivers. A resource manual for Head Start (National Pediatric HIV Resource Center, 1992) caregivers relates the following changes that may be noted:

Social—increased activity, irritability, and confusion.

Cognitive—decrease in intelligence, memory, or academic skills. Children may also exhibit decreases in previously displayed motor skills, such as the ability to hold a crayon or assemble puzzles.

Physical—clumsiness, staggering walk, and inability to perform usual physical tasks. Illness or infection may appear without warning.

Black (1999) reports that children need help coping with stressful events due to chronic illness, and problems with role transitions due to changes in their condition. Children with HIV/AIDS may also exhibit problems with appetite and difficulty with eating.

Caregivers need to adapt to the HIV/AIDS of children in care taking into consideration the stress and coping mechanisms that will be needed. Caregivers will need to view the situation from the ecological perspective (Lasar & Maldonado, 1994). There is also the ethical dilemma of caregiver confidentiality. HIV/AIDS may bring up personal values, prejudices, and beliefs. Disclosure involves the rights of the community dealing with a public health issue. Issues that surround this should be discussed, should it become known that a child in care or a parent or other relative has HIV or AIDS.

Caregivers should remember to always use universal sanitary precautions associated with this disease. Caregivers should apply strategies used with children with chronic illnesses as well as those for special needs. If a caregiver finds herself caring for a child with AIDS, extra reading and education on the subject might be helpful.

Seizure Disorders

Definition.   Seizure disorders is another term for epilepsy. Twenty types of seizure disorders may occur when there is temporary overactivity in the electrical impulses in the brain.

Significance.   One in every 100 persons has some form of seizure disorder on the continuum from rare to frequent displays.

How Does It Occur?   Seizure disorder can result from head injuries, infections, high fevers, lead poisoning, or may be hereditary.

When Does It Happen?   Possible triggers include:

- fast rising fevers
- fatigue
- disorientation from outside source such as flashing lights or rapid movement

Identifiers of Reaction.   Because there are twenty different types of seizure disorders the reaction range is wide. The following demonstrates the range:

- dazed behavior
- unusual sleepiness and irritability
- unexplained clumsiness, falls
- feeling strange, disoriented
- rapid eye movements, eyes rolling up
- head appears to move involuntarily
- involuntary, unnatural movements of body
- unconsciousness, drooling at the mouth

Child Care Support.   The first thing a caregiver should do is to become familiar with the type of disorder the child has and how to handle the reaction of that disorder. When the reaction occurs, remain calm. If a child is having a seizure that includes unconsciousness place the child on the floor and turn him on his side. Place something soft under the child's head. Patiently wait until the seizure has finished and help the child in the transition to normal activity. If the seizure lasts more than 10 minutes, call the parents or physician.

Sickle Cell Anemia

Definition.   Sickle cell anemia is a hereditary disease that affects the red blood cells. It is most often found in African American children and young adults.

Significance.   Sickle cell anemia occurs in one out of 400 African Americans.

How Does It Occur?   An abnormality in the red blood cells causes them to change shape and decrease the oxygen that they deliver to all parts of the body. When this causes blockage to tissues of an organ or joint, this leads to pain and may be damaging to the tissues in that location.

When Does It Happen?   Sickle cell anemia can be triggered by:

■ fatigue

■ overexertion from exercise

■ stress

Identifiers of Reaction.   There may be no apparent triggers. When it happens there may be intense pain in arms, legs, back, and chest.

Child Care Support.   A caregiver should be aware of the disease and watch the child for shortness of breath and fatigue. If a crisis occurs, the caregiver should remain calm, call the parents, and support the child until he is picked up. A preventive measure would be to protect the child from infection by offering a sanitary environment.

Working as a Team

Many of the issues that occur when caring for a child with a chronic illness are similar to those of a child with special needs. Some children with a chronic illness qualify as children with special needs under the ADA. Regardless of whether or not the child qualifies, using the strategies developed for children with special needs will help the caregiver meet most of the needs of the chronically ill child.

The team for a chronically ill child may only consist of the parent, the physician, and the caregiver. This supports the idea of a "medical home" for the child. The caregiver needs to ask questions and access any other resources available to help support the care for the child. The caregiver should have a plan for care of each child with a chronic illness if a reactive or crisis episode should occur. It is vital that the caregiver learn to recognize and identify reactions that may lead to crisis. She must also understand what to do in terms of a crisis situation. This includes understanding what constitutes an emergency needing outside help. The caregiver who possesses the knowledge of how to handle a crisis can remain calm and do what needs to be done.

KEY CONCEPT 13.3

Chronically Ill Children

Many caregivers will find themselves caring for one or more children with a chronic illness. A caregiver needs general knowledge of the chronic illness—especially the reactions leading to a crisis episode. She should also have understanding of what to do should this occur. Many of the strategies used for the child with special needs can be applied to the child with a chronic illness.

13.4 Children with Stress

Children today are dealing with many stressful events and life changes. Losses, events, or lifestyles that make the child feel she has no control may cause stress. Today, it appears that children have less time to relax and more time involved in some sort of planned activity (McCarthy, 2001). Some of the events or lifestyles that may produce stress in a child are listed in Table 13–2.

TABLE 13–2 Stressors in a Child's Life
• Divorce/single parent family/stepfamily adjustments
• Birth of a sibling
• Separation anxiety
• Loss (death) of a loved one or pet
• Too many scheduled activities
• A new care situation or being placed in care for the first time
• A friend leaves child care
• Lack of bonding or attachment
• Financial problems at home
• Fears, real or imagined
• Special needs or chronic illness
• Victim of child abuse
• Drug abuse in the home
• Frequent relocation
• Cultural considerations, including language and immigration
• Observing violence in the home, neighborhood, or other real situation
• Poverty
• Homelessness (see Reality Check: Poverty and Childhood p. 321)
• Peer pressure
• Too little privacy

This child may react differently to stress in her life than other children.

Stress may exhibit itself in aggressive behavior.

Children's reaction to stress may be visible in physical, emotional, or behavioral responses. Children have a limited understanding and a good imagination. When life feels out of control the child may magnify the significance of the stressor. Children do not have the same coping skills as an adult, so their reaction to stress may be somewhat different.

Children who react physically to stress may have headaches, stomachaches, or bouts of diarrhea. They may not have their regular appetites and may either not eat, or constantly be eating. Children who have normal language may have some language difficulties, such as rapid speech or stuttering. Children with allergies or asthma may have reactions that appear more often.

The emotional reaction to stress can be expressed in a number of ways. The spectra of behaviors range from regressive to aggressive. Children may show regressive behaviors in forms such as withdrawing or having toileting accidents. Children may become clingy, and too dependent. They may be unable to make simple decisions such as with what and whom to play. Children who are stressed may not laugh or smile and may cry more than usual. They may appear to escape into fantasy by constantly daydreaming or watching television. Children may appear fearful and nervous. Children may also become depressed. Five percent of children show signs of depression (Herbst, 1999).

Aggressive emotional behaviors are exhibited by acting out. This might range from throwing a tantrum to more violent behavior. Stressed children may bite or hit other children or adults. Children who use aggression to cope with stress may vandalize toys, equipment, or art of their own or others. They might have difficulty with social interactions. Children under stress may become easily frustrated and use colorful language to express their anger.

Regardless of how it is expressed, caregivers need to be alert to the fact that stress can be an important factor in children's behavior. If a child abruptly changes behavior, or is a constant source of regressive or aggressive behavior, stress may be a factor. The best way for the caregiver to help the child is to structure the environment so it supports the child. The environment should be protective and prevent more stress to the child. Robinson and Rotter (1991)

The caregiver and parent should always work together for the benefit of the child.

proposed three coping skills for adults to provide to children. These include giving the child security, a sense of control, and the feeling of self-worth to help prepare the child to cope with stress and fears.

Providing structure through a predictable routine allows the child the comfort of understanding what comes next. The caregiver can improve the quality of interaction with children by being consistent and reliable. The caregiver who forms an attachment to children helps them learn to trust the caregiver and the care environment. This gives some children a feeling of safety and stability that they may not otherwise have.

The caregiver can provide children under stress a sense of security in other ways. Some children under stress may need a quiet place to go to be free of stimulation. Providing a corner of a room that is not decorated and has a comfortable place to sit helps achieve this. Sometimes going from one activity to another can cause a child more stress. The caregiver can help children in their transition from one activity to another to reduce stress.

The caregiver also needs to help children under stress learn to identify and express their emotions. Role modeling, dramatic play, reading books, and discussions with the child help. A caregiver can support children by redirecting their anger, frustration, and aggression. Activities such as rocking horses, swings, and punching bags can alleviate anger. Water play and sand play are soothing and may help dissipate anger. A withdrawn child can be stimulated to act out emotions through play. A child who feels more in control will be able to cope with stress under other situations.

A caregiver who listens to children and responds with positive action and words allows them the opportunity to express problems and get in touch with feelings. The caregiver should reinforce positive behaviors and reward them with at least a positive comment. A caregiver who allows children choices where appropriate can help teach decision-making and problem-solving skills. Those actions show children that the caregiver respects them, and children who feel respected have a sense of self-worth.

The team approach of the caregiver and a parent working together can also be helpful with stress. A parent may be a source of stress for the child and may choose not to participate, although most parents will be cooperative. Some parents who are under stress themselves may welcome the caregiver's help. The caregiver can set up times with the parent to discuss the child. The caregiver should show the family respect and acknowledge their feelings. Being consistent and predictable in all dealings with the parent can build trust. The caregiver can also provide opportunities for the parent under stress to find additional help through counseling.

KEY CONCEPT 13.4

Children with Stress

Stress can have an effect on a child. It can cause physical, emotional, and behavioral difficulties. The caregiver needs to acknowledge stressors in a child's life and identify the reactions. Coping skills can be taught by the caregiver to provide a sense of security, control, and self-worth. The caregiver and parent can team up to help alleviate the child's stress.

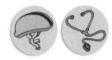

13.5 Working with Children from Drug-Abusing Families

It is estimated that 6 million women of childbearing age abuse drugs on a regular basis (Kelley, 1992). As many as 24 percent of children in this country may have been prenatally exposed to harmful substances (NIDA, 1998). Prenatal exposure to drugs can cause developmental difficulties in several areas:

- Children may be unable to organize their own play.
- Sporadic mastery is common.
- Learning strategies and problem solving may be hindered by a lack of organization of inner states.
- Communication and language development may be impaired by delayed acquisition of words and gestures, inability to express feelings, and speech difficulties.
- Difficulty with motor skills may be exhibited in both gross and fine motor skills.
- Acquiring a sense of self may be hampered by lack of attachment, inconsistent or negligent care.

All of these vulnerabilities can be assessed through observation and the use of assessment tools. A child who has any one of these difficulties can be very challenging for the caregiver. It would be helpful for the caregiver to work with the family. However, these families may present an even greater challenge. The families may be represented in several ways:

- the recovering family, who may be feeling vulnerable
- the addicted family living in chaos, who may be emotionally unavailable or negligent
- the foster family or relative caregiver, who may feel overwhelmed

Distrust

Unhappiness

Denial

Irritability

Loss of interest

Self-defense

Depression

Self-neglect

Loss of self-respect

Dishonesty

Isolation

Indefinable fears

Hostility

Blames others

Escape

Chronic depression

Increased drug use

Suicide attempts or admits defeat

Bottoming out and into recovery or death

Figure 13–3

Downward Spiral of Addiction

The Recovering Family

The recovering family may be in or out of a recovery program. The parent or parents may have few coping skills. The parents may be developmentally "frozen" at the stage they were in their own development when they began abusing drugs. They may be emotionally unavailable and struggling with attachment issues. They may be struggling to remain clean. The environment may be chaotic.

The Actively Abusing Family

The addictive family brings a whole series of problems. As people who abuse drugs go through the cycle of abuse, there is a tendency to get hostile when dealing with people in authority. Figure 13–3 shows the feelings that the downward spiral of addiction can cause in an active drug-using family.

Drug-abusing families live in an extremely chaotic environment. Children from this environment may have difficulty getting their physical needs met. There may not be food or clean clothes available for them. They may suffer great stress from negligent or inconsistent care at home. It is estimated that 675,000 children per year are maltreated or neglected by a drug abusive family caretaker (Kelley, 1992).

It is very difficult for a child to be able to count on a drug-abusing parent to meet the child's needs. Behavioral problems with a child may directly relate to active drug use in the home (Delaney-Black et al., 2000). An active substance abuser may have sudden mood swings that display the person as being either really up or really down and depressed. It is difficult to predict if the person will show up when expected to for appointments, including bringing the child to care. An addict may lose track of time or suffer from a hangover. Another common characteristic of an active abuser is the avoidance of contact with concerned persons. "Isolation is the core of addiction" ("The Battlefield," 1993, p. 37). A mother who is actively abusing drugs may have difficulty forming a bond of trust with anyone and may be emotionally unavailable to the child or the caregiver. Abusing families put their children at risk. They may fear that if help is sought, the child may be removed from the home. The family addictive system may discourage any behavior changes.

The Foster Family

Foster families or families where the caretaker is a relative may have their own difficulties. Legal custody of the child may be in flux. The parents may still have legal custody. The circumstances that led the child to this caretaker situation may have an effect on the caretakers. They may be sad, angry, depressed, or overwhelmed. If the parent of the child is around and wants to participate in the child's life, that can cause difficulties. There may be legal boundaries that have been or need to be mandated. The caregiver will need to be aware of this or any other legal custody issues. Caregivers can also assist these families by recognizing that extra help may be needed both at the center and in the home. Caregivers can help the family access social services to support them through the difficulties they may encounter.

Establishing a Relationship with the Family

Establishing a relationship with the family is a crucial step in the intervention process to help a child from a drug-abusing family. Providing a safe and secure environment for the parent and family is almost as critical as providing that type of care for the child. As difficult as it may be, the caregiver should try to establish communication with the parent concerning the child. The caregiver should be consistent and predictable in this relationship, and use cultural sensitivity if applicable. The caregiver who tries to show respect to the family is more likely to be accepted by them.

Many caregivers try to avoid difficult situations involving parents. They may also avoid difficult parents (Boutte, Keepler, Tyler, & Terry, 1992). Children in this situation need the support of the caregiver. The caregiver should avoid arguing with the parent, getting angry, being taken in by the parents defensiveness and becoming an enabler. The caregiver should model good coping skills, be flexible, remain calm and nonjudgmental, and be culturally competent. It might help the caregiver to practice possible parent responses and be prepared to answer them. If none of these suggestions work, respect the limitations of your abilities (Gonzalez-Mena & Stonehouse, 2000). You may need outside help in the form of a counselor or drug counselor in your area.

Working with the Children

The caregiver needs to provide a safe and protective environment. Good child development techniques are essential. A child at risk can be a challenge. The caregiver may need to add some protective and facilitative factors to her skills. The best thing that the caregiver can do is to provide consistent, predictable, and reliable care. These measures can improve the quality of interaction with the child and help to form an attachment bond.

The child at risk may need to be protected from overstimulation. The caregiver can help the child by creating a quiet, safe place to retreat. Transition times may stress the child at risk. The caregiver can provide structure and clear limits to help make the transition more manageable. These measures also allow the child to understand boundaries and acceptable behaviors. Recent studies have shown that if the child at risk is able to find someone with whom to develop a secure attachment, that child is likely to be able to overcome nonmedical, behavioral, and developmental difficulties (Groves et al., 2000). A child at risk from a drug environment will have to find reliable bonds with other people. The caregiver who helps a child in this way may give the child the tools needed to find other adults to rely on.

If the situation at home is intolerable, the caregiver may have to report the situation to the local Child Protective Services (CPS) office. If the child or children are removed from the drug environment, it is possible that CPS will work with the foster family or relative caring for the children to continue in the child care situation. The consistency of the caregiver and the caregiving situation will be a very important source of support to the child.

KEY CONCEPT 13.5

Children from Drug-Abusing Families

Many caregivers may find themselves working with children from drug-abusing families. They should learn to recognize the indicators for this condition. Caregivers who understand the family situation are more likely to be able to help. Families may be in recovery, may be active abusers, or may be a foster family that has complex issues to address. Caregivers can work more productively by developing good communication and trust with these families and their children.

13.6 Implications for Caregivers

The caregiver needs to understand that some children in care may have special circumstances that may be challenging. Children with special needs or chronic illnesses may be included in care. Some children may be suffering from a great deal of stress in their lives. Children may come from drug-abusing families with chaotic conditions in their lives. The caregiver needs to use tools such as education, supervision, and cultural competence to help these children and their families by providing an environment that will support the safety, nutrition, and health of these children.

Education

When children with special needs are included in care some modifications may need to be made in the child care environment. These may include toys, equipment, or nutritional requirements. Caregiver intervention may be needed to help the child interact and engage in exploration of the environment. The caregiver may need to use natural situations for activity-based learning. All of these situations require caregiver knowledge and awareness. The caregiver may need special training by the other IFSP team members in order to be fully able to support the child.

Children who are not disabled may need some instruction on how to act with a disabled child. Encouraging interaction may provide the best education. Parents of nondisabled children may also need education to help them understand the benefits of inclusion. Cultural competence is important with this issue because other cultures have different reactions to disabilities.

Many of the same strategies used for child abuse and children with special needs can be applied to children with chronic illnesses. Recognition of reactions that bring on crisis episodes may help to prevent them, and preparation for crisis episodes can help to minimize them. Teaching all children about the chronic disease(s) present in care can offer even more protection and prevention. This also provides understanding and the appreciation of diversity. Parents can be encouraged to appreciate how similar the chronically ill child is to the other children in care rather than to focus on the child's differences from other children.

The caregiver can use similar strategies when dealing with children who are experiencing stress in their lives. Recognizing stressors and identifying behaviors help the caregiver establish the presence of stress. Offering the child with stress skills that will help him to cope can alleviate stress and promote

Katy went to special school that mainstreamed healthy children with children with chronic diseases. Both she and her friend, Paul, had diabetes that required urine testing and shots of insulin as needed. Many of the other children watched as Katy and Paul and their caregiver, Charles, tested the urine to find out the condition of each of their systems for insulin. This process evolved into an activity for all the children. They would all gather around and most could identify what the insulin test result was. They often watched Katy and Paul get shots. Everyone was involved so there was nothing really "different" about Katy and Paul that the other children considered to be a problem.

well-being. Teaching children about stress and helping them learn to communicate offer a measure of protection. Providing resources for the parents may be stress reducing for the whole family.

Those same skills can be applied to children who come from drug-abusing families, although the caregiver may need more coping skills to work with these families. Knowledge of the family situation, such as whether drug abuse is active or the family is in recovery will help the caregiver understand which skills to employ.

It is important for the caregiver to remember that they are not alone in dealing with any of these issues. Outside support and resources are available from local and national organizations and agencies. Child care resource and referral services might be a good source of support. Another source would be professionals in the community who are often willing to help by discussing issues and solutions. Local child care organizations can offer support and may even have a support network in place.

Cultural Competence

If the child with special needs is from a different cultural background, the caregiver may need an additional tool, which is cultural competence. Many cultures have the tendency to either ignore or deny that a child has a problem. Other

Inclusion of children with special needs has many benefits.

cultures may focus on the problem to such a degree that it becomes an obsession. Values, childrearing practices, family roles, and outside support may all have an effect on how the disability is perceived. State departments of maternal and child health, departments of social services, and regional centers may be good resources for this information. The reactions and tendencies on the part of families may be equally true of chronically ill children.

Cultural competence may also be necessary for children with stress and their families. For some children, the stress may be a direct result of cultural differences and adjustment to a new environment. This may cause the parents more stress than the child. The caregiver who offers the culturally diverse family an opportunity to discuss the child's stress may help the parents reduce their own. The caregiver may help reduce family stress by providing resources for information on the difficulties they may be experiencing.

Drug-abusing families from different cultural backgrounds may look at the drug abuse differently than the caregiver. In some cultures drug abuse has less social stigma attached to it. Caregivers may need extra sensitivity when approaching these families.

Supervision

The caregiver who cares for a child with special needs, a chronically ill child, a child under a great deal of stress, or a child from drug-abusing families must supervise the child care environment, because these children are more at risk for health and safety issues as well as nutritional well-being. It is up to the caregiver to observe these children with a holistic approach.

The caregiver may need to observe more often and make certain that the special needs are met, that the health of the chronically ill child is assessed, and that a child under stress or from a chaotic family environment is offered relief through supportive behaviors.

Medication and nutritional needs must be maintained through careful supervision. Timing and frequency of medication for a child with special needs or a chronically ill child may be critical. These needs may have to be met by an outside source if the caregiver lives in a state where she is not allowed to offer medication. Nutritional needs may also be significant. In addition, the caregiver will need to supervise any team created for a child from the child care viewpoint in order to reinforce that child's goals.

KEY CONCEPT 13.6

Implications for Caregivers

A caregiver may take care of children who have special needs, chronic illness, significant stress, or come from chaotic environments. These children need a holistic approach to their care. The tools that the child caregiver will use are education, cultural competence, and supervision. The caregiver needs a knowledge base for these. Children who do not have these conditions may need to be taught to understand and support the other children who do. Cultural competence needs to be practiced because of the actions and reactions of other cultures to children who are disabled or ill. Supervision will provide an environment that offers maximum well-being for the children.

CHAPTER SUMMARY

Some children in care have special issues in their lives that will affect caregiving. Four issues that are the most likely to affect the caregiver and the child care site are inclusion of children with special needs, children with chronic illnesses, children who are suffering from stress in their lives, and children who come from drug-abusing families.

If children with disabilities are included the caregiver should work as part of a team and help support the child with special needs. Children with disabilities generally thrive in an environment that includes children from all backgrounds and capabilities.

Many caregivers will find themselves caring for one or more children with a chronic illness. A caregiver needs general knowledge of the chronic illness, the reactions leading to crisis episodes, and how to deal with the crisis.

Stress can cause physical, emotional, and behavioral difficulties in children. The caregiver needs to acknowledge stressors in children's lives, identify common reactions, and provide coping skills.

Caregivers need to be prepared to offer stability and support to children who may come from chaotic environments due to drug abuse. It is essential that they understand how to work with the families as well as the children. Caregivers are most effective in meeting children's needs when they use a holistic approach, including education, cultural competence, and supervision.

TO GO BEYOND

In this section you will find a number of activities that you can use to apply and improve your knowledge of this chapter. There are also thorough Online Resources that accompany this text that can be found at http://www.early childed.delmar.com/resources/robertson/index.html. Included on this site are chapter practice quizzes, PowerPoint outlines, Web links, a discussion forum, and various other activities to help you better understand the material in this chapter. This site is updated regularly so check back often to receive the latest information about the subjects in this chapter.

Chapter Review Critical Thinking Applications

1. How does the Americans with Disabilities Act impact child care? Describe the process of accommodating children with disabilities.

2. Discuss the presence of children with chronic illnesses in child care. Should a caregiver have more qualifications to work with these children?

3. Examine children's stress and situations that might cause the stress. What supportive measures can caregivers provide to help alleviate some of the stress children experience?

As an Individual

1. Research children's books that deal with the issues in this chapter. Create a list of 10 "special subjects" books and report to class on one of these books. These lists will be collated, duplicated, and distributed to the entire class.

2. Examine how individualized family service plans (IFSP) are handled in your community. List the agencies that handle the IFSP and deliver the services needed for the family and the child with special needs. Do these agencies offer any type of support to child caregivers who care for the child with special needs?

3. Find out what type of support that is available to help parents with a drug problem in your community. Be prepared to report and discuss this in class.

As a Group

1. Divide the class into small groups and send them into the community to gather information on what help is available for children with special needs. Collate the information, distribute to class, and discuss your findings. Was there any specific help available for caregivers of these children?

2. Discuss how cultural differences might impact working with families who have children with special needs or chronic illnesses. List measures that would help the caregiver bridge these differences.

3. In small groups of four or five, create a policy for emergency due to a chronic illness or special need. Evaluate what extra support might be needed for this type of an emergency.

4. Discuss AD/HD and how a child with this condition might impact child care. What measures could a caregiver use to support a child with AD/HD?

5. Examine the downward spiral of addiction and how it might effect families. Assign each small group a portion of that list. Create several scenarios where each behavior might be found. Role play these scenarios. Come back as a large group and report how the exercise might have helped the students to better understand these behaviors.

CHAPTER REFERENCES

Alexander, L. (1999). Chronic conditions in the classroom. *Healthy Child Care, 2*(5). Retrieved May 15, 2002, from http://www.healthychild.net/Articles.

Allred, K., Briem, R., & Black, S. (1998). Collaboratively addressing needs of young children with disabilities. *Young Children, 53*(5), 32–35.

Aronson, S. (2000, September). Updates on a new vaccine, TB screening and inclusion of children with special needs. *Child Care Information Exchange,* 78–80.

Barkley, R. (1998). *Attention-deficit hyperactivity disorder: A handobok for diagnosis and treatment.* New York: Guilford Press.

The Battlefield of addiction. (1993, July 19). *Maclean's.* Special report. 36–39.

Black, S. (1999). HIV/AIDS in early childhood centers: The ethical dilemma of confidentiality versus disclosure. *Young Children, 54*(2), 39–45.

Boutte, G., Keepler, D., Tyler, V., & Terry, B. (1992). Effective techniques for involving "difficult" parents. *Young Children, 47*(3), 19–23.

Bracer, D., & Cripe, J. (1992) *An activity based approach to early intervention.* Baltimore: Paul H. Brooks.

ChildStats.gov (CSG). (2002). America's children: Key national indicators of well-being, 2001. Retrieved May 1, 2002, from http://www.childstats.gov/americaschildren.

Delaney-Black, V., Covington, C., Templin, T., Ager, J., Nordstrom-Klee, B., Martier, S., Leddick, L., Czerwinski, R., & Sokol, R. (2000). Teacher-assessed behavior of children prenatally exposed to cocaine. *Pediatrics, 106*(4), 782–791.

Diamond, K., Hestenes, L., & O'Connor, C. (1994). Integrating children with disabilities in preschool: Problems and promise. *Young Children, 49,* 68–79.

Frieman, B., & Settle, J. (1994). What the classroom teacher needs to know about children with chronic medical problems. *Childhood Education, 70*(4), 196–201.

Gonzalez-Mena, J., & Stonehouse, A. (2000, January). High-maintenance parents. *Child Care Information Exchange,* 10–12.

Gorman, C. (1994, July 4). Women, kids and AIDS. *Time Magazine,* 60.

Grechus, M. (2000). Who's challenged? Children with special needs or their caregivers? *Healthy Child Care, 3*(3). Retrieved May 15, 2002, from http://www.healthychild.net/Articles.

Groves, B., Lieberman, A., Osofsky, J., & Fenichel, E. (2000, April/May). Protecting young children in violent environments: A framework to build on. *Zero to Three,* 5.

Health Resources and Services Administration (HRSA). (2001). *Children and youth with special health care needs: A 10-year action plan to accompany Healthy People 2010.* Washington, DC: Maternal and Child Health Bureau.

Herbst, A. (1999, September). What's wrong with our children? *Parents Magazine,* 108–115.

Jessee, P., Nagy, M., & Poteet-Johnson, D. (1993). Children with AIDS. *Childhood Education, 70*(1), 10–14.

Kelley, S. (1992). Parent stress and child maltreatment in drug-exposed children. *Child Abuse and Neglect, 16,* 317–328.

Lasar, S., & Maldonado, Y. (1994). Infants and young children with HIV infection: Service delivery considerations for family support. *Infants and Young Children, 49*(4), 70–81.

McCarthy, L. (2001, March). Raising a stress-free child. *Parenting Magazine,* 66–70.

Nadeau, K., & Dixon, E. (1997). Learning to slow down and pay attention: A book for kids about ADD. Washington, DC: ADA-Magination Press.

National Institute on Drug Abuse (NIDA). (1998). Pregnancy and drug use trends. National Institutes of Health. Retrieved May 15, 2002, from http://www.nida.nih.gov/Infofax/pregnancytrends.html.

National Network for Child Care (NNCC). (1998). Caring for children with special needs: The Americans with Disabilities Act. Retrieved May 15, 2002, from http://www.nncc.org.

National Pediatric HIV Resource Center. (1992). *Getting a head start on HIV.* New York: National Pediatric HIV Resource Center in cooperation with Region II Head Start Resource Center.

National Pediatric and Family HIV Resource Center (NPFHRC). (1997). *Children, adolescents and young adults with HIV: A fact sheet.* Retrieved May 15, 2002, from http://www.pedhivaids.org/fact/childfact/html.

Olson, J., Murphy, C., & Olson, P. (1999). Readying parents and teachers for inclusion of children with disabilities: A step-by-step process. *Young Children, 54*(3), 18–23.

Robinson, E., & Rotter, J. (1991). *Coping with fears and stress.* (ERIC Digest) Champaign, IL: Eric Clearinghouse.

Zamani, R. (2001a). Diabetes in the child care setting. *Child Care Health Connections, 13*(6), 6–7.

Zamani, R. (2000b). Diversity: Facing the diverse needs of all children. *Child Care Health Connections, 13*(6), 8.

SUGGESTIONS FOR READING

Black, S. (1994). *Providing psychoeducational support for children affected by AIDS.* Florida: Nova University.

Daniels, J. (1995). New beginnings: Transitions for difficult children. *Young Children, 50*(3), 17–23.

Furman, R. (1995). Helping children cope with stress and deal with feeling. *Young Children, 50*(2), 33–41.

Goldberg, E. (1994). Including children with chronic health conditions: Nebulizers in the classroom. *Young Children, 49*(1), 34–39.

Malick, M., Holder, G., & Walthers, V. (1994). Coping with childhood asthma: Caretakers view. *Health and Social Work, 19*(2), 103–110.

Needlman, R., & Needlman, G. (1996, March). HIV: Facts and myths. *Scholastic Early Childhood Today,* 8–10.

Newacheck, P., & Taylor, W. (1992). Childhood illness: Prevalence, severity and impact. *American Journal of Public Health, 82*(3), 364–371.

Putnam, F., & Trickett, P. (1993). Child sexual abuse: A model of chronic trauma. *Psychiatry: Interpersonal and Biological Process, 56*(1), 82–95.

Robertson, C. (1993). *Working with prenatally substance exposed children and their families. California Community College curriculum and resource guide.* Sacramento, CA: California Community Colleges Chancellor's Office.

Schwartz, S., & Heller-Miller, J. (1988). *The language of toys: Teaching communication skills to special needs children.* Bethesda, MD: Woodbine House.

Siegler, A. (1996, February). Preventing burnout: Why children need some unscheduled time. *Child Magazine,* 45–47.

Solit, G. (1993, September). A place for Marie. *Child Care Information Exchange,* 49–53.

Surr, J. (1992). Early childhood programs and the Americans with Disabilities Act. *Young Children, 47*(5), 18–21.

Wallach, L. (1994). Helping children cope with violence. *Young Children, 48*(4), 4–11.

Woolery, M., & Wilburs, J. (Eds.) (1994). *Including children with special needs in early childhood programs.* Washington, DC: NAEYC.

For additional information on safety, nutrition, and health in early education, visit our Web site at **http://www.earlychilded.delmar.com**

Creating Linkages

After reading this chapter, you should be able to:

14.1 Policies for Creating Linkages

Describe and discuss policies for creating linkages for better health and well-being within the child care environment and the community.

14.2 Toward Better Communication Skills

Describe and discuss how to develop good communication skills for working with parents and coworkers.

14.3 Managing Diversity

Describe and discuss the importance of understanding issues regarding diversity and how they may affect safety, nutrition, and health in child care.

14.4 Accessing Community Resources

Describe and discuss the importance of accessing and developing community safety, nutrition, and health resources for helping the caregiver, the child, and the parents.

14.5 Developing Effective Advocacy

Describe and discuss the advocacy role the child caregiver plays in linking the child, the family, the community, and beyond.

14.6 Creating a Team Approach

Describe and discuss how to create a team that provides the maximum protection for a child's health and well-being.

Linkages
connections that unify the caregiver, child, family, and community

14.1 Policies for Creating Linkages

Linkages should be formed within and without the child care environment in order to offer the maximum in protection and prevention for issues dealing with children's safety, nutrition, and health. The caregiver needs to secure the cooperation of coworkers, parents, and community resources to create these linkages. The following indicators reflect reasons for linkages to offer support to the child care environment:

■ Strategies should be initiated to break down cultural bias or racial attitudes and recognize diversity as positive (Hunt, 1999).

■ Professionals must be prepared to be agents of change as well as competent practitioners (Whitebook, 1994).

■ Leadership empowers people to effect change (Bloom, 1994).

■ Child caregivers should acknowledge community resources and use them for consultation and other services (American Public Health Association [APHA] & American Academy of Pediatrics [AAP], 2001).

■ Caregivers and parents who work together as a team can improve the quality of child care (Keyser, 2001).

Synergy
combined effort or action

Synergy or combined effort is much more effective than individual effort. This is especially true in child care. Policies should be in force to help develop approaches using synergy as often as possible. The holistic approach to child care allows the caregiver to understand that one person would be less effective than a combined effort. A child caregiver is called upon to be many things to the child. The physical, emotional, and cognitive care and education of a child is a very large task. Most caregivers are involved in this task on a daily basis for a number of children.

The caregiver can help make this job easier. The caregiver who learns to communicate about the child's safety, nutritional, and health needs can be more proactive in the care of children. This effort will involve communicating to the

Communicating with the child is the first step toward learning how to communicate with parents, coworkers, and directors regarding a child's safety, nutritional, and health needs.

The director posts available community resources for parents and caregivers to access.

parent as well as all those present in the child care environment. Coworkers, directors, assistants, and food preparers should all be involved in the effort to promote and protect the health and well-being of children in care. An important part of this communication is to let the parents know, in advance, what the policies are for safety, nutrition, and health (Dailey, 1999).

The communication effort helps the transition from child care to the home environment so the child might feel the sense of well-being as a constant. Many parents do not realize how they can actively affect their own environment. A child caregiver who passes on knowledge about safety, nutrition, and health can help parents create a better environment at home.

A caregiver who is sensitive about diversity is more effective in preventing problems and protecting the well-being of the child. The many cultures, races, and other diverse conditions of people in this country are rapidly causing change and this diversity should be understood instead of ignored. The caregiver who learns to celebrate the differences and understand the similarities will be more effective in offering the children in care the maximum environment. The caregiver who approaches situations from a diverse viewpoint will be more likely to pick nuances of how families approach safety, nutrition, and health. A caregiver should be comfortable knowing her limitations (Gonzalez-Mena & Stonehouse, 2000).

In addition to the parents and families, the caregiver also needs to seek help from outside the child care environment. A child caregiver is rarely a qualified health or nutritional professional. There will probably be instances where the caregiver will need to call on outside resources and professionals to deal with a situation that presents a challenge.

It is getting more difficult to remain in the child care environment without acknowledging that the caregiver be an advocate for the health, safety, and well-being of children. This not only occurs within the environment and to the parents, but in the greater community. The difficulties that communities are seeing with violence, poverty, homelessness, child abuse, and other family situations may have a residual effect in the child care environment. The caregiver may feel the need to take a leadership role to help improve the community or the situation.

A team effort is the best way to use the synergistic approach. A team can be created in working with people within the child care, with parents, and the greater community. A child caregiver who makes the most of the people and the resources available will offer the children in child care the best environment possible.

In order to provide the maximum benefit to the child, there should be policies that include:

1. *Communication Skills:* practices for supporting better communications between caregivers, parents, and others
2. *Managing Diversity:* understanding diverse cultures, race, and health conditions in order to recognize differences and similarities that will help maintain the well-being of children
3. *Accessing Community Resources:* understanding how to recognize and access community resources that will help the caregiver be more effective in providing for safety, nutrition, and health

4. *Developing Effective Advocacy:* understanding the importance of advocacy and how to perform it

5. *Creating a Team Approach:* understanding how to create a team for providing for the health and well-being of children in care

KEY CONCEPT 14.1

Policies for Linkages

Child care is an important part of many children's lives. Child care quality is greatly improved if there is good communication with parents and if cultural competence is practiced. The quality of care is promoted by accessing and using community resources. The caregiver who is an advocate for the child with the parents, others, and the greater community is offering maximum protection and prevention. A team approach combines efforts to provide for better safety, nutrition, and health.

14.2 Toward Better Communication Skills

Development of good communication is critical for the child care environment. Families come in many different forms. There may be two parents present, or only a single parent. There may be two parents present where one of them is a stepparent. Grandparents, aunts, uncles, and foster parents are becoming increasingly responsible for raising children. Mutual communication with the parent or guardian concerning the child should show respect and acknowledge feelings about certain situations. This helps both parties feel more comfortable. Keeping parents informed about the child's activities and any concerns you have helps families learn how to trust you and provide a basis for communication (Dailey, 1999; Powell, 1998).

A bond of trust between caregiver, parent, and child can be formed by consistency and respect.

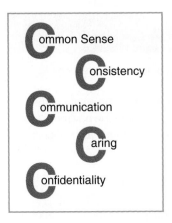

Figure 14–1

Five Cs of Parent Relations

Developing Trust and Respect

The child caregiver who is consistent and predictable in the relationship with parents helps develop a bond of trust. If the caregiver shows the child and the family respect, they are much more likely to be responsive to participate actively in the safety, nutrition, and health of the child (see Figure 14–1).

The caregiver should be supportive and responsive to concerns about a child. This should be established at the beginning of the relationship with the child and parent or guardian and should be continued on a daily basis. Establishing and continuing the communication relationship is often a matter of common sense as listed in Table 14–1.

Make sure that you do not make any assumptions about the child or the family culture (Shaw, 2000). Ask questions and, where applicable, be aware of cultural issues. If culture may be a part of the issue and a relationship has already been established, you might want to ask direct but sensitive questions about the culture or ethnicity to help you to understand (Sturm, 1997). Remember, when you are engaging in communication with parents, you should make sure to respect their comfort zone, as well as your own. Be sure to communicate thoroughly and ask questions about anything that might be relevant to the issue at hand. It is important to realize that "one size" or one solution does not fit all situations and people. Each child, each family, and each issue are different and the caregiver should be considerate of that fact (Ball & Pence, 1999; d'Entremont, 1998). You can ask parents for their opinions and ask them to clarify what they have said. A family's values should be supported, but both the caregiver and the family should realize that there are different perspectives. Always keep in mind that the goal is the well-being of the child (Gonzalez-Mena, 2000a). Without clear discussion, communication may break down, and both the parent and the caregiver may become frustrated. Clear communication must occur in order to understand differences, whether they be cultural, religious, or socioeconomic (Gonzalez-Mena & Bhavnagri, 2001).

TABLE 14–1 A Dozen Ways for a Child Caregiver to Successfully Communicate
• Show a genuine interest in the child and ask the parent to share feelings and concerns about the child.
• Encourage the parent to ask questions, visit the child care, and participate whenever possible. Seek input whenever possible.
• Be an active listener. Focus on the parent or guardian, not on how to respond. Assume nothing. Clarify any confusion or misunderstanding by repeating what was heard.
• Provide parents with verbal and written information about the child and the concerns or information that will help address the safety, nutritional, and health needs of the child.
• Think before speaking. What is it that needs to be communicated? What is the best way to do it? Practice through role play if you need to.
• Any concern about the child should be dealt with immediately and not be allowed to go unchecked. Never discuss a child in front of other children or adults.

(continued)

TABLE 14–1   A Dozen Ways for a Child Caregiver to Successfully Communicate *(continued)*
• Be positive and discuss good behaviors and accomplishments as well as problems.
• Be flexible. Each family is unique and has different needs. Be aware of the family situation, the cultural background, and the child's home environment.
• Be a good observer. Often it is what is not said or done that may be significant. Learn to read nonverbal cues such as body tension, avoidance of contact, a sense of chaos, or other vulnerabilities.
• Never compare the child or situations with others. This never accomplishes anything and can cause resentment and guilt.
• Always keep whatever is communicated in confidence. Use the information to help the child and family find resources or get any help necessary.
• Remain calm; do not argue or be defensive. Model good coping skills.

Developing a System of Communication in Child Care

Good communication skills are necessary for the child care staff. During a day the same child may have more than one caregiver. These caregivers need to communicate with each other as to the child's safety, nutritional, and health needs. The quality of any interactions concerning the child affect the care of the child. Children need to feel that their environment is constant and that the care is consistent. The degree of communication between staff can affect the morale of the child care environment. There can be problems if any one person feels that he is not being heard or his opinion is not respected. When the communication within a child care environment is consistent the children can also learn to communicate at a greater level.

Face-to-face verbal communication between caregivers and supervisors is the most effective way to monitor situations and identify problem areas and training possibilities.

Communication is most effective when it is verbal and face to face. However, the nature of child care may not always offer the opportunity. A system of communication through notes, after hours telephone conversations, and regular staff meetings can help to maintain an open line of communication about concerns and issues concerning the well-being of the children in care. If the child care environment includes a director, he or she should model good communication and help others on the staff to resolve any conflicts that may be present.

Another area that might be further developed in child care is communication with preverbal infants and toddlers. Recent research has shown that very young children can reduce their communication frustration level by learning simple signs to represent language (*Business Week,* 2000). Child care centers all over the United States are employing this method of communication for the preverbal children in care (Fawcett, 2001; Grabmeir, 1999; Meller, 2001; White, 1999). The idea is that children know what people are saying to them before they can talk, but they cannot reciprocate in spoken language (Helms, 1999). Children younger than 12 months are capable of learning and mastering simple signs (Baca, 2001; *Business Week,* 2000). Signing can encourage communication at least six months before children begin to form basic words (Daniels, 2000). The ability to learn to communicate gives preverbal children the opportunity to participate and decreases their frustration level. Signing has been found to be a major source of reducing tantrums and stress for very young children. Another benefit from this has been that children who use signs at this early stage of development can increase their cognitive abilities. (Goodwyn, Acredolo, & Brown, 2000). Communication like this has also shown an increase in the bonding level of the child and the person communicating with the child.

Opinions differ on what signs should be used with preverbal children. Some feel that using American Sign Language (ASL) is the best way. Others have been successful in making up signs that, when consistently used, seem to work fine. Videos such as *Baby Signs* and *Sign with Me* are available to help parents and caregivers understand this important communication pattern.

KEY CONCEPT 14.2

Good Communication Skills

Communication is a key factor in the success of a child care environment's effort to provide for the safety, nutrition, and health of the children present. Communication with the families of the children is vitally important and should be a priority. Asking for input and listening to parents is a key to consistency and optimum care. Communicating with others who participate in the child care environment allow protection and prevention to be at the highest level.

Diversity
differences; variety often related to culture

14.3 Managing Diversity

Culture is defined as parameters of behavior. Regardless of the culture of a home environment, when one steps into the outside world, **diversity** is everywhere. The increasing population of different cultural groups has had an impact on the United States (Loeb et al., 1993; O'Hare, 1992; Zamani, 2000). The society we live in is multicultural and multifaceted. Being culturally sensitive is no longer enough. To be a successful, effective child caregiver, one must be culturally competent (Shonkoff, 2000).

Everyone should learn how to handle this diversity, but that is especially true for people who care for children. The child caregiver has the opportunity to teach children positive values about gender, race, ethnicity, class, and disabling conditions. The child caregiver will also be dealing with families of children who may represent differing cultures, social class, ethnicity, and other variations of background and experiences.

Creating a cultural consistency between the home environment and the environment in care is important (Cronin & Jones, 1999; Gonzalez-Mena, 2000). If there is no representation for a child's culture in toys, language spoken, language in books, foods, or other people around them, then the child is likely to feel that they are in "stranger" care (Cronin & Jones, 1999). Children who are uncomfortable in care are less likely to play and learn and more likely at risk for safety, nutrition, and health. When a child is exposed to diversity in culture and cultural practices he is more likely to become comfortable and see the differences as normal (Gerstenblatt, 2000). When a child is comfortable in care he is more likely to develop a sense of identity (Hunt, 1999; Gonzalez-Mena, 2000b). The awareness of cultural diversity and differing values has the potential to greatly improve the child care environment. It will also allow the caregiver the ability to best meet the needs for safety, nutrition, and health for all children in child care.

Preparing for Diversity

Preparation for dealing with diversity begins with the child caregiver. The caregiver should examine her own cultural background, attitudes, beliefs, and guidelines for behavior (d'Entremont, 1998; Bromer, 1999). People can break down barriers to accept those who are different if they understand their own biases and ways of operating. If a child caregiver becomes aware that he has a strong prejudice that cannot be overcome, he should consider seriously whether or not he should be working with children.

Each person should appreciate his own uniqueness as well as the similarities to others (Gonzalez-Mena, 2000b). This is the first step that enables the child caregiver to create an environment where all children are able to accept who they are and value their backgrounds. In order to do this, there are several techniques that will help the caregiver learn about the diversity of the children and families in child care.

This approach should cover more than just how different cultures celebrate holidays or the foods they eat. A caregiver who is trying to understand diversity should learn how families behave on an ongoing and everyday basis (see Table 14–2). Values and beliefs regarding items such as family roles, child-rearing practices, gender differences, and communication are reflected in how families live their lives on a daily basis (Huntsinger et al., 2000).

Diverse classrooms present the immediate need of understanding and nurturing diversity. Caregivers play an important role in creating an antibias environment in which children can grow and learn about their own and others' uniqueness.

TABLE 14–2 Techniques for Understanding Diversity

- Develop a dialogue with parents about their own cultures. Invite them to share their culture with others in child care. Express a desire to learn from the parent. Ask for their opinions and encourage them to participate. This might include having them help plan curriculum and participate in activities.
- If language barriers exist, try to find someone who can help translate and break down any barriers to caregiver–parent communication.
- Have family evening potlucks where families bring dishes representing their backgrounds and share some of their histories with other families.
- Research games, songs, and so forth, from other cultures in books on child care curriculum and histories. If there are children in care who have disabilities, this can also be researched.
- Attend cultural fairs to get a greater understanding about the cultures represented in the child care. Learn everything you can about a child's home culture.
- Create a support group with other caregivers. This collaborative effort can share information, resources, and open discussion. This is a good way to remove barriers that the caregiver may have.
- Observe children who are from diverse cultures, socioeconomic levels, or who may be disabled. Watch the child with the parents and family members.
- Talk to others in the community who represent the diverse group to find out about the group.
- In larger child care situations, encourage the hiring of diverse staff.
- Acknowledge with parents that a topic may have many points of view and when necessary reach a consensus for the well-being of the child.

The child caregiver can gain insight into diversity issues by talking with parents individually or in groups.

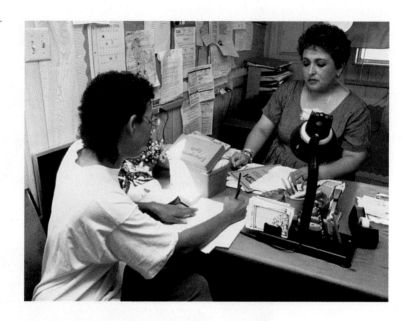

Personal Interactions

Personal interactions are the best way to adapt to the issues of cultural diversity (Smith, 1992). As diversity is explored and understood it allows the caregiver to be more able to communicate, be more sensitive, and be more willing to change and adapt. See Table 14–3 for some strategies to help with cross-cultural communication.

Differences in backgrounds may elicit necessary responses in order to maintain the safety, nutritional well-being, and health of the children in care.

An understanding of different cultural backgrounds provides a deeper understanding of parenting strategies. Socioeconomic differences are also an important factor.

TABLE 14–3 Keys to Cross-Cultural Communication
• Be open, honest, and respectful.
• Understand and respect personal space. Cultures have varying degrees of comfort about the amount of personal space between them and another person.
• Establish a rapport in the common interest of the child.
• Express interest and pay attention by listening carefully.
• Respect silence. It may be a cultural norm or the result of taking time to understand what is being said in a nonnative language.
• Watch how, when, and if eye contact is made. In some cultures making eye contact shows lack of respect.

Parents develop their philosophy of how to parent based on their own culture, socioeconomic background, personality, and family experiences.

Recent studies have shown that even though parents may come from diverse cultural backgrounds, it is the socioeconomic level that most greatly affects parenting styles (Julian, McKenry, & McKelvey, 1994). These and other studies have found that there were few differences in parenting based on culture alone. Low income status may bring with it emotional stress and decreased abilities of parents and families to provide the necessary support for the children. Social conditions such as large households, lack of access to health care, and unemployment were found to have an effect on the health of children of Mexican immigrants (Duarte & Rafanello, 2001).

As the caregiver realizes that families are more alike than different, it breaks down further barriers to providing care. The effects of low income may be more easily understood than a cultural difference. As the child caregiver recognizes the similarities to families of other cultures, the ability to discern differences may increase.

Understanding Family Actions

Acculturated
adopting attitudes and beliefs

There may be cultural differences that account for the actions of families. These are most likely to occur in families who are less **acculturated** to the social values commonly accepted by American society. Families who perceived difficulties in adapting to the patterns of social integration were more likely to place greater demands on children and were found to practice more strict control over them (Julian, McKenry, & McKelvey, 1994). The families that operate from the viewpoint of their own culture alone are more likely to have bicultural conflicts. These conflicts may include how children are expected to behave, how health is perceived, whether or not safety is seen as an issue, and how children are fed (Gonzalez-Mena, 2000; Zamani, 2000).

Integrating Diversity into Child Care

It should be understood that differences may present themselves between child care and the home environment. Children develop their attitudes and identity through experiences in their environments and with their bodies as

Diversity can be incorporated into any type of activity simply by presenting different types of people, food, or landscapes that encourage discussion of those differences.

they pass through developmental stages. When children are infants and toddlers they become self-aware. As they grow and explore their world they begin to identify differences as well as similarities. They will also begin to question differences. Caregivers should be able to respond appropriately. For example, color is an integral part of a person and children of color should be made to feel that who and what they are is good (Ellswood, 1999).

A caregiver should show appreciation for diversity and be aware of the dynamics involved when diverse cultures interact. She should be sensitive to group differences, but should not stereotype or minimalize the differences. This can lead children to form prejudgments (Biles, 1996). A caregiver should teach respect and tolerance for everyone in the child care environment. Tolerance should include people who are diverse culturally, racially, ethnically, or in abilities. Biracial, biethnic children may need extra support in this respect (CCHP, 2001). Children with racial or ethnic differences should be taught to stand up for themselves (Ellswood, 1999; Hunt, 1999).

The best way to manage diversity is on an ongoing basis. The child caregiver should continually interact with children and other adults with diversity in mind. The child care environment should integrate diversity into all aspects of providing for the safety, nutrition, and health of children.

Children who learn about diversity in a positive manner are more likely not to develop any biases as adults (Derman-Sparks, 1993, 1995, 1999). Children learn from what the people around them think, say, and do. Table 14–4 offers some suggestions to help integrate diversity into the curriculum for safety, nutrition, and health.

TABLE 14–4 Activities that Integrate Diversity

- Create a nonjudgmental atmosphere. Avoid isolating any child.
- Focus on the diversity of the children in your own child care. This includes not only culture, but also lifestyle and socioeconomic differences.
- Weave different cultures into the curriculum themes. This allows for greater depth of understanding.

(continued)

TABLE 14–4 Activities that Integrate Diversity *(continued)*

- Provide materials that depict diverse images. This might include pictures on the wall of children from all backgrounds, toys that are nonsexist and representative of the different cultures in your child care. Dolls should be anatomically correct. Books and stories should be from a cross-section of society, including those in different languages that represent children in your care.
- Include staff from diverse backgrounds at all levels of responsibility. It is important to have this representation reflect the diversity in your care.
- Actively involve parents. Have them and caregivers from diverse cultures share their knowledge of their home cultures.
- Encourage participation by community helpers from diverse backgrounds for special circle times or programs that deal with safety, nutritional, or health issues. A visiting nurse may be Filipino, a police officer may be African American, and a dietician may be in a wheelchair.
- Initiate activities that help provide self-esteem, self-identity, and well-being of mental health. Help children to learn to value the differences and similarities among themselves. This will help break down stereotypical viewpoints that may impair how a child feels about himself or others.
- Encourage children to develop critical thinking skills to resist prejudice and develop acceptance.
- Respond positively to children's questions about issues concerning diversity. A child who asks about a disabled person should be answered instead of being ignored or having the question sidestepped. What is not discussed becomes the foundation for bias. These are the times for the teachable moment.
- Discuss and try to find ways to support the differing values of the families in your care.

KEY CONCEPT 14.3

Managing Diversity

A child caregiver needs to manage diversity on an ongoing basis. Children in care represent a wide array of different family structures, ethnic and cultural backgrounds, and experiences. The child caregiver who employs techniques that help understand diversity is better prepared to interact with children and their parents. This is essential for the caregiver who wants to offer an environment that provides the best in safety, nutrition, and health for the child. The caregiver can initiate activities that promote the integration of diversity into the child care environment.

14.4 Accessing Community Resources

The child caregiver may need to access a host of resources to help in meeting the safety, nutritional, and health needs of the children in care. The number of resources available may depend on the type of community where the care is provided.

Surveying the Community for Resources

Larger urban communities such as major cities are more likely to have a number of resources that the caregiver may access. Smaller urban or suburban communities may offer a more limited number of resources, while rural communities may have even fewer. This is only one determining factor. The caregiver will have to attempt access to resources to determine the number available in the local community.

Another factor is the degree of commitment that the local governments have to the well-being of children. Some cities, counties, and states have a higher degree of commitment and therefore have more resources available for the caregiver. An example would be those cities that have a child care specialist on staff to help the area organize for child care. However, other states and counties and cities may have less commitment or fewer resources themselves that limits the information that they might otherwise provide.

Many states, counties, and cities have community child care resource and referral agencies. These agencies provide the much needed information that the child caregiver should attempt to access.

The federal government provides many resources that the caregiver can access. Government agencies such as the U.S. Department of Health and Human Services and the U.S. Department of Agriculture provide a great deal of information to promote safety, nutrition, and health. The information is readily available to all consumers and is easy to access through mail or the Internet. Some information may be available locally at government offices or through local programs such as the Women, Infants, and Children program (WIC) and Head Start.

Many national organizations have offices that provide information to promote the health and well-being of children. All the organizations have a national office and some have state and local affiliates that provide easier access to information. Examples of these are the American Red Cross and the American Cancer Society.

Child care resource and referral agencies are a good source for parents to find quality, licensed child care that meets their individual needs.

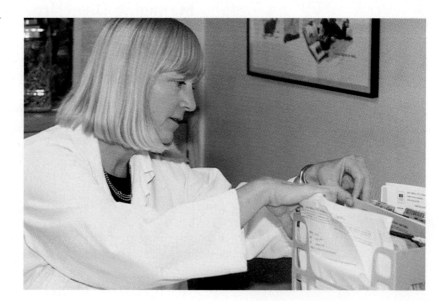

Bananas—A Few People Can Make a Difference

In 1973 in Oakland, California, three women organized a support group for other mothers who did not have extended families in their area. Originally, they wanted to exchange care and information, form a play group, and relate their child-rearing concerns. They called themselves "Bananas," which referred to how they were feeling as well as what was present in their lives at this point— children who were at the banana eating and squishing stage. They felt that this name would make them more accessible and would be easy to remember. Some mothers in the group were looking for nonparental child care so they could work outside the home. At about the same time, the state government was wondering if public monies for child care was really necessary. These women were afraid that the already scarce care available would become nonexistent, so they became politically active. They organized a survey and found that money for care was needed, especially for the care of infants. These women began a campaign to change the situation. They motivated legislators to introduce and pass the legislation that created the first resource and referral network in the nation.

Bananas found themselves in business as they became the first resource and referral agency in the country. They worked as volunteers for the first year or so and later found that there was enough money coming in that there could be some paid positions. They began offering caregiver workshops and classes, and organizing support groups for parents and caregivers.

Today, Bananas has evolved into one of the most effective linkages in the nation. They employ a staff of 26 people, with volunteers still donating their time and effort. Their mission is to help parents in any way that they can. They help find child care of all types. From experience in their area, they know that the preferred care for infants is an in-home caregiver who is shared by two families. They help create these family–family links through interviews and questionnaires. Bananas also helps families access needed resources and gives workshops for parents.

For 15 years they employed a nurse to handle health and safety issues. She not only interacted with the parents, but also created informational handouts on health and safety issues. Bananas entered new territory when an out-of-state move turned one woman from an employee to a health consultant who writes a column for their newsletter.

Bananas offers caregivers a place where they can link with families that need care, find information they need, and participate in caregiver training workshops. Bananas offers classes and workshops on site and they have created a linkage with the Peralta Community College District. They teach classes at Merritt College and the college gives credit for some of the classes held at Bananas.

Bananas is still actively involved in affecting legislation. One of its major achievements is the creation of TRUSTLINE, an 800 hotline number for parents to check the backgrounds of license-exempt caregivers such as nannies. This hotline has found a number of individuals with criminal backgrounds or who have been registered as sex offenders and are trying to care for children.

Bananas has formed another organization that shares their space and deals with children with special needs. This organization offers services to families, caregivers, and children. It organizes teams that include the family, the caregiver, and health and nutritional professionals, and offers support and access to resources and referrals.

None of the original founders of Bananas remain involved. Arlyce Curry joined Bananas when it was six months old and at the volunteer stage. For many years she has led Bananas to bigger and greater goals. Bananas is a shining example of what a few people can do to make a difference in the care of children. Check out the Bananas Web site at http://www.bananasinc.org/.

A parent bulletin board is an excellent way to provide parents with information on different types of resource and support organizations in the community.

Colleges and universities are resources for information. The departments most likely to have important information are child development, nutrition, human services, family studies, nursing, and schools of medicine. Both public and private institutions of higher learning are usually happy to share their information. Some might even be willing to share expertise, if time permits. Many child care health consultants come from this resource. Some universities offer extension services that are excellent sources of all types of information concerning children, families, nutrition, and health. Pennsylvania State University and Iowa State University are good examples of this type of support.

Hospitals, clinics and health centers, and poison control centers may also be good resources. They may have information readily available that concerns the health, safety, and well-being of children. These types of facilities may also offer speakers for specific information such as immunizations. These speakers can be utilized for special topic programs that the caregiver may provide for families. These people are also likely resources for seeking a health consultant for the child care environment.

Many common local resources exist for caregivers regardless of their location. These resources are included in Table 14–5.

TABLE 14–5 Common Local Resources for Safety, Nutritional, and Health Information or Assistance

- Department of Public Health
- Hospitals, children's hospitals
- Health centers and clinics
- Fire and police departments
- Child care licensing/foster care licensing
- Child care resource and referral agencies
- Children's protective services
- Gas and electric companies
- Colleges and universities
- Medical societies (e.g., American Academy of Pediatrics)

(continued)

TABLE 14–5 Common Local Resources for Safety, Nutritional, and Health Information or Assistance *(continued)*

- Local chapters of national organizations such as American Red Cross, American Dietetic Association, Girl Scouts, American Cancer Society, American Heart Association, and the March of Dimes
- Poison control centers
- Libraries
- Head Start
- Department of Social Services
- Dental societies
- Family day dare associations
- State and local affiliates of the National Association for the Education of Young Children (NAEYC)
- Schools and school districts (for screening, school nurses, and special education resources)
- Humane societies
- County extension services
- WIC
- Visiting Nurses Associations
- Department of Parks and Recreation
- Pharmacies and pharmacists
- Department of Environmental Protection
- Associations for cultural and ethnic affiliations

Prominent health organizations recommend that child caregivers create a community resource file that includes written information on different topics dealing with safety, nutrition, and health.

Organizing and Using the Resources

It is vitally important that the child caregiver have resources organized should need for access occur. The American Public Health Association and the American Academy of Pediatrics recommend that a child caregiver create a community resource file that includes written information on a number of topics dealing with safety, nutrition, and health. These resources are for the caregiver and the parents of children in care. If the information is available in the parent's native language, it should be provided or as an alternative, a translator should be used, whenever possible. These organizations also recommend that the child caregiver use consultants from local available resources. Consultants might include people from the fields of health care, nutrition, safety, mental health, or child abuse prevention. Since the child caregiver's time is often taken up with the business of care, the consultants can offer the caregiver an invaluable service.

KEY CONCEPT 14.4

Accessing Community Resources

Access to community resources is very important for the child caregiver. The caregiver should be prepared with a number of local resources for the safety, nutritional well-being, and health of the children in care. These resources include written information and people who might consult. Resources should be surveyed and organized so the caregiver is prepared to use them if the need arises.

Advocate

to support or speak on behalf of another

14.5 Developing Effective Advocacy

The majority of people who become child caregivers do so because of care and concern for children and their welfare. Regardless of the type of child care the caregiver is supplying, opportunity may present itself to **advocate** on behalf of a child. It is an inherent part of the job of a caregiver to make sure the children in care are supported for optimum health, safety, and well-being. This may require the caregiver to talk to parents, health professionals, and other sources of community resource and support.

For the Child Care Center

Center-based care may already anticipate this need. It may even be part of a director's job description. Teachers in center care may need to advocate to the director about problems or issues about children or the environment of care. In turn, directors may represent the child care to the parents and others. Directors should be prepared for this through their education, training, and experience. They should help the teachers in their facilities to learn to do the same. Staff meetings, daily consultation, and mentoring will help teachers learn to best represent the children in care. Education and training will provide added support for teachers.

For the Family Child Caregiver

New family child caregivers may not anticipate the need to intercede on behalf of a child. Veteran family child caregivers will report a great deal of advocacy on behalf of the children in care. Approaching parents is usually the first line of communication. However, community resources and support may be necessary to help the caregiver approach a situation with the parents.

Support from others in the same profession might prove to be very valuable to the family day caregiver. National organizations have local chapters

Child caregivers by nature of their profession also become child advocates to make sure that children in care are supported for optimum health, safety, and well-being.

Family caregivers can benefit from contact with other family caregivers. This promotes the sharing of information and support that are inherent in a center.

that may provide this support. Local child care resource and referrals may also help the family caregiver to find others to share concerns and solutions. Local licensing may also be a source of connecting with other family day caregivers. Education and training facilities are also a source of support and learning to advocate on behalf of children.

For the Nanny

The in-home care provided for by a nanny may appear to be an ideal caregiving situation. With lower caregiver–child ratio one might think there are few problems. Very few people performing the job of a nanny are trained and may

Nannies may find themselves in the awkward position of not being able to communicate effectively with parents about the child because of the employer–employee relationship. Nanny support groups are a good way for nannies to get together and share solutions to these and other common problems.

be surprised to find difficulties are present here too. Two issues raised by many nannies are home safety and nutritional needs. The families that employ nannies are not always aware of what is safe or healthy for children. It may be awkward for the nanny to approach the family because of the employer–employee relationship. Nannies need to understand the importance of advocacy for the children in care. Community resources and support can provide the foundations needed.

Nanny support groups are good sources of resources and solutions for advocacy. Local placement agencies may know of support groups in the area. Placing an ad in the local family press or newspaper to start a nanny support group has been effective in many parts of this country and in Canada. A list of support groups can be found at the National Association of Nannies Web site at: http://www.nannyassociation.com/support.html or the Nanny Network Web site at: http://www.nannynetwork.com/nannygroups.html.

The Health Advocate

The American Public Health Association and the American Academy of Pediatrics would like to see health advocacy in child care taken one step further. They recommend that child care facilities or large family child care homes should have one person who is designated as the health advocate. In most cases this would be an assigned caregiver. This designated caregiver would receive more training in issues concerning safety, nutrition, and health. In cases of small family child care homes and in-home caregivers, the health advocate is usually the caregiver. The designated health advocate could also be an outside community resource such as a health professional who is in the facility on a frequent basis and knows the children well. Many resource and referral networks and agencies have added a health consultant to their staff. These health consultants are generally available to child caregivers in the local area for questions and act as a resource. The California Child Care Health Program is a pioneer and innovator in the area of health consultants for child care. They offer a bimonthly newsletter that is available at: http://www.child carehealth.org/webpages/newsletter.htm.

The American Public Health Association and American Academy of Pedatrics recommends that child care centers designate a "health advocate" to receive additional training in the areas of safety, nutrition, and health.

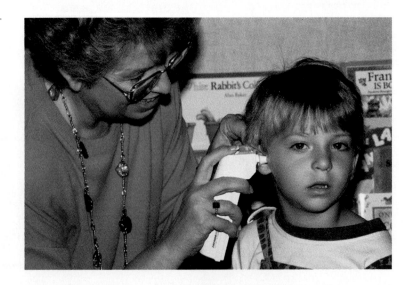

Leadership

Leadership may go beyond advocating for the children in care to the parents and others. Some issues may be of real concern and the caregiver may want to pursue the issue at another level. This may be involvement to make changes at the local level or even more sweeping changes at the state or national level.

Grassroots advocacy or leadership begins at the local level. Local affiliates of national organizations that represent child care or children may be a good starting point. The national office can provide the local contact. Some cities and counties have a child care coordinator. This office may be able to provide good information and may be willing to help change local ordinances, laws, and other matters affecting the care of children.

Another source of help, support, and need for change may be the local health department. Other local places of support for advocacy may be children's hospitals, school districts, and medical societies.

Some states and local areas have child law advocacy groups, and some have a child care lobbyist who may provide valuable information and assistance. These can be found by contacting the local or statewide legal societies.

The caregiver may have to take a greater leadership role if the preceding support for advocacy is not available. Pursuing the issue may call for directly working with townships, city councils, county board of supervisors, or aldermen. If the issue goes beyond local assistance, the caregiver may need to contact state legislators, the governor, the house representative or senators who represent the area in state or national matters.

Whatever the reason for advocacy or leadership, many caregivers feel it is their responsibility to go beyond just providing daily care. The issues involved in safety, nutrition, and health for children have a tremendous impact on the well-being of children and their future.

KEY CONCEPT 14.5

Advocacy for Children

Caregivers may need to advocate for the children in care on issues concerning safety, nutrition, and health. The caregiver can do this in all areas of child care. Child care centers, family child care homes, and nannies may all need advocacy at a point in time. The advocacy contact may be with parents, community resources, or other sources of support. Some issues may cause the caregiver to seek local, state, or national assistance to make changes.

14.6 Creating a Team Approach

Although the caregiver might want to be able to provide everything the children and their families need, no one caregiver is prepared to do it all. The best answer to providing the maximum protection and prevention for safety, nutritional, and health issues is to work as a part of a team.

The Team Members

The team includes the caregiver, the family, and the community resources and services (see Figure 14–2).

As a team member, the caregiver represents the issues dealing with safety, nutrition, and health that concern child care. The caregiver may have solutions to some of these issues. It is important for the caregiver to determine the areas in which she is well-informed, has had experience, and has received specialized training. This will allow the caregiver to form the base from which to seek help from outside sources.

Creating a file of safety, nutritional, and health information will allow the caregiver to have a great deal of necessary information available as it is needed. Keeping a current list of community resources will also help the caregiver function as a team member. Networking with other child caregivers will also help provide information.

The health records, daily observation, and assessments of a child will help the caregiver establish whether the child has an issue or problem that may affect the child's health or well-being. If a problem does exist and the parent denies it, then creating a team may be more difficult. Issues or problems that affect the safety, nutrition, or health of a child should not be ignored. The sooner a problem or issue is identified and dealt with, the greater the opportunity for preventing the problem from having a lifelong effect. Parents want to be able to feel a sense of control. If the issue is approached in a manner where assistance to empower the parent is offered, the parent may be more responsive to intervention.

Providing an Atmosphere for Teamwork

The caregiver can provide an atmosphere for teamwork that will encourage the parents to participate. Responsiveness to parental concerns, trust, modeling

Figure 14–2
The Team Approach to Child Care

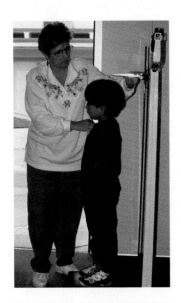

Periodic measurements of a child's height is one example of the type of information that might go in a child's safety, nutrition, and health file.

respect, and good communication skills provide the basis for a parent–caregiver relationship. Parents appreciate warmth, positive attitudes, and accessibility of the caregiver. When this type of climate is available to parents they are more likely to participate. Schwick (1992) noted that particular strategies are helpful to creating the family–school team. The needs and interests of the parents are important. These may be examined through surveys, conferences, parent information centers, parental involvement in the program, and home visits.

The caregiver should survey the parents and other adults in the child care environment on a regular basis to find out where help is needed on issues concerning safety, nutrition, and health of the children. Parents often respond to the call for information solicited from the caregiver. The survey might form the basis of special topics for newsletters, parent handouts, speakers, videos, or even field trips including both parents and children.

The survey could begin a dialogue between a parent and the caregiver relating to a specific issue with a child. Caregiver and parent conferences may help to continue this dialogue. For example, one of the answers you may find in your survey is that some families have no access to health care for their children. This also means that there is no "medical home" for those children. A caregiver can inform a family about available no- and low-cost public health insurance policies in the local area and can help them navigate the health care system to advocate for their children (Sokol-Guiterrez, 2000). Parents may recognize a problem but may be unwilling to admit that it exists if the caregiver approaches them first. Asking the parents for input may put the parent at ease and may help the parent to acknowledge the problem. If this approach does not work, soliciting the help of a community resource may be necessary.

Parents may also feel the need for specific help dealing with parenting issues that could affect the health and well-being of children. Posting a list of topics to be considered may help parents decide which issues are more pressing to them, so they can request information. Creating a parent center, even if

Annie was a family child caregiver who was very organized and really tried to help the parents of the children in her care. She printed a weekly newsletter telling parents what the children did that week and reminding them of future events. She included any new safety, nutrition, or health information she received from the local agencies that she was linked to.

One day, a mother came to her, worried and stressed. Lisa, a first generation Vietnamese American, was concerned that her extended family wanted to "coin" her son Vu when he was sick. Coining involves placing a hot coin on the child's neck that causes red streaks in this area. Normally, Lisa would have gone along with tradition, but she had read in the paper that this practice was dangerous. She wanted Annie to help her with this problem. Annie called several local health care agencies and confirmed that "coining" was indeed dangerous. The agencies mailed information to her that she gave to Lisa. Lisa was able to go to her family and tell them that although she appreciated their traditions, she could not allow her son to be put in danger with that particular tradition. She told them whenever Vu was ill, she would take him to the physician for care.

it is just a tabletop or rack for providing information may help engage the parent in a mutual effort. A parent who is used to accessing information may be better prepared to participate as a team member. If there are a significant number of non-English speaking families in care, the caregiver should attempt to provide information in the language of the family. Community support may be needed to accomplish this.

Home visits allow the caregiver to view the child in a more holistic manner, with all the environments considered (Shaw & Zehaye, 2000). Some parents and families are more than happy to encourage the caregiver to visit their homes, but this may not be possible due to time constraints. However, if an issue is creating difficulties, a home visit may provide a better picture or elicit more cooperation from the parents involved. A home visit should be handled carefully and it might be a good idea to consult with community resource professionals before visiting the family. Some families may refuse to participate in this strategy. The in-home caregiver may have an advantage in creating a partnership based on this aspect, because the care is provided in the family's own home and the caregiver is privy to most of what is occurring.

Providing Linkages to the Community

All of the strategies used to create a parent/caregiver network may also help to promote the partnership of the third party, the community resource. Caregivers should have access to a number of people who are resources for community support. Successful child care programs and family child care homes are those that involve community agencies and support networks (Lovejoy, 1998). These people may include health professionals, nutritionists, and those employed in safety professions such as police and firemen. Social workers, occupational therapists, family counselors, speech therapists, and child abuse prevention specialists are all good sources of community support. Team members may also be secured from organizations such as the American Red Cross,

The "team" of child care provider/worker and parent can also be expanded to include a resource and referral worker.

Head Start, community health services, resource and referral agencies, and special interest groups like the March of Dimes.

Prevention is one of the primary goals of the caregiver to protect the children's health, safety, and well-being. Providing linkages for families to many of the community resources can help prevent problems concerning these issues. Collaboration with people parents might turn to for guidance might help integrate the information into the child care environment, thus making the information more accessible and saving time in an issue of importance (Lally, Lerner, & Lurie-Hervitz, 2001). These linkages may occur by simply providing brochures and access information, and can occur by inviting these community resources to speak at special programs the caregiver provides for parents. Linkages may also occur through referrals to specific professionals to provide extra help or care to children who may need it. If caregivers understand the community system for a specific need of a child, they can help families get needed information and services (Shaw, 2000). A parent must participate for this linkage to be successful. Earlier groundwork for establishing good communication should make getting parent participation easier.

KEY CONCEPT 14.6

Creating a Team

Child caregivers need the help of parents and community resources in order to provide the optimum environment for good safety, nutrition, and health for children. Providing an atmosphere for teamwork can engage parents and create a linkage between the child care environment and the home environment. Providing families a linkage to community resources can help the caregiver to create a team that will help protect and provide the best for the children's health, safety, and well-being in and out of the child care environment.

CHAPTER SUMMARY

A child caregiver should provide an environment that meets the safety, nutritional, and health needs for the children while in care. Communication with the families of the children is vitally important and should be a priority.

The caregiver should access and use community resources that will help provide a greater degree of health and well-being for the child. The child caregiver should manage diversity on an ongoing basis. Children in care represent a wide array of different family structures, ethnic and cultural backgrounds, and experiences. The caregiver can initiate activities that promote the integration of diversity into the child care environment.

Caregivers may need to advocate for the children in care on issues concerning safety, nutrition, and health. Child caregivers need the help of parents and community resources in order to provide the optimum environment for good safety, nutrition, and health for children.

TO GO BEYOND

In this section you will find a number of activities that you can use to apply and improve your knowledge of this chapter. There are also thorough Online Resources that accompany this text that can be found at http://www.early childed.delmar.com/resources/robertson/index.html. Included on this site are chapter practice quizzes, PowerPoint outlines, Web links, a discussion forum, and various other activities to help you better understand the material in this chapter. This site is updated regularly so check back often to receive the latest information about the subjects in this chapter.

Chapter Review Critical Thinking Applications

1. Discuss the importance of communication in the child care environment. Include all the elements.
2. How does diversity impact child care? What steps should a caregiver take to manage diversity? How should parents in child care be involved?
3. Where would you begin to access resources in your local community?

As an Individual

1. List the resources in your area that a caregiver would utilize.
2. Research the topic of preverbal communication by finding two articles on signing with infants. Write a two to three paragraph paper and be prepared to discuss in class.
3. Survey the community for culturally diverse health and safety practices. Create a list to share with the class.
4. Go to your local resource and referral agency and find out what measures they are taking to advocate for the children in your community. List these measures and discuss in class. What more might be done to help children in the community?

As a Group

1. Working in small groups, create a list of resources for the child caregivers that is compiled from the lists individuals have collected. Do any of these deal with diversity or advocacy?
2. In these same groups, create a team of caregivers, parents, and resources. Role play these different roles.
3. Discuss the best methods to create a "cultural consistency" between child care and the home.

CHAPTER REFERENCES

American Public Health Association & American Academy of Pediatrics, (APHA & AAP). (2001). *Caring for our children: National health and safety performance standards: Guidelines for out-of-home care.* Washington, DC: American Public Health Association.

Baca. M. (2001, July 28). Baby talk: Signals may ease communication between parents and infants. *San Diego Union Tribune,* E1, 4.

Ball, J., & Pence, A. (1999). Beyond developmentally appropriate practice: Developing community and culturally appropriate practice. *Young Children, 54*(2), 46–50.

Biles, B. (1996). Activities that promote racial and cultural awareness. National Network for Childcare. Retrieved May 15, 2002, from http://www.nncc.org/Diversity/fc43_activ.rac.aware.html.

Bloom, P. (1994). Building a sense of community: A broader view. *Child Care Information Exchange, 101,* 47–50.

Bromer, J. (1999). Cultural variations in child care: Values and actions. *Young Children, 54*(5), 72–73.

Business Week. (2000, August 14). Look who's talking—with their hands: By signing, even infants can tell you what's on their mind. *Businessweek Online.* Retrieved May 15, 2002, from http://www.businessweek.com/2000/00_33/b3694165.htm?scriptFramed.

California Childcare Health Program (CCHP). (2001). Unique needs of biracial/biethnic children. *Child Care Health Connections, 14*(1), 8.

Cronin, S., & Jones, E. (1999, January). Play and cultural differences. *Child Care Information Exchange,* 46–47.

Dailey, L. (1999). Communicating health, safety and developmental concerns to parents. *Child Care Health Connections, 12*(5), 4.

Daniels, M. (2000). *Dancing with words: Signing for hearing children's literacy.* Westport, CT: Bergin & Garvey.

d'Entremont, L. (1998). A few words about diversity and rigidity: One director's perspective. *Young Children, 53*(1), 72–73.

Derman-Sparks, L. (1999). Markers of multicultural/antibias education. *Young Children, 54*(5), 43.

Derman-Sparks, L. (1995, November/December) Children and diversity. *Scholastic Early Childhood Today,* 42–45.

Derman-Sparks, L. (1993). Empowering children to create a caring culture in a world of differences. *Childhood Education, 70*(2), 66–71.

Duarte, G., & Rafanello, D. (2001). The migrant child: A special place in the field. *Young Children, 56*(2), 26–34.

Ellswood, R. (1999). Really including diversity into early childhood classrooms. *Young Children, 54*(4), 62–66.

Fawcett, A. (2001, July 3). Baby talk. *The Atlanta Journal-Constitution.* Retrieved May 1, 2002, from http://littlesigners.com/ajc_babytalk.html.

Gerstenblatt, P. (2000). Providing culturally sensitive child care environments. *Child Care Health Connections, 13*(1), 8.

Gonzalez-Mena, J. (2000a, July). High-maintenance parent or cultural differences? *Child Care Information Exchange,* 40–42.

Gonzalez-Mena, J. (2000b). *Multicultural issues in child care.* Menlo Park, CA: Mayfield Publishing.

Gonzalez-Mena, J., & Bhavnagri, N. (2001, March). Cultural differences in sleeping practices. *Child Care Information Exchange,* 91–93.

Gonzalez-Mena, J., & Stonehouse, A. (2000, January). High-maintenance parents. *Child Care Information Exchange,* 10–12.

Goodwyn, S., Acredolo, L., & Brown, C. (2000). Impact of symbols on early language development. *Journal of Nonverbal Behavior, 24.* Abstract available at: http://www.focusites.com/babysigns/symbolicgesturingarticle.htm.

Grabmeir, J. (1999, January 27). Teaching infants to use sign language. Ohio State University. Retrieved May 15, 2002, from http://www.newswise.com/articles/1999/1/SIGNLANG.OSU.html.

Helms, A. (1999, November 28). Teaching babies sign language before verbal speech. *Toronto Star.*

Hunt, R. (1999). Making positive multicultural early childhood education happen. *Young Children, 54*(5), 39–42.

Huntsinger, C., Huntsinger, P., Ching, W., & Lee, C. (2000). Understanding cultural contexts fosters sensitive caregiving of Chinese American children. *Young Children, 55*(5), 7–15.

Julian, T., McKenry, P., & McKelvey, M. (1994). Cultural variations in parenting: Perceptions of Caucasian, African-American, Hispanic-American and Asian-American families. *Family Relations, 43*(1), 30–38.

Keyser, J. (2001, March). Creating partnerships with families: Problem-solving through communication. *Child Care Information Exchange,* 44–47.

Lally, J., Lerner, C., & Lurie-Hervitz, E. (2001). National survey reveals gaps in the public's and parent's knowledge about early childhood development. *Young Children, 56*(2), 49–53.

Loeb, P., Friedman, D., Lord, M., Guttman, M., & Kukula, G. (1993, October 4). To make a nation: How immigrants are changing America for better or worse. *U.S. News and World Report,* 47–52.

Lovejoy, A. (1998). Components of successful parent education programs. NGA Center for the Best Practices. Retrieved May 15, 2002, from http://www.nga.org/center/divisions/1,1188,c_issue_brief^d_1833,00.html.

Meller, T. (2001, March 18). Looking for signs. *The Journal Newspapers.* Retrieved May 15, 2002, from http://www.signingwithkids.com/swkmedia.htm.

O'Hare, W. (1992). America's minorities: The demographics of diversity. *Population Bulletin, 47*(4), 82–125.

Powell, D. (1998). Reweaving parents into the fabric of early childhood programs. *Young Children, 53*(4), 60–67.

Schwick, K. (1992). *Teacher parent partnerships.* [ERIC Digest]. Champaign, IL: Eric Clearinghouse for Elementary and Early Childhood Education.

Shaw. P. (2000). Discussing provider concerns with parents. *Child Care Health Connections, 13*(1), 9.

Shaw, P., & Zehaye, S. (2000). Do I have the tools? *Child Care Health Connections, 13*(5), 10.

Shonkoff, J., & Phillips, J. (Eds.), & The Committee on Integrating the Science of Early Childhood Development. (2000). *Neurons to neighborhoods.* Committee on Integrating the Science of Early Childhood Development, Board of Children, Youth and Families. Washington, DC: National Academy Press. Retrieved May 15, 2002, from http://www.nap.edu.

Smith, D. (1992). Changing U.S. demographics: Implications for professional preparation. *Journal of Home Economics, 84*(1), 19–23.

Sokol-Gutierrez, K. (2000, January). Partners in health: Helping families advocate for their children's health. *Child Care Information Exchange,* 51–53.

Sturm, C. (1997). Creating parent-teacher dialogue: Intercultural communication in child care. *Young Children, 52*(4), 34–38.

White, D. (1999, August 9). Babies taught sign language often ahead of their peers later on. *The Memphis Commercial Appeal.* Retrieved May 15, 2002, from http://seattlep-1.nwsource.com/lifestyle.storya1.shtml.

Whitebook, M. (1994). Finding the support you need. *Scholastic Early Childhood Today, 8,* 14–15.

Zamani, R. (2000). Diversity: Facing the diverse needs of all children. *Child Care Health Connections, 13*(6), 8.

SUGGESTIONS FOR READING

Allen, J., McNeill, E., & Schmidt, V. (1992). *Cultural awareness for children.* Menlo Park, CA: Addison-Wesley.

Bassett, M. M. (1998). *The professional nanny.* Clifton Park, NY: Delmar Learning.

Brand, S. (1996). Making parent involvement a reality: Helping teachers develop partnerships with parents. *Young Children, 51*(1), 76–81.

Carter, M. (1996, July). Communicating with parents. *Child Care Information Exchange,* 80–83.

Copeland, M., & McCreedy, B. (1997). Creating family friendly policies. *Child Care Information Exchange, 113,* 7–12.

Copeland, T. (1997). How to help your staff cope with conflict—Using the three choice model. *Child Care Information Exchange, 113,* 83–84.

Gonzalez-Mena (1996, March). When values collide. *Child Care Information Exhange, 108,* 30–32.

Guendelman, S., English, P., & Chavez, G. (1995). Infants of Mexican immigrants: Health status of an emerging population. *Med Care, 33*(1), 41–52.

Hohensee, J., & Derman-Sparks, L. (1992). *Implementing an anti-bias curriculum in early childhood classrooms.* [ERIC Digest]. Champaign, IL: Eric Clearinghouse on Elementary and Early Childhood Education.

Kellaghan, R. (Ed.) (1993). *The home environment and school learning: Promoting parent involvement in the education of children.* New York: Macmillan.

Knitzer, J., & Page, S. (1996). Public policy report: Young children and families: The view from the states. *Young Children, 51*(5), 51–55.

Maddux, R. (1988). *Team building: An exercise in leadership.* Los Altos, CA: Crisp.

Morrison, J., & Rodgers, L. (1996) Being responsive to the needs of children from dual heritage backgrounds. *Young Children, 51*(1), 29–33.

Sontag, D. (1993, June 29). A fervent "no" to assimilation in new American children of immigrants: Rewriting an axiom. *New York Times,* A-6,10.

Sparrow, J. (1996). Speaking parents language. *Scholastic Early Childhood Today, 11,* 17–18.

Stanley, D. (1996). How to defuse an angry parent. *Child Care Information Exchange, 108,* 34–35.

Sturm, C. (1997). Creating a parent-teacher dialogue: Intercultural communication in child care. *Young Children, 52*(5), 34–38.

Surr, J. (1992). Early childhood programs and the Americans with Disabilities Act. *Young Children, 47*(5), 18–21.

For additional information on safety, nutrition, and health in early education, visit our Web site at **http://www.earlychilded.delmar.com**

Building Curriculum for Safety, Nutrition, and Health

After reading this chapter, you should be able to:

15.1 Curriculum

Describe and discuss the elements needed to design a curriculum for safety, nutrition, and health.

15.2 Lesson Planning

Summarize the steps in planning lessons for presenting safety, nutrition, and health concepts to children.

15.3 Sample Lesson Plans for Safety, Nutrition, and Health

Indicate an understanding of the application of concepts through lessons on safety, nutrition, and health.

Curriculum

course of study that relates to the subject being examined

15.1 Curriculum

Curriculum provides the mechanism for teaching children about safety, nutrition, and health. Caregivers teach children every day by role modeling behaviors and actions. However, role modeling does not provide enough information for children so that they may understand, change their actions, and practice healthy and safe behaviors. Caregivers need to use other methods to properly inform children.

Curriculum can be presented in a number of ways (see Table 15–1). Group or circle time is the perfect opportunity to introduce a subject, discuss it, and plan for further experiences. Those experiences may include field trips or having a resource person visit the child care. Social studies may apply the information to other areas. Experiences can include tapes and videos that offer either individual or group learning time. Songs may reinforce the subject. Large muscle activities and manipulative activities offer opportunity for physical expression or practicing of the information. Dramatic play allows the children opportunity to act out and practice information to gain a greater understanding. Cooking experiences can help children understand safety, nutrition, and health, if properly presented.

Bulletin boards offer constant reminders of the subject being discussed. Books may deal directly with the subject or may reinforce the subject from a different direction. Stories, flannelboards, and finger plays can apply the subject information in a specific way for the children to whom it is presented. Arts, crafts, and sensory experiences may reinforce information already presented.

Curriculum Design

Curriculum must include a number of elements in order for it to be effective. It should provide a holistic approach to the subject for the children, and should also address the children with a holistic approach. The abilities of the children

TABLE 15–1 Ways to Present Curriculum
• Group or circle time
• Field trips
• Dramatic play
• Resource people visiting child care
• Social studies
• Large muscle and manipulative experiences
• Cooking
• Books
• Bulletin boards
• Sensory experiences
• Tapes
• Videos
• Stories
• Finger plays
• Arts and crafts

should be taken into consideration, which include the cognitive, physical, and social abilities. The caregiver needs to be aware of these abilities in order to begin curriculum design.

Curriculum should be developmentally appropriate. The National Association for the Education of Young Children (NAEYC) offers this information for caregivers. Sue Bredekamp (1987) edited *Developmentally Appropriate Practice in Early Childhood Programs Serving Children from Birth through Age Eight,* which helps the teacher understand what positive practices apply to certain age groups. Infants, toddlers, preschoolers, and school-aged children have different abilities. They also have different interests that should be reflected in the curriculum. What is appropriate for a toddler may be boring to a preschooler.

Curriculum should offer children several important qualities, and should be flexible. Curriculum needs to allow for flow that may involve children's interest and attention span. Any curriculum that is used should promote positive feelings for children. It should help children to feel better about themselves. Curriculum also needs to offer children choice. If only one activity is planned and it does not interest a child, then the objective is lost for that child. If several choices are offered, one is bound to appeal to some of the children.

A variety of activities allows the children different ways to explore the subject. This may reinforce the information so that children grasp the idea that is being presented. Using different methods for presentation will also help reinforce the information. Some methods such as dramatic play and field trips allow children opportunities to explore and interact. Children may be able to retain the information better if these types of opportunities are available.

Another consideration should be the diversity of the audience. Curriculum should be **antibias**. Regardless of the method that the material is presented, all material should be checked for bias. The caregiver should be aware of any prejudice or limiting feelings that may prevent this from being done. Table 15–2 includes considerations when designing a curriculum.

Designing curriculum for the child care environment is an ongoing task. For new caregivers, this may seem an overwhelming task. Some caregivers find that designing curriculum for other areas is easier or more interesting than in the subjects of safety, nutrition, or health. This chapter addresses the subjects in order to help the caregiver make this task easier.

Antibias

an approach to curriculum that removes all inequities due to race, gender, and abilities

---

TABLE 15–2 Curriculum Design Considerations

- Is it developmentally appropriate?
- Does it provide for a holistic approach?
- Do children have choices?
- Does it promote positive feelings?
- Is it flexible?
- Can children explore and interact?
- Are there a variety of activities?
- Does it use a number of methods for presentation?
- Is the information presented in an antibiased manner?

There is a process that will help the caregiver to develop a lesson plan. First, the curriculum unit must be decided. The appropriate units that come from this text include:

Introduction—Children's Environment (Introduction)
Section 1—Safety Education (Chapters 1–4)
Section 2—Nutrition Education (Chapters 5–7)
Section 3—Health Education (Chapters 8–11)
Section 4—Current Issues Education (Chapters 12–13)

15.2 Lesson Planning

Lesson plans are the daily substance of curriculum. For some beginning care-takers, learning how to develop a lesson plan may help them develop an entire curriculum. Five lesson plans might equate to a week's curriculum unit on a particular subject. More experienced caregivers may design a week's curriculum first, then proceed to create lesson plans to match it. Both methods work if the information being presented is accepted and practiced by the children.

The **theme** or purpose for each lesson plan must be selected. Each unit may have a number of themes to help the caregiver address the subject. The theme should emphasize the point that is being made. The objectives or expected outcomes should be clearly connected to the theme. The **objectives** allow the caregiver a way to measure the success of the lesson.

This is time for a curriculum design check (see Table 15–2). The questions posed should be applied to the theme and the objectives. If the theme or objectives are not feasible or are not appropriate, try again.

The caregiver should select materials to use based on the theme, the developmental level of the children, and what is available. Materials may help to present the subject or reinforce what has been presented. Supportive materials may be available in the environment to emphasize and reinforce the theme.

Before the lesson plan is presented to the children, it helps to survey the children for their level of understanding on the subject. For example, hand washing is the theme and the plan is to present basic information to four-year-olds. The caregiver surveys the children and finds out that they all know the process. They may not be clear as to why they should wash their hands or when they should wash their hands. The caregiver may keep the theme, but may emphasize germs being the reason for hand washing and focus on the times to wash so that germs can be removed.

The caregiver also should have a tentative schedule for presenting the lesson plan. The schedule should offer a parameter for time or focus. The schedule should allow for flexibility and the teachable moment. The teachable moment occurs as a question is asked or a thought is expressed and the children are very receptive. This moment offers the caregiver the opportunity to focus on the subject in a way that is easily understood by the children.

After the lesson is presented, an evaluation process should take place. How did the children receive the information? Was it at the appropriate level for the children? Are they showing behavioral changes due to the lesson? If changes need to be made, the changes should be written down and added to the plan for future presentation.

Theme
subject being emphasized

Objectives
goals; expected outcomes

Another part of the process of lesson planning is to pass on to the parents the relevant information that has been given to children. This could happen in several ways:

■ There may be a notice on the bulletin board about the day's events.

■ A weekly newsletter may be sent to the parents about the next week's daily schedule.

■ A parent information sheet or learning card might be handed out to the parent concerning a particular lesson.

Whatever method is used, it is important for the parents to receive the information. They can help the caregiver reinforce the lessons and perhaps change practices at home.

An example of a lesson plan follows.

Lesson Plan ❖ **Example**	**Unit:**	Safety
	Theme:	Using Traffic Signs and Signals to be Safe
	Objectives:	Children will learn how signs and signals help them to be safe.
	Materials:	A standing pretend stoplight. A flannelboard and flannel cutouts. A hand-held stop sign. A whistle. A bulletin board about traffic safety. Block area set up for street, street signs, and cars.
	Lesson:	Tell a flannelboard story about Bobby and the traffic signs to children in group time. Ask children when they see these signs in their environment.

Practice what red lights, green lights, and yellow lights mean, using the standing stoplight. Repeat several times. Show the stop sign and ask them what it means. Demonstrate the whistle and talk about traffic guards and how they help children. Ask the children what signs are around when they cross the street. Talk about crossing safety.

■ Always cross the street in a crosswalk.

■ Stay on the curb and look both ways.

■ When there is no traffic or the traffic is stopped, it is safe to cross.

■ Look both ways again and then cross.

Discuss how this would be different in the case of a stoplight. Practice traffic light crossing safety by playing "Red Light, Green Light" for several minutes to reinforce the idea.

Follow-Up: Have traffic lines drawn outside on playground surface. Take out the traffic signal and traffic sign. Children can get on trikes and wagons and practice traffic safety. Whistles are available for guiding traffic. A handout to parents requesting they practice the traffic safety procedures that are included.

Age-Appropriate: This may be presented to mixed age or preschoolers only. Toddlers may not grasp idea by themselves, but may model behaviors of older children.

15.3 Sample Lesson Plans for Safety, Nutrition, and Health

Sample lesson plans for every chapter of this text are provided for the caregiver to help reinforce the information that is being learned. In addition to the information provided, there is a list of resources available at the conclusion of this chapter. These resources include children's books and sources for further help. For example, there are a number of songs or finger plays that can be looked up in the Suggested Readings section. For that reason, we will not include many of these in the lesson plans. Caregivers can help design their own curriculum by adding to the lesson plans provided.

Lesson Plan ❖ **Introduction**	**Unit:**	Children's Environment
	Suggested Themes:	My Neighborhood, My Family, Where Do You Live?
	Theme:	Where Do You Live?
	Objectives:	Helping children become familiar with their physical environment.
	Materials:	Books about different lifestyles; living in the country, the city, and the suburbs. Dramatic play materials to play house or farm. Bulletin board with pictures depicting different lifestyles. Magazines for children to cut out pictures.
	Lesson:	Talk about different lifestyles and read book *A Crack in the Wall.* Discuss how the boy who lived in the city brought happiness to his environment by changing how he viewed the crack in the wall. Talk about what life is or might be like to live in a city. Ask how living in the country would be different.
	Follow-Up:	Provide dress-up materials for playing house in the city or the country. Have children cut out pictures of houses, apartments, and so forth, in cities and in the country. Have them circle those places that represent their own lifestyles. Put a note on bulletin board about what was discussed today. Read *Come Home with Us* later in the day. Talk about how people in different places in the city live. Discuss different ways families do things. Compare differences and similarities.
	Age-Appropriate:	Preschoolers.

Lesson Plan ❖ **Chapter I**	

Unit: Safety

Suggested Themes: Injury Prevention, Practicing Safe Behaviors, Hazards in My Environment.

Theme: Practicing Safe Behaviors.

Objectives: Children should be able to understand and practice safe behaviors.

Materials: Books. Pictures from magazines. Paper in the shape of a badge and crayons. Police officer badges and hats. Stop sign, stop light. Box of items to sort for safety.

Lesson: Talk about safe behaviors to practice on a daily basis like crossing the street, staying away from medicines or poisons, using seat belts, staying away from strangers, not playing with matches or guns, and so forth. Talk about people who help keep us safe, like police officers, firefighters, and so on. Have a box of items. Show them one at a time and have children sort those items that promote safety, such as a stop sign, from those that may cause problems, such as a cigarette lighter. Sort them into two boxes. Talk about things that may keep young children safe in child care. Take a safety walk around the indoor and outdoor environment. Point out the things that help keep the children safe.

Follow-Up: Have safety books available in the library. Read *Dinosaurs Beware: A Safety Guide*. Observe dramatic area for play with props such as police badges, uniforms. Offer badge-shaped paper to color on. Hand out parent information sheet about safe practices.

Age-Appropriate: Preschoolers.

Lesson Plan ❖ Chapter 2		
	Unit:	Safety
	Suggested Themes:	Fire Safety/Stop, Drop, Roll, Cool, and Call; Poison Safety; Indoor Water Safety; Toy Safety; Electrical Safety.
	Theme:	Fire Safety.
	Objectives:	Children should be able to protect themselves by understanding fire safety and fire safety strategies.
	Materials:	Fire hats, uniforms, and other props for dramatic play area. Books. Cut shapes of a smoke alarm to color. Bulletin board featuring STOP! DROP! ROLL! COOL! and CALL!
	Lesson:	Visit a firestation or firehouse. A firefighter will show a uniform, including full gear. Talk about how important it is to listen to firefighters if they are trying to rescue us. Have a firefighter show the fire engine and other equipment and how it works. If the children are not allowed in the fire station, have the firefighter come to you. This varies from area to area.
		Have a firefighter demonstrate stop, drop, roll, cool and call. If possible, have children practice now. Otherwise, practice when children have returned to care.
	Follow-Up:	A great number of books available in library. Read *Fire Diary*. Observe dramatic play area for firefighter/fire station play. Talk about safe behaviors that help support firefighters. Talk about smoke alarms and how they work. Listen to one. Put out smoke alarm cutouts for coloring.
		Talk about how to get out of fires. Talk about fire drills. Hand out information sheets for parents. Include a request to have them diagram home and create a fire drill for evacuation, then practice it. Several days later, have a fire drill.
	Age-Appropriate:	Preschoolers.

Lesson Plan ❖ Chapter 3	**Unit:**	Safety
	Suggested Themes:	Poisonous Plants, Car Travel Safety, Bicycle or Riding Toy Safety, Water Safety, Playground Safety, Neighborhood Safety. Choose only those that are appropriate to care site.
	Theme:	Car Travel Safety/Buckle Up.
	Objectives:	Children should understand how to be safe when in a car, truck, or bus.
	Materials:	Chairs set up in dramatic play area to simulate a four- or six-passenger car with a steering wheel for the driver. Books. Bulletin board on travel safety. Toy cars to paint on paper. Toy cars, buses, and trucks. Outside, a gas station set up for trikes and wagons. Magazines for pictures of vehicles.
	Lesson:	During group time, read *When I Ride in a Car.* Talk about safety in the car. Always buckle up, no hands out the windows, speak with indoor voices, and so forth. Talk about how safety might be different in a bus or in a truck. Compare behaviors.
	Follow-Up:	Go on a field trip in a car or bus. Practice what children learned. Observe children in dramatic play area playing car or bus. Put books about vehicles in library. Encourage children to play gas station in outdoor area and have them practice safe behaviors while on their "vehicles."
		Have children use toy cars for painting. Have children cut pictures of vehicles out of magazine. Discuss safety while they are doing the task. Give parents an information sheet on travel safety. Include a few tips on how to survive travel with children.
	Age-Appropriate:	Preschoolers.

Lesson Plan
❖
Chapter 4

Unit: Safety

Suggested Themes: First Aid, Disaster Preparedness, Fire Drills, Earthquake, Tornado, Hurricane.

Theme: Fire Drills.

Objectives: Children will learn the importance of fire drills and how to protect themselves in case of fire.

Materials: A fire drill bell or buzzer. Clearly marked exits. Sign or poster that shows stop, drop, roll, cool, and call concept. A bulletin board with fire safety, fire drill information. A safe place outdoors to meet during the fire drill.

Lesson: Invite a firefighter to talk about fires and how they destroy things and hurt people. Talk about how things can be replaced, but that people cannot. Discuss the importance of getting out of a fire. Have students practice a fire drill. Have fireman demonstrate stop, drop, roll, cool, and call. Children will practice stop, drop, roll, cool, and call. At one point during the day, have a random fire drill so children can practice while the ideas are fresh in their minds.

Follow-Up: Read the book *When There Is a Fire, Go Outside.* Give parents information about home fire drills and ask them to practice at home. Once a month conduct a random fire drill in child care.

Age-Appropriate: Toddlers, preschoolers, and school-aged children are all capable of understanding this information at some level. Toddlers may model the behavior without understanding it, but that modeling could save their lives.

Lesson Plan ❖ **Chapter 5**	**Unit:**	Nutrition
	Suggested Themes:	Food Guide Pyramid, Fruits and Vegetables, Milk and Milk Products, Strong Bones and Teeth, How Food Helps Us Grow, Where Do Foods Come From, and Breads and Grains.
	Theme:	Breads and Grains.
	Objectives:	Children will understand how breads and grains fit into the Food Guide Pyramid and how they help them grow and have energy. They will be able to identify foods that fit into this category.
	Materials:	Examples of fresh bread, bagels, rice, cereals, and pasta and other products that belong in this category of the pyramid. Poster of the Food Guide Pyramid. Magazine pictures of foods including numerous breads and grains, an empty poster board, and glue or paste.
	Lesson:	Read the book *Bread, Bread, Bread.* Have children name all the different kinds of breads they can think of. Talk about how bread helps children grow and have energy. Show children examples of other foods that fit into the breads and grains categories. Have them select and cut out pictures of this category from magazine pictures of foods. Using glue sticks, have all children glue their pictures of these foods on a large poster board, creating a collage of breads and grains.
	Follow-Up:	Snack and lunch items will feature bread and cereal group foods such as cereal, spaghetti, tortillas, pancakes, and rice cakes. Read the book *On Top of Spaghetti, Pancakes for Breakfast,* or *Strega Nona.* If children bring their lunches, have all children participate in identifying the bread or grain food group items.
	Age-Appropriate:	Preschool-age children will be able to identify these foods.

Lesson Plan ❖ **Chapter 6**	

Unit: Nutrition

Suggested Themes: Junk Foods, Television Ads Influence Food Choices. Learning to Feed Ourselves (for Toddlers), and Exercise Our Bodies.

Themes: Exercise Our Bodies.

Objectives: Children will understand how exercise makes their bodies strong and healthy.

Materials: A flannelboard and flannel cutouts. An exercise video. Balls, trikes, and a whistle.

Lesson: Explain the importance of exercise to children. Have them give examples of what they think is exercise, clarifying as you go. Tell a flannelboard story about a little boy who didn't exercise and how it made him unhealthy and how he felt after he started exercising. Put on an exercise video and have everyone participate. Take a walk and walk at different speeds from slow to fast. Read the book *Willie Takes a Hike.*

Follow-Up: Plan some organized exercises for the rest of the week. Include foot races and trike races; play Red Light, Green Light, and Simon Says. Use exercise video for kids again. Read books like *Too Much Junk Food, Too Much T.V.,* and *I Went Walking,* and discuss how these might affect children and their exercise effort and time.

Age-Appropriate: Preschoolers will enjoy using their energies in this lesson.

Lesson Plan
❖
Chapter 7

Unit:	Nutrition
Suggested Themes:	Breakfast Starts My Day, Lunch Helps Me Grow, Snacks are Important, and Good Fast Food Selections.
Theme:	Lunch Helps Me Grow.
Objectives:	Children will learn how to make good selections for lunch box meals.
Materials:	Labels from typical convenience foods such as Lunchables and snack items often packed in lunches. Lunch snacks, breads, condiments, meats, cheese, peanut butter and jelly, chips, veggies, juices, sodas, junk food selections. Magazine pictures of foods, paper, scissors, and glue or paste.
Lesson:	Show children labels from typical lunch and snack foods. Help them learn how to look at the labels to see what is healthy and what is not. Talk about good selections for a lunch box. Read *Lunch Boxes.* Have children discuss how many different items from different cultures are healthy lunch selections. Have children practice good selections by choosing lunch items from magazine pictures and pasting them on paper. Have children select their own lunch items and make their own lunches. Talk about their selections, and help them make better choices, if necessary.
Follow-Up:	Send home a handout of good lunch box selections and those foods you do not want to see in child care (such as candy and soda). Read *What's on My Plate?, Lunch,* and *Gregory, the Terrible Eater.* During lunch time for the rest of the week, read labels from children's lunch box selections. Have children discuss their food choices.
Age-Appropriate:	Preschoolers and school-aged children are most likely to be receptive to this information.

Lesson Plan ❖ **Chapter 8**	**Unit:**	Health
	Suggested Themes:	My Family, Myself, Being a Friend, Showing and Sharing My Feelings.
	Theme:	Showing and Sharing My Feelings.
	Objectives:	Children will develop an understanding of the feelings they experience. They will learn ways to express their feelings.
	Materials:	Marking pens and paper. Books. Magazines. Finger paints and paper. Paints and paper. Play dough. Cut out cardstock circles 3 to 4 inches in diameter.
	Lesson:	Talk with children about feelings. Read book *Feelings: Inside and Outloud Too.* Discuss book. Have children practice feelings on their faces as you read the book. Talk about ways to verbalize feelings like singing, yelling, and so forth.
		Talk about positive ways that children might express anger (punching bag, play dough, painting, and so forth). Talk about inappropriate ways to express emotions (biting, kicking, hitting, and so forth). Show pictures from magazines or books and have children identify feelings. Let children have free time to express a feeling they have had. This can be done by drawing a happy picture, drawing or painting faces to match moods, picking out a magazine picture, or making a finger paint to match a mood. Some children may have difficulty with this concept, while others will easily be able to do it.
	Follow-Up:	Provide more books on feelings for children to read. When reading any book and a feeling is shown, note that feeling and the expression or ask children to tell you what it is. Have materials available for children to make a mobile with circles that they can draw or cut out faces with feelings that express a range of emotions. Learning card given to parents to explain the importance of encouraging children to express their feelings in socially accepted ways.
	Age-Appropriate:	Preschoolers. If handled correctly even toddlers can benefit.

Lesson Plan

❖

Chapter 9

Unit:	Health
Suggested Themes:	Hearing, Smelling, Seeing, Tasting, Doctor Checkups, A Visit to the Dentist, My Body and Its Parts, How Tall Am I and What Do I Weigh?
Theme:	A Visit to the Dentist.
Objectives:	Children should understand the importance of healthy teeth and who can help them keep healthy.
Materials:	A new toothbrush for each child (supplied by dentist). Clothing for the dramatic play area to emulate dentist uniform. Books. Bulletin board on dental health.
Lesson:	Have a dentist come visit children. A toothbrush is given to teach child. Dentist explains how to brush teeth. Children do a "dry" run with toothbrushes. Dentist talks about what he/she does when children visit. After dentist leaves, children brush teeth with water in bathroom. Reinforce proper toothbrushing techniques. Put each toothbrush in baggy and place in each child's cubby.
Follow-Up:	Read *Doctor De Soto* about a mouse who is the dentist to a number of different animals. Talk about how different the teeth are. Talk about how they would brush teeth. Discuss other ways to help keep teeth healthy such as good diet. Watch dramatic play for reinforcement. Give parents information sheet provided by dentist or create one on proper brushing. Play the song "Brush Your Teeth" by Raffi.
Age-Appropriate:	Toddlers and preschoolers.

Lesson Plan
❖
Chapter 10

Unit:	Health
Suggested Themes:	What is a Germ? Wash Those Germs Right Off of Your Hands! Keeping Food Safe. What Is an Immunization?
Theme:	Wash Those Germs Right Off of Your Hands!
Objectives:	Children should know how and when to wash their hands.
Materials:	Plaster of Paris. Magazines. Books. Sink, liquid soap. Bulletin board on hand washing procedures with pictures of when to wash.
Lesson:	In circle or group time. Discuss germs. Read *Germs Make Me Sick!* Discuss the importance of hand washing and the occasions that hands should be washed. Demonstrate how to wash hands. Have children show you how to wash hands. Move into bathroom area with sinks. Show children how you wash your hands. Sing "This is the Way We Wash our Hands" ("All Around the Mulberry Bush" tune) as children show the caregiver how hands should be washed. Correct if needed. Query as to when hands should be washed.
Follow-Up:	Make plaster of Paris handprints for children to take home. Wash hands at appropriate times. Have children wash hands at appropriate times. Do several finger plays including "My Hands" (Herr & Libby, 1995). This makes children more aware of their hands. See if they can add a line to the finger play that indicates hand washing and the importance of it. Hand out parent information sheet or learning card so parents are aware of correct procedures and times for children to wash their hands.
Age-Appropriate:	Toddlers and preschoolers. Toddlers may not understand but they are sensory and will wash hands properly with encouragement and reinforcement.

Lesson Plan
❖
Chapter 11

Unit:	Health
Suggested Themes:	Keeping My Body Healthy, Getting Enough Sleep, Taking Care of Myself When I Am Sick, How Do I Feel?
Theme:	Taking Care of Myself When I Am Sick.
Objectives:	Children should be able to help themselves get well.
Materials:	Blankets and pillows, doctor kit, and so forth, for dramatic play area. Books. Paints, pens, and paper.
Lesson:	Have a nurse visit to explain what a child needs when she is sick. Talk about rest, drinking liquids, and taking the medicines the doctor gives. Discuss ways to rest, what drinks might be appealing, and how you never take medicine unless the doctor says you should. Also talk about preventing other people from getting sick by washing hands, not sharing cups.
Follow-Up:	Read *Sick in Bed.* Let children play patient and nurse or doctor. Have children draw picture of things they could do for themselves to make them well. Put a note on the bulletin board to parents on what was discussed today.
Age-Appropriate:	Preschoolers.

Lesson Plan
❖
Chapter 12

Unit:	Special Topics—Child Abuse Prevention
Suggested Themes:	I Know My Body, Stranger Safety, Good Touches and Bad Touches.
Theme:	Stranger Safety.
Objectives:	To be safe, children are made aware of some of the lures that a stranger may use.
Materials:	Puppets—an adult and several children. Pictures of child lures strangers use such as candy, emergencies, open car doors, and so forth.
Lesson:	Using the puppets, depict some of the lures that strangers use that put children's safety at risk. Show children pictures of some of the items or conditions that may occur during a child lure situation. Discuss the use of candy, asking for directions, and the open car door. Talk about safe people to go to for help. Discuss having a password for an emergency lure.
Follow-Up:	Reminders on the bulletin board. Parent handout on child lures. Have a parent meeting to discuss the importance of training children about child lures.
Age-Appropriate:	Older preschoolers and school-aged children are able to assimilate this information.

Lesson Plan

❖

Chapter 13

Unit: Special Topics—Inclusion, Chronically Ill Children, Children with Stress

Suggested Themes: Being Different/Being Alike, How to Help Our Friends, Sometimes I Feel Sad, Sometimes I Feel Angry, Sometimes I Feel Lonely.

Theme: Being Different/Being Alike.

Objectives: Children learn to recognize that they are more alike children with disabilities than different. They also learn to accept differences.

Materials: Pictures of children with disabilities. Dolls with disabilities.

Lesson: Read *My Buddy* and *In Other Words.* Have a discussion comparing the two themes. Talk about how both boys might feel. Ask children to recognize how both boys are the same, then ask the children to recognize how they are similar to both boys. Have children who are willing to wear a patch over one eye during snack time. Discuss how it felt. Ask them to tell you in what ways they felt similar to when they did not wear a patch. How did the two compare?

Follow-Up: Read *Our Teacher's in a Wheelchair.* Ask the children if being the different/same changes when someone is grown up. Place pictures in room of children with different disabilities. Have dolls with disabilities available to play with in dramatic play area.

Age-Appropriate: Preschoolers can discern the same and different.

Resources for Building Curriculum

Children's Environment

Aliki. (1992). *I'm Growing.* New York: HarperCollins Publishers.

Aliki. (1984). *My Five Senses.* New York: HarperCollins Publishers.

Berenstain, S., & Berenstain, J. (1994). *The New Neighbors.* New York: Random House.

Bertrand, L. (1994). *Who Sleeps in the City?* Shelburne, VT: Chapters.

Bliss, C. D. (1994). *The Shortest Kid in the World.* New York: Random House.

Boyd, L. (1987). *The Not-so-Wicked Stepmother.* New York: Viking Press.

Bridwell, N. (1985). *Clifford and the Grouchy Neighbors.* New York: Scholastic.

Cole, J. (1997). *I'm a Big Brother.* New York: William Morrow & Company.

Cole, J. (1997). *I'm a Big Sister.* New York: William Morrow & Company.

de Paola, T. (1996). *The Baby Sister.* New York: G. S. Putnam and Son.

Haggerty, M. E. (1993). *A Crack in the Wall.* New York: Lee and Low Books. A new home in a poverty situation and the fears that it brings.

Kadish, S. (1994). *Discovering Friendship.* Austin, TX: Steck-Vaughn.

Kubler, A., & Formby, C. (1995). *Come Home with Us.* Swindon, England: Child's Play. Multicultural homes.

Kubler, A., & Formby, C. (1995). *Come Play with Us.* Multicultural play.

Meyer, M. (1988). *Just My Friend and Me.* New York: Golden Book.

Meyer, M. (1983). *All by Myself.* New York: Golden Book.

Murkoff, H. (2001). *What to Expect at a Play Date (What to Expect Kids).* New York: Harperfestival. Kids want to make friends, and they should—but they're not born knowing how to *be* friends.

Pinkney A., Pinkney, B., & Pinkney, J. (1997). *Pretty Brown Face.* Lake Worth, FL: Red Wagon. An African American baby boy discovers the unique features that make his face so special.

Raffi. (1988). *One Light, One Son.* New York: Crown Publishing. We are all the same.

Shelby, A. (1995). *Homeplace.* New York: Orchard Books. Living in the country, history of an old house and the people in it, including today.

Silverstein, S. (1999). *The Giving Tree: 35th Anniversary.* New York: HarperCollins Juvenile Books. To say that this particular apple tree is a "giving tree" is an understatement.

Simon, N. (1975). *All Kinds of Families.* Niles, IL.: A. Whitman.

Spier, P. (1980). *People.* New York: Doubleday.

Williams, V. B. (1986). *Cherries and Cherry Pitts.* New York: William Morrow and Co. Life in the city.

Wing, N. (2001). *The Night Before Kindergarten (Reading Railroad Books).* New York: Grosset & Dunlap. Join the kids as they prepare for kindergarten, packing school supplies, posing for pictures, and the hardest part of all—saying good-bye to Mom and Dad.

Health Subjects

Agassi, M. (2000). *Hands Are Not for Hitting.* Minneapolis: Free Spirit Publishing.

Aliki. (1992). *I'm Growing.* New York: HarperCollins Publishers.

Aliki. (1984). *My Five Senses.* New York: HarperCollins Publishers.

Allington, R., & Kriell, K. (1985). *Hearing.* Milwaukee: Raintree.

Berenstain, S., & Berenstain, J. (1988). *The Bad Dream.* New York: Random House.

Berenstain, S., & Berenstain, J. (1988). *Ready, Set, Go.* Exercise. New York: Random House.

Berenstain, S., & Berenstain, J. (1983). *The Messy Room.* New York: Random House.

Berenstain, S., & Berenstain, J. (1981). *Visit to the Dentist.* New York: Random House.

Berger, M. (1995). *Germs Make Me Sick!* New York: HarperCollins Publishers.

Brandenburg, F. (1979). *I Wish I Was Sick ,Too!* New York: Mulberry Books.

Bridwell, N. (1996). *Clifford's Sports Day.* New York: Scholastic Books. About exercise during a sports day.

Charlip, R., & Supree, B. (2001). *Mother Mother I Feel Sick Send for the Doctor Quick Quick Quick.* Berkeley, CA: Tricycle Press.

Cole, J. (1994). *You Can Smell Forever with Your Ear.* New York: Grosset and Dunlap. Five senses.

Creative Group at PSS! (1996). *The Boo Boo Book.* New York: Putnam and Grosset.

Demuth, P. (1997). *Achoo!: All About Colds.* New York: Grosset & Dunlap. A children's story that explains how germs spread diseases such as colds.

Dunn, S. (1994). *Keeping Fit.* Chicago: Good Year Books.

Fowler, A. (1991). *Feeling Things.* Chicago: Children's Press.

Fowler, A. (1991). *Hearing Things.* Chicago: Children's Press.

Fowler, A. (1991). *Seeing Things.* Chicago: Children's Press.

Fowler, A. (1991). *Smelling Things.* Chicago: Children's Press.

Frandsen, K. (1987). *I'd Rather Get a Spanking Than Go to the Doctor.* Chicago: Children's Press.

Katz, B. (1996). *Germs! Germs! Germs!* New York: Cartwheel Books. A children's story about germs, from the germ's point of view.

Leonard, M. (1988). *Getting Dressed.* New York: Bantam Books.

Leonard, M. (1988). *Taking a Bath.* New York: Bantam Books.

Numeroff, L. (1995). *Chimps Don't Wear Glasses.* New York: Simon & Schuster.

Oremerod, J. (1983). *Be Brave Billy.* London: J.M. Dent and Sons Ltd. Being brave about going to doctor and dentist.

Oxenbury, H. (1983). *The Check-up.* New York: Penguin Books.

Payne, L. M. (1994). *Just Because I Am.* Minneapolis: Free Spirit Publishing Inc.

Polland, B. K. (1975) *Feelings: Inside and Outloud Too.* Berkeley, CA: Celestial Arts.

Ready, D. (1998). *Dentists.* Mankato, MN: Capstone Press.

Reasoner, C. (1995). *Little Box Book's First Aid Kit.* New York: Putnam and Grosset. Four small books including Stethoscope, Cough Syrup, Adhesive Tape, and First Aid Kits.

Rey, H. A. *Curious George Goes to the Hospital.* Boston: Houghton Mifflin.

Rice, J. (1997). *Those Mean, Nasty, Dirty, Downright Disgusting but Invisible Germs.* Saint Paul, MN: Redleaf Press. A little girl gets germs off her hands by washing them down the drain.

Rockwell, A. (1982). *Sick in Bed.* New York: Macmillan.

Rogers, F. (1989). *Going to the Dentist.* New York: G.P. Putman and Sons.

Rogers, F. (1986). *Going to the Doctor.* New York: G.P. Putman and Sons.

Sesame Street. (1985). *Sign Language ABC with Linda Bove.* New York: Children's Television Workshop, Random House.

Silverstein, A., Silverstein, V., & Nunn, L. (1999). *Allergies.* New York: Grolier Publishers.

Simon, N. (1974). *I Was So Mad.* Morton Grove, IL: A. Whitman.

Steig, W. (1982). *Doctor De Soto.* New York: Farrar, Straus & Giroux. Mouse dentist works on all kinds of animals.

Wells, R. (1995). *Edward's Overwhelming Overnight.* New York: Penguin Books. Edward the unready bear has fears about spending the night with a friend.

Ziefert, H., & Smith, M. (1988). *What Do I Hear?* New York: Bantam Books.

Ziefert, H., & Smith, M. (1988). *What Do I See?* New York: Bantam Books.

Ziefert, H., & Smith, M. (1988). *What Do I Smell?* New York: Bantam Books.

Ziefert, H., & Smith, M. (1988). *What Do I Taste?* New York: Bantam Books.

Ziefert, H., & Smith, M. (1988). *What Do I Touch?* New York: Bantam Books.

Safety Subjects

Bingham, C. (1995). *Mighty Machines: Fire Truck.* New York: Dorling Kendersly Publishing.

Branley, F. M. (1985). *Flash, Crash, Rumble, and Roll.* New York: HarperCollins Publishers.

Bridwell, N. (1994). *Clifford the Firehouse Dog.* New York: Scholastic Books.

Brown, M., & Krensky, S. (1982). *Dinosaurs Beware: A Safety Guide.* Boston: Little, Brown and Company.

Canizares, S., & Chanko, P. (1999). *First Aid.* New York: Scholastic. Photographs and simple text explore different aspects of first aid.

Chlad, D. (1984). *Bicycles Are Fun to Ride.* Chicago: Children's.

Chlad, D. (1983). *When I Ride in a Car.* Chicago: Children's.

Chlad, D. (1982). *When There Is a Fire, Go Outside.* Chicago: Children's.

Cole, J. (1995). *The Magic School Bus: Inside a Hurricane.* New York: Scholastic Books.

Hankin, R. (1985). *I Can Be a Firefighter.* Chicago: Children's.

Hill, S. (1998). *Playground Problem Solvers.* Cypress, CA: Creative Teaching Press.

Holub, J. (1998). *Red Yellow Green What Do Signs Mean.* New York: Scholastic Incorporated. This book describes signs in the environment.

Hopping, L. (1994). *Tornadoes!* New York: Scholastic Books.

Keats, E. J. (1987). *The Trip.* New York: Morrow.

Kubler, A., & Formby, C. (1995). *Come Ride with Us.* Swindon, England: Child's Play.

Kupperstein, J. (1996). *Safety Counts.* Cypress, CA: Creative Teaching Press.

Leaf, M. (1988). *Safety Can Be Fun.* New York: Harper and Row.

Packard, M. (1995). *I Am a Firefighter.* New York: Scholastic Books.

Polacco, P. (1990). *Thunder Cake.* New York: Philomel Books. Cake must go in oven before storm hits.

Polacco, P. (1999). *Meteor.* New York: Philomel Books. Funny book about what happens when a meteor lands.

Raffi, (1988). *Wheels on the Bus.* New York: Crown Publishing. With song.

Rex, M. (1999). *My Fire Engine.* New York: Henry Holt and Co. A little boy lives out a fantasy of being a hero.

Rey, H. A. (1973). *Curious George Rides a Bike.* Boston: Houghton Mifflin Company.

Rey, M., & Rey, H.A. (1985). *Curious George at the Fire Station.* Boston: Houghton Mifflin Company.

Rosenblatt, L. (1994). *Fire Diary.* Morton Grove, IL: A. Whitman.

Seuling, B. (1985). *Stay Safe, Play Safe.* New York: Western Publishing, Golden Books.

Stater, T. (1991). *All About Fire Trucks.* New York: Grosset and Dunlap.

Stoltz, M. (1988). *Storm in the Night.* New York: HarperCollins. Story about a thunderstorm where electricity goes off.

Wells, R. (1995). *Edward in Deep Water.* New York: Penguin Books. Edward the unready bear is afraid of the water.

Nutrition Subjects

Barrett, J., & Nelson, M. (2000). *Food (Elmo's World).* New York: Random House (Merchandising). Elmo learns that food helps him to grow big and strong.

Berenstain, S., & Berenstain, J. (1985). *Too Much Junk Food.* New York: Random House.

Berenstain, S., & Berenstain, J. (1984). *Too Much T.V.* New York: Random House.

Brown, M. (1986). *Stone Soup.* New York: Macmillan.

Canizares, S., & Chanko, P. (1998). *Water.* New York: Scholastic. Describes liquid, solid, and frozen forms of water.

Canizares, S., & Chessen, B. (1999). *In the Kitchen.* New York: Scholastic. Exploring what happens in the kitchen.

Carle, E. (1987). *The Very Hungry Caterpillar.* New York: Philomel Books.

Chanko, P., & Berger, S. (1999). *Markets.* New York: Scholastic. Exploring things that can be found in markets.

Coplans, P. (1993). *Spaghetti for Suzy.* New York: Houghton Mifflin.

dePaola, T. (1989). *Tony's Bread.* New York: Putnam.

dePaola, T. (1988) *Strega Nona.* New York: Simon & Schuster.

dePaola, T. (1978). *Pancakes for Breakfast.* San Diego: Harcourt Brace Jovanovich.

Eagan, R. (1997). *From Wheat to Pasta.* New York: Children's Press.

Ehlert, L. (1989). *Eating the Alphabet from A to Z.* San Diego: Harcourt Brace Jovanovich. Fruits and vegetables from A to Z.

Ehlert, L. (1987). *Growing Vegetable Soup.* San Diego: Harcourt Brace Jovanovich.

Erlich, F. (1991). *Lunch Boxes.* New York: Puffin Books.

Fleming, D. (1992). *Lunch.* New York: Holt.

Fowler, A. (1995). *Corn On and Off the Cob.* Chicago: Children's Press.

French, V. (1995). *Oliver's Vegetables.* New York: Orchard Books. A boy learns about fresh vegetables in the garden.

Glazer, T. (1995). *On Top of Spaghetti.* Chicago: Good Year Books.

Golden, B. (2001). *A Mountain of Blintzes.* San Diego: Gulliver Books.

Gomi, T. (1991). *Who Ate It?* Brookfield, CT: Millbrook Press.

Gross, R. (1990). *What's on My Plate?* New York: Macmillan.

Haduch, B. (2001). *Food Rules!* New York: Puffin Books.

Hoban, R. (1964). *Bread and Jam for Frances.* New York: Harper and Row.

Julius, J. (2001). *I Like Berries.* New York: Children's Press.

Julius, J. (2001). *I Like Cereal.* New York: Children's Press.

Julius, J. (2001). *I Like Juice.* New York: Children's Press.

Julius, J. (2001). *I Like Potatoes.* New York: Children's Press.

Krauss, R. (1944). *The Carrot Seed.* New York: Harper and Row.

Kubler, A., & Formby, C. (1995). *Come Eat with Us.* Swindon, England: Child's Play. Multi-cultural foods and eating methods.

Landau, E. (1999). *A True Book of Apples.* New York: Children's Press.

Landau, E. (2000). *A True Book of Tomatoes.* New York: Children's Press.

Lord, J. (1987). *The Giant Jam Sandwich.* Boston: Houghton Mifflin.

Lottridge, C. (1986). *One Watermelon Seed.* London: Oxford University Press.

McCloskey, R. (1976). *Blueberries for Sal.* New York: Penguin.

Morris, A. (1989). *Bread, Bread, Bread.* New York: William Morrow.

Napoli, D., & Tchen, R. (2001). *How Hungry Are You?* New York: Simon & Schuster. Two friends try to plan a picnic.

Nechaev, M. (1998). *Apron Annie's Pies.* Cypress, CA: Creative Teaching Press.

Numeroff, L. (1985). *If You Give a Mouse a Cookie.* New York: HarperCollins.

Oda, M. (1984). *Happy Veggies.* Boston: Houghton Mifflin.

Passen, L. (1991). *Fat, Fat Rose Marie.* New York: Holt.

Preiss, L. (1990). *The Pig's Alphabet.* Boston: David R. Goding.

Pruemin, M. (1994). *How to Make an Apple Pie and See the World.* New York: Alfred Knopf.

Rand, G. (1996). *Willie Takes a Hike.* San Diego: Harcourt Brace Jovanovich.

Schwartz, D. (1998). *Plant Fruits and Seeds.* Cypress, CA: Creative Teaching Press.

Seuss, Dr. (1960). *Green Eggs and Ham.* New York: Random House.

Sharmat, M. (1987). *Gregory, the Terrible Eater.* New York: Macmillan.

Sinykin, S. C. (1990). *Come Out, Come Out, Wherever You Are.* Hazeldon, MN: Hazeldon Educational Materials. Story about an overweight girl and her changing perception of herself.

Smalls-Hector, I. (1992). *Apple Picking Time.* New York: Crown Publishing. American tradition of picking apples.

Stevens, J. (1995). *Tops and Bottoms.* San Diego: Harcourt Brace and Co. Bear and Hare learn about plants that grow on top of the ground and under the ground.

Williams, B. (1978). *Jeremy Isn't Hungry.* New York: Penguin Books. Older brother tries to feed Jeremy, but he wants to feed himself.

Williams, R. (1996). *Oranges for Orange Juice.* Cypress, CA: Creative Teaching Press.

Williams, S. (1989). *I Went Walking.* San Diego: Harcourt Brace Jovanovich.

Wood, D., & Wood, A. (1984). *The Little Mouse, The Red Ripe Strawberry, and the Big Hungry Bear.* Swindon, England: Child's Play.

Special Topics Subjects

Arthur, C. (1979). *My Sister's Silent World.* Chicago: Children's.

Bunnett, R. (1992). *Friends in the Park.* Bellingham, WA: Our Kids Press. A typical day in the neighborhood park with children with varying abilities and diverse cultures.

Carter, A. (1997). *Big Brother Dustin.* Morton Grove, IL: Albert Whitman & Co. A young boy with Down syndrome learns his parents are expecting a baby.

Charlip, R. (1979). *Handtalk: An ABC of Finger Spelling and Sign Language.* New York: Macmillan.

Cohn, J. (1994). *Why Did It Happen?: Helping Children Cope in a Violent World.* New York: Morrow.

Corman, C., & Trevino, E. (1995). *The Jumpy Jumpy Elephant.* Milwaukee: Specialty Press. A smart little elephant learns he has ADD.

Cowen-Fletcher, J. (1993). *Mama Zooms.* New York: Scholastic. A mother takes her son everywhere in her wheelchair.

Damrell, L. (1991). *With the Wind.* New York: Orchid Books. A boy who enjoys the freedom of horseback riding just happens to have a disability.

Dwyer, K. (1991). *What Do You Mean I Have a Learning Disability?* New York: Walker and Co. A boy having problems in school is tested and finds out he has a learning disability.

Emmert, M. (1989). *I'm the Big Sister Now.* Morton Grove, IL: Albert Whitman. A young girl tells the story of her older sister who has multiple disabilities.

Foreman, M. (1996). *Seal Surfer.* San Diego: Harcourt Brace & Co. A boy with a disability learns to surf and enjoy the ocean.

Heelan, J. (2000). *Rolling Along: The Story of Taylor and His Wheelchair.* Chicago: Rehabilitation Institute of Chicago. A young boy with cerebral palsy enjoys his new mobility with his first wheelchair.

Hesse, K. (1993). *Lester's Dog.* New York: Crown. A deaf child overcomes his fear of a dog.

Hoban, T, (1987). *I Read Signs.* New York: Morrow.

Karim, R. (1994). *Mandy Sue's Day.* New York: Clarion Books. A blind girl is more like other children than different.

Kastner, J. (1993). *Naomi Knows It's Springtime.* Honesdale, PA: Boyds Mills. A blind child knows the signs of spring.

Lears, L, (1998). *Ian's Walk: A Story About Autism.* Morton Grove, IL: Albert Whitman & Co. A young girl learns to appreciate the way her autistic brother experiences the world.

Mayer, M. (1983). *I Was So Mad.* New York: Golden Books.

Ofosky, A. (1992). *My Buddy.* New York: Henry Holt and Company. About a boy's disabilities.

Peterson, J. W. (1977). *I Have a Sister and My Sister Is Deaf.* New York: HarperCollins Publishers.

Polland, B. K. (1975). *Feelings: Inside and Outloud Too.* Berkeley, CA: Celestial Arts.

Powers, M. E. (1986). *Our Teacher's in a Wheelchair.* Niles, IL: A. Whitman.

Rabe, B. (1998). *Where's Chimpy?* Morton Grove, IL: Albert Whitman. A story about a girl with Down syndrome and her father.

Rickert, J. (1992). *Russ and the Fire House.* Bethesda, MD: Woodbine House. A boy with Down syndrome goes "on duty" with his uncle, a fireman.

Rickert, J. (2001). *Russ and the Almost Perfect Day.* Bethesda, MD: Woodbine House. A boy with Down syndrome has a great day going to school and playing with friends.

Simon, N. (1974). *I Was So Mad.* Morton Grove, IL: A. Whitman.

Thompson, M. (1996). *Andy and His Yellow Frisbee.* Bethesda, MD: Woodbine House. Kids dealing with autism.

Walker, J. (1993). *In Other Words.* Toronto, Canada: Annick Press. A boy with disabilities imagines what it would be like to live without them.

Watson, E. (1996). *Talking to Angels.* San Diego: Harcourt Brace Jovanovich. Girl who talks to her autistic sister.

Winn, C., & Walsh, D. (1996). *Clover's Secret.* Minneapolis: Fairview Press. Clover attempts to hide family violence.

Suggested Readings

Anderson, L. (1996). *Early Childhood Health and Curriculum.* Grand Rapids, MI: T.S. Denison.

Berman, C., & Fromer, J. (1991). *Teach Children About Food: A Teaching and Activities Guide.* Palo Alto, CA: Bull Publishing Company.

Bickert, G. (1994). *Food to Grow and Learn On.* Nashville, TN: Incentive Publications.

Cook, D. (1995). *The Kids Multi-Cultural Cookbook-Food and Fun Around the World.* Charlotte, VT: Williamson Publishing Co.

Greene, K. (1987). *Once Upon a Recipe.* New York: Putnam.

Harms, T. (1981). *Learning from Cooking Experiences.* Menlo Park, CA: Addison-Wesley and Co.

Jacobson, M., & Hill, L. (1991). *Kitchen Fun for Kids.* New York: Henry Holt and Company.

Knox, G. (Ed.). (1989). *Better Homes and Gardens New Junior Cookbook.* Des Moines, IA: Meredith Corporation.

M'Guinness, J. (Illustrator). (1987). *Kids Cooking: A Very Slightly Messy Manual.* Palo Alto, CA: Klutz Press.

Ralph, J., & Gompf, R. (1995). *The Peanut Butter Cookbook for Kids.* New York: Hyperion Paperbacks for Children.

Veitch, B., & Harms, T. (1981). *Cook and Learn: Nutritious Foods from Various Cultures.* Menlo Park, CA: Addison-Wesley Publishing Co.

Winget, M. (Ed.). (1992). *Vegetarian Cooking Around the World.* Minneapolis: Lerner Publications, Co.

CHAPTER REFERENCES

Bredekamp, S. (1987). *Developmentally appropriate practice in early childhood programs serving children from birth through age eight.* Washington, DC: NAEYC.

Herr, J., & Libby, Y. (1995). *Creative resources for the early childhood classroom.* Clifton Park, NY: Delmar Learning.

SUGGESTIONS FOR READING

Allen, J., McNeill, E., & Schmidt, V. (1992). *Cultural awareness for children.* Menlo Park, CA: Addison-Wesley.

Allen, K. (1992). *The exceptional child: Mainstreaming in early childhood education.* Clifton Park, NY: Delmar Learning.

Bassett, M. M. (1998). *The professional nanny.* Clifton Park, NY: Delmar Learning.

Berman, C., & Fromer, J. (1991). *Teaching children about food. A teachers and activities guide.* Palo Alto, CA: Bull Publishing Co.

Cook, R., Tessier, A., & Klein, M. (1992). *Adapting early childhood curricula for children with special needs.* New York: Macmillan.

Gestwicki, C. (1995). *Developmentally appropriate practice: Curriculum and development in early education.* Clifton Park, NY: Delmar Learning.

Hendrick, J. (1995). *Total learning.* Englewood Cliffs, NJ: Merrill.

Moore, C., Kerr, M., & Shulman, R. (1990). *Young chef's nutrition guide and cookbook.* New York: Barron's.

Nutrition and wellness for the young child: A curriculum for adults. (1984). Pleasant Hills, CA: Diablo Valley College.

Taylor, B. (1995). *A child goes forth: A curriculum guide for preschool children.* Englewood Cliffs, NJ: Prentice-Hall.

For additional information on safety, nutrition, and health in early education, visit our Web site at **http://www.earlychilded.delmar.com**

Appendix A

FORMS

- Child's Health History

- Developmental Health History

- Caregiver Health History

- Immunization Schedule for Children Not Immunized in Early Infancy

- Consent for Medical Treatment

- Physician's Report

- Physician to Be Called in Emergency

- Identification and Emergency Information for Day Care Centers

- Consent for Child Care Provider Access to Physician Records

- Authorization for Emergency Medical Care

- Symptom Record

- Sample Letter to Parents about Exposure to Communicable Disease

- Incident Report Form

- Evacuation Procedure

- Stop, Drop, Roll, Cool, and Call

CHILD'S HEALTH HISTORY
(Sample)

Child's Name _____   Nickname _____

Date of Birth _____   Telephone No. _____

Address _____

Parents' Names

1. _____   2. _____

   Employed at _____   Employed at _____

   Telephone No. _____   Telephone No. _____

Emergency Numbers

If the above cannot be reached, call

1. _____

   Relationship to Child _____   Telephone No. _____

2. _____

   Relationship to Child _____   Telephone No. _____

State of Child's Health

Please put N/A if not applicable.

Any recent health problems? _____

_____

Does the child have any dietary restrictions, including food allergies? _____

Does the child have any allergies? _____

_____

Does the child have any condition that would warrant special consideration or attention in our care?

Please explain. _____

Any special problems or fears? _____

_____

Is the child under treatment of a doctor or dentist for previous illness or injury? Please explain.

_____

If yes, please give name of doctor or dentist.

Name _____   Telephone No. _____

Is the child taking medication? If yes, what? _____

Name of prescribing physician

Name _____   Telephone No. _____

DEVELOPMENTAL HEALTH HISTORY

Child's Name _____   Nickname _____

Date of Birth _____   Telephone No. _____

Address _____

Parents' Names

1. _____   2. _____

   Employed at _____   Employed at _____

   Telephone No. _____   Telephone No. _____

Physical

Does your child have any problems

1. with speech or language? _____
2. seeing? _____
3. running, walking, or moving? _____
4. hearing? _____
5. using their hands? _____

If so, please explain. _____

6. What is the child's favorite food? _____
7. What foods does the child dislike? _____
8. How does the child indicate the need to use the bathroom? _____
9. Any special words for bodily functions or body parts? _____
10. What are the regular bowel and bladder patterns? _____
11. Does the child take naps regularly? _____
12. What help does the child need in getting dressed? _____

Social/Emotional

1. Describe the child's personality. _____
2. What are the child's favorite toys? _____
3. What ages are the children that the child frequently plays with? _____
4. Does the child play happily alone? _____
5. Describe the child's home environment. _____
6. Does anything frighten your child? _____
7. Does the child have a special comforting article (blanket, etc.)? _____

CAREGIVER HEALTH HISTORY
(Sample)

Your Facility Name _____

Address _____

Name _____

Address _____ Telephone No. _____

Date of Birth _____ Social Security No. _____

Position Title _____

Duty Statement _____

_____

Authorization for Release of Medical Information

I hereby authorize the release of medical information contained in this report.

_____   _____   _____
Signature of Applicant   Address   Date

Physician Fills Out

Evaluation of general health

_____

_____

Evaluation of physical ability to perform duties

_____

_____

Note Any Condition That May Create a Hazard to Children or Staff

_____

_____

TB Test   Positive _____   If positive, what action taken? _____

             Negative _____   _____

Date of Test _____

Vision _____

Hearing _____

	Chicken pox	Measles	Mumps	Rubella	DPT	Polio
History of Childhood Diseases (Date)	_____	_____	_____	_____	_____	_____
Immunization Status	_____	_____	_____	_____	_____	_____

Any special medications? _____

_____

Name of Physician _____

Address _____ Telephone No. _____

Physician's Signature _____

IMMUNIZATION SCHEDULE FOR CHILDREN NOT IMMUNIZED IN EARLY INFANCY

Schedule	Immunization
First Visit	DPT-1, Polio-1, MMR*, HBCV
2 Months Later	DPT-2, Polio-2, HBCV
4 Months Later	DPT-3
6–12 Months Later	DPT-4, Polio 3
Kindergarten Entry	DPT-5, Polio 4

*MMR to be given if 15 months of age or older

NOTE: Children who are in the process of immunization and in the specified waiting period may be admitted to or remain in care until next dose is due. Those children who exceed the specified waiting period must be excluded. Immunization requirements vary with each state. Be sure to check your state's requirements before admitting a child to care.

STATE OF CALIFORNIA HEALTH AND WELFARE AGENCY

DEPARTMENT OF SOCIAL SERVICES
COMMUNITY CARE LICENSING

CONSENT FOR MEDICAL TREATMENT

As the parent, agency representative, or legal guardian, I hereby give consent to

_____ to provide all emergency dental or medical care
Facility Name

prescribed by a duly licensed physician (MD) or dentist (DDS) for _____.
Name

This care may be given under whatever conditions are necessary to preserve the life, limb, or well-being of my dependent.

Child has the following medication allergies:

_____   _____
Date   Parent/Agency Representative/Guardian Signature

Home Address _____

Home Telephone (___)_____Work Telephone (___)_____

UC 627 (10/88) (Confidential)   89 51494

*This form is required by California Law for all Day Care Centers and Family Day Care Centers.

Sample consent for medical treatment form. Different states may have different requirements; check with your state agency for the correct form. (*Courtesy of the State of California Health and Welfare Agency*)

PHYSICIAN'S REPORT

Facility name _____

Address _____ Telephone _____

Dear _____ :

_____ is in child care. We have observed

_____ and would like your diagnosis of the condition so that we can best protect the health of all the children in care.

Results of Examination

_____ No illness found

_____ Noncommunicable disease (Specify) _____

    Describe any treatment required at the child care setting. _____

    _____

    _____

_____ Communicable disease (Specify) _____

    Describe any treatment required before this child can be readmitted. _____

    _____

    _____

_____ Describe any actions required for this child's contacts. _____

    _____

    _____

List Medications Prescribed

Name _____

Dosage _____ From _____ Until _____

Date child can return to care _____

Physician's Signature _____

I, _____, give permission for Dr. _____
    Parent's Name

to release information about _____ to _____ .
                 Child's Name   Facility Name

_____
                 Parent's Signature

When to Use: This form allows you to share information with the child's physician. It can help reduce misunderstandings that result when information is related verbally.

PHYSICIAN TO BE CALLED IN EMERGENCY

Name _____   Telephone No. _____

Medical Plan No. _____

If physician cannot be reached, what action should be taken? _____

_____

Allergies or Other Medical Limitations

_____

Permission for Medical Treatment

Administrative procedures vary among medical personnel and medical facilities with regard to provision of medical care for a child in the absence of the parent. The exact procedure required by the physician or hospital to be used in emergencies should be verified in advance.

In case of an accident or an emergency, I authorize a staff member of Grossmont College Child Development Center to take my child to the above-named physician or to the nearest emergency hospital for such emergency treatment and measures as are deemed necessary for the safety and protection of the child, at my expense.

This authorization is given pursuant to the provisions of Section 25.8 of the Civil Code of California.

Parent's Signature _____   Date _____

Policies

I hereby grant permission for my child(ren) to use all of the play equipment and participate in all of the activities of school.

I hereby grant permission for my child to leave the school premises under the supervision of a staff member for campus walks and on pre-announced field trips.

I understand that students may be making observations at the Center as part of class assignments.

I have no objection to my child being included in photographs, slides, or movies taken at the Grossmont College Child Development Center which might be used for purposes of interpreting the school program. I understand that any photography or observation will be done only with the consent of and under the supervision of the classroom teacher.

I understand that I must notify the Center Office of any college class-related field trips that will take me off campus while my child is at the Center.

I understand that children left after their regular contract time without permission from the Center Office will be subject to termination of child care services.

I agree to inform the Child Development Center of any and all personal changes in circumstances that would affect my status in the Center; e.g., marriage, separation, divorce, change in employment or education, change in address or telephone number.

Parent's Signature _____   Date _____

(Courtesy of the Grossmont College Child Development Center)

Department of Social Services
Community Care Licensing

IDENTIFICATION AND EMERGENCY INFORMATION
FOR DAY CARE CENTERS

To Be Completed by Parent or Guardian

Child's Name Last	Middle		First	Sex	Telephone ( )
Address Number Street		City	State	Zip	Birthdate
Father's Name Last	Middle		First		Business Telephone ( )
Home Address Number Street		City	State	Zip	Home Telephone ( )
Mother's Name Last	Middle		First		Business Telephone ( )
Home Address Number Street		City	State	Zip	Home Telephone ( )
Person Responsible for Child Last Name Middle First			Home Telephone ( )		Business Telephone ( )

Additional Persons Who May Be Called in Emergency

Name	Address	Telephone	Relationship

Physician or Dentist to Be Called in Emergency

Physician	Address	Medical Plan and Number	Telephone ( )
Dentist	Address	Medical Plan and Number	Telephone ( )

If Physician Cannot Be Reached, What Action Should Be Taken?

☐ Call Emergency Hospital ☐ Other Explain _____

Names of Persons Authorized to Take Child from the Facility

(Child will not be allowed to leave with any other person without written authorization from parent or guardian)

Name	Relationship

Time Child Will Be Called For

Signature of Parent or Guardian	Date

To Be Completed by Facility Director/Administrator

Date of Admission	Date Left

LIC 700 (8/86) (Confidential)   86   41957

*This form is required for all day care centers and family day care centers.

(Courtesy of the State of California Department of Social Services)

CONSENT FOR CHILD CARE PROVIDER ACCESS
TO PHYSICIAN RECORDS

I, _____, give my consent for

the following individual to have access to my child's medical records while my child is enrolled in

_____.

My child's caregiver: _____

Address: _____

Telephone Number: _____

I understand that information in my child's record will not be released to any other individuals without my specific written consent.

Signed: _____   Date: _____
                 (Parent/Legal Guardian)

Witnessed: _____

AUTHORIZATION FOR EMERGENCY MEDICAL CARE
(Sample)

Minor's name _____

The undersigned has entrusted the above-named minor for care with _____
child care. I hereby authorize such adult person to consent to any x-ray, examination, anesthetic, medical or surgical diagnosis or treatment, and hospital care to be rendered to said minor under the general or specific supervision and upon the advice of a physician and surgeon licensed under the provisions of the Medicine Practice Act or to consent to an x-ray examination, anesthetic, dental or surgical diagnosis or treatment, and hospital care to be rendered to said minor by a dentist licensed under the provisions of the Dental Practice Act.

A photocopy of this *Authorization for Emergency Medical Care* shall be as valid as the original.

Child's birthdate: _____

Father's work telephone number: _____

Father's Social Security number: _____

Mother's work telephone number: _____

Mother's Social Security number: _____

Father's Insurance Company and policy number: _____

_____

Mother's Insurance Company and policy number: _____

_____

Name of child's physician and telephone number: _____

_____

Date: _____   _____
Signed/Relationship

_____
Signed/Relationship

_____
Child Care Provider Signature

SYMPTOM RECORD

Child's Name: _____

Date: _____ Symptom: _____

When symptoms began, how long they last, how severe, how often? _____
_____

Any change in child's behavior? _____
_____

Child's temperature _____ ☐ axillary ☐ oral ☐ rectal

Food and fluid intake in the past 12 hours: _____
_____

Urine, bowel movement, vomiting in the past 12 hours: _____
_____

Circle or write in other symptoms:

runny nose   sore throat   cough   vomiting   diarrhea   rash

trouble breathing   stiff neck   itching   trouble urinating   pain

Other symptoms: _____

Exposure to medications, animals, insects, soaps, new foods: _____
_____

Exposure to other people who were sick? Who, and what sickness? _____
_____

Other problems that might affect this illness: (asthma, anemia, diabetes, allergy, emotional trauma)
_____

What has been done so far? _____

Health provider's advice for this illness: _____

Name of person completing this form: _____

SAMPLE LETTER TO PARENTS ABOUT EXPOSURE TO COMMUNICABLE DISEASE

Name of Child Care Program: _____

Address of Child Care Program: _____

Telephone Number of Child Care Program: _____

Date: _____

Dear Parents:

A child in our program has or is suspected of having: _____

The disease is spread by: _____

The symptoms are: _____

_____ and may appear for this length of time: _____

To prevent this disease: _____

_____

_____

_____

_____

_____

_____

_____

_____

_____

_____

_____

_____

_____

_____

_____

_____

If your child has any symptoms of this disease, call your doctor to find out what to do. Be sure to tell your doctor about this notice. If you do not have a regular doctor to care for your child, contact your local health department for instructions on how to find a doctor or ask other parents for names of their children's doctors. If you have any questions, please contact:

_____ at (_____)_____
      (Caregiver's name)   (Telephone number)

(Courtesy of Pennsylvania Chapter, American Academy of Pediatrics)

INCIDENT REPORT FORM

Fill in all blanks and boxes that apply.

Name of Program: _____ Telephone No.: _____

Address of Facility: _____

Child's Name: _____ Sex: M F Birthdate:__/__/__ Incident Date: __/__/__

Time of Incident: ___:___AM/PM Witnesses: _____

Parent(s) Notified By: _____ Time Notified: ___:___AM/PM

Location where incident occurred: ☐ playground ☐ classroom ☐ bathroom ☐ hall
☐ kitchen ☐ doorway ☐ large muscle room or gym ☐ office ☐ dining room
☐ stairway ☐ unknown ☐ other (specify) _____

Equipment/product involved: ☐ climber ☐ slide ☐ swing ☐ playground surface
☐ sandbox ☐ trike/bike ☐ hand toy (specify): _____

☐ other equipment (specify): _____

Cause of injury (describe): _____

☐ fall to surface; estimated height of fall _____ feet; type of surface: _____

☐ fall from running or tripping ☐ bitten by child ☐ motor vehicle ☐ hit or pushed by child
☐ injured by object ☐ eating or choking ☐ insect sting/bite ☐ animal bite
☐ injury from exposure to cold ☐ other (specify): _____
_____

Parts of body injured: ☐ eye ☐ ear ☐ nose ☐ mouth ☐ tooth ☐ other face
☐ other part of head ☐ neck ☐ arm/wrist/hand ☐ leg/ankle/foot ☐ trunk
☐ other (specify): _____

Type of injury: ☐ cut ☐ bruise or swelling ☐ puncture ☐ scrape ☐ broken bone
or dislocation ☐ sprain ☐ crushing injury ☐ burn ☐ loss of consciousness
☐ unknown ☐ other (specify): _____

First aid given at the facility: (e.g., pressure, elevation, cold pack, washing, bandage): _____
_____

Treatment provided by: _____
☐ no doctor's or dentist's treatment required
☐ treated as an outpatient (e.g., office or emergency room)
☐ hospitalized (overnight) no. of days: _____

Number of days of limited activity from this incident: _____ Follow-up plan for care of the
child: _____

Corrective action needed to prevent reoccurrence: _____

Name of official/agency notified: _____ Date: _____

Signature of staff member: _____ Date: _____

Signature of parent: _____ Date: _____

(Courtesy of Pennsylvania Chapter, American Academy of Pediatrics)

EVACUATION PROCEDURE

1. All staff must give children proper information on exiting the facility.

2. Children's activities will stop immediately at the sound of the drill, and they are to proceed to the classroom door.

3. _____ will lead children out of the facility to the designated area.
   Staff Title/Name

4. _____ will check bathrooms, closets, and hallways to assure all children have exited.
   Staff Title/Name
   (Window and doors will be closed on the way out.)

5. _____ will bring the attendance and emergency contact records to the designated area.
   Staff Title/Name

6. In case of fire, _____ will notify the fire department.
   Staff Title/Name

7. When the building cannot be reentered, children will be taken to _____.
   Name of Facility

8. Parents will be notified by telephone or radio broadcast on _____.
   Station Call Letters

9. No one should reenter the building unless given permission by the fire department.

10. _____ will complete the evacuation log at the end of each drill.
    Staff Title/Name

11. The local fire marshall will be invited to observe a drill annually, and teach staff use of fire extinguishers.

12. If there is a power failure _____ will activate the emergency lighting systems.
    Staff Title/Name
    Flashlights are available in each classroom closet.

13. If there is a severe storm or tornado, children should be taken to _____.
    Place in Facility

14. Staff should remain calm and speak to children in a reassuring manner. Take appropriate toys and books to keep children involved in an activity.

Scheduling of Fire Drills

■ Fire drills will be held monthly.

■ Drills will be held at different times during the day, after nap time, and after lunch to familiarize children with the proper evacuation procedure.

■ Select a location in the building for the site of a "pretend" fire which would change the usual evacuation route. Plan and conduct an evacuation drill using alternate exits.

(Courtesy of Pennsylvania Chapter, American Academy of Pediatrics)

Note: Stop, Drop, Roll, Cool, and Call logo not available at the time of this printing. *(Courtesy of the Burn Institute, 3702 Ruffin Rd., Ste. 101, San Diego, CA)*

Appendix B

PHYSICAL GROWTH NATIONAL CENTER FOR HEALTH STATISTICS (NCHS) PERCENTILES

- Girls: Birth to 36 Months (Length and Weight)

- Boys: Birth to 36 Months (Length and Weight)

- Girls: 2 to 18 Years (Stature and Weight)

- Boys: 2 to 18 Years (Stature and Weight)

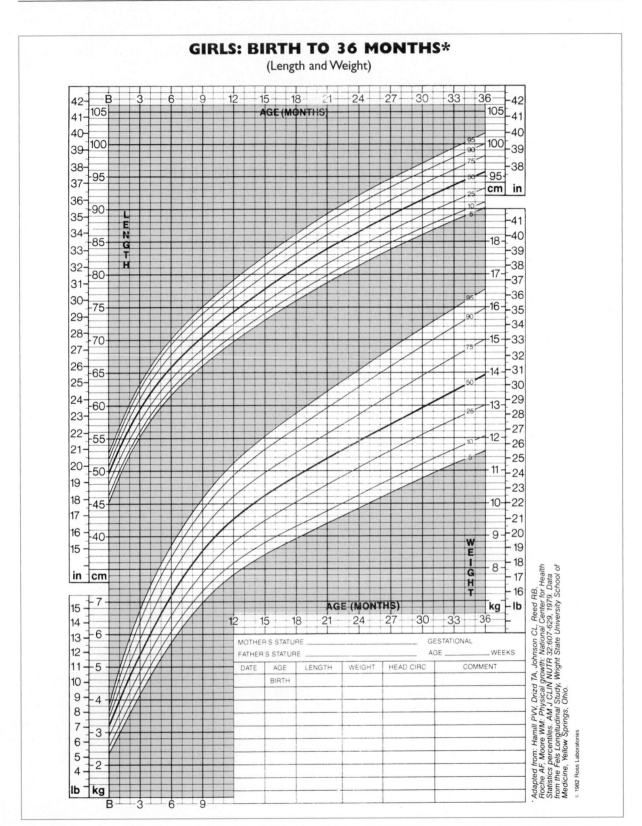

GIRLS: BIRTH TO 36 MONTHS*
(Length and Weight)

(Used with permission of Ross Products Division, Abbott Laboratories, Columbus, OH 43216. From Ross Laboratories. © 1982 Ross Products Division, Abbott Laboratories)

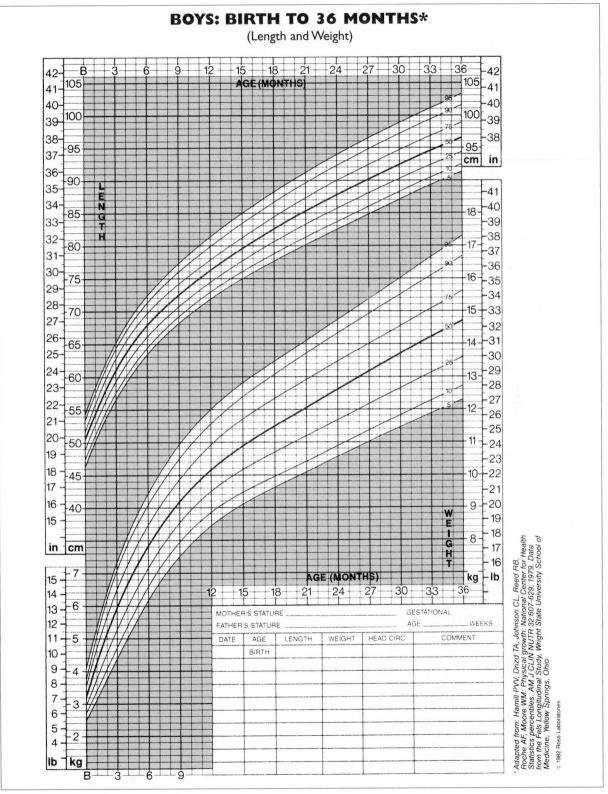

BOYS: BIRTH TO 36 MONTHS*
(Length and Weight)

(Used with permission of Ross Products Division, Abbott Laboratories, Columbus, OH 43216. From Ross Laboratories. © 1982 Ross Products Division, Abbott Laboratories)

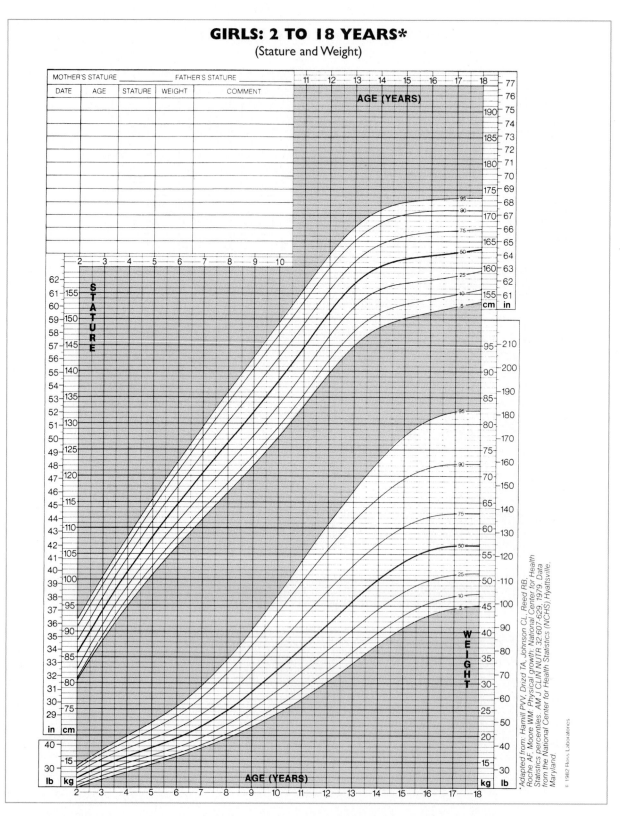

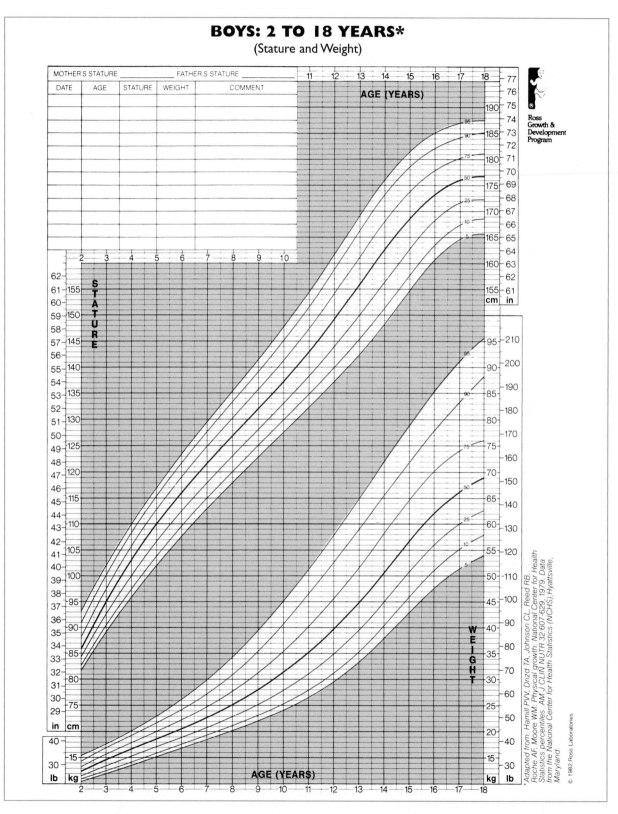

BOYS: 2 TO 18 YEARS*
(Stature and Weight)

(Used with permission of Ross Products Division, Abbott Laboratories, Columbus, OH 43216. From Ross Laboratories. © 1982 Ross Products Division, Abbott Laboratories)

Appendix C

CHILDREN'S DEVELOPMENT

- Denver II Developmental Screening Test

- Developmental Milestones—Birth to Five Years

- Selected Screening and Assessment Tools

- Suggested Readings on Children's Developmental Norms

523

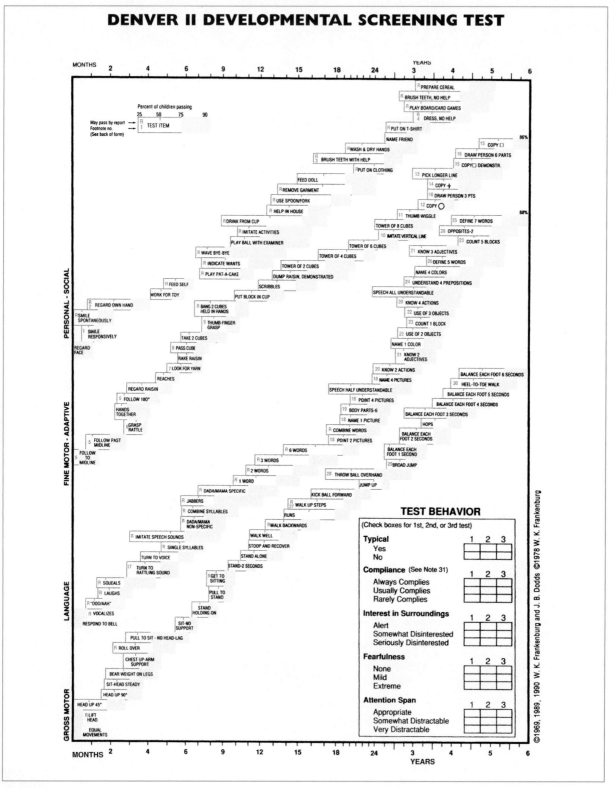

DENVER II DEVELOPMENTAL SCREENING TEST

(Reprinted with permission of DDM)

DIRECTIONS FOR ADMINISTRATION

1. Try to get child to smile by smiling, talking, or waving. Do not touch him/her.
2. Child must stare at hand several seconds.
3. Parent may help guide toothbrush and put toothpaste on brush.
4. Child does not have to be able to tie shoes or button/zip in the back.
5. Move yarn slowly in an arc from one side to the other, about 8" above child's face.
6. Pass if child grasps rattle when it is touched to the backs or tips of fingers.
7. Pass if child tries to see where yarn went. Yarn should be dropped quickly from sight from tester's hand without arm movement.
8. Child must transfer cube from hand to hand without help of body, mouth, or table.
9. Pass if child picks up raisin with any part of thumb and finger.
10. Line can vary only 30 degrees or less from tester's line. ✓
11. Make a fist with thumb pointing upward and wiggle only the thumb. Pass if child imitates and does not move any fingers other than the thumb.

| 12. Pass any enclosed form. Fail continuous round motions. | 13. Which line is longer? (Not bigger.) Turn paper upside down and repeat. (pass 3 of 3 or 5 of 6) | 14. Pass any lines crossing near midpoint. | 15. Have child copy first. If failed, demonstrate. |

When giving items 12, 14, and 15, do not name the forms. Do not demonstrate 12 and 14.

16. When scoring, each pair (2 arms, 2 legs, etc.) counts as one part.
17. Place one cube in cup and shake gently near child's ear, but out of sight. Repeat for other ear.
18. Point to picture and have child name it. (No credit is given for sounds only.)
    If less than 4 pictures are named correctly, have child point to picture as each is named by tester.

19. Using doll, tell child: Show me the nose, eyes, ears, mouth, hands, feet, tummy, hair. Pass 6 of 8.
20. Using pictures, ask child: Which one flies?... says meow?... talks?... barks?... gallops? Pass 2 of 5, 4 of 5.
21. Ask child: What do you do when you are cold?... tired?... hungry? Pass 2 of 3, 3 of 3.
22. Ask child: What do you do with a cup? What is a chair used for? What is a pencil used for? Action words must be included in answers.
23. Pass if child correctly places and says how many blocks are on paper. (1, 5).
24. Tell child: Put block **on** table; **under** table; **in front of** me, **behind** me. Pass 4 of 4. (Do not help child by pointing, moving head or eyes.)
25. Ask child: What is a ball?... lake?... desk?... house?... banana?... curtain?... fence?... ceiling? Pass if defined in terms of use, shape, what it is made of, or general category (such as banana is fruit, not just yellow). Pass 5 of 8, 7 of 8.
26. Ask child: If a horse is big, a mouse is __? If fire is hot, ice is __? If the sun shines during the day, the moon shines during the __? Pass 2 of 3.
27. Child may use wall or rail only, not person. May not crawl.
28. Child must throw ball overhand 3 feet to within arm's reach of tester.
29. Child must perform standing broad jump over width of test sheet (8 1/2 inches).
30. Tell child to walk forward, ⚬▭⚬ ⚬▭⚬ ➤ heel within 1 inch of toe. Tester may demonstrate. Child must walk 4 consecutive steps.
31. In the second year, half of normal children are noncompliant.

OBSERVATIONS:

DEVELOPMENTAL MILESTONES—

Skills	Birth to 12 Months	One Year to Two Years	
Cognitive Skills	Follows moving object with eyes. Looks directly at faces and responds to gestures. Places toy in and takes toy out of containers. Beginning of memory—object permanence. Looks for hidden objects. Listens to and follows simple directions.	Imitates adults through actions and words. Names simple objects. Listens to and follows commands and requests. Explores the environment. Acts like "little scientist." Matches simple objects.	
Language Skills	Cries, babbles, and coos. Looks at speaker when spoken to and responds using variety of sounds. Capable of vowel and consonant sounds, often using repetition. Begins to imitate sounds. Begins to use intonation for meaning.	Speaks first words. Able to speak 50 meaningful words to communicate. Identifies and names simple objects. Uses gestures to enhance communication. Indicates possession by using words *mine, me*. Uses the word *no* frequently to voice autonomy.	
Fine Motor Skills	Reaches for objects; grasps and plays with them. Puts objects in mouth. Uses pincer grasp. Shifts objects between hands. Drops objects; picks them up.	Stacks three objects, such as blocks, in a tower. Turns pages (two or three at a time). Turns doorknobs. Throws small ball. Scribbles, paints with large movements, holds brush with whole hand. Drinks from a cup without help. Begins using a spoon. Places round objects into holes.	
Gross Motor Skills	Lifts head. Turns from side to side; rolls over. Sits with back straight and head steady. Able to crouch. Crawls. Pulls self up into a standing position, then walks along furniture, using both hands. Stands without support.	Takes first steps. Walks alone without help. Stands without support. Walks backwards. Walks upstairs using one hand. Jumps using both feet. Pulls and pushes toys. Throws a ball with overhand motion without falling.	
Social Skills	Smiles spontaneously. Discriminates between familiar people and strangers. Responds to own name. Understands words *no-no*. Imitates simple actions of others.	Shows emotions such as affection, joy, fear, anger, and jealousy. Recognizes self in mirror. Refers to self by name. Hugs and kisses. Throws temper tantrums. Loves to help put things away. Imitates adult activities. Initiates play.	
Self-Mastery Skills	Holds bottle. Feeds self finger foods. Holds cup with two hands; needs assistance to drink from it. Cooperates with being dressed.	Takes off shoes and other clothing; can unzip. Verbalizes needs such as food, drink, and toileting. Eats and drinks well without assistance.	

BIRTH TO FIVE YEARS

Two to Three Years	Three to Four Years	Four to Five Years
Can name and recognize one color. Matches shapes and objects by function. Stacks objects, such as blocks, five high. Responds to simple direction. Has limited attention span. Identifies objects in picture books. Can describe own activity. Begins to understand function of objects in familiar environments.	Can name and recognize six colors. Begins to understand concept of time, including past and present. Understands concept of pretending. Knows own full name and age. Attention span is somewhat longer, but easily distracted. Can match by "family" group or function.	Matches pictures of familiar objects. Draws people figures with recognizable parts. Counts to five. Knows street and town where he lives. Points to and names six colors. Matches commonly related objects. Has extended attention span. Has increased understanding of time, function, and whole and part.
Talks constantly. Refers to self by proper pronouns. Uses plurals. Uses complete sentences consisting of three to four words. Asks questions: why, where, how?	Talks in sentences. Can relate present or past experiences. Uses past tense for verbs. Has extensive vocabulary. Can repeat a song or nursery rhyme. Can understand and use size comparisons. Asks questions for information.	Has basic grammatical structure in use. Uses increasingly complex language. Has large vocabulary base. Understands more complex directions. Uses directions in play. Able to listen to long stories.
Can turn pages of book one at a time. Paints using wrist action. Holds crayon with fingers, not whole hand. Moves fingers independently of others. Strings beads. Cuts using scissors, but hasn't mastered it. Shows hand preference. Manipulates clay by rolling and pounding.	Drives pegs into holes, nails into wood. Can copy circle or cross. Manipulates clay and play dough into recognizable objects. Able to stack objects nine high. Cuts using scissors.	Cuts on a straight line. Copies simple figures. Prints a few capital letters.
Runs well. Kicks ball without losing balance. Stands on one foot. Jumps short distances with both feet. Rides a tricycle, but has not necessarily mastered both steering and peddling. Walks upstairs alternating feet. Walks on tiptoe.	Runs around obstacles. Throws ball overhand, with direction. Hops on one foot. Climbs up slide and slides down unassisted. Walks a line. Can catch ball bounced to her. Masters riding a tricycle.	Turns somersault. Walks up and down stairs unassisted, alternating feet. Jumps forward as many as ten times without falling. Walks backward in a line, heel to toe. Can swing at a stationary ball with a bat.
Better control of temper tantrums. Begins to share toys. Plays near other children (parallel play). Begins real dramatic play. Participates in group activities like circle time.	Plays with others (associative play). Able to share and take turns. Acts out whole scenes in dramatic play.	Plays with other children (cooperative play). Dramatic play resembles reality, including dressing up. Pretending is acknowledged. Acknowledges sex differences.
Understands gender identity. Feeds self. Drinks from drinking fountain. Takes off jacket or coat. Toilets with help. Opens doors.	Knows own gender identity. Buttons and unbuttons clothing. Washes hands without help. Pours well from small pitcher. Spreads with knife. Toilets without help.	Laces shoes. Follows instructions given in a group. Uses knife to cut food. Can help set table. Can help in simple food preparation. Knows name of city she lives in.

SELECTED SCREENING AND ASSESSMENT TOOLS

Bayley Scales of Infant Development
Two to Thirty Months
Developed in 1969, this tool measures mental, motor, and behavioral development. It helps to identify developmental difficulties in very young children.

Gessell Assessment Tool
Birth to Six Years
This tool was first developed in 1940 and then revised in 1980. Measures motor, adaptive, language, and personal and social behavior.

Denver Developmental Screening Test
Birth to Six Years
This tool was developed in 1967 and measures fine motor, gross motor, language, adaptive, and personal and social skills. It is best used as an indicator for further assessment needs. It is limited due to its broad spectrum.

Early Learning Accomplishment Profile
Birth to Three Years
This profile offers programming guidance for infants and young children with special needs.

Learning Accomplishment Profile Diagnostic Test
Thirty Months to Five Years
This tool measures fine motor and gross motor skills, cognition, and language development. It can also provide appropriate learning objectives and assist in measuring progress. It is intended primarily for children with special needs.

Learning Accomplishment Profile Diagnostic Screening
Birth to Five Years
This short test (15 minutes) shows cut-off points in norms that may indicate the need for early intervention. It assesses fine and gross motor skills, language, cognition, social, and self-help skills.

Uniform Performance Assessment System
Birth to Six Years
This assessment tool is based on criteria that directly refers to the areas of communication, social and self-help skills, cognition, and general motor skills.

Portage Guide to Early Education
Birth to Six Years
A checklist is the main instrument used to assess developmental skill performance. This tool also includes lesson plans and other aids to develop optimum skill building for young children.

Hawaii Early Learning Profile
Birth to Three Years
This tool, developed in 1979, measures cognition, language, social, and self-help skills as well as fine and gross motor skills.

Early Childhood Environment Rating Scale
Birth to Five Years
The primary purpose of this tool is to rate the quality of the child care or preschool setting, the materials and activities provided, children's development, and scheduling. The resulting assessment can point out areas that need improvement to enhance the child care or preschool experience.

SUGGESTED READINGS ON
CHILDREN'S DEVELOPMENTAL NORMS

Ainsworth, M., Blehar, M., Waters, E., & Wall, S. (1979) *Patterns of attachment: Observation in the strange situation and at home.* Hillsdale, NJ: Erlbaum.

Bayley, N. (1969). *The Bayley scales of infant development.* New York: The Psychological Corporation.

ERIC. (1989). *Early intervention for infants and toddlers: A team effort* (#461). Urbana, IL: The University of Illinois.

Frankenburg, W. K., Dodds, J. B., & Fandal, A. (1975). *Denver developmental screening test.* Denver, CO: Ladoca Publishing.

Furuno, S., O'Reilly, D., Hosaka, C., Inatuska, T., Aleman, T., & Zeisloft, B. (1979). *Hawaii early learning profile.* Palo Alto, CA: Vort Corporation.

Harel, I., & Anastasian, N. (1985). *The at-risk infant.* Baltimore: Brookes Publishing.

Harms, T., & Clifford, R. (1980). *Early education environmental rating scale.* New York: Teacher's College Press.

Shearer, D., Billingsley, J., Froman, A., Hilliard, J., Johnson, F., & Shearer, M. (1976). *Portage guide to early education* (Rev. ed.). Portage, WI: Portage Project.

Smith P., & Pederson, D. (1988). Maternal sensitivity and patterns of infant and mother attachment. *Child Development, (59),* 1097–1101.

Terr, L., & Tyler, R. (1992, May). Prenatal drug exposure: An overview of associated problems and intervention strategies. *Phi Delta Kappan,* 705–707.

Ungerer, J., & Signman, M. (1983). Developmental lags in preterm infants from one to three years. *Child Development, (54),* 1217–1228.

Weiss, R. (1981). INREAL intervention for language handicapped and bilingual children. *Journal of the Division of Early Childhood, (4),* 24–27.

White, O., Edgar, E., Haring, N., Afflectk, J., Hayden, A., & Benderesky, M. (1981). *Uniform performance assessment system (UPAS).* Columbus, OH: Charles E. Merrill.

Appendix D

NUTRITIONAL ASSESSMENT TOOLS

- The Food Guide Pyramid

- Hard-to-Place Foods

- Mexican American Foods and the Food Guide Pyramid

- Nutritional Breakdown of Typical Lunch Menus

531

The Food Guide Pyramid
A guide to daily food choices

Fats, Oils, and Sweets
Use Sparingly

Milk, Yogurt,
and Cheese Group
2–3 Servings

Meat, Poultry, Fish, Dry Beans,
Eggs, and Nut Group
2–3 Servings

Vegetable Group
**3–5
Servings**

Fruit Group
2–4 Servings

Bread, Cereal, Rice,
and Pasta Group
6–11 Servings

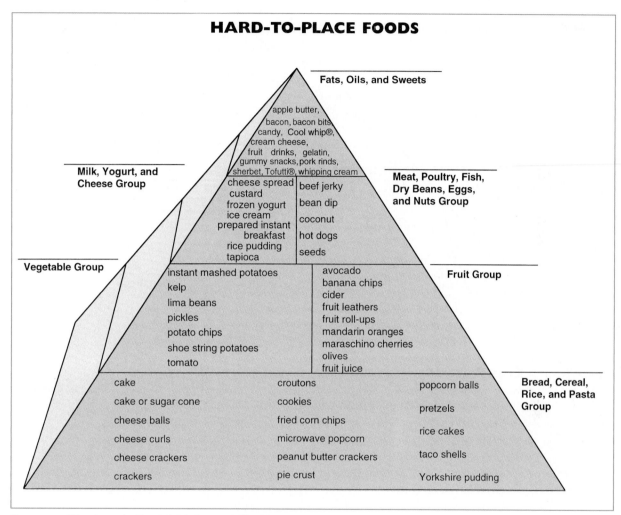

HARD-TO-PLACE FOODS

Fats, Oils, and Sweets

apple butter, bacon, bacon bits, candy, Cool whip®, cream cheese, fruit drinks, gelatin, gummy snacks, pork rinds, sherbet, Tofutti®, whipping cream

Milk, Yogurt, and Cheese Group

cheese spread
custard
frozen yogurt
ice cream
prepared instant breakfast
rice pudding
tapioca

Meat, Poultry, Fish, Dry Beans, Eggs, and Nuts Group

beef jerky
bean dip
coconut
hot dogs
seeds

Vegetable Group

instant mashed potatoes
kelp
lima beans
pickles
potato chips
shoe string potatoes
tomato

Fruit Group

avocado
banana chips
cider
fruit leathers
fruit roll-ups
mandarin oranges
maraschino cherries
olives
fruit juice

Bread, Cereal, Rice, and Pasta Group

cake
cake or sugar cone
cheese balls
cheese curls
cheese crackers
crackers

croutons
cookies
fried corn chips
microwave popcorn
peanut butter crackers
pie crust

popcorn balls
pretzels
rice cakes
taco shells
Yorkshire pudding

Placement of Foods on the Food Guide Pyramid (© 1993 Pyramid Packet, Penn State Nutrition Center, 417 East Calder Way, University Park, PA 16801-5633; 814-865-6323)

MEXICAN AMERICAN FOODS AND THE FOOD GUIDE PYRAMID

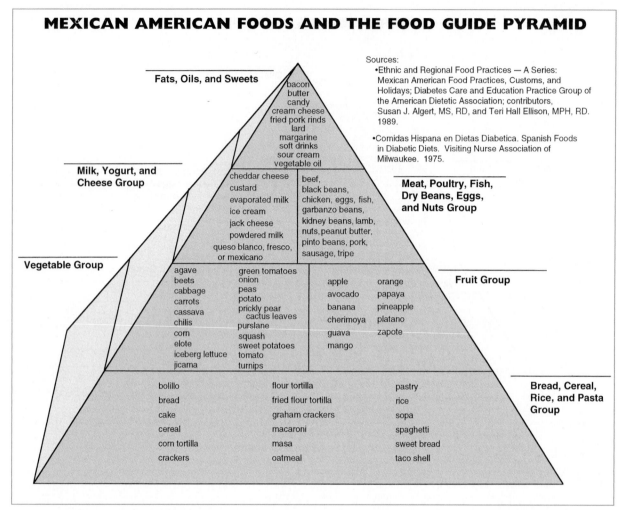

Fats, Oils, and Sweets

bacon
butter
candy
cream cheese
fried pork rinds
lard
margarine
soft drinks
sour cream
vegetable oil

Milk, Yogurt, and Cheese Group

cheddar cheese
custard
evaporated milk
ice cream
jack cheese
powdered milk
queso blanco, fresco, or mexicano

Meat, Poultry, Fish, Dry Beans, Eggs, and Nuts Group

beef,
black beans,
chicken, eggs, fish,
garbanzo beans,
kidney beans, lamb,
nuts, peanut butter,
pinto beans, pork,
sausage, tripe

Sources:
•Ethnic and Regional Food Practices — A Series: Mexican American Food Practices, Customs, and Holidays; Diabetes Care and Education Practice Group of the American Dietetic Association; contributors, Susan J. Algert, MS, RD, and Teri Hall Ellison, MPH, RD. 1989.

•Comidas Hispana en Dietas Diabetica. Spanish Foods in Diabetic Diets. Visiting Nurse Association of Milwaukee. 1975.

Vegetable Group

agave
beets
cabbage
carrots
cassava
chilis
corn
elote
iceberg lettuce
jicama

green tomatoes
onion
peas
potato
prickly pear cactus leaves
purslane
squash
sweet potatoes
tomato
turnips

Fruit Group

apple
avocado
banana
cherimoya
guava
mango

orange
papaya
pineapple
platano
zapote

Bread, Cereal, Rice, and Pasta Group

bolillo
bread
cake
cereal
corn tortilla
crackers

flour tortilla
fried flour tortilla
graham crackers
macaroni
masa
oatmeal

pastry
rice
sopa
spaghetti
sweet bread
taco shell

Placement of Foods on the Food Guide Pyramid (© 1993 Pyramid Packet, Penn State Nutrition Center, 417 East Calder Way, University Park, PA 16801-5633; 814-865-6323)

NUTRITIONAL BREAKDOWN OF TYPICAL LUNCH MENUS

SCHOOL LUNCH PROGRAM

	Calories	Protein (grams)	Fat (grams)	% Calories from fat	Sodium (milligrams)
Char-broiled hamburger	346	20	12	31	1,272
French fries	138	2	6	39	19
Coleslaw	100	1	6	54	180
8 oz. milk (1% fat)	141	8	4	26	136
2 chocolate-chip cookes	90	1	4	40	70
Total	**815**	**32**	**32**	**38**	**1,677**
Chicken chili	220	18	7	29	1,000
1 oz. tortilla chips	155	2	6	53	233
Chunky applesauce	125	trace	0	0	15
Brownie	225	3	13	54	95
8 oz. milk (1% fat)	141	8	4	26	136
Total	**866**	**33**	**30**	**32**	**1,479**

HOME-PACKED LUNCH

	Calories	Protein (grams)	Fat (grams)	% Calories from fat	Sodium (milligrams)
Bologna sandwich	420	17	28	59	1,089
1 oz. potato chips	150	2	10	60	233
1 cherry gelatin snack	70	1	0	0	40
6.75 oz. apple juice	90	0	0	0	25
6 mini ginger snaps	140	2	5	36	130
Total	**870**	**22**	**43**	**31**	**1,517**
1 slice sausage pizza (leftover)	250	12	9	32	576
1 roll fruit leather	74	0	trace	trace	13
1 medium apple	125	trace	trace	5	2
8.45 oz. cranberry drink	160	trace	trace	4	5
2 creme-filled spongecakes	310	2	10	29	311
Total	**919**	**14**	**19**	**14**	**907**

FAST-FOOD LUNCH

McDonald's	Calories	Protein (grams)	Fat (grams)	% Calories from fat	Sodium (milligrams)
1 regular hamburger	250	12	9	32	490
1 small French fries	231	3	9	35	175
Vanilla shake	310	11	5	15	170
Chocolate-chip cookies	330	4	15	42	280
Total	**1,121**	**30**	**38**	**31**	**1,115**
Taco Bell					
1 regular taco	180	10	11	56	276
Nachos	320	5	18	51	560
Cinnamon twist	180	trace	8	40	190
16 oz. cola	150	0	0	0	15
Total	**830**	**15**	**37**	**49**	**1,041**

Data for 1% fat milk vary because brands of milk differ in the amount of milk solids added.

Appendix E

SOURCES OF MATERIALS RELATED TO SAFETY, NUTRITION, AND HEALTH

Abbott Laboratories
100 Abbott Park Road
Abbott Park, IL 60064–3500
http://www.abbott.com

Aetna Life, Casualty, and Health Companies
151 Farmington Avenue
Hartford, CT 06156
http://www.aetna.com/index/.htm

Alexander Graham Bell Association
    for the Deaf, Inc,
3417 Volta Place, NW
Washington, DC 20007
http://www.agbell.org

Alliance to End Childhood Lead Poisoning
227 Massachusetts Avenue
Suite 200
Washington, DC 20002
http://www.aeclp.org

American Academy of Pediatrics
141 Northwest Point Boulevard
Elk Grove Village, IL 60009–1098
http://www.aap.org

American Allergy Association
P.O. Box 7273
Menlo Park, CA 94026
http://www.parentsoup.com/library/organizations

American Alliance for Health, Physical Education,
    Recreation, and Dance
1900 Association Drive
Reston, VA 20191
http://www.aahperd.org

American Automobile Association
1000 AAA Drive
Heathrow, FL 32746
http://www.aaa.com

American Cancer Society
1599 Clifton Road, NE
Atlanta, GA 30329
http://www.cancer.org/

American Dairy Association
O'Hare International Center
10255 W. Higgins Road
Suite 900
Rosemont, IL 60018–5616
http://www.realseal.com/home.html

American Dairy Products Institute
300 W. Washington Street
Suite 400
Chicago, IL 60606–1704
http://americandairyproducts.com/
    goals.html

American Dental Association
211 E. Chicago Avenue
Chicago, IL 60611
http://www.ada.org/

American Diabetes Association, Inc.
1701 N. Beauregard Street
Alexandria, VA 22311
http://www.diabetes.org/

American Dietetic Association
216 W. Jackson Boulevard
Chicago, IL 60606–6995
http://www.eatright.org/

American Foundation for the Blind
11 Penn Plaza
Suite 300
New York, NY 10001
http://www.afb.org/

American Heart Association
7272 Greenville Avenue
Dallas, TX 75231
http://www.americanheart.org/

American Hospital Association
One N. Franklin
27th Floor
Chicago, IL 60606
http://www.aha.org/index.asp

American Institute of Baking
1213 Bakers Way
Manhattan, KS 66505–3999
http://www.bakinguniversity.com/
(nutrition education and food safety)

American Insurance Association
1130 Connecticut Avenue, NW
Suite 1000
Washington, DC 20036
http://www.aiadc.org/

American Lung Association
1740 Broadway
New York, NY 10019
http://www.lungusa.org/

American Medical Association
515 N. State Street
Chicago, IL 60610
http://www.ama-assn.org/ama/pub/category/
    3457.html

American National Red Cross
431 18th Street, NW
Washington, DC 20006
http://www.redcross.org/news/

American Optometric Association
243 N. Lindbergh Boulevard
St. Louis, MO 63141
http://www.aoanet.org/

American Printing House for the Blind
1839 Frankfort Avenue
Mailing Address: P.O. Box 6085
Louisville, KY 40206–0085
http://www.aph.org/aph1.htm

American Public Health Association
800 I Street, NW
Washington, DC 20001–3710
http://www.apha.org/

American School Health Association
7263 State Route 43
P.O. Box 708
Kent, OH 44240
http://www.ashaweb.org/

American Social Health Association
P.O. Box 13827
Research Triangle Park, NC 27709
http://www.ashastd.org/

American Speech, Language, and Hearing
    Association
10801 Rockville Pike
Rockville, MD 20852
http://www.asha.org/siteindex.cfm

The ARC of the United States
1010 Wayne Avenue
Suite 650
Silver Spring, MD 20910
http://www.thearc.org/

The Arthritis Foundation
1330 W. Peachtree Street
Atlanta, GA 30309
http://www.arthritis.org/

Association for the Care of Children's Health
7910 Woodmont Avenue
Suite 300
Bethesda, MD 20814
http://www.babycenter.com/refcap/1445.
    html?CP_bid=

Asthma and Allergy Foundation of America
1233 20th Street, NW
Suite 402
Washington, DC 20036
http://www.aafa.org/

Better Vision Institute
1655 N. Ft. Meyer Drive
Suite 200
Arlington, VA 22209
http://www.visionsite.org/

Childhood and Youth Division
Health Canada
Jeanne Mance Building
9th Floor
Tunney's Pasture
Ottawa, Ontario
K1A 1B4 Canada
http://consumerinformation.ca/cgi-
    bin/document.cgi?SeqId=28711&
    Language=E&Session=361475984269030

Children's Defense Fund
25 E Street, NW
Washington, DC 20001
http://www.childrensdefense.org/

Clearinghouse on Child Abuse and Neglect
    Information
330 C Street, SW
Washington, DC 20447
http://www.calib.com/nccanch/

Committee for Children
2203 Airport Way South
Suite 500
Seattle, WA 98134
http://www.cfchildren.org/

Consumer Information Center
Pueblo, CO 81009
http://www.pueblo.gsa.gov/health.htm

Consumer and Professional Relations Division
of HIAA
1201 F Street, NW
Suite 500
Washington, DC 20004–1204
http://www.hiaa.org/cons/cons.htm

Council for Exceptional Children
Division of Early Childhood
P.O. Box 79026
Baltimore, MD 21279–0026
http://www.cec.sped.org/mb/join.htm

Cystic Fibrosis Foundation
6931 Arlington Road
Suite 200
Bethesda, MD 20814
http://cff.org/

Department of Health and Human Services
Food and Drug Administration
5600 Fishers Lane
Rockville, MD 20857–0001
http://www.fda.gov/

Easter Seals National Headquarters
230 W. Monroe Street
Suite 1800
Chicago, IL 60606
http://www.easter-seals.org/

Environmental Protection Agency
1200 Pennsylvania Avenue, NW
Washington, DC 20460
http://www.epa.gov/

Epilepsy Foundation of America
4351 Garden City Drive
Landover, MD 20785
http://www.epilepsyfoundation.org/epusa/index.html

Federal Emergency Management Agency
500 C Street, SW
Washington, DC 20472
http://www.fema.gov/

Feingold Association of the United States
P.O. Box 6550
Alexandria, VA 22306
http://www.feingold.org/2index_internatl.html

Florida Department of Citrus Fruit
Box 148
Lakeland, FL 33802–0148
http://www.floridajuice.com/floridacitrus/intro.html

Food and Nutrition Information Center
National Agricultural Library Room 304
10301 Baltimore Avenue
Beltsville, MD 20705–2351
http://www.nal.usda.gov/fnic/general/ general.html

General Mills
Educational Services
P.O. Box 1113
Minneapolis, MN 55440
http://www.generalmills.com/explore/

Health Education Associates, Inc.
8 Jan Sebastian Way #13
Sandwich, MA 02563
http://www.aboutus.com/a100/healthed/

Health Education Foundation
2600 Virginia Avenue, NW
Suite 502
Washington, DC 20037

Healthy Choices for Kids
P.O. Box 39
Ellensburg, WA 98926
http://www.healthychoices.org/

The Huntington's Disease Society of America
158 W. 29th Street
7th Floor
New York, NY 10011–2420
http://www.hdsa.org/

International Life Sciences Institute
1126 Sixteenth Street, NW
Suite 300
Washington, DC 20036–4804
http://www.ilsi.org/

Johnson & Johnson
http://www.jnj.com/who_is_jnj/baby_care.html

The Joseph P. Kennedy, Jr. Foundation
1325 G Street, NW
Suite 500
Washington, DC 20005–4709
http://www.familyvillage.wisc.edu/
jpkf/index.html

Kellogg Company
One Kellogg Square
Battle Creek, MI 49016
http://www.kelloggs.com

Learning Disabilities Association of America
4156 Library Road
Pittsburgh, PA 15234
http://www.ldanatl.org/

Lefthanders International
P.O. Box 8249
Topeka, KS 66608

Lever Brothers
http://www.leverbrothers.com/

March of Dimes Birth Defects Foundation
1275 Mamaroneck Avenue
White Plains, NY 10605
http://www.modimes.org/

Metropolitan Life Insurance Company
One Madison Avenue
New York, NY 10010
http://www.metlife.com/

Muscular Dystrophy Association—USA
National Headquarters
3300 E. Sunrise Drive
Tucson, AZ 85718
http://www.mdausa.org/

National Academy of Sciences
National Research Council
Office of News and Public Information
2101 Constitution Avenue, NW
Washington, DC 20418
http://www4.nationalacademies.org/news.nsf

National Association for Down Syndrome
P.O. Box 4542
Oak Brook, IL 60522
http://www.nads.org/

National Association for the Education of Young
   Children
1509 16th Street, NW
Washington, DC 20036–1426
http://www.naeyc.org/

National Association for Visually Handicapped
22 W. 21st Street
New York, NY 10010
http://www.navh.org/

National Center for Nutrition and Dietetics
216 W. Jackson Boulevard
Chicago, IL 60606–6995
http://www.eatright.org/ncnd.html

National Education Association
1201 16th Street, NW
Washington, DC 20036
http://www.nea.org/issues/safescho/

National Council on Family Relations
3989 Central Avenue, NE
Suite 550
Minneapolis, MN 55421
http://www.ncfr.org/

The National Dairy Council
http://www.nationaldairycouncil.org/news/
   nwindex.html

National Fire Protection Association
1 Batterymarch Park
P.O. Box 9101
Quincy, MA 02269–9101
http://www.nfpa.org/

National Health Council
1730 M Street, NW
Suite 500
Washington, DC 20036
http://www.nhcouncil.org/

National Health Information Center
Office of Disease Prevention and Health Promotion
P.O. Box 1133
Washington, DC 29913–1133
http://www.health.gov/nhic

National Hemophilia Foundation
116 W. 32nd Street
11th Floor
New York, NY 10001
http://www.hemophilia.org/

The National Information Center
for Children and Youth with Disabilities
P.O. Box 1492
Washington, DC 20013–1492
http://www.nichcy.org/

The National Institute of Allergy and Infectious
   Diseases
Office of Communications and Public Liaison
Building 31, Room 7A-50
31 Center Drive MSC 2520
Bethesda, MD 20892–2520
http://www.niaid.nih.gov/

National Institutes of Health
Department of Health and Human Services
Bethesda, MD 20892
http://www.nih.gov/

National Kidney Foundation
30 E. 33rd Street
Suite 1100
New York, NY 10016
http://www.kidney.org/

National Livestock and Meat Board
444 N. Michigan Avenue
Chicago, IL 60611
http://www.agen.ufl.edu/~foodsaf/sf203.html

CHAPTER #   *Chapter Title*   ■ **541**

National Maternal and Child Health Clearinghouse
5600 Fishers Lane, Room 18–05
Rockville, MD 20857
http://www.nmchc.org/

The National Pediculosis Association
P.O. Box 610189
Newton, MA 02461
http://www.headlice.org/

National Reye's Syndrome Foundation
P.O. Box 829
Bryan, OH 43506–0829
http://www.reyessyndrome.org/

National Safety Council
1121 Spring Lake Drive
Itasca, IL 60143–3201
http://www.nsc.org/

National Spinal Cord Injury Association
6701 Democracy Boulevard
Suite 300, #300–9
Bethesda, MD 20817
http://www.spinalcord.org/

National Sudden Infant Death Syndrome
    Resource Center
2070 Chain Bridge Road
Suite 450
Vienna, VA 22182
http://www.circsol.com/SIDS/index.HTM

National Wildlife Federation
1400 16th Street, NW
Washington, DC 20036–2266
http://www.nwf.org/

Nutrition Action Plan for Canada
http://www.hc-sc.gc.ca/hppb/ nutrition/

Nutrition and Food on the WEB
School of Kinesiology, Simon Fraser University
Burnaby, British Columbia
Canada
http://www.sfu.ca/~jfremont/index.html

Nutrition-Health Canada
Brooke Claxton Building
11th Floor
Tunney's Pasture
Ottawa, Ontario
K1A 0K9 Canada
http://www.hc-sc.gc.ca/english/ food.htm

Office of Early Childhood Development
Department of Human Services
717 14th Street, NW
Suite 700
Washington, DC 20005
http://www.dhs.washington.dc.us/Office_of_Early_
    Childhood_Deve/office_of_early_childhood_
    deve.html

Parents Anonymous, Inc.
675 W. Foothill Boulevard
Suite 220
Claremont, CA 91711
http://www.parentsanonymous-natl. org/

Poison Prevention Week Council
P.O. Box 1543
Washington, DC 20013
http://www.cpsc.gov/cpscpub/pubs/386.html

Prevent Blindness America
500 E. Remington Road
Schaumburg, IL 60173
http://www.preventblindness.org

Public Health Services for Children
U.S. Department of Health and Human Services
200 Independence Avenue, SW
Washington, DC 20201
http://www.hhs.gov/kids/

Ross Products Division
Abbott Laboratories
625 Cleveland Avenue
Columbus, OH 43215–1724
http://www.ross.com/html/unifiedsite.cfm

Sex Information and Education Council of the
    United States
130 W. 42nd Street
Suite 2500
New York, NY 10036–7901

State Farm Insurance
One State Farm Plaza
Bloomington, IL 61710
http://www.statefarm.com/consumer/consum.htm

United Cerebral Palsy Association
1000 Elmwood Avenue
Rochester, NY 14620
http://www.ggw.org/AlSigl/ucpa.html

U.S. Department of Agriculture
Agricultural Research Service
14th & Independence Avenue, SW
Washington, DC 20250
http://www.ars.usda.gov/

U.S. Department of Education
400 Maryland Avenue, SW
Washington, DC 20202–0498
http://www.ed.gov/

U.S. Government Printing Office
Superintendent of Documents
710 N. Capitol Street, NW
Washington, DC 20402
http://www.gpo.gov/

Veterans of Safety—Student Chapter
Central Missouri State University
Humphreys 327
Department of Safety Science and Technology
Warrensburg, MO 64093
http://cmsu2.cmsu.edu/~vos/

The World Health Organization
Liaison Office in Washington, DC
1775 K Street, NW
Suite 430
Washington, DC 20006
http://www.who.int/

Glossary

A

accident—unforeseen occurrence that results in injury.

acculturated—adopting attitudes and beliefs.

activity based—activities that promote adaptive behavior.

advocate—to support or speak on behalf of another.

age appropriateness—consideration of the developmental abilities of a particular age group in the selection of toys, materials, and equipment.

agile—easy, flexible, fast movement.

amblyopia—an unequal balance of a child's eye muscles often referred to as "lazy eye." Condition is improved through the use of eye patches to enable the weaker eye to strengthen with greater use.

amino acids—organic compounds containing carbon, hydrogen, oxygen, and nitrogen; the key components of proteins.

anaphylaxis—sensitivity to an allergen that causes an attack that can result in collapse or death.

anecdotal—a brief narrative account that describes a child's behavior that is significant to the observer.

antibias—an approach to curriculum that removes all inequities due to race, gender, and abilities.

antibodies—proteins produced in the body to react with antigens in order to neutralize or react with the antigen to protect the body.

appraisals—regular process of evaluation of a child's health or developmental norms.

assessment—in-depth appraisal to determine if a particular health or developmental condition is occurring.

assimilate—to absorb and incorporate in order to make alike.

at risk—exposure to chance of injury, damage, or hazard.

attachment—the bond that develops between a child and another person as a result of a long-term relationship.

audiologist—person trained to identify types of hearing losses, to interpret audiometric tests, and to recommend equipment and procedures to assist the hearing impaired.

B

baby bottle tooth decay—tooth decay that results from the remains of milk left on the teeth as a result of drinking from a baby bottle.

bacteria—organisms that can survive within or outside of the body, some of which cause diseases.

basal metabolism—the amount of energy used by the body while at rest.

behaviors—actions or conduct that put safety at risk.

blood contact—passing of germs through the blood from one person's circulatory system to another person's circulatory system.

C

calories—the unit of measurement for the energy found in foods.

cardiovascular disease—disease resulting from impaired function of the heart and/or surrounding arteries.

caregivers—persons who care for children: teachers, family child care providers, nannies.

cephalocaudal—development from the top to the bottom of the body or from the head down toward the toes.

cholesterol—a steroid or fatty alcohol found in animal fats that is produced by the liver of the animal.

chronic illnesses—medical conditions requiring continuous treatment.

communicable diseases—a disease spread from one person to another through means of respiratory spray or infected body fluids.

complete protein—protein that contains all essential amino acids.

concrete operational stage—third stage of cognitive development in which logical ideas can be applied to concrete or specific situations.

condition—circumstance or situation under which safety is at risk.

confidential—keeping information private.

contact—touching.

coronary atherosclerosis—disease of the heart resulting in the walls of arteries degenerating due to fat buildup.

coronary heart disease—disease of the arteries feeding the heart muscle.

cultural—relationship to traits and ascribed membership of a given group.

cultural competence—perceptive, responsive behavior to cultural differences.

curriculum—course of study that relates to the subject being examined.

D

dehydrated—loss of water in the body that may impair normal bodily functions.

dental caries—tooth decay.

developmental disabilities—physical or mental incapacities that interfere with normal progress of development.

developmental norms—statistically average age that children will demonstrate certain developmental abilities and behaviors.

dilated—pupils of the eye that are enlarged due to shock or injury.

direct contact transmission—passing of germs from one person's body or clothing to another person through direct contact.

disabled—incapacitated.

disaster preparedness—ability to be ready or prepared for any type of disaster that may occur.

disinfecting—procedures to eliminate all germs through use of chemicals or heat.

diversion—something that changes the focus of attention.

diversity—differences; variety often related to culture.

E

early intervention—decision to modify a child's at-risk behavior or condition in its early stage(s) in order to lessen the impact of the behavior or condition on the life of the child.

ecological—pertaining to the relationship of the individual to the environment.

economic—the satisfaction of the material needs of people.

emergency contact—the person or persons to notify in case of an emergency.

environment—all the conditions, circumstances, and influences surrounding and affecting the development of an individual.

environmental hazards—chance for risk resulting from environmental conditions.

enzymes—organic substances produced in body cells that can cause changes in other substances through catalytic reaction.

ethnicity—relationship to a national, cultural, or racial group.

evacuation—removal of persons from a site where a disaster or emergency exists.

event sampling—when an observer records a specific preselected behavior as it occurs, every time it occurs.

F

failure to thrive—failure of a child to grow physically and develop mentally according to the norms. This condition may occur because of organic defects, or may be due to lack of emotional bonding.

fat soluble—vitamins that dissolve in fat, but not in water, such as vitamins A, D, E, and K.

fecal contamination—contamination occurring through exposure to feces.

fecal-oral transmission—passing of germs from an infected person's bowel movement via the hand into another person's system via the mouth.

feedback—a technique for encouraging desired behaviors in children through communication.

fine motor skills—physical skills related to small body movements, particularly of the hands and fingers. These skills include using scissors, holding a crayon, or working a puzzle.

food frequency questionnaire—an estimate of the frequency of foods eaten during the period of one week.

food jag—preference for one particular food over all others, normally occurring during the preschool years.

friction—rubbing together.

functional skills—skills that allow children to adapt to their environment.

G

generalizable skills—common skills that can be practiced and used in different settings.

genetic—the origin of features of an individual.

germs—microscopic organisms that can cause disease.

gross motor skills—physical skills using large body movements such as running, jumping, and climbing.

growth retardation—the hindering of progress of normal growth and development.

guidelines—statements of advice or instruction pertaining to practice.

H

health policies—framework for ensuring health and well-being in child care settings.

health promotion—the improvement of health conditions by encouraging healthful characteristics and customs.

health status—the condition of health of an individual.

heredity—the transmission from parent to child of certain characteristics.

holistic—consideration of the whole being.

hormones—chemical substances formed in one organ of the body and carried to another organ or tissue where they have specific effects.

hygiene—protective measures and sanitary practices to limit the spread of infection and help to promote health.

hypertension—very high blood pressure.

I

immigrant—one who leaves a country to settle in another.

immunization—vaccines given in order to protect individuals through the development of antibodies against specific infectious diseases.

inclusion—to include or integrate.

indicators—a sign or characteristic that signifies a problem may exist.

individualized family service plan—plan that coordinates services to meet the needs of the child with special needs and assist his or her family.

infection control—control of infectious agents by sanitary practices.

infectious diseases—diseases capable of invading the body and causing an infection to occur; may or may not be contagious.

ingestion—putting into the digestive system through swallowing.

inhalation—breathing in through the nose and mouth.

injection—the force of fluid or poison into the body via a sharp object such as an animal bite or an insect bite.

injury prevention—forestalling or anticipating injury risk.

iron deficiency—lack of adequate supplies of iron needed for normal growth, development, and production of red blood cells.

isolation—situation that causes a person or persons to be set apart or separated from other people.

J

job burnout—inability to perform job due to excessive stress.

L

lactose intolerance—inability of body to process lactose found in milk and milk products.

laws—rules of conduct established and enforced by authority.

liabilities—safety risks or hazards.

linkages—connections that unify the caregiver, child, family, and community.

low center of gravity toy—riding toy where the center of weight is low and balanced, making it difficult to tip over.

lyme disease—disease transmitted via the bite of a tick or deer tick.

M

macronutrients—major nutrients needed for the body, such as fats, protein, and carbohydrates.

malnutrion—inadequate nutrition as a result of improper diet or lack of food.

mandate—an order by law.

metabolism—chemical changes that take place as nutrients are taken into the blood, processed and absorbed by the blood, or eliminated from the body.

metabolize—change occurring by chemical and physical processes in living cells.

micronutrients—supporting nutrients, such as vitamins, minerals, and water, needed by the body.

migrant—a transient who travels from place to place to find work.

mobile—ability to move about easily.

multi-use facilities—child care sites that are used for other functions.

N

nearsightedness—lack of ability to see well, other than close up.

nutrients—substances found in foods that provide for the growth, development, maintenance, and repair of the body.

O

obesity—condition of overweight to the extent that the body is carrying 20 percent more weight than the normal body for the size and bone structure.

objectives—goals; expected outcomes.

observation—primary means of data gathering in order to understand children's development and behavior.

orientation—meeting or discussion of a child new to care regarding health, special needs, and developmental history.

otitis media—infection of the middle ear.

overnutrition—excess intake of foods that provide more than adequate amounts of the substances needed for growth, development, maintenance, and repair of the body, often resulting in overweight.

P

parasites—organisms that live off of another organism.

poison control center—a resource available through a phone call in case of poisoning.

positive reinforcement—reward given in response to a particular behavior that increases the chance of that behavior occurring again.

preoperational stage—second stage of cognitive development in which logic is limited.

primary caregiver—the person assigned to be a child's main caregiver throughout the day in order to form a positive attachment bond.

primary health assessor—caregiver who knows the children very well and can observe for health and well-being.

profusely—pouring forth freely or abundantly.

proximodistal—development of the body from the inside toward the outside or the torso through the arms and out to the fingers.

R

referral—sending a child for further testing or screening and making available resources that will intervene and aid risk that is posed to the child.

regional center—a center in a particular geographic area dedicated to helping families that have children with special needs. The center acts as a resource, a referral agency, and a source of support for families.

regulations—recommendations that are made a requirement by law.

rescue breathing—the process of steps to help a person who is not breathing to resume normal breathing.

resilient—the ability to recover after being exposed to risk.

respiratory diseases—diseases of the nose, ears, sinuses, throat, and lungs.

respiratory tract transmission—germs that are passed through the air from the respiratory tract of one person to another person.

risk—the chance of injury, damage, or loss.

risk management—the act of managing risk.

role modeling—setting a behavioral example.

running records—a detailed narrative account that describes a child's behavior in sequence, as it occurs.

S

safety zones—areas that offer little risk.

sanitary practices—practices that remove bacteria, filth, and dirt that cut down on disease transmission.

sanitized—removal of bacteria, filth, and dirt that makes transmission of disease unlikely.

screenings—to select or evaluate through a process.

secretions—saliva, mucus, urine, and blood produced by the body for specific purposes.

self-esteem—positive sense of self.

self-regulation—to control and direct one's actions.

sensorimotor cognitive development—first stage of cognitive development that utilizes motor abilities and senses.

shock—an imbalance of the circulatory system as a result of injury that includes a decrease in blood pressure, a rapid pulse, and possible unconsciousness.

shock absorbers—materials that lessen the force of a fall.

staff-to-child ratio—the number of staff required to provide proper care for the number of children of a certain age group.

standards—statements that define a goal of practice.

strabismus—a condition that occurs in children that causes one or both eyes to appear crossed.

stress—nonspecific response of the body to any demand put on it.

survival procedures—preparation and steps to follow to stay in place in case of disaster or weather emergency.

synergy—combined effort or action.

syrup of ipecac—a liquid substance used to induce vomiting.

T

theme—subject being emphasized.

time sampling—occurs when an observer records a particular behavior over a specific period of time.

travel information sheet—check-off sheet that monitors all conditions for travel safety.

triggers—substances or conditions that activate a response.

24-hour dietary recall method—record of what was eaten for a 24-hour period that relies heavily upon memory.

U

undernutrition—less than adequate intake of foods that provide the substances needed for growth, development, maintenance, and repair of the body.

unintentional injury—physical injury that is the result of an unintentional event.

V

vaccinations—inactivated, dead, or weakened live organism of infectious diseases to which the body builds resistance.

virus—a microorganism that is produced in living cells and that can cause disease.

vulnerability—inability to protect from risk.

W

water-soluble—vitamins that dissolve in water, such as vitamins B and C.

Index

References are to pages, tables, forms and appendices. Page numbers followed by a "t" or "f" denote tables or forms respectively.